D1406182

ASPECTS OF DIAGENESIS

Based on symposia

Sponsored by the Eastern and by the Rocky Mountain Sections,

The Society of Economic Paleontologists and Mineralogists

Edited by

Peter A. Scholle, *U.S. Geological Survey, Denver, Colorado*

and

Paul R. Schluger, *General Crude Oil Co., Denver, Colorado*

Copyright © 1979 *by*

SOCIETY OF ECONOMIC PALEONTOLOGISTS AND MINERALOGISTS

Special Publication No. 26

Tulsa, Oklahoma, U.S.A.

March, 1979

SEPM 1979

Library
I.U.P.
Indiana, Pa

552.5   As63p

c.1

A Publication of

The Society of Economic Paleontologists and Mineralogists

a division of

The American Association of Petroleum Geologists

PREFACE

There are a number of gaping holes in accumulated knowledge within the discipline of sedimentology. Perhaps one of the largest holes has been the general subject of diagenesis in clastic rocks. It was therefore fortuitous that two symposia covering various aspects of diagenesis (mainly in clastics) were presented a year apart in different parts of the country but with the same motivation—to contribute to the closing of that knowledge gap. Sedimentologists now have a fairly good idea of the what and the how of sediment deposition. What happens after the sediments are lithified has frequently been ignored. It was the aim of both editors of this publication to approach the subject from two different viewpoints. Paul Schluger directed a symposium which looked mainly at clastic reservoirs, and Peter Scholle presented a symposium which examined various aspects of paleotemperature control of diagenesis.

This special publication is not, by any means, the final definitive word on these subjects, but the editors and authors sincerely hope that SEPM Special Publication 26 will be a convenient and good starting place for those interested in pursuing and enlarging our knowledge of diagenesis.

Finally we would like to offer particular thanks to Ray Ethington who provided invaluable assistance with technical editing and Kim A. Schwab who did much of the manuscript proofing.

PETER A. SCHOLLE AND PAUL R. SCHLUGER
Editors

CONTENTS

PART 1. DETERMINATION OF DIAGENETIC PALEOTEMPERATURE—INTRODUCTION

PETER A. SCHOLLE

U.S. Geological Survey, Denver, Colorado 80225

This symposium on "The Determination of Diagenetic Paleotemperatures" was originally sponsored by the Eastern Section of the Society of Economic Paleontologists and Mineralogists. All but one of the papers published here were presented orally at the 11th Annual Northeastern Section, Geological Society of America meeting on March 27, 1976. The original concept of the symposium was to bring together people using a wide variety of geochemical and mineralogical techniques and to discuss the application of such techniques to a common geological problem. Although a number of these tools are used routinely within the petroleum industry, they are not necessarily generally applied throughout the geological profession. Thus, the symposium served the function of familiarizing a broad range of geologists with a significant part of the spectrum of techniques available for the quantitative or semi-quantitative determination of burial temperatures of sediments. The reader should be aware, however, that many other techniques, not discussed here, are also available for such studies. All the techniques presented have some degree of uncertainty in their determinations and may be affected by one or more factors such as water chemistry, pressure, organic carbon or hydrocarbon concentration, or geologic time. Therefore, it is often advisable to use two or more complementary techniques which provide a cross-check. The papers in this volume, written mostly as review articles rather than descriptions of new applications, provide the reader with the background needed to select and apply the technique most useful for a given problem.

The papers in this volume fall into two natural groupings:

1. Articles dealing with examination of organic matter or fossil remains in sediments. Anita Harris discusses the technique of using color alteration of conodonts as an index of burial temperature. This tool is especially valuable in Paleozoic sediments as shown by the examples presented from the Appalachian area. Neely Bostick discusses the examination of solid organic matter, particularly vitrinite, in sediments and summarizes relations between degree of reflectivity of grains and the level of thermal maturation. William Harrison further examines the degree of graphitization of organic matter as a function of diagenetic temperature.

2. Articles dealing with the examination of inorganic minerals in sediments. Janet Hoffman and John Hower deal with clay mineral assemblages as a function of burial depth and present examples from the Disturbed Belt of Montana. Zeolite reactions as paleothermometers in sedimentary rocks are discussed by Edward Ghent. Two further papers deal with inclusions or imperfections in crystals as paleotemperature indicators. Edwin Roedder discusses the significance of fluid inclusions, work which has particular application in many mineralized areas, and Charles Naeser presents data on the uses of fission-track counting in apatites and other heavy minerals to discern whether sediments have been heated beyond certain temperatures, as well as to date their cooling history. In the final paper, Eric Eslinger, Samuel Savin, and Hsueh-Wen Yeh examine the oxygen-isotope geothermometry of shales.

Clearly, many other papers and topics could have been included in this volume, but it is hoped that these articles will show the range of available techniques and will stimulate further studies and better correlation between various workers.

Copyright © 1979, The Society of Economic Paleontologists and Mineralogists

SEPM Special Publication No. 26, p. 3–16, March 1979

CONODONT COLOR ALTERATION, AN ORGANO-MINERAL METAMORPHIC INDEX, AND ITS APPLICATION TO APPALACHIAN BASIN GEOLOGY

ANITA G. HARRIS

U.S. Geological Survey, U.S. National Museum E-501, Washington, D.C. 20560

ABSTRACT

Conodonts are apatitic marine microfossils of Cambrian through Triassic age. During incipient metamorphism (50°–300° C) they change color from pale yellow to brown to black due to carbon-fixing within the trace amount of organic matter in their skeletons. As thermal metamorphism continues (300°–550° C), conodonts change from black to gray to white to crystal clear as a result of carbon loss, release of water of crystallization, and recrystallization. The conodont color alteration technique provides a unique link between mineral and organic indexing of thermal metamorphism and is best suited for carbonate rocks.

Conodont color alteration index (CAI) isograd maps for three stratigraphic intervals in the Appalachian basin show: (1) Conodont color alteration is directly related to the depth and duration of burial and the geothermal gradient. (2) Tectonics affect color alteration only where folding and faulting act to significantly increase depth of burial. (3) Isograds and overburden isopachs are conformable throughout most of the northern half and in the western part of the southern Appalachian basin; in these areas, isograd values gradually increase eastward except for a major disruption in the area of the Rome trough. (4) South of central Virginia, isograds are disrupted and irregular because late Paleozoic thrusting has severed and telescoped original burial metamorphism isograd patterns. (5) Basin restoration using conodont CAI isograds indicates a maximum shortening in northeast Tennessee of about 115 miles (185 km). (6) The CAI 2 isograd (=brown conodonts) for each stratigraphic interval lies near the eastern limit of oil production for that interval; this limit shifts eastward for each successively younger stratigraphic interval concomitant with decreasing overburden. (7) Gas production is less related to isograds and depends mostly on primary and (or) secondary porosity and permeability. The CAI 4 isograd (=brownish-black conodonts), however, approximates the eastern limit of gas production because the temperature (depth of burial) necessary to produce this high level of organic metamorphism concurrently produces mineral metamorphism that reduces porosity and permeability and the likelihood of commercial reservoirs.

INTRODUCTION

The thermal level of diagenesis or metamorphism of a rock can be evaluated from its mineral and (or) organic constituents. Incipient to high-grade metamorphic mineral assemblages (50° to +800° C) have been determined for pelitic sedimentary and volcanogenic rocks (Hower, 1976 and this volume; Turner and Verhoogen, 1960). Identification techniques for determining incipient to high-grade metamorphic mineral facies range from X-ray diffraction analysis of clay minerals to megascopic field identification of porphyroblasts, respectively. The equivalents of incipient to low-grade mineral metamorphic indices (30°–300° C) have been determined for organic materials such as kerogen, vitrinite, and palynomorphs (see Bostick and Damberger, 1971, Table 1). Indexing of organic materials is accomplished by means of chemical analysis, spectral fluorescence, reflectance or transluscence photometry, or visual color comparison. Organic indices are generally used for assessing temperatures of <300° C, whereas mineral indices are used for higher temperatures. It is noteworthy that the mineralogy and the depositional and post-depositional environments of pelitic rocks have made them the chief source of most organic and mineral metamorphic indices. For the same reasons, carbonate rocks have been, until now, unsuitable for assessing thermal metamorphism.

A unique link between mineral and organic indexing of thermal metamorphism is provided by the conodont color alteration technique which combines both mineral and organic indexing in one element. This technique is applicable in the temperature range of 50° to 550° C and is best suited for carbonate rocks.

Although most of the earlier work concerning conodont color alteration indexing (Epstein, 1976; Epstein and others, 1977) dealt with the experimental laboratory data that justify the technique, this report deals chiefly with its application, as the experimental data are now published.

I wish to thank J. E. Repetski and P. A. Scholle, U.S. Geological Survey, for their review of the manuscript.

CONODONTS

Conodonts (Fig. 1) are apatitic marine microfossils (generally 0.1–1 mm) that contain trace amounts of organic matter. They are the hard parts of an unknown organic group of worldwide distribution in Cambrian through Triassic rocks and are valuable index fossils for biostratigraphic

Copyright © 1979, The Society of Economic Paleontologists and Mineralogists

correlation throughout most of their geologic range. Because of their mineral composition (carbonate apatite according to Pietzner and others, 1968), conodonts are readily recovered from carbonate rocks by organic-acid treatment and are then further concentrated by heavy-liquid and (or) magnetic separation. They readily persist into greenschist metamorphic terranes and have been recovered from marbles interbedded with garnet-mica schists (Schönlaub and Zezula, 1975). Conodonts are most abundant in slowly deposited and (or) hydraulically reworked carbonate or clastic sediments. Though in the laboratory they are most easily extracted and concentrated from carbonate rocks, in the field they are most easily recognized in black shales because of the color contrast between the dull black shale and the vitreous lighter colored conodont (and even more noticeable if the conodonts are weathered and thus chalky white).

Conodont Color Alteration

Unweathered conodonts are pale yellow (Fig. 1a–d), light to dark brown (Fig. 1e–j), black (Fig. 1k, l), opaque white (Fig. 1m), and crystal clear (Fig. 1n, o); if unweathered and thermally unaltered, they are pale yellow (Fig. 1a–d). Using controlled time-temperature-pressure experiments with and without water, Epstein and others (1977) have shown that:

1. The sequence of color change from pale yellow to black to white conodonts found in field collections is the same as that produced by heating alone.

2. Conodont color alteration is progressive, cumulative, and irreversible.

3. Color alteration is time and temperature dependent.

4. Pressure neither retards nor accelerates color alteration.

5. In an open system, water neither retards nor accelerates color alteration, but in a sealed system, water in combination with pressure and heat retards color alteration by 50 percent.

6. Color alteration from pale yellow to black probably results from a carbon-fixing process within the trace amounts of organic matter in the apatitic conodont. Progressive color alteration from black through gray and opaque white, to crystal clear is the result of carbon loss, release of water of crystallization, and recrystallization.

7. Eight distinct levels of color alteration (termed indices) can be discriminated visually.

8. An Arrhenius plot of the experimental data and field data indicate that conodont color alteration begins at about 50° C and continues into garnet-grade metamorphism (about 550° C).
In addition, conodont color alteration has been correlated with other optical organic indices and with percent fixed carbon (Epstein and others, 1977; Table 1).

0.2 mm

Fig. 1.—A selection of conodont elements of diverse form, age, and color. Even though this is a black and white photograph, some concept of the color change in conodonts can be appreciated. Letter symbols are explained in text.

TABLE 1.—CORRELATION OF THREE ORGANIC METAMORPHISM INDEXES (ALL ARE OPTICAL TECHNIQUES), PERCENT FIXED CARBON, AND OVERBURDEN RANGES FOR CONODONT COLOR ALTERATION INDEXES (CAI) IN THE APPALACHIAN BASIN FOR MIDDLE ORDOVICIAN ROCKS

CAI[2]	Conodonts			Palynomorphs[1]		Vitrinite[1]	Percent Fixed Carbon
	Temperature °C[3]	Approx. overburden, in ft. (m) (values for Ordovician rocks in Appalachian basin)[4]		Translucency index (AMOCO)[5]	Weight percent carbon in kerogen	Reflectance	
1	<50–80	<4,000–(<1,220)		1–5	<82	<0.8	<60
1.5	50–90	4,000–8,000 (1,220–2,440)		5–up. 5	81–84	0.7–0.85	60–65
2	60–140	8,000–12,000 (2,440–3,660)		5–6	81–87	0.85–1.3	65–73
3	110–200	12,000–18,000 (3,660–5,490)		up. 5–6	83–89	1.4–1.95	74–84
4	190–300	18,000–26,000 (5,490–7,930)		6	84–90	1.95–3.6	84–95
5	300–400	begins at 26,000–30,000 (7,930–9,150)		up. 6–7	+90	+3.6	+95

[1] Palynomorph translucency and vitrinite reflectance determinations were made on the same rock samples from which conodont CAI had been determined.
[2] Data for CAI >5 are not given because CAI values >5.5 have not been found in the Appalachian basin. Several localities in North America (chiefly in Idaho, central-easternmost California, and Arizona) and Europe do have high CAI values that can be correlated with mineral indices.
[3] The temperature ranges for conodonts are from an Arrhenius plot of experimental data (Epstein and others, 1977) and represent heating durations of 500 million to 1 million years (lower temperature (500 m.y.-value) is applicable to heating durations of greater than about 50 million years).
[4] Overburden ranges are minimum estimates and were read frc t-Ordovician overburden isopach map (Harris and others, 1978) in areas where most of the post-Ordovician section is intact and deforn iinimal.
[5] The translucency indexes are mean range values and are visual c estimates and not photometric determinations.

APPLICATIONS OF THE CONODONT COLOR ALTERATION INDEX (CAI) IN THE APPALACHIAN BASIN

Conodont CAI as a geothermometer.—The CAI of a conodont sample can be determined by comparing unindexed conodonts with a set of laboratory-produced or field-assembled conodont standards or with a conodont color chart or soil color chip chart. These techniques are described in Epstein and others (1977).

Once a sample is indexed, a temperature range can be determined using an Arrhenius plot of the experimental data of Epstein and others (1977, fig. 3; Fig. 2). For example, late Middle Ordovician conodonts from Monterey, Virginia, in the Valley and Ridge province of the Appalachians, have a CAI value of 4 to 4.5. The age of the conodonts gives a maximum possible time for burial and heating of 470 m.y., but this can be further refined from a knowledge of Appalachian geology. In this part of the Appalachians, the latest possible time for beginning of unloading by erosion is Middle Triassic. Therefore, 270 m.y. is the maximum possible time for burial and heating, thus providing the lowest possible temperature for conodonts of CAI 4–4.5 (Fig. 2, heavy solid lines). Using Figure 2 and projecting the 4–4.5 field segment of the 270 m.y.-line to the X axis yields a temperature range of 185°–220° C for these conodonts. If, however, unloading began in the Late Pennsylvanian, which is the earliest possible

time for unloading in this part of the Appalachians, the maximum time for burial and heating is 210 m.y. (Fig. 2, dashed lines), thus a maximum temperature range of 190°–230° C. The total possible temperature range for this sample therefore is 185°–230° C.

This temperature range is compatible with other geologic data. In the vicinity of Monterey, at least 14,300 feet (4,359 m) of rock is known to overlie the Middle Ordovician (Fig. 2). If we assume an average geothermal gradient of 1° C per 100 feet, known overburden alone can account for a temperature of 160° C. Thickening and (or) duplication of section by folding and faulting combined with restoration of section missing by erosion could easily account for the additional 30°–70° C. Moreover, Paleozoic rocks in the Monterey area are cut by Cenozoic intrusions which could also indicate a higher than average Cenozoic geothermal gradient.

Conodont CAI isograd maps.—Conodont CAI isograd maps aid in basin analysis of thickness of overburden, structural history, and oil and gas potential.

The Appalachian basin is an ideal area to test and apply conodont CAI because (1) most of the bedrock is of Paleozoic age, (2) fairly abundant geologic data are available in a basin where geologic investigation has been going on for more than a century, (3) a variety of structural settings are available from near horizontal beds on the

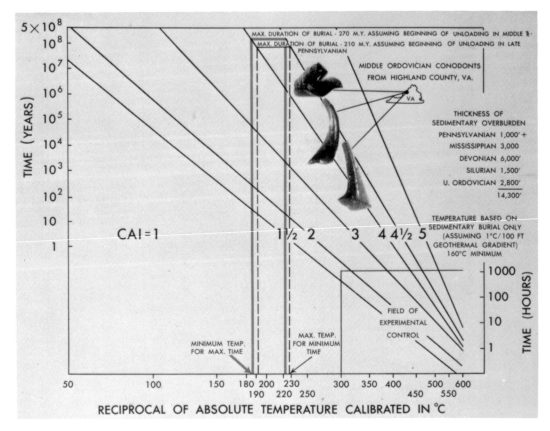

FIG. 2.—Arrhenius plot of data from conodont open-air heating runs of Epstein and others (1977, fig. 3) showing best color fit for late Middle Ordovician conodonts from the Valley and Ridge province near Monterey, Va. The CAI of these conodonts was determined by comparing them with index standards. Use of this plot for determination of minimum and maximum temperature ranges of conodont samples is explained in the text.

north and west to increasingly folded and faulted terrane on the east and south, (4) post-Paleozoic deposits are negligible, (5) igneous activity is negligible, and (6) more than a century of hydrocarbon exploration has broadly outlined the limits of oil and gas production.

Isograd maps were compiled for the Appalachian basin using U.S. Geological Survey collections and many specimens and samples provided by colleagues in universities, state surveys, and the petroleum industry. All collections are from carbonate rocks and almost all are from limestone. Conodonts from noncarbonate rocks were not used, so that variation in host-rock lithology could be neglected.

Because depth (temperature) and duration of burial affect color alteration, conodont CAI isograd maps were compiled for three stratigraphic intervals—Ordovician, Silurian through Middle Devonian, and Upper Devonian through Mississippian. These intervals were chosen because each

contains at least one widespread marine carbonate unit.

The best analysis of a conodont CAI isograd map is achieved when used in conjunction with an overburden isopach map. Such maps were compiled for each isograd interval (not shown in this report, but available in Harris and others, 1978) using data given in de Witt (1975), de Witt and others (1975), and Miller (1975). In general, in the Appalachian basin, overburden and CAI increase eastward for almost all stratigraphic intervals in post-Middle Ordovician rocks. CAI 1 is in areas having a history of minimal burial, which are along the western edge of the basin. CAI isograd and isopach trends are conformable throughout most of the basin, especially in western and central areas where most of the Paleozoic section is preserved and deformation was minimal.

CAI isograd map for Ordovician rocks (Fig. 3).—Conodonts from 60 Lower Ordovician, 318 Middle Ordovician, and 29 Upper Ordovician

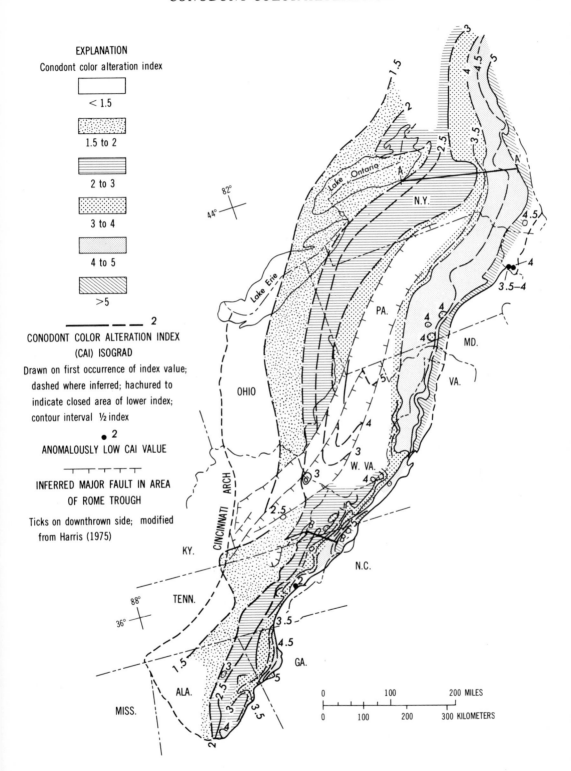

EXPLANATION

Conodont color alteration index

< 1.5

1.5 to 2

2 to 3

3 to 4

4 to 5

>5

————— — 2

CONODONT COLOR ALTERATION INDEX
(CAI) ISOGRAD

Drawn on first occurrence of index value;
dashed where inferred; hachured to
indicate closed area of lower index;
contour interval ½ index

• 2

ANOMALOUSLY LOW CAI VALUE

INFERRED MAJOR FAULT IN AREA
OF ROME TROUGH

Ticks on downthrown side; modified
from Harris (1975)

Fig. 3.—Conodont color alteration isograd map for Ordovician carbonate rocks, chiefly limestone, in the Appalachian basin. Lettered lines are explained in text.

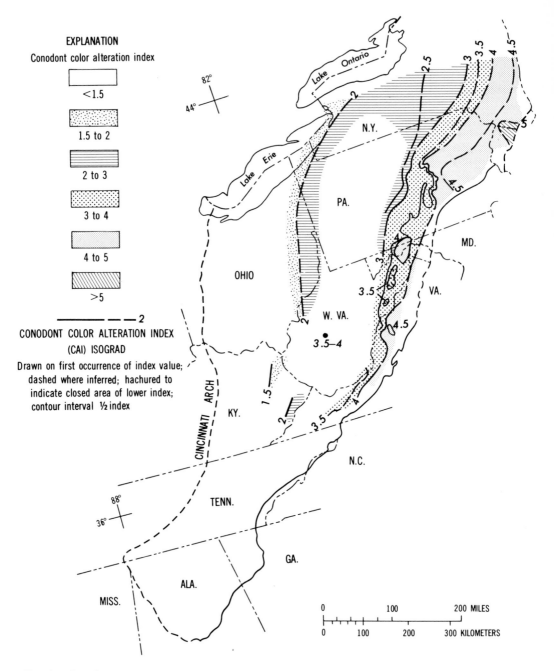

EXPLANATION

Conodont color alteration index

<1.5

1.5 to 2

2 to 3

3 to 4

4 to 5

>5

—————— — — 2

CONODONT COLOR ALTERATION INDEX
(CAI) ISOGRAD

Drawn on first occurrence of index value;
dashed where inferred; hachured to
indicate closed area of lower index;
contour interval ½ index

Fig. 4.—Conodont color alteration isograd map for Silurian through Middle Devonian limestones in the
Appalachian basin.

samples, for a total of 407 localities, were indexed
(sample localities are shown in Harris and others,
1978). Wherever possible, lower to middle
Middle Ordovician collections were used in order
to provide as uniform a stratigraphic position as
possible. Isograds are drawn on the first occur-

rence of an index value, so that the 2 isograd
passes through localities having conodonts with
index values of 1.5 to 2.

The consistent westward bulge of Ordovician
isograds in Pennsylvania reflects the composite
effect of eastward-thickening Silurian through

Permian clastic wedges that are superimposed in that area. Here too, as in much of the western and central part of the basin, the relatively even spacing of isograds indicates that the original post-Ordovician overburden patterns are not tectonically disrupted. One major isograd disruption occurs within the central Appalachian basin, in the Rome trough area. Well data indicate higher CAI and isopach values in the trough than to the east or west. Although data are meager, I have taken the liberty of presenting one possible interpretation of this area, rather than continuing the regional isograd trend through it with most of the data points appearing as anomalous hot spots. Interestingly, isograds in the Rome trough mimic Silurian isopachs (de Witt and others, 1975) as well as structure contours on the top of the Ordovician (Miller, 1975).

South of central Virginia, in the southeastern part of the Appalachian basin, isograds are disrupted and irregular, because late Paleozoic thrusting has severed and telescoped original metamorphic isograd patterns. In some areas tectonic burial by overriding thrust sheets appears to have had little influence on organic metamorphism levels in underlying autochthonous rocks indicating that the allochthonous sheet(s) was not thick enough to raise the metamorphic level of the autochthonous plate. In Tennessee, for example, along the present eastern limit of the basin where surface control is good, isograd trends in Ordovician rocks and the strike of the overriding Great Smoky thrust sheet (carrying older rocks of chlorite to biotite grade along its western edge) are discordant. Thrusting from the east can and does place more thermally mature strata over less thermally mature strata to the west. As a consequence, isograds on the surface of a thrust sheet do not necessarily characterize the organic maturity of rock in the autochthonous plate. This relationship is illustrated by the fact that autochthonous rock exposed in windows through the Blue Ridge thrust sheet in Tennessee and in the Pulaski thrust sheet in Virginia are thermally less mature than the overlying allochthonous sheet. Even more striking is the fact that conodonts from a window in the Great Smoky thrust sheet have a CAI of only 2, indicating that these Ordovician carbonate rocks could not have been buried as deeply or reached the same degree of thermal maturity as correlative rocks 10–15 miles (16–24 km) to the west which are exactly the same age but contain conodonts having a CAI of 4. The conodonts that have anomalously low CAI may be from rocks representing the eastern edge of the Appalachian basin, which were thrust

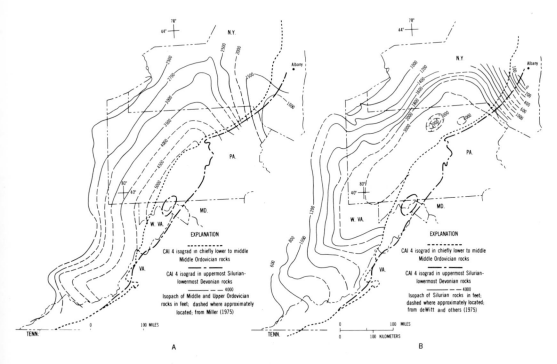

Fig. 5.—Maps showing the relationship of the same isograd in two stratigraphic intervals to the thickness of intervening strata (see text for detailed explanation).

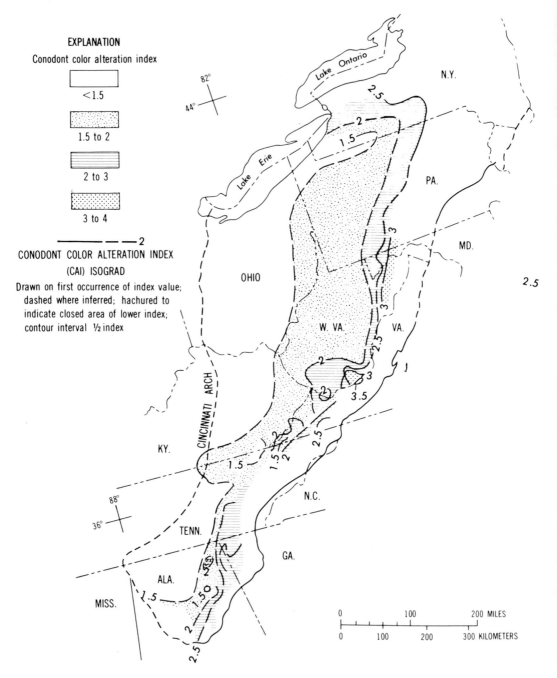

FIG. 6.—Conodont color alteration isograd map for Upper Devonian through Mississippian carbonate rocks in the Appalachian basin (sample localities are shown in Harris and others, 1978).

westward during a late tectonic event and are now near the depocenter of the basin. Similar anomalies are found in the thrusted terranes east of the main Ordovician outcrop belt in New Jersey and New York.

The isograd map also provides a guide for basin restoration. The CAI 2 and 5 isograds are about 175 miles (280 km) apart in New York (A-A′, Fig. 3) in an area of little deformation. These isograds bound an area that contained a minimum

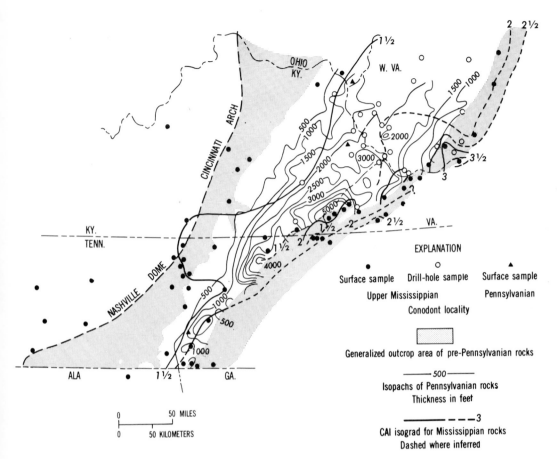

Fig. 7.—Part of the Appalachian basin showing Upper Mississippian CAI isograds superimposed on isopachs for Pennsylvanian rocks (from Epstein and others, 1977, fig. 18).

of 8,000 feet (on the northwest) to 25,000 feet (on the southeast) (2,440–7,625 m) of fill. Depositional patterns and strike appear to have been reasonably consistent throughout most of the basin during the Paleozoic. The distance between the 2 and 5 isograds remains remarkably consistent southward to central Virginia at which point the 5, 4.5, and 4 isograds disappear and reappear beneath the Blue Ridge thrust sheet and eastern isograd bands narrow. In the Appalachian basin, the shortest distance between the 2 and 5 isograd is 60 miles (95 km), in northeast Tennessee (B-B', Fig. 3), indicating a maximum shortening of the basin in this area of 115 miles (185 km). Using different methods of basin reconstruction, Dennison and Woodward (1963) show a minimum late Paleozoic shortening of 65 miles (105 km) in this same area. Still another estimate of shortening for part of this area is given by Harris (1974). His restoration of an Upper Cambrian stromatolite

bank edge indicates 40 miles (64 km) of shortening in the less tectonically disturbed west half of the Valley and Ridge province in northeast Tennessee.

If the geothermal gradient was reasonably consistent throughout the basin (isopach and isograd maps indicate it was), then overburden isopachs could be restored from isograd values in areas of erosion. The 4.5 isograd area in eastern Pennsylvania now contains a minimum of 24,000 feet (7,880 m) of overburden which can be used as a base value. Table 1 gives minimum overburden ranges for Ordovician CAI values in the Appalachian basin.

CAI isograd map for Silurian through Middle Devonian rocks (Fig. 4).—Conodonts from 43 Silurian and 111 Lower and Middle Devonian localities, a total of 154 points, were indexed (sample localities are shown in Harris and others, 1978). Most points are for uppermost Silurian and lowermost Devonian limestones. Isograds do

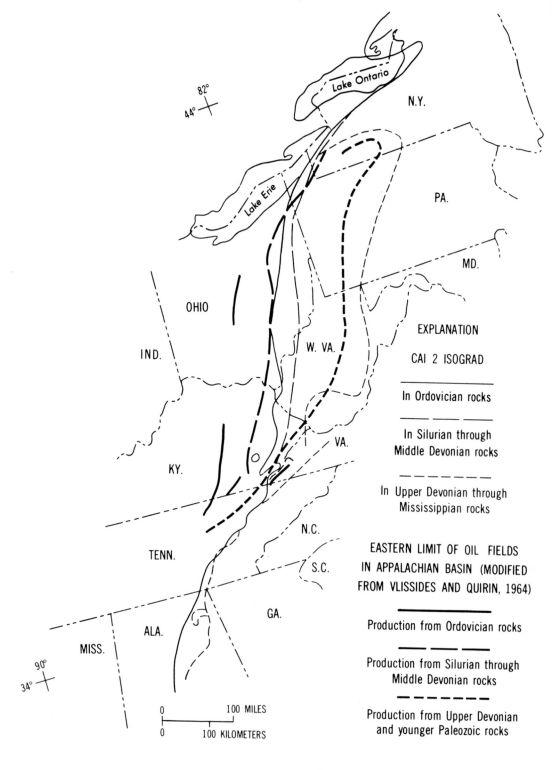

EXPLANATION

CAI 2 ISOGRAD

In Ordovician rocks

In Silurian through
Middle Devonian rocks

In Upper Devonian through
Mississippian rocks

EASTERN LIMIT OF OIL FIELDS
IN APPALACHIAN BASIN (MODIFIED
FROM VLISSIDES AND QUIRIN, 1964)

Production from Ordovician rocks

Production from Silurian through
Middle Devonian rocks

Production from Upper Devonian
and younger Paleozoic rocks

A

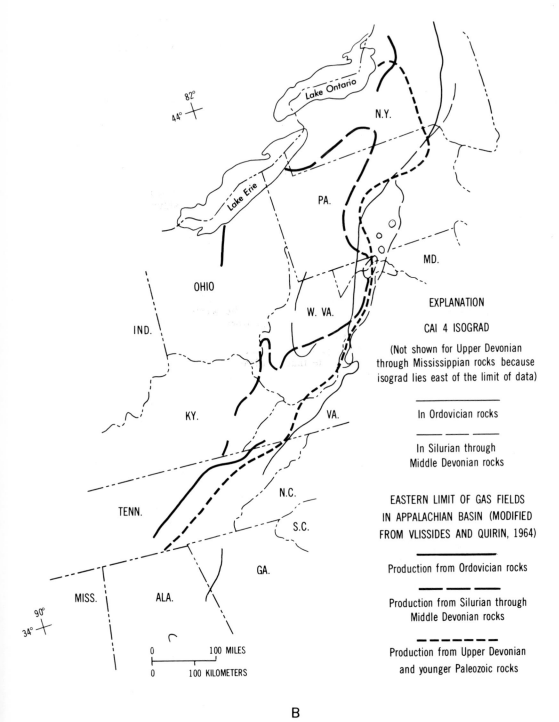

CAI 4 ISOGRAD

(Not shown for Upper Devonian
through Mississippian rocks because
isograd lies east of the limit of data)

In Ordovician rocks

In Silurian through
Middle Devonian rocks

EASTERN LIMIT OF GAS FIELDS
IN APPALACHIAN BASIN (MODIFIED
FROM VLISSIDES AND QUIRIN, 1964)

Production from Ordovician rocks

Production from Silurian through
Middle Devonian rocks

Production from Upper Devonian
and younger Paleozoic rocks

B

FIG. 8.—Maps showing the eastern limit of oil (*A*) and gas (*B*) production for three stratigraphic intervals in the Appalachian basin.

not extend south of southern Virginia because carbonate rocks of this age are generally absent in the outcrop belt.

The Silurian through Middle Devonian isograd map readily shows the correlation of conodont color with thickness of overburden regardless of tectonic setting. In western New York overburden is relatively thin (4,000–8,000 ft; 1,220–2,440 m) and conodonts are only slightly altered (CAI 1.5–2). Devonian rocks are virtually flat lying across New York. Only the easternmost part of the outcrop belt, just west of Albany, New York, is within the folded and faulted Valley and Ridge province. Conodont color gradually darkens across New York and no abrupt color change occurs at the tectonic front. The color alteration in New York conforms to an eastward-thickening wedge of Upper Devonian clastic rocks. Conodonts in south-central Pennsylvania, in the western part of the folded and faulted Valley and Ridge province, are the same color as conodonts in flat-lying rocks having comparable overburden in east-central New York. The darkest conodonts are in outliers east of the main outcrop belts and adjacent to the anthracite fields in eastern Pennsylvania, where Mississippian and Pennsylvanian rocks are thickest. These data demonstrate that tectonics do not affect color alteration in conodonts.

Comparison of the same isograd value at different stratigraphic levels provides information on the thickness of intervening strata. Near coincidence of two such isograds indicates a thin intervening section, an unconformity, and (or) tectonic superposition. Figure 5 shows the relationship between the CAI 4 isograd in chiefly lower to middle Middle Ordovician rocks and the same isograd in Upper Silurian-lowermost Devonian rocks in the northern half of the Appalachian basin. The two isograds are nearly coincident from their northern limit to central Pennsylvania at which point they abruptly spread 60 miles (95 km) apart. They begin reconvergence at the Pennsylvania-Maryland border and finally merge in central Virginia. This configuration results from regional variation in erosional, depositional, and structural patterns. From central Pennsylvania to northeastern New York (near Albany), Upper Ordovician and Silurian rocks thin and are gradually cut out along a post-Middle Ordovician unconformity (Taconic unconformity), so that near Albany, uppermost Silurian rocks lie on Middle to Upper Ordovician rocks. Thus overburden for both units is nearly identical and isograds are nearly coincident. A Middle and Upper Ordovician chiefly clastic marine sequence thickens from 2,000 to about 15,000 feet (610–4,575 m) southeastward across Pennsylvania and thins gradually southwestward and rapidly northeastward (Fig.

5A). A much thinner series of Silurian rocks follows nearly the same regional pattern (compare Fig. 5A with 5B). Both intervals combine to produce the isograd pattern shown on Figure 5. The reversal in isograd position (upper Silurian-lowermost Devonian isograds west of Middle Ordovician isograds) in southern Virginia results from westward thrusting of more thermally mature younger strata over less thermally mature older strata.

CAI isograd map for Upper Devonian through Mississippian rocks (Fig. 6).—Conodonts from 143 Upper Devonian through Mississippian and from 14 Pennsylvanian localities were indexed. Pennsylvanian localities were used only as a guide to contouring. Pennsylvanian-Permian rocks probably represent most of the post-Mississippian deposits in the Appalachian basin because younger deposits were very thin or absent.

A comparison of Upper Mississippian isograds and Pennsylvanian isopachs (Fig. 7) in the central Appalachian basin shows:

1. The westward-projecting lobe of the CAI 1.5 isograd at the Kentucky-Tennessee border may conform to a lobe of Pennsylvanian rocks that at one time extended farther westward. Significantly the CAI 1.5 isograd outlines an area of oil and gas production from Mississippian rocks in Tennessee and Kentucky (de Witt, 1975, sheet 4).

2. The CAI 2 isograd in West Virginia encompasses the 2,500-foot-thick (762-m-thick) outlier of Pennsylvanian rock that must have at one time been part of a much thicker continuous northwest-trending clastic wedge.

3. The northwest-trending area of CAI 2 to 3.5 in southeast West Virginia coincides with anomalous Ordovician CAI highs and with an area of modern hot spring activity. The high heat flow in this area possibly results from a buried pluton (see Dennison and Johnson, 1971).

Assessment of hydrocarbon potential from CAI isograd maps.—Because organic maturity within conodonts is related to depth of burial, more than one isograd map is needed to assess oil and gas potential. Accordingly, the three isograd maps were produced (Figs. 3, 4, and 6). Figure 8 shows the eastern limit of commercial oil (Fig. 8A) and gas (Fig. 8B) production in the Appalachian basin for three stratigraphic intervals and the CAI isograd that best approximates this boundary. It is important to note that the cutoff for oil production for different stratigraphic intervals is not geographically coincident. The limit for oil production for each successively younger stratigraphic interval generally shifts eastward concomitant with decreasing overburden values (indicated by the eastward shift of the associated CAI 2 isograd). In Figure 8A, the CAI 2 isograd lies near the eastern limit of oil production for each stratigraphic interval. It appears that the CAI 2 isograd which correlates with a fixed carbon value of 65 percent (Table 1) marks the cutoff for commercial oil and condensate production (Bostick and Damberger, 1971, Table 1). Gas production (Fig. 8B), on the other hand, shows less relation to isograds. The eastern limit of Silurian through Middle Devonian production broadly meanders across the basin and across isograd trends. Gas generation occurs below, within, and well above the thermal limits for oil generation (from soon after burial into chlorite-grade metamorphism; from CAI 1 to +4). Gas production depends mostly on primary and (or) secondary porosity and permeability for accumulation in structural and stratigraphic traps. Thus it appears odd that the CAI 4 isograd approximates the eastern limit for gas production over large areas of the Appalachian basin. However, the temperature (depth of burial) necessary to produce this high level of organic metamorphism (CAI 4) concurrently produces mineral metamorphism that reduces porosity and permeability and the likelihood of commercial reservoirs.

From the standpoint of organic diagenesis, the entire Paleozoic section provides potential target horizons for oil production only in the westernmost part of the northern Appalachian basin and throughout the western half of the southern Appalachian basin. However, younger Paleozoic rocks within this terrane may not have even reached the thermal threshold for oil generation. Conodont color alteration begins near the upper thermal limit for oil generation, so that this technique can only be used for assessing the thermal cutoff, not the thermal threshold for oil generation.

The requirements for natural gas production are far less restrictive than those for oil. Gas can be generated from a greater variety of organic materials and can be generated and preserved through a much larger thermal range than oil. As a consequence, almost the entire Appalachian basin has a thermal potential for gas production. But the increase in thermal metamorphism and tectonic deformation eastward in the basin decreases the potential for gas production in that area for the following reasons. Although gas generation continues into the high levels of thermal metamorphism found in the eastern part of the basin, mineral metamorphism simultaneously acts to reduce porosity and permeability. In this same area, major and minor tectonic fractures can produce permeability and serve as channelways and traps for gas migration and accumulation. These same channelways, however, can contribute to the loss of gas from otherwise suitable traps. Therefore, exploration in the eastern part of the basin must be preceeded by detailed geologic investigation to identify appropriate targets.

REFERENCES

Bostick, N. H., and Damberger, H. H., 1971, The carbon ratio rule and petroleum potential in NPC region 9: Illinois Geol. Survey, Illinois Petroleum, no. 95, p. 142–151.

Dennison, J. M., and Johnson, R. W., Jr., 1971, Tertiary intrusions and associated phenomena near the thirty-eighth parallel fracture zone in Virginia and West Virginia: Geol. Soc. America Bull., v. 82, p. 501–508.

—— and Woodward, H. P., 1963, Palinspastic maps of central Appalachians: Am. Assoc. Petroleum Geologists Bull., v. 47, p. 666–680.

De Witt, Wallace, Jr., 1975, Oil and gas data from the upper Paleozoic rocks in the Appalachian basin: U.S. Geol. Survey Misc. Geol. Inv. Map I-917 A, 4 sheets, scale 1:2,500,000.

Epstein, A. G., 1976, Conodont color alteration—an index to incipient through garnet-grade metamorphism [abs.]: Geol. Soc. America Abs. with Programs, v. 8, p. 167.

——, Epstein, J. B., and Harris, L. D., 1977, Conodont color alteration—an index to organic metamorphism: U.S. Geol. Survey Prof. Paper 995, 27 p.

Harris, A. G., Harris, L. D., and Epstein, J. B., 1978, Oil and gas data from Paleozoic rocks of the Appalachian basin: maps for assessing hydrocarbon potential and thermal maturity (conodont color alteration isograds and overburden isopachs): U.S. Geol. Survey Misc. Geol. Inv. Map I-917 E, scale 1:2,500,000.

Harris, L. D., 1974, Cambrian facies trends—tool for estimating shortening in the southern Valley and Ridge province [abs.]: Am. Assoc. Petroleum Geologists Bull., v. 58, p. 1892.

——, 1975, Oil and gas data from the Lower Ordovician and Cambrian rocks of the Appalachian basin: U.S. Geol. Survey Misc. Geol. Inv. Map I-917 D, 3 sheets, scale 1:2,500,000.

Hower, John, 1976, The determination of diagenetic and metamorphic temperatures using clay mineral assemblages [abs.]: Geol. Soc. America Abs. with Programs, v. 8, p. 201.

Miller, R. L., 1975, Oil and gas data from the Upper and Middle Ordovician rocks in the Appalachian basin: U.S. Geol. Survey Misc. Geol. Inv. Map I-917 C, 2 sheets, scale 1:2,500,000.

PIETZNER, HORST, AND OTHERS, 1968, Zur chemischen Zusammensetzung und Mikromorphologie der Conodonten: Palaeontographica, v. 128, pt. A, p. 115–152.

SCHÖNLAUB, H. P., AND ZEZULA, GERHARD, 1975, Silur-Conodonten aus einer Phyllonitzone im Muralpen-Kristallin (Lungau/Salzburg): Geol. Bundesanst. Verh., no. 4, p. 253–269.

TURNER, F. J., AND VERHOOGEN, JOHN, 1960, Igneous and metamorphic petrology: New York, McGraw-Hill Book Co., 694 p.

VLISSIDES, S. D., AND QUIRIN, R. A., 1964, Oil and gas fields of the United States exclusive of Alaska and Hawaii: Washington, D.C., U.S. Geol. Survey, scale 1:2,500,000.

SEPM Special Publication No. 26, p. 17–43, March 1979

MICROSCOPIC MEASUREMENT OF THE LEVEL OF CATAGENESIS OF SOLID ORGANIC MATTER IN SEDIMENTARY ROCKS TO AID EXPLORATION FOR PETROLEUM AND TO DETERMINE FORMER BURIAL TEMPERATURES—A REVIEW

NEELY H. BOSTICK

Programmgruppe für Erdöl und organische Geochemie Kernforschungsanlage-Jülich, German Federal Republic*

ABSTRACT

Dispersed solid organic matter occurs as a minor constituent in most sedimentary rocks. It consists of diverse materials that' are like the macerals in coals (though usually in different proportions than in normal coals), and its maturation is chemically and physically like coalification. Reflected-light microscopy enables one to recognize the different organic grains and to select the best type for optical measurement to indicate the indigenous maturation of organic matter in the rock. The organic constituent selected should have the following characters. It (1) is virgin when deposited with the sediment, (2) matures regularly, (3) is not subject to retrograde alteration, (4) resists reaction with adjacent fluids and solids, (5) is not significantly affected by pressure, (6) occurs widely in rocks of diverse lithology and facies, (7) is distinguishable from pre-altered and redeposited material, (8) can be analyzed separately, (9) persists through a broad range of catagenesis and metamorphism, and (10) has properties that can be analyzed throughout the alteration range by a relatively inexpensive technique.

Vitrinite grains that are not recycled from previous rocks satisfy the above requirements, and reflectance is normally the property measured. Data from experimental studies in the laboratory and from a number of sedimentary basins show that, for the most part, temperature and duration of heating determine the progress of catagenesis.

Regional and vertical studies of organic catagenesis indicate a correlation between rank of solid organic matter and occurrence of oil and gas—even though the fluids migrate extensively. Oil is generated first at about 0.5% vitrinite reflectance (oil immersion) and occurs last, associated with gas condensate, at about 1.3%. Above that rank, abundant methane can be generated from types of kerogen that do not yield oil. Petroleum occurrence is limited in much of the eastern United States because the sedimentary rocks have been too hot in the past (mostly as a result of former deep burial). The regions that are favorable or unfavorable for exploration for petroleum or gas, from the point of view of level of organic maturation, are indicated on a map. On the continental shelf, especially where sediments are less than two kilometers thick, it is most important to determine whether burial temperature has been adequate for petroleum formation.

Determination of actual past temperatures is not required for correlation with petroleum occurrence. Measured level of organic catagenesis can be used, however, to estimate actual former temperatures from our knowledge of the general time-temperature-rank function of the reactions and from geologic information on the burial history of the rocks in question.

INTRODUCTION

Organic matter is a minor constituent in most sedimentary rocks. The study of organic matter has little appeal to people trained in mineralogy compared to the study of rare heavy minerals. It is not surprising, therefore, that the organic matter has been neglected in work by sedimentary petrologists. However, some organic matter is present in most sedimentary rocks; its analysis helps understand the origin and burial history of the rocks and aids exploration for petroleum.

A practical distinction is made between the solid organic matter and the fluid organic matter in rocks, for the latter consists of compounds that can be analyzed in detail by methods of organic geochemistry. With rare, but economically important, exceptions (oil-rich sandstones and limestones, asphalt sands and deposits of solid bitumens), more than 90% of the organic matter in sedimentary rocks is solid grains (Fig. 1). They have been deposited in the sediment just as clastic mineral grains have. Analysis of the solid organic matter is the subject of this paper.

Chemical studies have shown that the solid organic matter consists of carbon-oxygen-hydrogen-nitrogen-sulfur compounds similar to those found in coals. Data from elemental chemical analyses and chemical structural studies allow some interpretation of the types and the changes of solid organic matter in sedimentary rocks. However, the data are difficult to interpret because the grains are of mixed kind and origin,

*Present address: U.S. Geological Survey, Box 25046, Denver Federal Center, Denver, Colorado 80225.

Copyright © 1979, The Society of Economic Paleontologists and Mineralogists

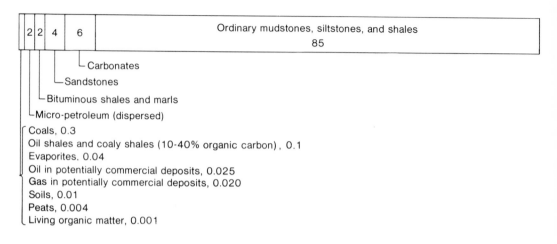

Fig. 1.—Distribution of organic matter (measured in percent by mass of organic carbon) in sedimentary rocks of the continents. This portrayal does not include hydrocarbon gas dissolved in water, which may amount to as much as 10% of the total continental carbon. Modified from Vassoyevich (1973) and from Vassoeyvich and others (1976).

even in a single rock. Microscopy reveals the separate grains of all but the organic groundmass (below one micrometer in size). Hence it is possible to analyze separate types of organic matter under the microscope and to record their changes under different conditions in the laboratory and in nature.

Solid organic matter composes, by weight, 0.1–1% of most siltstones and sandstones. It is usually less abundant in limestones and may be absent in pure limestones and in red beds. "Petroleum source rock" shales generally have 1–10% solid organic matter. Oil shales, carbonaceous shales, and, of course, coals are even richer.

From studies of coal it has long been recognized that after the biochemical changes during peat diagenesis the chemical and physical changes continue until the coal is in a clearly metamorphic state—anthracite or even graphite. These coalification changes also have been called rank change, anthralithification, eometamorphism, anchimetamorphism, maturation, (late) diagenesis, and catagenesis. I follow the suggestion and example of N. B. Vassoyevich and use the term catagenesis when referring to the change in solid organic matter in sedimentary rocks after the peat stage (diagenesis) and into the anthracite stage (metamorphism).

The foundation for microscopy of dispersed organic matter is mainly the field of coal petrology, with significant contributions from palynology. The most commonly used techniques and terms to describe solid organic matter are derived from coal petrology studies, and these will be summarized and illustrated in the next two sections.

BASIC METHODS

The "ideal constituent."—Because organic matter dispersed in clastic rocks is rarely of one predominant type as it is in many coals, bulk analysis is not reliable. A particular constituent must be selected to measure indigenous catagenetic change. This can be done under the microscope. Such a constituent should have the following characteristics. It: (1) is virgin when deposited with the sediment, (2) matures regularly, (3) is not subject to retrograde alteration, (4) resists reaction with adjacent fluids and solids, (5) is not significantly affected by pressure, (6) occurs widely in rocks of diverse lithology and facies, (7) is distinguishable from pre-altered and redeposited material, (8) can be analyzed separately, (9) persists through a broad range of catagenesis and metamorphism, and (10) has properties that can be analyzed by a relatively inexpensive technique throughout the alteration range.

Vitrinite (Table 1) serves well as the "ideal constituent" having the foregoing characteristics, and by using reflectance microscopy it can be identified and its rank can be measured accurately. Vitrinite occurs widely in dispersed form, and it is the major constituent in most coals. (Huminite in lignites is equivalent.)

Reflectance microscopy.—When solid organic matter undergoes increasing catagenesis, its reflectance, absorption index, and refractive index increase progressively. The method of reflectance microscopy relies on microscopes that illuminate and image the specimen from the same side, normal to its flat polished surface. Such microscopes are used to study metals and opaque ores.

TABLE 1.—PHYTOCLAST GROUPS DISTINGUISHED IN REFLECTANCE ANALYSIS

Terms used in this study	Plant material or possible equivalent coal maceral
Liptinite (Lp)	Spores and pollen (exine) (E) Plant cuticles (C) Resin particles or cell filling (R) Structured or coherent algal bodies (Al) (Liptinite [= exinite])
Floccules and groundmass (D)	Mostly algal debris plus finely comminuted liptinite and "low-gray", and solid bitumen. (Groundmass, liptinite, colloalginite, sorbomixtinite, granular micrinite)
Low-gray vitrinite (L)	Structured or apparently unstructured woody tissues plus tissue impregnations. (First-cycle vitrinite.)
High-gray (H) and fusinite (F)	Redeposited and biochemically altered plant fragments and products of alteration (re-cycled vitrinite, pre-altered vitrinite, semifusinite, sclerotinite (S), micrinite fusinite; approximately inertinite).

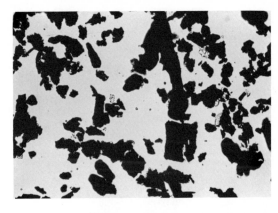

FIG. 2.—Concentrate of dispersed solid organic matter from a Jurassic shale, viewed by transmitted light. Field width is about 300 micrometers. Rank is 1.3% R_{oil}^{max} (vitrinite).

Generally, oil immersion objectives are used for organic petrography, for they give greater contrast and enable the constituents to be recognized better than do objectives in air. The quantitative measure of the level of catagenesis is the reflectance from the polished surface of one type of constituent. This measurement is made with a photomultiplier photometer which is calibrated on the microscope using polished glass or mineral standards. The advantage of reflectance microscopy is that both morphology, with internal structure, and approximate rank (reflectance of the organic matter can be *seen* simultaneously.

Transmitted light microscopy.—The color or light absorption of organic matter is measured by comparison with a set of reference slides or color standards or by photometry of the absorption of transmitted light. Particle strew mounts are used as in palynological preparations (Figs. 2, 3). Unfortunately, with this technique it is difficult to obtain materials of a constant thickness except when microspores of a given type occur in a set of samples. Furthermore, it requires a skilled palynologist to recognize pre-altered or redeposited grains. When these conditions are

met, however, very accurate results can be obtained in the lower range of organic catagenesis (Grayson, 1975).

Refractive index of liptinite or vitrinite is a measure of organic catagenesis that has been used extensively in the Soviet Union. With this technique it is difficult to eliminate redeposited grains, and the Becke line movement with respect to the immersion liquids is hard to see, especially with materials of high rank.

Fluorescence microscopy.—Different kinds of solid organic matter can be distinguished and maturation can be measured using fluorescence microscopy (Jacob, 1973; Van Gijzel, 1975; Ottenjahn, Teichmüller, and Wolf, 1975). Blue or ultraviolet excitation causes liptinite, low rank

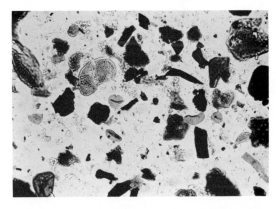

FIG. 3.—Concentrate of dispersed solid organic matter from an Eocene siltstone, viewed by transmitted light. Field width is about 300 micrometers. Rank is 0.4% R_{oil}^{max} (vitrinite).

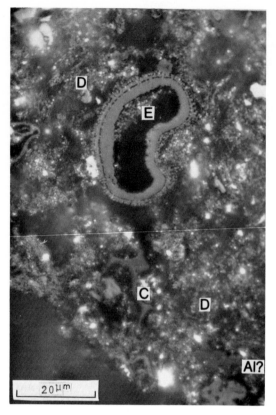

FIG. 4.—Concentrate of solid organic matter from an Eocene argillaceous lignite after hydrothermal reaction for 64 days at 300° C, 41,000 kPa. See Table 1 for symbols. Vitrinite reflectance is 0.95% R_{oil}^{max}.

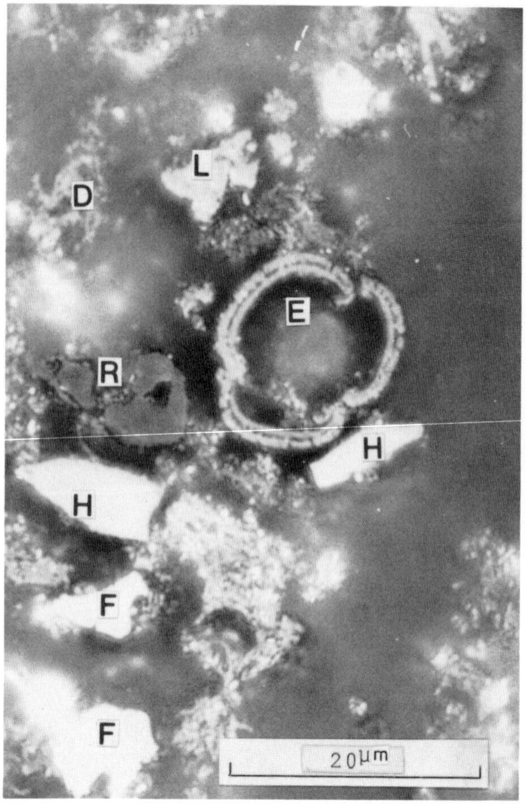

FIG. 5.—Concentrate of solid organic matter from an Eocene argillaceous lignite after hydrothermal reaction for 64 days at 300 C, 41,000 kPa. See Table 1 for symbols. Vitrinite reflectance is 0.95% R_{oil}^{max}.

vitrinite (huminite), and some organic groundmass and solid bitumens to reradiate light in the range from yellow-green to orange. The fluorescence helps greatly in distinguishing these substances in polished section, and careful analysis has shown systematic changes in the spectrum and the intensity of fluorescence with change in rank. This method is promising for measuring both diagenesis and catagenesis of low-rank organic matter and for determining the initiation of petroleum generation—particularly in rocks that contain algal remains or a fine organic groundmass but have no vitrinite.

Preparation of samples.—The whole rock or a concentrate of organic particles after demineralization may be prepared for microscope study. The whole rock is preferred especially for analysis of solid bitumens and for fluorescence study, the concentrate for measurement of vitrinite reflectance, refractive index, and translucency of microspores. Organic particles are concentrated from a rock with some combination of hand picking, crushing, ultrasonic disintegration, flotation, heavy liquid separation, and demineralization with HCl and HF (Bostick and Alpern, 1977). Preparations for reflectance microscopy include polished rock slabs or chips and polished organic concentrates embedded in plastic pellets or on microscope slides. Specimens are ground and polished on rotating laps with sequentially finer diamonds or silicon carbide and then with powders such as aluminum, chromium, or cerium oxides. For transmitted light microscopy, organic concentrates are mounted on slides by means of glycerine jelly, Canada balsam or artificial media.

KINDS OF SOLID ORGANIC MATTER

Microscopy of solid organic matter shows grains and groundmass with great diversity of color, structure, refractive index, and reflectance. The solid organic matter consists of spores and pollen,

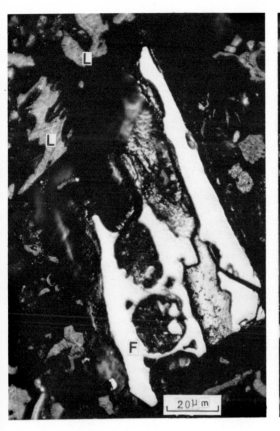

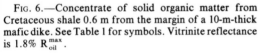

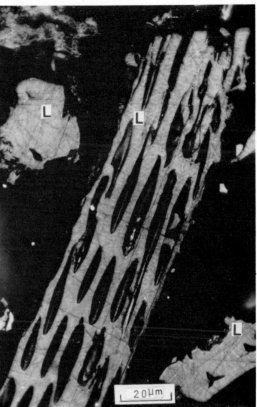

FIG. 6.—Concentrate of solid organic matter from Cretaceous shale 0.6 m from the margin of a 10-m-thick mafic dike. See Table 1 for symbols. Vitrinite reflectance is 1.8% R_{oil}^{max} .

FIG. 7.—Concentrate of solid organic matter from Cretaceous shale 0.6 m from the margin of a 10-m-thick mafic dike. See Table 1 for symbols. Vitrinite reflectance is 1.8% R_{oil}^{max} .

leaf cuticle, resin balls and fillings, and woody fragments that have bordered pits, ribs, fibers, or cellular structure (Figs. 2–14). Compact particles, apparently unstructured, also are revealed. These probably are equivalent to the collinite described by coal petrologists or to insoluble humate reported by geochemists. Some rocks, especially organic-rich ones, contain irregular or flocculent masses, mostly of algal origin, solid bitumens, and organic groundmass too fine-grained to differentiate under the microscope. Protista and fragments of animal fossils are occasionally found.

The solid organic matter is approximately the same as the "kerogen" of organic geochemists. The individual grains have been termed macerals, phytoclasts, organoliths, or organoclasts. Since the constituents dealt with in this paper are mainly plant fragments, I will call them phytoclasts.

Classification of solid organic matter.—Detailed classification and description of solid or-ganic matter is not included in this paper. Examples of classification for dispersed organic matter are the works by Alpern (1970), Combaz (1975), Ginsburg, Lapo, and Letushova (1976), and Parparova (1969). Parparova's work is correlated closely with geochemical studies of solid organic matter. Summaries of classifications used in coal petrology are found in Stach and others (1975), and Ginsburg, Lapo, and Letushova (1976). Expressions used frequently to describe the total assemblage of solid organic matter are non-petrologic and include sapropelic or "oily" (oil-prone) and humic or "coaly" kerogen. The first kind contains dominantly what petrologists call liptinite, especially alginite, and the second contains mainly vitrinite and inertinite. Other expressions in recent use by the French are "type I" through "type III", and these are discussed below in the section called "Applications of organic petrography to petroleum exploration."

Simplified classification for measurement of

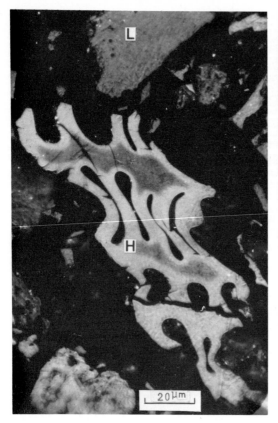

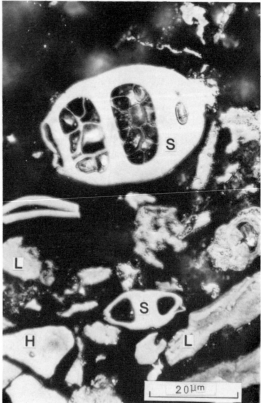

Fig. 8.—Concentrate of solid organic matter from a Cretaceous fine-grained sandstone 6 m from the margin of a 4-m-thick felsic dike. See Table 1 for symbols. Vitrinite reflectance is 0.5% R_{oil}^{max}.

Fig. 9.—Organic concentrate from an Eocene fine-grained sandstone 1.2 m from the margin of a 2-m-thick basalt dike. See Table 1 for symbols. Vitrinite reflectance is 1.5% R_{oil}^{max}.

alteration.—I find it useful to separate organic matter into four groups to facilitate selection of a constituent that can be measured to determine what degree of catagenetic change is indigenous to the rock. Table 1 summarizes these groups. Coal maceral names are given in parentheses where they make up part or all of the group. The phytoclasts with the lowest reflectance (liptinite) and highest reflectance (fusinite) are usually minor constituents; those with intermediate reflectance (the "grays") make up the bulk of most assemblages.

Liptinite includes plant spores and pollen, recognizable from their form, resin particles or cell fillings, irregular fragments of plant cuticle (Figs. 4, 5), algal remains, and probably some solid bitumen or other secondary matter. These phytoclasts are usually a dull gray in polished section, but in samples with vitrinite reflectance above 1.5% their reflectance approaches that of other constituents. Liptinite appears yellow or yellow-

gray in transmitted light, becoming amber, then opaque, with increasing catagenesis.

Floccules, irregular masses, or a fine-grained groundmass are difficult to polish and offer no surfaces adequate for reflectance measurement (Figs. 4, 5). These occur especially in limestones and organic-rich shales. These materials are mainly algal debris plus finely comminuted liptinite and other macerals. In transmitted light they appear as the lightest material on a slide. When they are a fine groundmass they are commonly lost during rock maceration.

The *low-gray* vitrinite group is separated from similar phytoclasts to designate those particles whose rank represents maturation *within* the host rock. "Low-gray" is equivalent to vitrinite in normal coals. This is illustrated schematically in Figure 15 as if a polished rock section were seen in reflected light (the relative size of the organic particles is greatly exaggerated).

The phytoclast assemblage deposited in a given

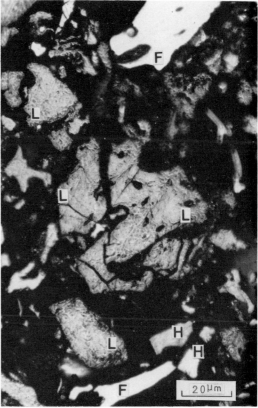

FIG. 10.—Concentrate of solid organic matter from Cretaceous shales 46 m from the margin of a 10-m-thick mafic dike. See Table 1 for symbols. Vitrinite reflectance is 0.50% R_{oil}^{max} (no influence).

FIG. 11.—Concentrate of solid organic matter from Cretaceous shales 1.9 m from the margin of a 10-m-thick mafic dike. See Table 1 for symbols. Vitrinite reflectance is 1.2% R_{oil}^{max}.

rock consists of organic debris having diverse origins and different histories of transportation. Some phytoclasts are eroded from older rocks, and part of their present rank was attained in the former host rock; some may be plant fragments, relatively fresh from the plant or altered and filled by flavonoid or humic compounds; and some have been biochemically altered during the history of a complicated trip from plant to site of final deposition. Only the reflectance of phytoclasts which had *minimum* rank when the sediment was deposited indicates the level of catagenesis inherent to the host rock.

In practice, low-gray and high-gray groups are separated mainly on the basis of reflectance as judged by the observer, or a low-gray value is picked from a histogram of reflectance values of the entire suite—low-gray being the dullest gray particles (excepting liptinite, solid bitumens, or contaminant from borehole caving) in the sample (Fig. 16). In the majority of samples, low-gray is easily definable, for many grains with uniform low reflectance are visible in the microscope field at one time (Figs. 7, 10). In a few cases, where low-gray is sparse (Fig. 5), or in high-rank samples where all materials have nearly the same reflectance (Figs. 9, 13), the distinction of low-gray within the diverse assemblage is difficult. Low-gray grains generally are amber in transmitted light, though they may be opaque if thick or of high rank.

High-gray encompasses materials similar to the low-gray vitrinite, but with a more complicated history. Some of the high-gray grains are vitrinite and other phytoclasts redeposited from older sedimentary rocks. Some may be plant or peat material which is biochemically altered before it is incorporated in the sediment. The fusinite is mainly plant charcoal. In some samples, the reflectance commonly differs in different zones of the same grain (Fig. 8); very likely these are weathered or pre-altered grains. The high-gray

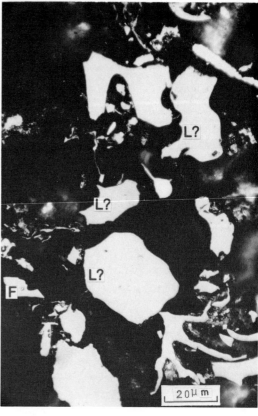

F_{IG}. 12.—Concentrate of solid organic matter from Cretaceous shales 0.60 m from the margin of a 10-m-thick mafic dike. See Table 1 for symbols. Vitrinite reflectance is 1.8% R_{oil}^{max}.

F_{IG}. 13.—Concentrate of solid organic matter from Cretaceous shales 0.31 m from the margin of a 10-m-thick mafic dike. See Table 1 for symbols. Vitrinite reflectance is 3.3% R_{oil}^{max}.

group may contain the coal macerals semifusinite, micrinite, sclerotinite (Fig. 9), and fusinite, plus redeposited macerals of other groups. These materials are dark amber or opaque in transmitted light.

CATAGENESIS OF SOLID ORGANIC MATTER

Catagenesis of solid organic matter has been studied and discussed in relation to coal for many years, so much of our knowledge about it comes from coal science. However, the mass of solid organic matter dispersed in sedimentary rocks on the continents is about three hundred times that of coal (Fig. 1). The different properties observed in coals in early studies could not be explained wholly by differences in original plant material or in biochemical alteration during diagenesis. It was found that coal reacts to contact, dynamothermal and regional burial metamorphism, though differently than do minerals. Heat plays the most

important role in coal alteration. However, heat near dikes or sills acts differently from the heat in deeply buried sediments at corresponding temperatures because of the greatly different duration of the reactions (Bostick, 1973).

Catagenesis of solid organic matter shows on a regional scale regardless of whether it results from regional differences in burial depth or in geothermal gradient. Maps of organic catagenesis may portray classic coal rank parameters (Fig. 17), rank of dispersed solid organic matter (Fig. 18), or derived parameters such as paleodepth or paleotemperature (Fig. 19).

Importance of temperature.—In the laboratory the relation between rank of solid organic matter (whether measured chemically or optically) and heating is clearly shown (Fig. 20). In nature the same relation of increased rank with increased temperature is found adjacent to volcanic dikes (Figs. 10–14, 21), although here only relative

Library
I.U.P.
Indiana, Pa

552.5   As63p
L.1

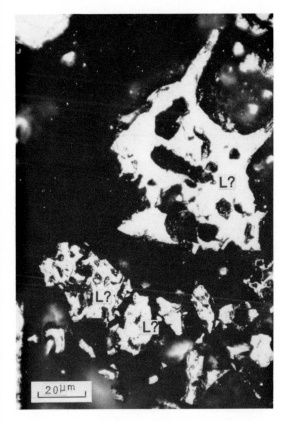

FIG. 14.—Concentrate of solid organic matter from Cretaceous shales 0.05 m from the margin of a 10-m-thick mafic dike. See Table 1 for symbols. Vitrinite reflectance is 4.6% R_{oil}^{max} .

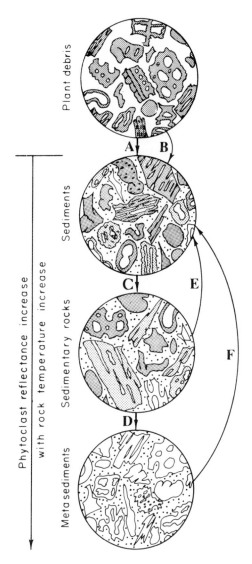

temperatures are inferred. The level of catagenesis resulting from normal sedimentary burial also increases with temperature. Laboratory data can be used as a "thermometer" to determine from measured organic rank the former maximum temperatures in dike contact zones. Values so derived agree with theoretical heat studies (Bostick, 1971). The lab data cannot be used to indicate former burial temperatures, however, because a given level of catagenesis is produced by much lower temperatures under natural conditions of sediment burial. The difference in rate or kind of reaction appears to result mainly from a difference in reaction duration. (This topic will be discussed in the section on paleotemperature measurement.) Organic catagenesis normally increases regularly with increasing depth, as shown in the example

FIG. 15.—Schematic representation of solid organic matter dispersed in sedimentary rocks, as seen by reflected-light microscopy. The arrows indicate the

following history of the organic matter: *A*, plant material is deposited with mineral grains in a sediment; *B*, some organic matter is altered biochemically during delayed transport from plant to sediment; *C*, the sediment is buried and indurated to become rock; *D*, with further burial and heating, the organic matter that has not been greatly altered previously acquires higher reflectance (lighter tone in the figure); and *E, F*, some organic particles may be eroded and redeposited in younger sediments, where they will have relatively high rank. The measure of rank increase (diagenesis plus catagenesis) from sediment to rock of the given sample is the reflectance of the least altered detrital organic matter in the sample. An additional possibility not considered in this figure is that fluid organic matter can migrate into the rock and be altered into a solid bitumen that can possibly be confused with vitrinite under the microscope. From Bostick (1974, fig. 5).

of Figure 22. Extremely irregular changes are occasionally reported, however, such as those reported from boreholes near the deep-seated intrusion of the Bramsche Massif, northern Germany. It has been suggested that such irregularity may result from alteration by hydrothermal fluids (Koch, 1974).

Pressure and shear.—The question arises whether burial catagenesis results from heat alone or from the combination of heat and pressure. Early workers in coal geology ascribed a large role to pressure, but they did not have a clear conception of temperatures deep in sedimentary basins or of former deep burial of parts of some coal basins. Rank and temperature data from different boreholes, such as those shown in figure 23, show that organic catagenesis increases with temperature (geothermal gradient) rather than with depth (pressure gradient). The results of a statistical analysis by Kontorovich, Parparova, and Trushkov (1967) of several hundred boreholes showed a better correlation of rank with temperature than with depth, despite the general parallelism of these two parameters (Table 2).

Shear appears to have generally no influence on the course of catagenesis, though some examples of increased vitrinite anisotropy in shear zones in anthracite are known (Stach and others,

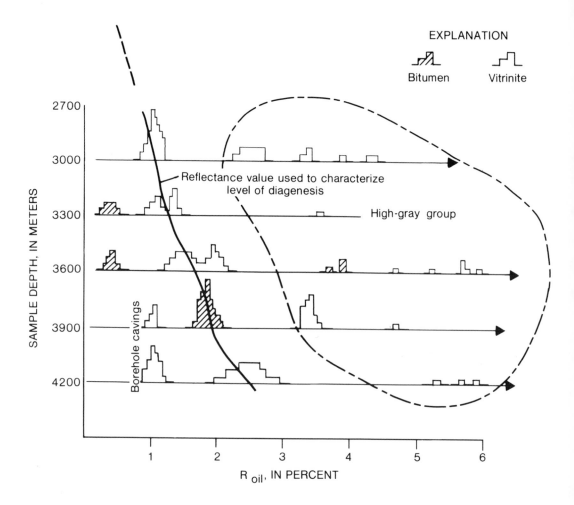

Fig. 16.—Reflectograms of solid organic matter from five samples of borehole cuttings from various depths. The analytical problem in measuring organic catagenesis is to distinguish first-cycle vitrinite from redeposited grains, well cavings, and possible solid bitumens. These other types of particles are recognized by such features as high reflectance, enclosure of clastic mineral grains, high fluorescence, or persistent occurrence of the same materials in several samples. After Robert (1974).

TABLE 2.—STATISTICAL ANALYSIS OF VITRINITE
REFRACTIVE INDEX WITH RESPECT TO OTHER BOREHOLE
DATA (FROM KONTOROVICH, PARPAROVA,
AND TRUSHKOV, 1967)

TABLE 2.—STATISTICAL ANALYSIS OF VITRINITE
REFRACTIVE INDEX WITH RESPECT TO OTHER BOREHOLE
DATA (FROM KONTOROVICH, PARPAROVA,
AND TRUSHKOV, 1967)

Paired coefficient		Partial coefficient	
		Depth constant Temperature	Temperature constant Depth
Temperature	Depth		
0.81	0.65	0.67	0.22

1975). Kalkreuth (1976) measured illite crystallinity and vitrinite reflectance of samples from tightly sheared anticlines in Carboniferous slates. Although the illite crystallinity was relatively higher in the axial zones than elsewhere, the vitrinite maximum reflectance and bireflectance did not vary systematically with position in the structures.

APPLICATION OF ORGANIC PETROGRAPHY TO PETROLEUM
EXPLORATION

The connection between catagenesis of solid organic matter and the occurrence of petroleum deposits has been known since the publication of works by White (1915, 1935) and Fuller (1919, 1920). Since then many studies have shown that the vertical distribution of oil and gas (Fig. 24) and the level of catagenesis of solid organic matter (Fig. 20) both change systematically with rock temperature. Table 3 summarizes the relationship between organic catagenesis and petroleum occurrence, regardless of depth, in many parts of the world. These examples emphasize the *occurrence* of commercial hydrocarbon deposits, many

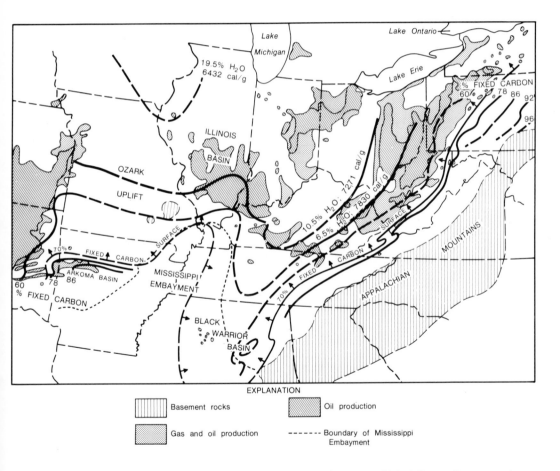

FIG. 17.—Coalification pattern of Pennsylvanian coal basins of the eastern United States. Data on rank are plotted for near-surface Pennsylvanian coals regardless of their stratigraphic position. The isorank lines are superimposed on a map of oil and gas occurrence in upper Paleozoic strata. Modified from Bostick and Damberger (1971) and from Damberger (1974).

TABLE 3.—RELATIONSHIPS BETWEEN CATAGENESIS OF COAL AND DISPERSED SOLID ORGANIC MATTER AND OCCURRENCE OF OIL AND GAS DEPOSITS BOSTICK AND DAMBERGER (1971) AND BARTENSTEIN AND TEICHMÜLLER (1974), WITH ADDITIONS.

Refl. %R oil	Volatile matter % d.a.f	Btu/1b (moist. minerai-matter free)	ASTM coal classes and groups	Internat. coal classes	White, 1915 Eastern United States	Fuller, 1919 North Texas, Paleozoic	Lilley, 1924 Eastern U.S. and Midcontinent, Pennsylvanian	Ammosov, 1961 (Intl. Geol. Review, 1962) Ural-Volga and North Caucasus Districts	Rodionova, 1967 North Caspian Basin Paleozoic	Vassoevich et al. 1967 Review of world picture	Correia, 1967 Sahara, Paleozoic	Staplin 1969 Canadian Great Plains	Vassoevich et al. 1969 Review of world picture	Ammosov and Gorshkov (1969, fig. 14) West Siberian platform Density of oil in near-source deposits (at 20°C, g/cm³)	Kontorovich (1970, table 6) (Western Siberia) Intensity of process of oil formation	Kontorovich (1970, table 6) Evaluation of prospects for oil and gas	Preobrazhenskaya, Klucheva and Ivanova (1971) (Giant oil and gas deposits of the U.S.S.R.) (% of total)
0.3	50	8,300	Lignite	13						Occasional dry gas	Oil deposits	Wet or dry hydro- carbons			Oil formation does not take place. Gas product is CO_2	Syngenetic oil absent	
0.4	45	9,500	Subbituminous C	12	Commercial oil fields		Mixed base below 35°	Major oil fields	Main formation of bitum-inoids	Naptphene-methane oil; wet gas			Methane formation in early catagenesis	0.90			
0.5		11,000	Subbituminous B / A, 9, 10	11		Principal oil fields	Mixed base 35-40°			Methane oil increases over napthene; more solid paraffins and light aromatics; wet gas	Gas and shows of oil		Oil formation (plus gas)	0.88	Weak oil formation. Methane is main product of gas formation	Main zone of oil and gas occurrence	
0.6	40	13,000	High-volatile C / B	8		Principal fields of light oil and gas	Paraffin base above 40°					hydro- carbons		0.86	Main zone of oil formation. Methane is main product of gas formation		
0.7		14,000	High-volatile A	7				Minor oil fields, but of high quality		Highly paraffinic oil, rich in normal alkanes				0.84		Various kinds of oil	
0.8	35		Medium-volatile	6		Rare high-gravity oil; common gas fields				Gas condensates	Gas	Dry gas	Wet gas and gas condensates	0.82 / 0.80	Oil formation dies out. Gas formation continues		Oil / Gas
0.9	30		Low-volatile	5	Oil deadline	Usually no commercial production	Dry gas only	Rare oil occur-rences		Lowest limit of commercial oil. Gas	Hydro-carbon traces	Dry gas or barren			No oil formation. Gas formation continues, with dry methane as main product	Subordinate oil occurrence	
1.0	20		Semi-anthracite	4	No commercial oil fields; gas fields may occur	No oil or gas, with rare exceptions	No hydro-carbons			Lowest limit of commercial gas			Late catagenetic methane			Oil usually absent. Possible deposits of gas and, more rarely, gas condensate	
2.0	10		Anthracite	3 / 2 / 1													
3.0																	

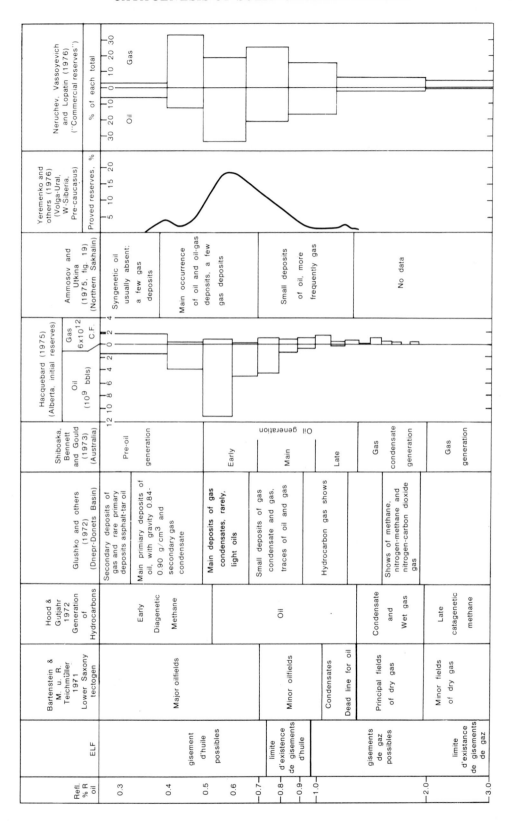

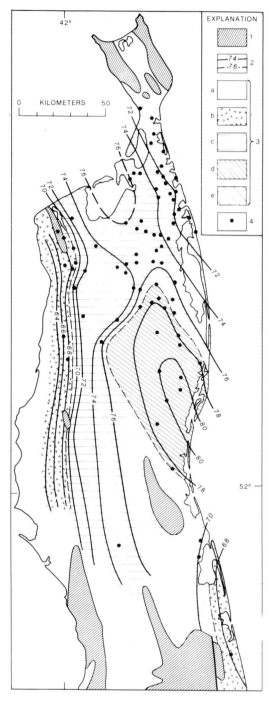

FIG. 18.—Map of "isoresplends" (equal-reflectance isopleths) of the Dagin Horizon (Neogene), northern Sakhalin Island, USSR. *1,* Horizon eroded (missing); *2,* isoresplends, $10 \times \% \ R_{air}$; *3,* stages of lithification, $10 \times \% \ R_{air}$: a, < 62; b, 62–70, c, 70–76, d, 77–84, e, 84–90; *4,* sample localities. Modified from Ammosov and Utkina (1975).

of which may have migrated from the site of origin. A comparison between oil and gas occurrence and generation is shown in Figure 25. Note that the resources (columns C and D) of oil and gas occur at depths somewhat shallower than those indicated for generation of most oil and gas (columns A and B). In particular, shallow gas has been lost and deep gas appears to be as yet largely not accounted for in known resources. The preponderance of gas over oil generation in deep strata does, however, show in the resources (column E)—as well as in Table 3. Note also that sapropelic organic matter (column A) has greater oil and gas generation potential than organic matter of dominantly humic type. The question of origin of hydrocarbons must be answered to predict better the location and total quantity of hydrocarbons generated. This requires geochemical studies of indigenous hydrocarbons with respect to the type and level of catagenesis of their associated solid organic matter.

Geochemical study of coals shows well the relation between the catagenesis of solid matter, and that of organic fluids, although most coals have a low capacity to generate petroleum. Figure 26 shows the carbon preference index (CPI) of hydrocarbons from a ranked series of Australian coals. Low CPI correlates with late-generated and mature petroleum, and is shown in the figure to correlate also with high coal rank. Hydrocarbons and the total bitumen content are related systematically to level of catagenesis of dispersed solid organic matter. For example, Figure 27 shows chloroform-extracted bitumens (D) and hydrocarbons (F) extracted from Carboniferous shales, arranged on a scale of increasing paleodepth and level of organic catagenesis (indicated by vitrinite reflectance (A), %C of coals and dispersed organic matter (B), and %H of dispersed organic matter). From such studies it is possible to demonstrate the relationships between hydrocarbon generation and the level of organic catagenesis.

The empirical relationships between oil and gas occurrence, and the level of catagenesis of solid organic matter are applied in petroleum exploration and prediction of resources. An early example by Hacquebard and Donaldson (1970) from the northern extension of the Appalachians is shown in Figure 28. From just a few vitrinite reflectance data they plotted the relative depth of exploration boreholes with respect to an "oil dead line" and showed which boreholes were "favorable" or "unfavorable" for oil occurrence. It is clear that boreholes 1, 6, 7, and 8 were drilled well beyond the depth of likely oil preservation.

Figure 17 is a regional map of the present level of organic catagenesis in the eastern United States from classical work by White (1915), modified by more recent data. The "oil dead line" (70%

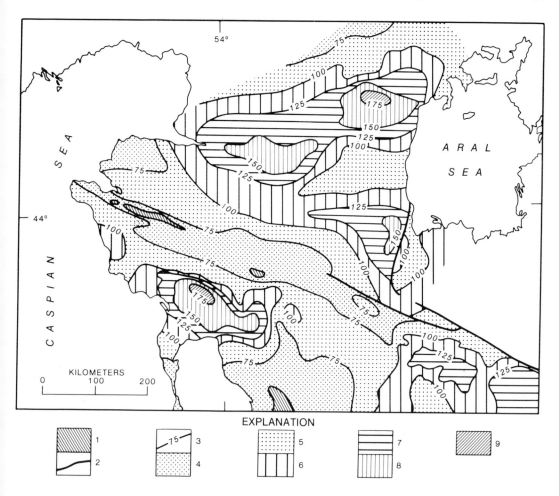

FIG. 19.—Map of paleoisotherms of the topmost Jurassic strata in part of Kazakhstan and central Asia. *1,* Jurassic strata partly eroded; *2,* major faults; *3,* paleoisotherm zones, in degrees C; *4,* < 75; *5,* 75–100; *6,* 100–125; *7,* 125–150; *8,* 150–175; *9,* 175–200. Modified from Ammosov and Sharkova (1975). The paleoisotherms were derived from vitrinite reflectance.

fixed carbon, 1.1% R_o) is an isorank *surface;* wells spudded below (southeast and south of) this (eroded) isorank surface can be expected to yield gas or only small amounts of high-gravity oil. Wells started above (northwest or north of) this surface may strike oil, or, depending on their distance above the surface, they may drill through it into strata barren of petroleum. In this example there are no strata preserved that are above a shallower "immaturity surface" (except in the younger Mississippi Embayment). An "immaturity surface" above which catagenesis has not yet generated petroleum will be an important concept, however, in exploration for oil offshore on the Atlantic coastal margin.

Composition of dispersed organic matter.—In addition to the level of organic catagenesis, the bulk chemical composition of different kinds of solid organic matter and the basin history are also important in predicting petroleum occurrence. Figure 29 illustrates elemental composition (C, H, and O) of four basic varieties of organic matter. Type I (floccules, colloalginite, or sapropelic or "oily" kerogen) is the most important for generation of hydrocarbons because of its very high hydrogen content. Type III ("low-gray" vitrinite, or humic or "coaly" kerogen) is the main organic constituent of most shales and sandstones and all coals except the rare algal types. In its pure form, Type III appears to have potential

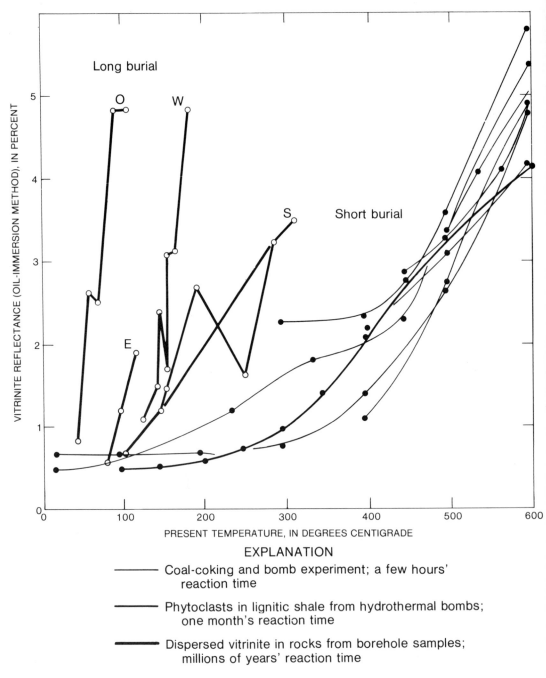

FIG. 20.—Reflectance of vitrinite from coals and from lignitic shale altered by laboratory reactions and of dispersed vitrinite from deep boreholes. *O*, Carboniferous, Arkoma Basin, Oklahoma—maximum present depth 3,750 m; *E*, Lower Cretaceous, Angelina County, Texas—maximum present depth 3,500 m; *W*, Upper Jurassic and Lower Cretaceous, La Salle County, Texas—maximum present depth 6,520 m; *S*, Salton geothermal field, California—maximum present depth 2,460 m. Modified from Bostick (1974).

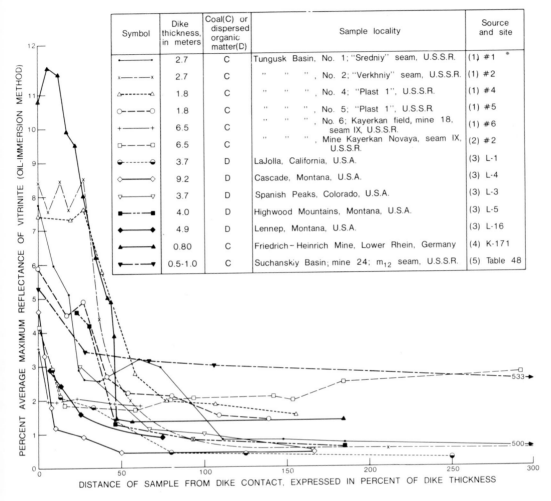

Symbol	Dike thickness, in meters	Coal(C) or dispersed organic matter(D)	Sample locality	Source and site
•——————•	2.7	C	Tungusk Basin, No. 1; "Sredniy" seam, U.S.S.R.	(1) #1
x— — —x	2.7	C	" " ", No. 2; "Verkhniy" seam, U.S.S.R.	(1) #2
▵·······▵	1.8	C	" " ", No. 4; "Plast 1", U.S.S.R.	(1) #4
○— — —○	1.8	C	" " ", No. 5; "Plast 1", U.S.S.R.	(1) #5
+——————+	6.5	C	" " ", No. 6; Kayerkan field, mine 18, seam IX, U.S.S.R.	(1) #6
□— — —□	6.5	C	" " ", Mine Kayerkan Novaya, seam IX, U.S.S.R.	(2) #2
●·······●	3.7	D	LaJolla, California, U.S.A.	(3) L-1
◇——————◇	9.2	D	Cascade, Montana, U.S.A.	(3) L-4
▽——————▽	3.7	D	Spanish Peaks, Colorado, U.S.A.	(3) L-3
■— — —■	4.0	D	Highwood Mountains, Montana, U.S.A.	(3) L-5
◆——————◆	4.9	D	Lennep, Montana, U.S.A.	(3) L-16
▲——————▲	0.80	C	Friedrich–Heinrich Mine, Lower Rhein, Germany	(4) K-171
▼— — —▼	0.5-1.0	C	Suchanskiy Basin; mine 24; m_{12} seam, U.S.S.R.	(5) Table 48

Fig. 21.—Contact alteration of solid organic matter adjacent to volcanic dikes, measured by vitrinite reflectance. Data sources: *1*, Bogdanova (1968); *2*, Bogdanova (1965); *3*, Bostick (1971); *4*, Teichmüller (1973); *5*, Ivanov (1975).

mainly for generating deep dry gas. Type II (liptinite, except alginite) has relatively high hydrogen content like type I, but generation of significant amounts of the hydrocarbons predominant in oils has not been demonstrated from type II. A fourth type, significant in some rocks, is lower in hydrogen and oxygen than Type III and has very little hydrocarbon potential. It consists of fusinite (fossil charcoal) and other "high-gray" material that has been redeposited from older high rank rocks or has been strongly altered biochemically.

Sedimentary rocks commonly contain a mixture of these materials. However, many oil shales contain dominantly type I, and coals and many

clastic rocks contain mainly type III. The materials of these chemical types can be distinguished microscopically except when they occur as a fine groundmass. Present research is aimed at better analysis of the groundmass organic materials, particularly by means of fluorescence microscopy.

Basin history.—The relation between burial history and petroleum generation deserves more consideration than it receives. Figure 30 is a plot of the burial history of a hypothetical particular rock unit, with its contained organic matter, superimposed on a diagram of the phases of petroleum and gas generation. The depth of these phases in this example is typical, but in some

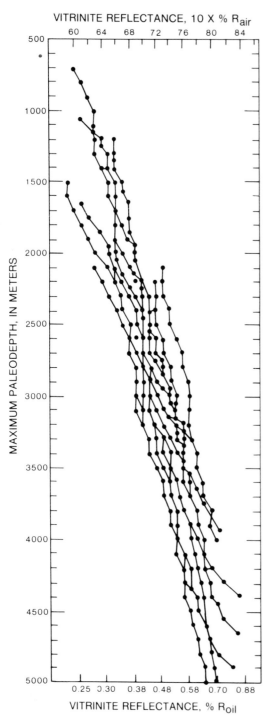

VITRINITE REFLECTANCE, 10 X % R_{air}

MAXIMUM PALEODEPTH, IN METERS

VITRINITE REFLECTANCE, % R_{oil}

FIG. 22.—Vitrinite reflectance for series of samples from boreholes in northern Sakhalin Island, USSR. The same data appear in Figure 31. After Ammosov and Utkina (1975). R_{oil} figures were derived from % R_{air} by use of data in van Krevelen (1961, p. 350) and in Sarbeyeva and Krylova (1968, Table 1).

TABLE 4.—VITRINITE REFLECTANCE AND MINIMUM BURIAL PALEOTEMPERATURE NEEDED TO ATTAIN A GIVEN REFLECTANCE LEVEL. AFTER AMMOSOV, BABASHKIN, AND SHARKOVA (1975). R_{oil} HAS BEEN ADDED BY CONVERSION FROM % R_{air} AS IN FIGURE 22.

Vitrinite reflectance		Paleo-temperature (°C, minimum)
$10xR_{air}$	R_{oil}	
72	0.48	100
76	0.59	125
80	0.72	145
84	0.86	165
88	1.00	180
92	1.16	195
96	1.42	210
100	1.50	220
104	1.70	230
108	1.92	235
112	2.14	240

petroleum basins they have been found to be much shallower or deeper. In a given basin their depth must be determined by analysis of the level of organic catagenesis. In this example about 25 million years, with burial totaling 2,300 meters, are required for the rock unit to reach a degree of catagenesis at which oil begins to form. The main phase of oil formation occurs between 35 and 45 million years after deposition. Two alternatives are illustrated for the period between 50 and 75 million years after deposition: (1) uplift and erosion reduces or stops organic catagenesis, or (2) continued maturation at 3,500 meters brings the organic matter beyond the main phase of petroleum generation, with likely expulsion of fluids in large quantity. Beyond 75 million years condensate and gas remain in the rock, and beyond 80 million years only methane is generated. Additional information on the time of formation of structures and consolidation of impermeable traps would be required for complete evaluation of this sample situation for petroleum exploration.

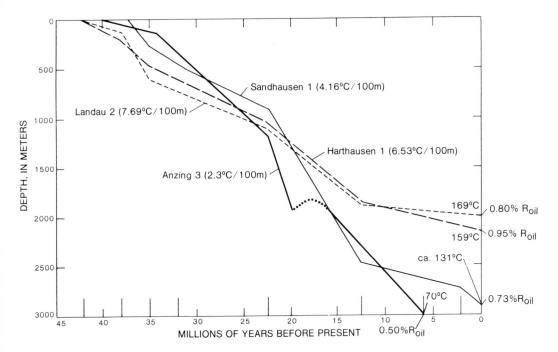

FIG. 23.—Diagrams of burial history of Eocene strata in four boreholes in the Upper Rhein graben, with comparison of present temperature and rank (% R_{oil}^{random}, vitrinite) and average temperature gradient. After Teichmüller and Teichmüller (1975).

PALEOTEMPERATURE MEASUREMENT

The further use of studies of the level of organic maturation to determine paleotemperatures in sedimentary basins depends greatly on definition of the time-temperature-rank function and the use of geologic information to find the reaction duration. One expedient is to construct a table of minimum temperatures needed to attain various levels of organic catagenesis (Table 4). This table

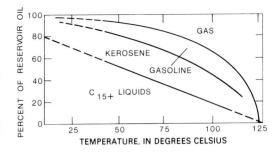

FIG. 24.—Generalized plot of reservoir hydrocarbon composition versus presentday reservoir temperature, western Canada. Modified from Evans, Rogers, and Bailey (1971).

is based on measured reflectance and present temperatures in boreholes where, from geologic studies, the present thermal gradients are hoped to be nearly representative of past gradients. A rank-temperature table appears to give good results if applied in sedimentary basins with similar burial histories and with rather long burial times, such as the stable Mesozoic and Paleozoic basins.

In many cases it is difficult to determine accurately the former burial history of a particular set of strata, and changed heat flow can seldom be ruled out. Nonetheless, many data indicate that the reactions of organic catagenesis are very slow at the temperatures in sedimentary basins, so the reaction duration must be considered in evaluating past temperatures. This factor shows in Figure 20. Natural samples from boreholes reach a given level of organic maturation at much lower temperature than do artificially heated samples. In addition, the natural samples exposed to heating for tens of millions of years are altered at lower temperatures than are those exposed to heating only a few million years. A similar relationship shows in Figure 31 in the plot of vitrinite reflectance against maximum paleodepth for samples from northern Sakhalin. The Neogene samples have consistently lower reflectance at a given depth than do Paleogene and Cretaceous samples.

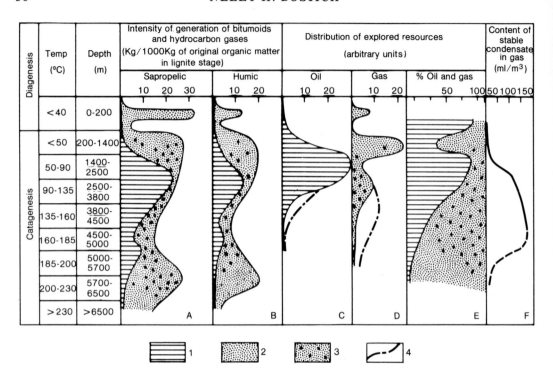

Fig. 25.—Generation oil and gas and distribution of their resources in the sedimentary crust. *1*, Oil and bitumoids; *2*, gas (CH₄); *3*, gas (C₂H₆ to C₅H₁₂); *4*, predicted resource distribution after more thorough exploration below 1–3 km depth. Modified from Kontorovich and Trofimuk (1976).

Time-temperature-rank models.—Several schemes for relating temperature, duration and rank are in use; most are based on the first-order reaction equations applied by Huck and Karweil (1955) to coal catagenesis. Lopatin uses a numerical summation to integrate time-temperature increments (Lopatin and Bostick, 1973; Lopatin, 1976). Bostick (1973) and Hood and Castaño (1974) use graphical techniques, the latter incorporating an "effective heating time" during which the rock is within 15° C of its maximum burial temperature. The accuracy of these schemes will be difficult to judge until the accuracy of the raw data used to build and test them can be better evaluated. Expressed in terms of temperature, the precision of determining temperature, duration, or rank appears to be on the order of ±20° C in most cases. When the reaction model is defined better, the accuracy should approach this value.

In contradiction with the above ideas about the rate of organic catagenesis, some researchers state that the duration of the reaction makes little difference in the level of catagenesis after about the first million years. Neruchev (Neruchev and Parparova, 1972; Neruchev and others, 1976) is a strong proponent of this view. If this should prove to be correct, or nearly so, the rank and maximum burial temperature could be correlated more simply and accurately than many workers now believe. In the middle range of data published recently by Neruchev and others (Fig. 32, this report) there is little difference in rank between Neogene, Mesozoic, and Paleozoic samples (actual burial time is not given) for any paleodepth.

Fig. 27.—Content of organic matter extracted from Carboniferous shales in Donets Basin, USSR. The data are plotted on a vertical scale of maximum paleodepth of the samples. Columns B and C show rank of kerogen and coals in the same sequence in terms of classical coal chemical analysis. Vitrinite reflectance in column A has been estimated from the chemical data for the coals. Modified from Neruchev, Vassoyevich and Lopatin (1976).

$$CPI = \frac{(\%C_{25} \text{ to } C_{33} \text{ odd})+(\%C_{23} \text{ to } C_{31} \text{ odd})}{2(\%C_{24} \text{ to } C_{32} \text{ even})}$$

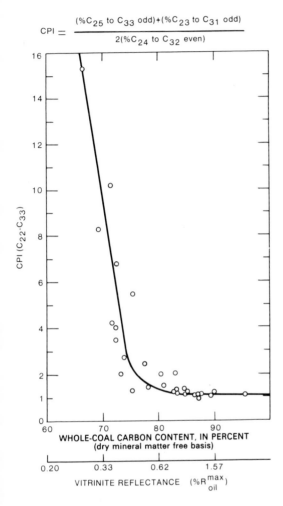

However, for the shallower and deeper points at a given paleodepth the vitrinite reflectance tends to be greater for the older samples.

Despite our incomplete knowledge of the exact catagenetic reaction rate, using the techniques described it is already possible to compile paleotemperature maps that are relatively accurate (Fig. 19). Data on level of organic catagenesis, hence approximate temperature, have been correlated with mineral metamorphic facies (Fig. 33) and with open porosity of clastic rocks (Fig. 34). These correlations can be used to help confirm other geologic studies. Alpern (1975) contains six papers on this subject. Analysis of the level of organic catagenesis aids greatly in understanding the place and time of hydrocarbon generation in sedimentary basins, and in predicting whether potential source rocks are still immature or are dominantly in the petroleum or gas generation range. It is important to realize that these applications of organic petrology to petroleum exploration do not require that temperature *per se* be determined. Measurement of the level of organic catagenesis will become more important in other fields of geology, however, when the relationship between temperature and rank is more exactly known.

FIG. 26.—Carbon preference index (CPI) of paraffin hydrocarbons from Australian coals plotted against whole-coal carbon content. Low CPI correlates with late-generated and mature petroleum. Modified from Brooks (1970). Vitrinite reflectance is approximate, and is based on its general correlation with %C. For additional CPI data from coals see Leythaeuser and Welte (1969).

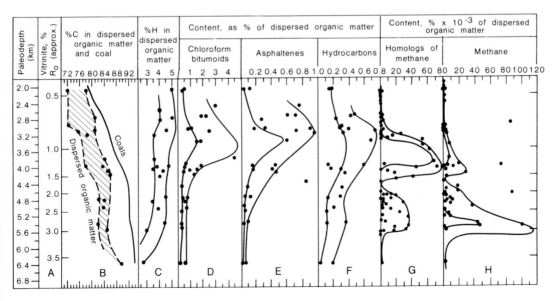

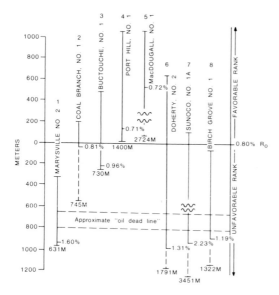

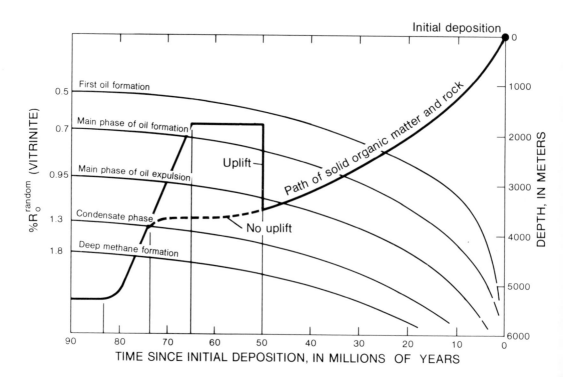

Fig. 28.—Depths, observed vitrinite reflectances, and position of an "oil dead line" in eight oil exploration boreholes in the upper Paleozoic of the Atlantic provinces, Canada. Modified from Hacquebard and Donaldson (1970). Today the "dead line" would probably be placed at higher rank than Hacquebard and Donaldson assumed—at about 1.1% vitrinite reflectance. The lines indicating the boreholes are dashed where they extend below the lowest reflectance data.

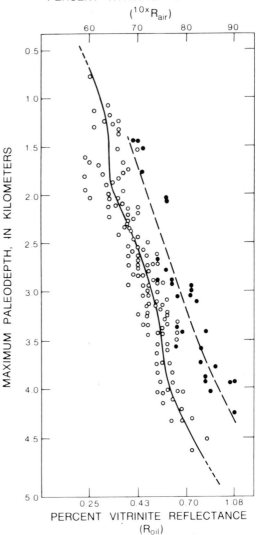

FIG. 31.—Vitrinite reflectance of samples from northern Sakhalin Island, USSR, plotted at maximum paleodepth. Open circles, Neogene samples; closed circles, Paleogene and Cretaceous samples. Modified from Ammosov and Utkina (1975). The same data appear in Figure 22.

FIG. 29.—Elemental composition (atomic ratios H/C and O/C) of four types of kerogen. The arrows show direction of change with increasing catagenesis. O, Formation of oxygenated products (CO_2, H_2O, heavy heteroatomic molecules); P, formation of petroleum; G, formation of gas. Modified from Tissot and Espitalie (1975).

FIG. 30.—Plot of burial history of a hypothetical rock unit to illustrate generation and possible expulsion and trapping of oil and gas. The depths shown for the zones of hydrocarbon genesis are typical, but these depths are determined by the local geothermal gradient. Modified from Cornelius (1974).

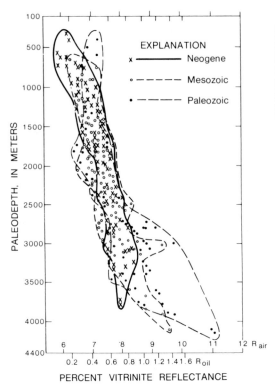

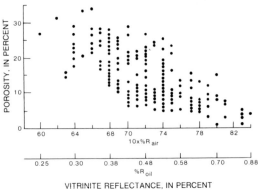

FIG. 34.—Relationship between sandstone open porosity and organic catagenesis (vitrinite reflectance) in Cenozoic and Cretaceous strata in northern Sakhalin Island, USSR. Modified from Ammosov and Utkina (1975). % R_{oil} is converted from % R_{air} as explained in Figure 22.

FIG. 32.—Paleodepth and vitrinite reflectance of coals and dispersed organic matter of various ages. Modified from Neruchev and others (1976). % R_{oil} is converted from % R_{air} as explained in Figure 22.

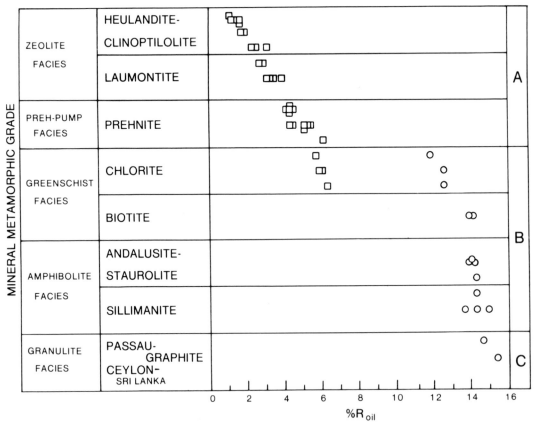

REFERENCES

ALPERN, B., 1970, Classification pétrographique des constituants organiques fossiles des roches sédimentaires: Inst. Francais Pétrole Rev., v. 25, p. 1233–1266.

—— (ed.), 1975, Pétrographie de la matière organique des sédiments, relations avec la paléotempérature et le potentiel pétrolier, Paris, 1973: Paris, Centre National de la Recherche Scientifique, 278 p.

AMMOSOV, I. I., 1961, Stadii izmeneniya osadochnykh porod i paragenticheskie otnosheniya goryuchikh iskopaemykh [Stages in the alteration of sedimentary rocks and paragenetic relations of combustible minerals]: Sov. Geol., 1961, no. 4, p. 7–24 [English transl., Internat. Geol. Rev., v. 4, p. 1105–1117].

——, BABASHKIN, B. G., AND SHARKOVA, L. S., 1975, Bituminit nizhnekembriyskikh otlozheniy Irkutskoy neftegazonosnoy oblasti [Bituminite of Lower Cambrian deposits in the Irkutsk oil and gas region], in I. V. Yeremin (ed.), Paleotemperatury zon nefteobrazovaniya: Moscow, Nauka Press, p. 25–59.

—— AND GORSHKOV, V. I., 1969, Vzaimosvyaz' katageneza i neftegazonosnosti otlozhenii Zapadno-Sibirskoy Nizmennosti [The relationship between catagenesis and petroleum content of strata in the West-Siberian lowland], in Rasseyannye vklyucheniya uglya v osadochnykh porodakh: Moscow, Nauka Press, p. 5–80.

—— AND SHARKOVA, L. S., 1975, Paleotemperatury, litifikatsiya i neftegazonosnost' yurskikh otlozheniy zapadnoy chasti Kazakhstana i sredney Asii [Paleotemperatures, lithification and oil and gas occurrence in Jurassic deposits in western Kazakhstan and central Asia], in I. V. Yeremin (ed.), Paleotemperatury zon nefteobrazovaniya: Moscow, Nauka press, p. 60–69.

—— AND UTKINA, A. I., 1975, Paleotemperatury, litifikatsiya i neftegazonosnost' neogenovykh otlozheniy severnogo Sakhalina [Paleotemperatures, lithification and oil and gas occurrence in Neogene deposits of northern Sakhalin], in I. V. Yeremin (ed.), Paleotemperatury zon nefteobrazovaniya: Moscow, Nauka Press, p. 70–93.

BARTENSTEIN, H., TEICHMÜLLER, M., AND TEICHMÜLLER, R., 1971, Die Umwandlung der organischen Substanz im Dach des Bramscher Massivs: Fortschr. Geologie Rheinland u. Westfalen, v. 18, p. 501–538.

—— AND TEICHMÜLLER, R., 1974, Inkohlunguntersuchungen, ein Schlüssel zur Prospektierung von Paläozoischen Kohlenwasserstoff-Lagerstatten?: Fortschr. Geologie Rheinland u. Westfalen, v. 24, p. 129–160.

BOGDANOVA, L. A., 1965, Petorgraficheskiye osobennosti termal'nometamorfizovannykh ugley Tunguskogo Basseyna [Petrographic features of thermally metamorphosed coals in the Tungusk Basin]: Litilogia i Poleznye Iskopayemye, 1965, no. 5, p. 43–56.

——, 1968, Resul'taty petrograficheskogo izucheniya kontaktogo-metamorfizovannykh ugley Tunguskogo Basseyna [Results of a petrographic study of contact-metamorphic coals in the Tungusk Basin], in Voprosy metamorizma ugley i epigeneza vmeshcayuschikh porod: Leningrad, Nauka Press, p. 205–211.

BOSTICK, N. H., 1971, Thermal alteration of clastic organic particles as an indicator of contact and burial metamorphism in sedimentary rocks: Am. Assoc. Stratigr. Palynologists Proc., 2nd, Geoscience Man., v. 3, p. 83–92.

——, 1973, Time as a factor in thermal metamorphism of phytoclasts (coaly particles): Cong. Internat. Strat. Geol. Carbonif., 7th, Krefeld, 1971, Compte Rendu, v. 2, p. 183–193.

——, 1974, Phytoclasts as indicators of thermal metamorphism, Franciscan Assemblage and Great Valley Sequence (upper Mesozoic), California: Geol. Soc. America, Spec. Paper 153, p. 1–17.

—— AND ALPERN, B., 1977, Principles of sampling, preparation and constituent selection for microphotometry in measurement of maturation of sedimentary organic matter: Jour. Microscopy, v. 109, p. 41–47.

—— AND DAMBERGER, H. H., 1971, The carbon ratio rule and petroleum potential in NPC region 9: Illinois Geol. Survey, Illinois Petroleum, no. 95, p. 142–151.

BROOKS, J. D., 1970, The use of coals as indicators of the occurrence of oil and gas: Australian Petroleum Explor. Assoc. Jour., v. 10, pt. 2, p. 35–40.

COMBAZ, A., 1975, Essai de classification des roches carbonées et des constituants organiques des roches sédimentaires, in B. Alpern (ed.), Pétrographie de la matière organique des sèdiments, relations avec la paléotempérature et le potentiel pétrolier: Paris, Centre National de la Recherche Scientifique, p. 93–101.

CORNELIUS, C. E., 1974, Geothermal aspects of hydrocarbon exploration in the North Sea area [preprint]: Bergen Conf. Petroleum Geol. North Sea, 1973, 34 p.

CORREIA, M., 1967, Relations possibles entre l'état de conservation des éléments figurés de la matière organique (microfossiles, palynoplanctologiques) et l'existence de gisements d'hydrocarbures: Inst. Francais Petrole Rev., v. 22, p. 1285–1306.

DAMBERGER, H. H., 1974, Coalification patterns of Pennsylvanian coal basins of the USA: Geol. Soc. America, Spec. Paper 153, p. 53–74.

DIESSEL, C. F. K., AND OFFLER, R., 1975, Change in physical properties of coalified and graphitized phytoclasts with grade of metamorphism: Neues Jahrb. Mineralogie Monatsh., Jahrg. 1975, p. 11–26.

EVANS, C. R., ROGERS, M. A., AND BAILEY, N. J. L., 1971, Evolution and alteration of petroleum in western Canada: Chem. Geology, v. 8, p. 147–170.

FULLER, M. L., 1919, Relation of oil to carbon ratios of Pennsylvanian coals in north Texas: Econ. Geology, v. 14, p. 536–542.

——, 1920, Carbon ratios of Carboniferous coals of Oklahoma and their relation to petroleum: Econ. Geology, v. 15, p. 225–235.

←

FIG. 33.—Relationship between mineral metamorphic grade and organic catagenesis in Carboniferous (A), Precambrian-Cambrian (B), and other strata (C). From Diessel and Offler (1975).

GINSBURG, A. I., LAPO, A. V., AND LETUSHOVA, I. A., 1976, Ratsional'ny kompleks petrograficheskikh metodov issledovaniya ugley i goryuchikh slantsev [Coordinated petrographic methods of analyzing coals and oil shales]: Leningrad, Nedra Press, p. 14–15.

GLUSHKO, V. V., NOVOSILETSKIY, P. M., AND KORCHINSKAYA, I. A., 1972, Osnovnyye zakonomernosti gazokondensat-nykh i neftyanykh zalezhey v Dneprovo-Donetskoy vpadine [The main features of gas condensate and oil deposits in the Dnepr-Donets Basin]: Geol. Nefti Gaza. 1972, no. 1, p. 10–15.

GRAYSON, J. F., 1975, Relationship of palynomorph translucency to carbon and hydrocarbons in clastic sediments, *in* Pétrographie de la matière organique des sédiments, relations avec la paléotempérature et le potentiel pétrolier: Paris, Centre National de la Recherche Scientifique, p. 261–273.

HACQUEBARD, P. A., 1975, Correlation between coal rank, paleotemperature and petroleum occurrences in Alberta: Canada Geol. Survey Paper 75-1, Part B, p. 5–8.

—— AND DONALDSON, J. R., 1970, Coal metamorphism and hydrocarbon potential in the upper Paleozoic of the Atlantic provinces, Canada: Canadian Jour. Earth Sci., v. 7, p. 1139–1163.

HOOD, A., AND CASTAÑO, J. R., 1974, Organic metamorphism: its relationship to petroleum generation and application to studies of authigenic minerals: U. S. Econ. Comm. Asia Far East, Comm. Coord. Joint Prospect. Miner. Resour. Asian Offshore Areas, Tech. Bull. 8, p. 85–118.

—— AND GUTJAHR, C. C. M., 1972, Organic metamorphism and the generation of petroleum: Geol. Soc. America Abs. with Programs, v. 4, p. 542–543.

HUCK, G., AND KARWEIL, J., 1955, Physikalisch-chemische Probleme der Inkohlung: Brennstoff-Chemie, v. 36, p. 1–11.

IVANOV, G. A. (ED.), 1975, Metamorfizm ugley i epigenez vmeshchayushchikh porod [Metamorphism of coals and epigenesis of the coal-bearing strata]: Moscow, Nedra Press. 256 p.

JACOB, H., 1973, Kombination von Fluoreszenz- und reflexions-mikroskop-photometrie der organischen Stoffe von Sedimenten und Boden: Leitz Mitt. Wiss. Tech., v. 6, p. 21–27.

KALKREUTH, W., 1976, Kohlenpetrologische und geochemische Untersuchungen an organischem Material Palä-ozoischer Sedimentgesteine aus der variskischen Geosynklinale: Dissertation, Rheinish-Westfälische Tech-nische Hochschule Aachen, German Federal Republic, 137 p.

KOCH, J., 1974, Untersuchungen über die Zunahme der Vitrinitreflexion mit der Tiefe in einigen Sedimentbecken: Erdol Kohle, v. 27, p. 121–124.

KONTOROVICH, A. E., 1970, Teoreticheskiye osnovy ob'yemno-geneticheskogo metoda otsenki potensial'nykh resurov nefti i gaza [The theoretical foundations of a volume-genetic method for evaluating oil and gas resources]: Sibir. Nauchno-Issled. Inst. Geologii, Geofizikii Mineral'nogo Syr'ya Trudy, v. 95, p. 4–51.

——, PARPAROVA, G. M., AND TRUSHKOV, P. A., 1967, Metamorfizm organicheskogo veshchestva i nekotorye voprosy neftegazonsnosti na primere mezozoiskikh otlozheniy Zapadno-Sibirskoy Nizmennosti [Metamorphism of organic matter and several questions of oil content (by example from Mesozoic deposits of the West-Siberian Lowland)]: Akad. Nauk SSSR Sibirsk. Otdeleniye Geologiya i Geofizika, 1967, no. 2, p. 16–29.

—— AND TROFIMUK, A. A., 1976, Litogenez i neftegazoobrazovaniye [Lithogenesis and formation of oil and gas], *in* N. B. Vassoyevich and others (eds.), Goryuchiye iskopayeme—problemy geologii i geokhimi naftidov i bituminoznykh porod (Mezhdunarodnyy geologicheskiy kongress, XXV sessiya, doklady sovetskikh geolo-gov): Moscow, Nauka Press, p. 19–36.

LEYTHAEUSER, C., AND WELTE, D., 1969, Relation between distribution of heavy N-Paraffins and coalification in Carboniferous coals from the Saar district, Germany, *in* Advances in organic geochemistry, 1968. Internat. Ser. Monogr. Earth Sci., v. 31, p. 429–442.

LILLEY, E. R., 1924, Coal as an aid in oil exploration. Eng. and Mining Jour., v. 117, p. 1009–1012.

LOPATIN, N. V., 1976, K opredeleniyu vliyaniya temperatury i geologicheskogo vremeni na katageneticheskiye protsessy uglefikatsii i neftegazoobrazovaniya [The influence of temperature and geologic time on the catagenetic processes of coalification and petroleum and gas formation], *in* Issledovaniya organicheskogo veshchestva sovremennykh i iskopayemykh osadkov: Moscow, Nauka Press, p. 361–366.

—— AND BOSTICK, N. H., 1973, Geologicheskiye faktory katageneza ugley [The geologic factors in coal catagenesis], *in* Priroda organicheskogo veshchestva sovremennykh i iskopayemykh osadkov: Akad. Nauk SSSR Otdeleniye Geologii, Geofiziki, Geokhimi, Kom. Osad. Porodam, Moscow, Nauka Press, p. 79–90 [English transl.: Illinois Geol. Survey Reprint 1974-Q, 16 p.].

NERUCHEV, S. G., AND PARPAROVA, G. M., 1972, O roli geologicheskogo vremeni v protsessakh metamorfizma ugley i rasseyannogo organicheskogo veshchestva porod [The role of geologic time in processes of metamorphism of coal and dispersed organic matter in rocks]: Akad. Nauk SSSR Sibirsk. Otdeleniye Geologiya i Geofizika, 1972, no. 10, p. 3–10.

——, ——, ZHUKOVA, A. V., FAYZULLINA, YE. M., AND KOZLOVA, L. YE., 1976, Diagnostika stadiy metamorfizma i zakonomernosti metamorficheskogo (katageneticheskogo) preobrazovaniya nebituminoznoy chasti sapro-planktonitovogo ROV [Diagnosis of the stage of metamorphism and the nature of the metamorphic (catagenetic) alteration of the non-bituminous part of saproplanktonic dispersed organic matter]: *in* Generatsiya uglevodoro-dov v protsesse litogeneza osadkov: Akad. Nauk SSSR Sibirsk. Otdeleniye Inst. Geologii i Geofiziki Trudy, Vyp. 330, p. 30–78.

——, VASSOYEVICH, N. B., AND LOPATIN, N. V., 1976, O shkale katageneza v svyazi c neftegazoobrazovaniyem [A scale of catagenesis in relation to formation of oil and gas], *in* N. V. Vassoyevich and others (eds.), Goryuchiye iskopayemye—problemy geologii i geokhimi naftidov i bituminoznykh porod (Mezhdunarodnyy geologicheskiy kongress, XXV sessiya, doklady sovetskikh geologov): Moscow, Nauka Press, p. 47–62.

OTTENJAHN, K., TEICHMÜLLER, M., AND WOLF, M., 1975, Spectral fluorescence measurements of sporinites in reflected light and their applicability for coalification studies, in B. Alpern (ed.), Pétrographie de la matière organique des sédiments, relations avec la paléotempérature et la potentiel pétrolier, Paris, 1973: Paris, Centre National de la Recherche Scientifique, p. 49–65.

PARPAROVA, G. M., 1969, Izucheniye rasseyannogo organicheskogo veshchestva porod neftenosnykh rayonov uglepetrograficheskim metodom [Coal petrographic study of dispersed organic matter in rocks of petroleum regions]: Vses. Neft. Nauchno-Issled. Geol.-Razved. Inst. Trudy, Vyp. 279, p. 270–300.

PREOBRAZHENSKAYA, G. S., KLUCHEVA, N. YU, AND IVANOVA, K. P., 1971, Geologicheskiye zakonomemosti rasprostraneniya krupnykh mestorozhdeniy nefti i gaza v SSSR [Distribution features of giant oil and gas deposits in the USSR]: Vses. Nauchno-Issled. Geol. Inst. Trudy, v. 286, 175 p.

ROBERT, P., 1974, Analyse microscopique des charbons et des bitumes dispersés dans les roches et mesure de leur pouvoir réflecteur—application a l'étude de la paléogéothermie des bassins sédimentaires et de la genèse des hydrocarbures: Advances in Organic Geochemistry, 1973, p. 549–569.

RODIONOVA, K. F., 1967, Organicheskoe veshchestvo i neftematerinskie porody devona Volgo-Uralskoi neftegazonosnoi oblasti [Organic matter and oil source rocks of the Devonian in the Volga-Ural petroleum region]: Moscow, Nauka Press, 358 p.

SHIBAOKA, M., BENNETT, A. J. R., AND GOULD, K. W., 1973, Diagenesis of organic matter and occurrence of hydrocarbons in some Australian sedimentary basins: Australian Petroleum Explor. Assoc. Jour., v. 13, p. 73–80.

STACH, E., MACKOWSKY, M-TH, TEICHMÜLLER, M., TAYLOR, G. H., CHANDRA, D., AND TEICHMÜLLER, R., 1975, Stach's textbook of coal petrology, 2d ed.: Berlin and Stuttgart, Gebrüder Borntraeger, 428 p.

SARBEYEVA, L. I., AND KRYLOVA, N. M., 1968, Otrazhatel'naya sposobnost' mikrokomponnetov ugely metamorficheskogo ryada [Reflectance of coal microcomponents in relation to the metamorphic series], in Voprosy metamorfizma uglei i epigeneza vmeshchayushchikh porod: Leningrad, Nauka Press, p. 87–106.

TEICHMÜLLER, M., 1973, Zur Petrographie und Genese von Naturkoksen im Flöz Präsident/Helene der Zeche Friedrich Heinrich bei Kamp-Lintfort (Linker Niederrhein): Geol. Mitt. (Aachen), v. 12, p. 219–254.

———AND TEICHMÜLLER, R., 1975, Inkohlungsuntersuchungen in der Molasse des Alpenvorlandes: Geologica Bavarica, v. 73, p. 123–142.

TISSOT, B., AND ESPITALIE, J., 1975, L'evolution thermique de la matière organique des sédiments: Application d'une simulation mathematique: Inst. Francais Pétrole Rev., v. 30, p. 743–777.

VAN GIJZEL, P., 1975, Plychromatic UV—Fluorescence microphotometry of fresh and fossil plant substances with special reference to the location and identification of dispersed organic material in rocks, in B. Alpern (ed.), Pétrographie de la matière organique des sédiments, relations avec la paleotempérature et le potentiel pétrolier, Paris, 1973: Paris, Centre National de la Recherche Scientifique, p. 67–91.

VAN KREVELEN, D. W., 1961, Coal: Amsterdam, Elsevier Pub. Co., 514 p.

VASSOYEVICH, N. B., 1973, Osnovnyye zakonomernosti, kharakterizuyuschiye organicheskoye veshchestvo sovremennykh i iskopayemykh osadkov [Characterization of organic matter in Recent and fossil sediments], in Priroda organicheskogo veshchestva sovremennykh i iskopayemykh osadkov: Akad. Nauk SSSR Otdeleniye Geologii, Geofiziki, Geokhimi, Kom. Osad. Porodam, Moscow, Nauka Press, p. 11–59.

———, 1974, Litologiya i organicheskaya geokhimiya [Lithogenesis and organic geochemistry], in Organicheskoye veshchestvo sovremennykh i iskopayemykh osadkov i metody yego izucheniya: Akad. Nauk SSSR Otdeleniye Geologii, Geofiziki, Geokhimi, Kom. Osad. Porodam, Moscow, Nauka Press, p. 16–32.

———, KONYUKHOV, A. I., AND LOPATIN, N. V., 1976, Obshcheye i osobennoye v obrazovanii ugley, nefti i uglevodorodnykh gazov [General and specific features in formation of coals, oil, and hydrocarbon gases], in N. B. Vassoyevich and others (eds.), Goryuchiye iskopayeme—problemy geologii i geokhimii naftidov i bituminoznykh porod (Mezhdunarodnyy geologicheskiy kongress, XXV sessiya, doklady sovetskikh geologov): Moscow, Nauka press, p. 7–19.

———, KORCHAGINA, YU. I., LOPATIN, N. V., AND CHERNYSHEV, V. V., 1969, Glavnaya faza nefteobrazovaniya [The main phase of oil formation]: Moskov. Univ. Vestnik, Ser. Geol., v. 24, no. 6, p. 3–27.

———, VYSOTSKII, I. V., GUSEVA, A. N., AND OLENIN, V. B., 1967, Uglevodorody v osadochno obolochke zemli [Hydrocarbons in the sedimentary mantle of the Earth]: Moskov. Univ. Vestnik, Ser. Geol., v. 22, no. 5, p. 36–48.

WHITE, C. D., 1915, Some relations in origin between coal and petroleum: Washington Acad. Sci. Jour., v. 5, p. 189–212.

———, 1935, Metamorphism of organic sediments and derived oils: Am. Assoc. Petroleum Geologists Bull., v. 19, p. 589–617.

YEREMENKO, N. A., AMMOSOV, I. I., PETROV, A. A., AND OKUN'KOVA, F. E., 1976, Sotnosheniye mezhdu mineral'nymi i organicheskimi komponentami na razlichnykh stadiyakh obrazovaniy neftegazonoshykh tolshch [The relationship between mineral and organic components at various stages of formation of oil and gas bearing strata], in N. B. Vassoyevich and others (eds.), Goryuchiye iskopayemye—problemy geologii i geokhimi naftidov i bituminoznykh porod (Mezhdunarodnyy geologicheskiy kongress, XXV sessiya, doklady sovetskikh geologov): Moscow, Nauka Press, p. 37–47.

SEPM Special Publication No. 26, p. 45–53, March 1979

LEVELS OF GRAPHITIZATION OF KEROGEN AS A POTENTIALLY USEFUL METHOD OF ASSESSING PALEOTEMPERATURES

WILLIAM E. HARRISON
Oklahoma Geological Survey, Norman, 73019

ABSTRACT

Catagenesis of sedimentary organic matter leads to end products of methane and a carbonaceous, graphite-like residue. Kerogens heated in the laboratory as well as those that have experienced natural catagenesis demonstrate progressively better developed graphite-like atomic arrangement as a function of increased temperature conditions. The height/width ratios of the d_{002} X-ray diffraction peak of graphite are useful in expressing various levels of graphitization and thus are potentially useful in paleothermometry.

INTRODUCTION

Organic matter in sediments can be divided into two broad classes on the basis of solubility in non-polar organic solvents. That material insoluble in such solvents is called kerogen and constitutes the bulk of the organic matter in the crust of the earth. As individual components of kerogen experience increased temperature conditions or are held at a fixed temperature for geologically significant periods of time, two types of reactions occur simultaneously.

Dobryansky (1963) described these reactions as being primarily those which lead to (1) molecules of smaller size and increased volatility (degradation) with methane as the final product, and (2) a carbon-rich residue that has lost most of its hydrogen (condensation). The condensation reactions lead toward an end product of graphite. The ordering or atomic arrangement of graphite is dependent on temperature history; thus determination of the level of graphite development in kerogen may be a useful tool for paleothermometry.

Welte (1974) used the coal model of Karweil as a possible analog for the basic structural configuration of kerogen and indicated several features common to both. The analogy is pursued in this study, and the common features have considerable appeal in the formulation of a physical model for kerogen.

COAL MACERALS AND KEROGEN

One of the most useful methods of comparing coal macerals with each other and with kerogens of fine-grained rocks is on the basis of elemental ratios. A relationship commonly used is the atomic H/C–O/C ratio plot or Van Krevelen diagram.

Figure 1 is a Van Krevelen diagram of three types of coal macerals. Position A for each maceral type is the H/C–O/C relationship at a low diagenetic or coalification level; positions B-D represent higher levels. At low to moderate levels

(positions A and B), the three fold separation of macerals on the basis of elemental ratios is quite apparent. At higher catagenetic/coalification levels the macerals lose their identity until, at D, they are indistinguishable.

The biochemicals that give rise to each of the three types of coal macerals play an important role in the H/C–O/C ratios.

Alginites are macerals that are composed of the remains of lipid-rich algal bodies. The lipids include metabolically derived fats, waxes, and oils that are characterized by relatively high hydrogen content. This is reflected in the high H/C ratios that alginites have at low diagenetic and catagenetic levels.

Vitrinites owe their origin to the carbohydrate-rich woody tissue of higher plants. Woody material consists mainly of structural carbohydrates (cellulose, hemicellulose, etc.) and lignin, all of which contain considerable quantities of oxygen. The relatively high oxygen content in woody tissue gives the corresponding coal maceral (vitrinite) a high O/C ratio.

Exinites occupy an intermediate position on the Van Krevelen diagram and consist of the resistant parts of spores and cuticular material.

Elemental analyses of kerogen have been published by several workers (*Forsman and Hunt,* 1958; *Forsman,* 1963; *McIver,* 1967; *Tissot et al.,* 1974). Van Krevelen diagrams of various types of kerogen show a three fold subdivision that is remarkably similar to that of coal macerals (see Figure 2). The three major kerogen types and the effects of catagenesis (increasing burial) are obvious. Components of kerogen are affected by initial biochemical input in much the same manner as are coal macerals. Lipid-rich or sapropelic depositional settings give rise to an organic matrix that contains compounds such as waxes, fatty acids and alcohols, and paraffinic hydrocarbons. This mixture has high concentrations of carbon and hydrogen and little oxygen.

Copyright © 1979, The Society of Economic Paleontologists and Mineralogists

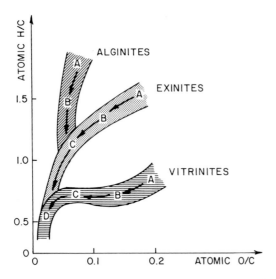

Fig. 1.—Van Krevelen diagram, showing elemental ratios for three coal macerals. A positions indicate ratios at low coalification levels. Positions B-D mark the changes that result from increasing coalification. The threefold subdivision apparent at A positions is gradually lost as the macerals attain higher fixed-carbon content. At D, the macerals are indistinguishable on the basis of elemental ratios.

By comparison, organic matter derived from cellulose, lignin, and humic acids has considerably more oxygen.

Using the data of Figures 1 and 2 as general guidelines, one may expect (1) lignitic or humic

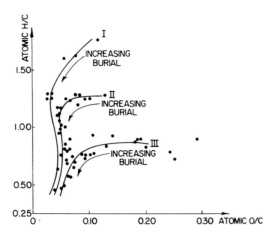

Fig. 2.—Van Krevelen diagram of kerogen. Type I kerogen includes lipid-rich (algal) source material. Type III kerogen consists predominantly of woody material and has relatively high oxygen content. Notice the similarity between elemental ratios of coal macerals (Fig. 1) and kerogens. (After Tissot et al., 1974).

materials at low catagenetic levels to be characterized by H/C ratios of about 0.85 or less, and (2) lipid or sapropelic materials at low catagenetic levels to have H/C ratios greater than 0.85. This general relation is used in the present study to assess lipid and humic character.

Physical characteristics of kerogen also can be used as a means of classification. A relationship between precursor material, physical appearance of kerogen, and generated hydrocarbon products has been proposed by Burgess (1974). Figure 3 is a modification of his scheme. He also presented photographs of several kerogens showing various morphological characteristics.

A similar exercise was conducted in this study for two end-member kerogens via scanning-electron microscopy. Figure 4 shows kerogens from a sample of Green River Shale collected in Garfield County, Colorado, and from a sample of Eocene lignite collected in Houston County, Texas. Kerogen samples were obtained by the demineralization, purification, and concentration methods described by Robinson (1969a). The H/C ratios for the Green River and lignitic kerogens were 1.35 and 0.75, respectively. The Green River kerogen has no shape characteristics (amorphous), whereas the lignitic kerogen consists of particles that have a distinct form and angular characteristics (structured).

A final consideration of differences in end-member kerogens concerns molecular structures of compounds that give rise to each type. Lipid mixtures commonly contain biochemicals that have straight-chain structural configurations. Examples of such compounds include the long-chain waxes, n-paraffins, and fatty acids and alcohols. The association of straight-chain components with marine-derived or lipid organic matter and ring (aromatic) components with humic organic matter persists even to high-temperature pyrolysis conditions. Thus Giraud (1970) noted that pyrolysis of humic material (coals) yielded products that were strongly dominated by benzene, toluene, and xylene, all ring compounds. Conversely, samples

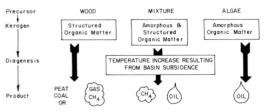

Fig. 3.—Proposed relationship between precursor material, kerogen type, diagenesis, and final generated products. (After Burgess, 1974.)

Fig. 4.—Scanning-electron photomicrographs of end-member-type kerogens. Left—Green River kerogen (Eocene), which is essentially structureless (amorphous). Right—is an Eocene lignitic kerogen, which has distinct (structured) morphology. Magnification, X1300.

identified as "marine sediments" yielded product mixtures with a predominance of straight-chain hydrocarbons.

INCREASING GRAPHITIZATION OF SEDIMENTARY ORGANIC MATTER

Chemical thermodynamics drives all carbonaceous material toward the most stable forms of carbon. In the case of sedimentary organic matter, there are two carbon species that result from catagenesis. These species, methane and a carbonaceous residue approaching graphite, are the final products of the degradation and condensation reactions described by Dobryansky (1963) and summarized by Hood *et al.* (1975).

Graphite consists of sheets of condensed aromatic rings (Fig. 5). The rings that form the sheets are bound tightly to each other, but the individual layers or sheets are held only by weak Van der Waals bonds. The individual sheets or aromatic layers are parallel to each other in well-ordered graphite; subparallel sheets result in poorly developed or a total lack of graphite structure.

Again, the analogy between coalification and kerogen catagenesis is useful. Figure 6 shows the structural changes that occur as coal transcends various rank to anthracite. These structural changes are reflected by other parameters, such as (1) increased aromaticity, (2) more highly condensed ring systems, and (3) increased dimensions of aromatic clusters, as coals attain higher rank (Teichmüller and Teichmüller, 1967). Notice

that anthracite has a structure that is similar to graphite, both in the direction of and normal to the C crystallographic axis. As sedimentary organic matter proceeds along its catagenetic path, it becomes more aromatic. When the aromatic layers become ordered enough, a graphite-like structure develops. Thus increased levels of graphitization of sedimentary organic matter and increased aromaticity occur together.

A relationship between changes in aromaticity in kerogen and the generation of petroleum was

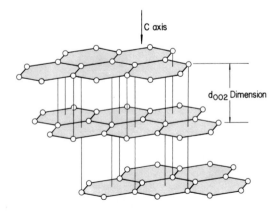

Fig. 5.—Structure of graphite. Well-ordered graphite consists of parallel polyaromatic sheets. In poorly ordered graphite, the sheets are subparallel.

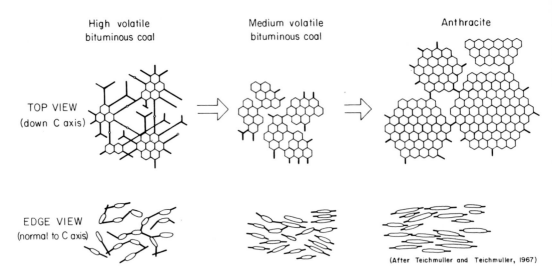

High volatile bituminous coal   Medium volatile bituminous coal   Anthracite

TOP VIEW (down C axis)

EDGE VIEW (normal to C axis)

(After Teichmuller and Teichmuller, 1967)

FIG. 6.—Structural changes that occur as coals progress through higher rank to anthracite. Notice the similarity between the structure of anthracite and graphite.

suggested by Welte (1974). He described the Karweil coal model in which the aromatic nuclei are bound by aliphatic side chains and peripheral groups. Aromaticity increases as the aliphatics are liberated as hydrocarbon products. Structural rearrangement during catagenetic processes, as illustrated by Figure 6, may also occur in kerogen. If the straight heavy lines of Figure 6 are considered as aliphatic components, then the thermal "splitting off" of these components may result in condensation of aromatic nuclei. If similar conditions prevail during maturation of kerogen, increasing aromaticity may be a consequence of the formation of aliphatic petroleum hydrocarbons.

Graphite development in coals has been described by several workers. Such investigations have been primarily directed toward evaluating the increasing levels of graphitization of organic matter that accompanies increased rank of humic material (Blayden et al., 1939; Quinn and Glass, 1958; Griffin, 1967; Robinson, 1969b). Several workers have examined the changes in carbonaceous material as a function of increasing metamorphic grade. Diessel and Offler (1975) showed that development of graphitic structure and increased reflectance occurs together in phytoclasts contained in rocks of increasingly higher metamorphic level. Grew (1974) studied carbonaceous material in coal, slate, phyllite, and schist samples in New England and concluded that the "well-ordered graphite" of the Narragansett basin was formed under pressure-temperature conditions similar to those required to produce the sillimanite

metamorphic facies (660–690° C and 4.5–5.0 kilobars).

Gorokhov et al. (1974) studied the alteration of marine algae under varying conditions of temperature, pressure, and exposure period and demonstrated an experimental transformation of biogenic residue to graphite-like material.

Oberlin et al. (1974) used high resolution electron microscopy to show ordering of aromatic layers as a function of simulated and natural catagenesis.

Some studies have been concerned specifically with graphite development in kerogen (Forsman and Hunt, 1948; Blyuman et al., 1972; Powell et al., 1975; Harrison, 1976).

Landis (1971) suggested a method of evaluating various levels of graphitization on the basis of parameters derived from X-ray diffraction patterns. This method involved quantification of graphite-peak height and base dimensions and relating these parameters to crystal order. Peaks that have broad bases and relatively low intensities reflect low-order crystallinities and poor graphite development. In kerogen, as with coals, increased crystal order can be related to thermal conditions, and a quantitative assessment of graphite development represents a measure of the maximum temperature attained. One of the parameters that reflects changes in the crystallinity is the height/width ratio measured at one-half the peak height (Landis, 1971). Greater values of this ratio for the d_{002} reflection of graphite indicate better crystal order and hence a higher temperature history.

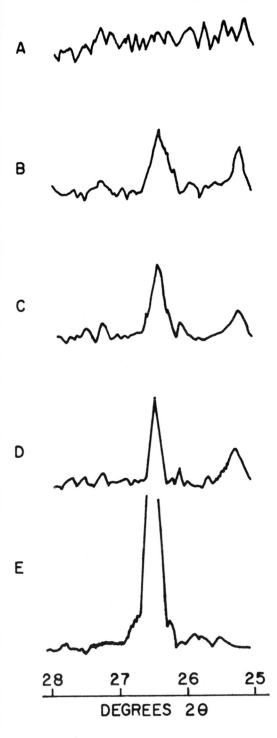

A

B

C

D

E

28 27 26 25

DEGREES 2θ

Fig. 7.—X-ray diffraction patterns, showing development of graphite-like structure. *A*, unheated kerogen; *B-D*, kerogen subjected to temperatures of 300° C, 600° C, and 900° C, respectively; *E*, graphite standard Cu_{ka} radiation, (35 kV, 18mA, 1666 counts/sec.).

TABLE 1.—HEIGHT/WIDTH PARAMETERS FOR A MODERN ESTUARINE KEROGEN SUBJECTED TO LABORATORY TEMPERATURES FOR 50 HOURS

	Height/width (@ 1/2 height)
Graphite standard	29.6
Kerogen @ 900° C	12.6
Kerogen @ 600° C	1.6
Kerogen @ 300° C	1.2

Harrison (1976) heated a modern estuarine kerogen (under laboratory conditions), which resulted in the X-ray diffraction patterns shown in Figure 7. The elemental composition of the initial (demineralized) kerogen concentrate, expressed as wt % (d.a.f.) was: carbon, 62.1; hydrogen, 5.2; oxygen, 29.2; and nitrogen, 3.5.

The d_{002} reflection is shown to have increasing peak height and decreasing peak width as temperature increased (Table 1). Although the thermal conditions employed in the study of estuarine kerogen were somewhat high when compared to temperatures encountered in sedimentary basins, the fact that kerogen undergoes progressive graphitization with increased laboratory temperatures was established. Table 1 shows the systematic increase in the H/W ratio as a function of laboratory temperature; all samples were heated for 50 hours.

In view of variation in precursor materials for end-member-type kerogens (i.e., predominantly cyclic compounds in humic sediments and straight-chain components in lipid sediments), additional laboratory studies were limited to pairs (one humic- and one lipid-rich) of similar geologic age. The H/C ratio was the primary means of distinguishing humic- and lipid-rich organic matter. Further, the kerogens were examined via visual (palynological) techniques to ascertain that samples were of a comparable carbonization level prior to laboratory treatment.

TABLE 2.—HEIGHT/WIDTH PARAMETERS FOR EOCENE LIPID- AND HUMIC-RICH KEROGENS SUBJECTED TO VARIOUS LABORATORY TEMPERATURES FOR 50 HOURS

Temperature °C	Height/width parameters (@ 1/2 height)	
	Lipid	Humic
100	not measurable	not measurable
200	not measurable	not measurable
300	2.13	2.33
400	1.73	2.50
500	3.33	3.57
600	4.00	4.67

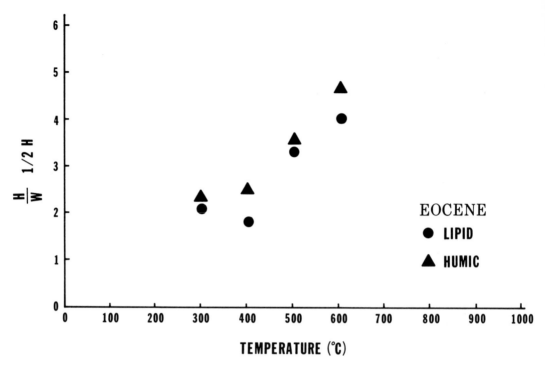

FIG. 8.—Height/width ratios of Eocene kerogens as a function of laboratory temperatures. Conditions as for Figure 7.

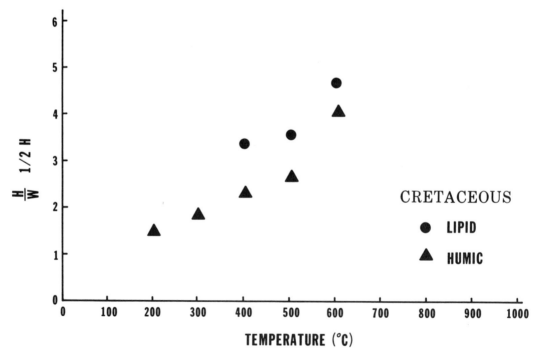

FIG. 9.—Height/width ratios of Cretaceous kerogens as a function of laboratory temperatures. Conditions as for Figure 7.

TABLE 3.—HEIGHT/WIDTH PARAMETERS FOR CRETACEOUS LIPID- AND HUMIC-RICH KEROGENS SUBJECTED TO VARIOUS LABORATORY TEMPERATURES FOR 50 HOURS

Temperature °C	Height/width parameters (@ 1/2 height)	
	Lipid	Humic
100	not measurable	not measurable
200	not measurable	1.56
300	not measurable	1.71
400	3.38	2.28
500	3.50	2.60
600	4.57	4.00

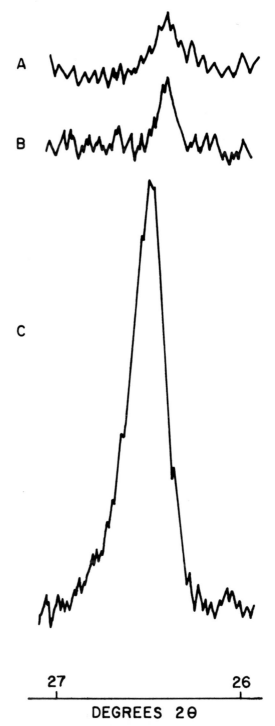

Eocene samples were the same as those shown in Figure 4. Height/width parameters were determined from the X-ray diffraction patterns and are presented in Table 2. The graphite d_{002} peak was not detected in samples heated to 100° C and 200° C but was present after heating at 300° C. The H/W ratios increased in value with increased temperature level with one exception: the lipid-rich kerogen had an anomalously low H/W ratio at 400° C, but the reason for such a value is not apparent. Figure 8 shows the relation between H/W and temperature, for Eocene kerogens.

Cretaceous samples consisted of a Lower Cretaceous organic-rich shale of the Viking Formation in Alberta and the Eagle Ford Shale (Upper Cretaceous). The Eagle Ford sample was from a well drilled in Jasper County, Texas. The H/C ratio of the Viking kerogen was 0.74 and possibly was influenced by continental-plant debris (Tissot *et al.*, 1974). The H/C ratio of the Eagle Ford kerogen was 1.74. The H/W ratios obtained by laboratory heating of these kerogens are shown in Table 3. Viking kerogen attained a graphite-like structure at 200° C whereas the Eagle Ford kerogen required a temperature of 400° C for similar development. Figure 9 shows H/W changes as a function of temperature. If the coal analogy discussed by Welte is again assumed, the lack of graphitization of the lipid kerogen may be the result of early catagenetic processes that involve elimination of the aliphatic groups. Measurable increases in aromaticity (graphitization) might not occur until a significant portion of the aliphatic chains and groups are released, thus permitting greater condensation of aromatic nuclei.

NATURAL GRAPHITIZATION OF KEROGEN

Figure 10 shows diffraction patterns of three kerogens that have experienced varying degrees of catagenesis. Sample A is a Miocene kerogen from Long Beach field in California and is considered equivalent to the sequences that are the sources of Los Angeles Basin oil fields. Relatively

FIG. 10.—X-ray diffraction patterns of three kerogens that have experienced varying levels of natural diagenesis. *A*, Los Angeles Basin Miocene kerogen; *B*, southwest Texas Cretaceous kerogen; *C*, southeastern Oklahoma Ordovician kerogen. See text for details. X-ray conditions as for Figure 7.

small peak height and a broad base indicate lack of graphitization and a low-temperature history. Diffractogram B is from a Lower Cretaceous (Pearsall Shale) kerogen in Bee County, Texas, and came from a depth of over 15,000 feet. The well produced dry gas for a short time before engineering problems curtailed operation. The diffraction pattern shows that a low level of graphitization has occurred and is suggestive of moderate thermal conditions. An Ordovician organic-rich shale from a well in McCurtain County, Oklahoma, was the source of the kerogen whose diffraction pattern is shown as C. The well from which this sample was taken penetrated more than 10,000 feet of metasedimentary rocks (Goldstein, 1975). This metamorphosed section yielded the best developed graphitic structure of any kerogen analyzed to date.

SUMMARY

All compounds are driven by chemical thermodynamics toward products that have the greatest stability. Organic matter in sediments is affected by processes of degradation and condensation that yield methane and a carbonaceous residue changing toward graphite. Increased aromaticity and development of graphite-like atomic structure occur together as a function of increased catagenetic level (temperature).

Kerogens derived from humic material are characterized by relatively high concentrations of aromatic or ring compounds. At low catagenetic levels, humic kerogens have H/C elemental ratios of about 0.85 or less. Kerogens that owe their origin to lipid biochemicals have significant quantities of straight-chain compounds and, at low catagenetic levels, have H/C elemental ratios greater than 0.85. A proposed model for the physical structure of coal suggests that aromatic or ring nuclei are bound to each other by straight-chain compounds and that increased coalification eliminates the chains and condenses the rings. Welte (1974) proposed an analogy between this coal model and kerogens of fine-grained rocks. Thus as kerogens are subjected to elevated temperatures, straight-chain paraffinic hydrocarbons are liberated from the kerogen matrix. Within the matrix, the aromatics are concentrated and condensed into large polyaromatic layers, a process herein called graphitization.

Graphite is an extremely well-ordered arrangement of carbon atoms. Various levels of ordering reflect varying levels of graphitization. Landis (1971) proposed a graphitization series based on parameters derived from X-ray diffraction data. This method provides a means to help assess the thermal conditions to which kerogens have been subjected.

An Eocene and Cretaceous pair of kerogens (one humic and one lipid) were heated in laboratory experiments, and graphitization parameters were determined. The Eocene humic kerogen (lignitic) developed a more graphite-like structural arrangement than did the lipid kerogen heated at the same temperature. This may partially be caused by the variation in initial concentrations of ring-type components that are indigenous to the depositional environments that give rise to humic and lipid kerogen. The Cretaceous humic kerogen did not develop better graphitic structure than its lipid counterpart. The humic kerogen did, however, attain a detectable graphite-position peak at a lower temperature. Various degrees of graphitization (or aromaticity) in kerogen can be related to temperature history. Thus this relation has potential as a tool in paleothermometry.

ACKNOWLEDGEMENTS

I would like to thank the Atlantic Richfield Company for permission to publish elemental-analysis data. David Foster of the Oklahoma Geological Survey assisted with the X-ray diffraction work. Archie Hood of Shell Development Company kindly reviewed the manuscript and made suggestions for its improvement.

REFERENCES

BLAYDEN, H. E., GIBSON, J., RILEY, H. L., AND TAYLOR, A., 1939, An X-ray study of carbonization: Fuel Sci. Practices, v. 19, p. 24–27.

BLYUMAN, B. A., DYAKONOV, YU. S., AND KRASAVINA, T. N., 1972, Izmeneniye strukturnogo sostoyaniya grafita pri progressivnom regional'nom metamorfizme [Change in the structural state of graphite during progressive regional metamorphism]: Akad. Nauk SSSR Doklady, v. 206, p, 1198–1200.

BURGESS, J. D., 1974, Microscopic examination of kerogen (dispersed organic matter) in petroleum exploration: Geol. Soc. America Spec. Paper 153, p. 19–30.

DIESSEL, C. F. K., AND OFFLER, R., 1975, Change in physical properties of coalified and graphitized phytoclasts with grade of metamorphism: Neues Jahrb. Mineralogie Monatsh., Jahrg. 1975, p. 11–26.

DOBRYANSKY, A. F., 1963, La transformation du pétrole brut dans la nature: Inst. Francais Pétrole Rev., v. 18, p. 41–49.

FORSMAN, J. P., 1963, Geochemistry of kerogen, in I. A. Breger (ed.), Organic geochemistry: New York, Macmillan Co., p. 148–182.

—— AND HUNT, J. M., 1958, Insoluble organic matter (kerogen) in sedimentary rocks of marine origin, in L. G. Weeks (ed.), Habitat of oil: Tulsa, Oklahoma, Am. Assoc. Petroleum Geologists, p. 747–778.

GIRAUD, A., 1970, Application of pyrolysis and gas chromatography to geochemical characterization of kerogen in sedimentary rocks: Am. Assoc. Petroleum Geologists Bull., v. 54, p. 439–451.

GOLDSTEIN, A. J., 1975, Geologic interpretation of Viersen and Cochran's 25-1 Weyerhaeuser well: Oklahoma Geology Notes, v. 35, p. 167–181.

GOROKHOV, S. S., PETROVA, N. I., AND KOVALENKO, V. S., 1973, Eksperimental'noye izucheniye evolyutsii biogennogo ugleroda pri vysokikh temperaturakh i vysokikh davleniyakh [Experimental study of the alteration of biogenic carbon at high temperatures and pressures]: Akad. Nauk SSSR Doklady, v. 209, p. 197–200 [AGI Translation Doklady, Earth Sci. Sect., April 1974, p. 194–196].

GREW, E. S., 1974, Carbonaceous material in some metamorphic rocks of New England and other areas: Jour. Geology, v. 82, p. 50–73.

GRIFFIN, G. M., 1967, X-ray diffraction techniques applicable to studies of diagenesis and low rank metamorphism in humic sediments: Jour. Sed. Petrology, v. 37, p. 1006–1011.

HARRISON, W. E., 1976, Laboratory graphitization of a modern estuarine kerogen: Geochim. et Cosmochim. Acta, v. 40, p. 247–248.

HOOD, A., GUTJAHR, C. C. M., AND HEACOCK, R. L., 1975, Organic metamorphism and the generation of petroleum. Am. Assoc. Petroleum Geologists Bull., v. 59, p. 986–996.

LANDIS, C. A., 1971, Graphitization of dispersed carbonaceous material in metamorphic rocks. Contr. Mineralogy and Petrology, v. 30, p. 34–45.

McIVER, R. D., 1967, Composition of kerogen—Clue to its role in the origin of petroleum, *in* Seventh World Petroleum Congress, Mexico, Proceedings, v. 2: London, Elsevier, p. 25–36.

OBERLIN, A., BOULMIER, J. L., AND DURAND, B., 1974, Electron microscope investigation of the structure of naturally and artificially metamorphosed kerogen: Geochim. et Cosmochim. Acta, v. 38, p. 647–650.

POWELL, T. G., COOK, P. J., AND McKIRDY, D. M., 1975, Organic geochemistry of phosphorites: Relevance to petroleum genesis: Am. Assoc. Petroleum Geologists Bull., v. 59, p. 618–632.

QUINN, A. W., AND GLASS, H. D., 1958, Rank of coal and metamorphic grade of rocks of the Narragansett Basin of Rhode Island: Econ. Geology, v. 53, p. 563–576.

ROBINSON, W. E., 1969a, Isolation procedures for kerogens and associated soluble organic materials, *in* E. G. Eglinton and M. T. J. Murphy (eds.), Organic geochemistry: Methods and results: New York, Springer-Verlag, p. 181–195.

——, 1969b, Kerogen of the Green River Formation, *in* E. G. Eglinton and M. T. J. Murphy (eds.), Organic geochemistry: Methods and results: New York, Springer-Verlag, p. 619–637.

TEICHMÜLLER, M., AND TEICHMÜLLER, R., 1967, Diagenesis of coals, *in* G. Larsen and G. V. Chilingar (eds.), Diagenesis in sediments: Amsterdam, Elsevier, p. 391–415.

TISSOT, B., DURAND, B., ESPITALIE, J., AND COMBAZ, A., 1974, Influence of nature and diagenesis of organic matter in formation of petroleum: Am. Assoc. Petroleum Geologists Bull, v. 58, p. 499–506.

WELTE, D., 1974, Recent advances in organic geochemistry of humic substances and kerogen. A review, *in* B. Tissot and F. Bienner (eds.), Advances in geochemistry 1973: Paris, Editions Technip, p. 3–13.

SEPM Special Publication No. 26, p. 55–79, March 1979

CLAY MINERAL ASSEMBLAGES AS LOW GRADE METAMORPHIC GEOTHERMOMETERS: APPLICATION TO THE THRUST FAULTED DISTURBED BELT OF MONTANA, U.S.A.

JANET HOFFMAN[1] AND JOHN HOWER[2]
Case Western Reserve University, Cleveland, Ohio 44106

ABSTRACT

Clay mineral assemblages in sedimentary rocks can be indicative of the maximum temperature (below 300° C) and metamorphic grade to which these rocks have been subjected. The chemical composition of the rock and pore fluid, along with the detrital mineralogy are also influential in determining the mineral assemblages that form at higher temperatures. Clay mineral assemblages are also dependent on reaction time at low temperatures. The most useful minerals which can be used as geothermometers are as follows: (1) for shales: illite/smectites, illite, and chlorite; (2) for sandstones: chlorite, chlorite/smectite (corrensite) and dickite; and (3) for volcanics and volcanogenic rocks: chlorite/smectites and zeolites. In pelitic sediments the conversion of smectite to illite and its subsequent recrystallization to 2M muscovite allow a detailed temperature zonation of these rocks into a sequence of temperature ranges.

These temperature (grade) sequences are applied to the disturbed belt of Montana. Mesozoic strata involved in Laramide thrust faulting events have mineral assemblages, principally the mixed-layer clays and zeolites, which reflect a low grade metamorphic environment and indicate metamorphic temperatures between 100° and 200° C. These metamorphic mineral assemblages are displayed by strata as lithologically diverse as shales, sandstones, volcanogenic rocks, and bentonites. Field evidence indicates that these strata were never sufficiently buried during sinking of the sedimentary basin to produce the observed mineralogic and chemical changes. Comparison of stratigraphically equivalent sediments on the adjacent undisturbed Sweetgrass Arch show mineral assemblages indicative of low temperature (<<100° C) conditions. Heating to a degree higher than that predicted from normal geothermal gradients is inferred to be caused by burial beneath thrust plates. This is suggested as the mechanism that generated the temperatures indicated by observed mineral assemblages in the disturbed belt.

INTRODUCTION

As is well known from the petrology of igneous and metamorphic rocks, the mineral assemblage present in a rock is determined by the chemical composition of the rock (plus the fluid phase that may have been present), the pressure-temperature regime to which it was subjected, and the extent to which it has reacted—i.e., how closely it has approached equilibrium. Pelitic rocks have proved to be the most useful in delineating metamorphic grade. Thus, regional metamorphic facies have generally been defined on the basis of mineral assemblages present in metamorphosed shales. The Barrovian sequence of isograds first described in a field study of the Dalradian schists of the Scottish Highlands: biotite-almandine garnet-staurolite-kyanite-sillimanite, is based on minerals observed in metamorphosed pelitic rocks. It is now known that this classical sequence is indicative of regional metamorphism of intermediate P_{H_2O} (2–6 Kb) and temperatures ranging

from about 300° to 600° C. Temperatures less than 300° C generally do not result in readily visible reconstitution of the shale or in startling growth of crystals. Argillites and slates are the immediate precursors to greenschist facies pelitic rocks. Because of their fine-grained nature the mineral assemblages of these pelites were neglected by metamorphic petrologists until relatively recent times. Therefore, metamorphic mineral reactions that take place between earth surface conditions and 300° C long remained unknown.

The first modern investigations of pregreenschist facies metamorphism were carried out on rocks of nonpelitic composition. The mineral sequence described by Coombs (1954) and Coombs et al. (1959) was an investigation of deeply buried, but incompletely reacted, andesitic volcanic rocks containing zeolite assemblages rather than the layer silicates that are the critical minerals of the well-known Barrovian assemblages. It has been observed that zeolites more commonly form in volcanic and volcanogenic rocks while the clay mineral-carbonate assemblages form in pelitic sediments (Zen, 1974). Both these trends occur in response to temperatures produced during and after burial of the sediments.

[1] U.S. Geological Survey, Reston, Va. 22092. Deceased August 1977.
[2] Present address: Department of Geology, University of Illinois, Urbana, Illinois 61801.

Copyright ℗ 1979, The Society of Economic Paleontologists and Mineralogists

The purpose of this paper is to assemble and synthesize the published evidence for pre-greenschist facies mineral sequences in shales and sandstones, and to apply this synthesis to the low grade metamorphism in the disturbed belt of Montana. The lithologies in the disturbed belt—shales, sandstones, and volcanics—permit us , to relate these temperature-compositional trends to those of the zeolite facies. We will end up by translating mineral assemblages for these lithologies into metamorphic temperatures.

TERMINOLOGY AND DEFINITIONS

The authors realize that there is considerable concern among some workers about the proper terminology to apply to pre-greenschist conditions (grades). We consider the temperatures associated with these grades below the biotite isograd to be less than approximately 300° C. Many descriptive terms (e.g., epigenesis, catagenesis, and anchimetamorphism) have been used. There may be some value in using these terms, but we prefer to go (almost) back to Van Hise (1904) and refer to all post-depositional changes as metamorphism.

The use of the metamorphic petrologist's term "grade" to indicate a specific mineral assemblage rather than a range of pressure-temperature conditions (Carmichael *et al.*, 1974) is important to our discussion of pre-greenschist facies rocks. At low temperatures only the most reactive phases in a rock begin to transform and make their way toward becoming stable phases under these conditions (Yeh and Savin, 1977; Aronson and Hower, 1976). Reaction times appear to be significant, even on the basis of geologic time, not going to completion even in tens of millions of years (Perry and Hower, 1970; Aronson and Hower, 1976). Experimental studies (Eberl and Hower, 1976) show that smectite, one of the most reactive minerals in shales, should have survived since the Paleozoic Era at earth surface conditions even if illite is the stable phase. As will be seen in the discussion of the temperature dependence of mineral assemblages of shales, kinetic aspects play an important role in the persistence or appearance of a mineral. At the same temperature, deeply buried Pliocene-Pleistocene shales have a much lower grade assemblage than do shales which have been buried since the early Tertiary.

MINERAL DEFINITIONS

Kaolin mineral species discussed are kaolinite and kaolin$_d$ (kaolinite with a disordered stacking arrangement), dickite, and nacrite. These kaolin polytypes are described by Bailey (1963) in terms of direction and amount of shift in the 1:1 layers and the location of the vacant octahedral site in successive layers. For the hydrated kaolin miner-

als we propose, in this paper, to follow the terminology suggested by Keller and Johns (1976), using endellite as the fully hydrated form and halloysite as the partially or totally dehydrated form.

Chlorite polytypes discussed are those described by Bailey and Brown (1962) and Hayes (1970). For complete mineral definitions and descriptions of the layer silicate minerals to be discussed, we refer the reader to Grim (1968) and Carroll (1970). However, because mixed-layer clays, particularly illite/smectite, have proven to be the most useful indicators of metamorphic grade, further mention of their composition and structure is merited. As can be seen in Figure 1, between pyrophyllite with no interlayer charge and dioctahedral micas with an interlayer charge deficiency of 1.0 equivalent per $O_{10}(OH)_2$, lie smectites, mixed-layer clays, and illite. Smectites have a charge deficiency approximately between 0.2 and 0.4 equivalents per $O_{10}(OH)_2$ on the 2:1 layer structure, enabling the structure to expand. Illites have a higher charge, approximately 0.8 equivalents per $O_{10}(OH)_2$, too high to allow the layers to expand when potassium is the interlayer cation. Thus illite is quite similar to muscovite. Mixed-layer illite/smectite is an interlayering of expanded smectite layers and nonexpanded illite layers. This interlayering can be in a random or in an ordered fashion. As a function of an increasing number of illite layers in the mixed-layer structure, many degrees of ordering are possible. Two types, however, are distinguished. They are: (1) the allevardite-like (ISISISIS . . .) or "short

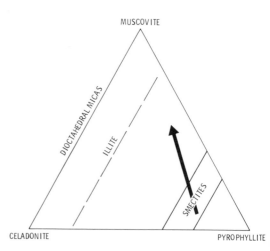

FIG. 1.—Distribution of smectites, illites, and mixed-layer illite/smectites within the compositional triangle pyrophyllite-muscovite celadonite (from Hower and Mowatt, 1966).

range" ordering commonly found where clays contain less than 40 percent expanded (smectite) layers and (2) the Kalkberg-type (ISIIISIIISII . . .) or "long range" ordering. For a more detailed discussion of ordering in mixed-layer clays see Reynolds and Hower (1970). The relative proportions of expanded (smectite) and non-expanded (illite) layers is determined by X-ray diffraction methods which are summarized by Hoffman (1976). The other mixed-layer clay referred to by the authors is corrensite, a completely ordered interlayering of chlorite and smectite layers. The interlayering schemes for corrensite and corrensite-like mineral species are analogous to those for mixed-layer illite/smectites.

Bentonites referred to in the literature as "classical," are the alteration products of acid or intermediate unconsolidated volcanic ash, usually in an aqueous environment. The dominant alteration mineral of this unconsolidated ash is dioctahedral smectite. The alteration process involves extensive interchange of constituents with the overlying aqueous environment or enclosing sediments (cf. Kiersch and Keller, 1955).

Potash (potassium or meta-) bentonites are alteration products of what were originally "classical" smectite bentonites. They contain as the major mineral a mixed-layer illite/smectite in place of the smectite of "classical" bentonites. The potassium content is consonant with the proportion of illite layers in the illite/smectite (Weaver, 1953; Byström, 1956; Hower and Mowatt, 1966; Hoffman, 1976).

PRE-GREENSCHIST FACIES METAMORPHIC MINERAL ASSEMBLAGES

The rock types that will be considered in this section are shales and sandstones. Temperature- (grade-) dependent mineral assemblages in these rock types will be correlated with each other and, in a later section, equated with the assemblages present in K-bentonites and intermediate volcanic (zeolite facies) rocks.

Shales.—The first published investigation of shales that have undergone deep burial is that of Burst (1959) in the U.S. Gulf Coast. Superposed on mineral assemblages that may have differed at the time of deposition because of differential sedimentation during transport (Parham, 1966) or conditions in the environment of deposition, he found that smectite was converted to illite as a function of burial depth and that chlorite may form under these conditions. Subsequent to Burst's publication, a number of workers reported the non-persistence of smectites in pelitic sediments that had been deeply buried, as well as other mineralogic changes (Weaver, 1967; Ehinger et al., 1965; Long and Neglia, 1968; Dunoyer,

1964, 1970; Perry and Hower, 1970; Weaver and Beck, 1971).

These data were summarized and supplemented by Hower and others (1976), who concluded that the generally reliable mineralogic criteria indicating increasing grade in shales include: (1) conversion of smectite to illite through a mixed-layer illite/smectite series, (2) appearance of chlorite, and (3) disappearance of potassium feldspar by decomposition. These mineralogic changes are represented by the reaction:

$$Smectite + K\text{-}feldspar = Illite$$
$$+ \; Chlorite + Quartz$$

The proportion of illite layers in the illite/smectite series is the most sensitive indicator of metamorphic grade in shales. In addition to the grade-dependent proportion of illite layers, illite/smectites exhibit a sequence of interlayering schemes that begins with random interstratification, proceeds to short range ordering and then to long range ordering of the illite and smectite layers.

The conversion of illite to a dioctahedral mica is the highest grade pre-greenschist facies reaction in pelitic rocks. This reaction was observed by Maxwell and Hower (1967) in a burial metamorphic sequence involving argillites of the Precambrian Belt Supergroup. In this occurrence the completion of this reaction is coincident with the biotite isograd of the greenschist facies. Kaolinite frequently coexists with illite but is absent from greenschist facies pelites (Weaver, 1958; Dunoyer, 1964; Perry, 1969).

Figure 2 displays mineralogic changes as a function of increasing metamorphic grade caused

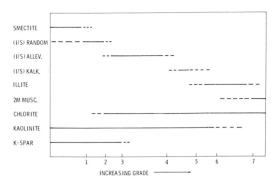

FIG. 2.—Metamorphic grade index minerals in pre-greenschist facies pelitic rocks. Numbers indicate significant grade-dependent changes in assemblage.

by progressive burial metamorphism of shales. Table 1 translates grade into temperature, the temperatures being the actual logged well temperatures. Two sets of temperatures are given, one for very young (Pliocene-Pleistocene) and one for older (upper Mesozoic–lower Tertiary) sequences. No temperatures are given for the short range order → long range order illite/smectite (stages 3 to 5 in Fig. 2) or for the long range order illite/smectite → illite conversions (stages 5 to 7 in Fig. 2) for the "young" set because they have not been observed in Pliocene-Pleistocene burial metamorphic sequences.

Sandstones.—The diagenetic-metamorphic clay mineral assemblage in sandstones is considerably more diverse than that of shales. This diversity is undoubtedly caused by the high permeability of sandstones in contrast to the low permeability of shales. In shales the pore-water chemistry appears to be controlled largely by the chemistry of the solids: the decomposition of unstable detrital minerals, the (probable) equilibrium solution of stable phases, and membrane filtration processes (Berry and Hanshaw, 1960). In contrast, the high permeability of sandstones results in a regime in which the solution/solid ratio is high. The phases that form are controlled by the solution composition. Clay minerals that have been reported to form diagenetically (metamorphically) from solution include Ib chlorite (Hayes, 1970), dickite/nacrite (Weaver, 1959; Shutov *et al.*, 1970; Dunoyer, 1970) and 1M illite (Triplehorn, 1967). Clay minerals that have been reported to form as (metastable?) decomposition products of pre-existing minerals include kaolinite (after feldspar) and corrensite (after ferromagnesium minerals) (Kübler, 1973). Illite has also been reported as a metamorphic product (of pre-exist-

ing smectite ?) in sandstones (Sommer, 1975).

Shutov and others (1970), largely on the basis of studies of Paleozoic sedimentary rocks of the Russian Platform, have suggested an evolutionary change in kaolin type as a function of burial metamorphic grade. They state (most likely on the basis of Petrov's (1958) detailed studies of the Cretaceous "great weathering crust") that kaolinite (triclinic) is the dominant kaolin mineral formed by weathering processes. During transport mechanical abrasion results in disordering of the layer stacking, so that the main kaolin mineral in unconsolidated sediments is kaolin$_d$. Burial metamorphism reverses the process, with the initial reaction being to reorder the kaolin$_d$ to kaolinite, followed by conversion of kaolinite to dickite or nacrite. According to Shutov and others (1970), nacrite is a "stress" mineral, occurring at the same grade as dickite, but as a vein mineral in slickensided fractures. Their evolutionary sequence is thus: Kaolinite (soils) → kaolin$_d$ (sediments) → kaolinite (shallow burial) → dickite/nacrite (deep burial). In this sequence they ignore halloysite/endellite, which appears to be an important—if not the dominant—kaolin that forms by the weathering of feldspars in recent soils (Parham, 1969). For the purpose of the present paper we will include halloysite as a sedimentary mineral with kaolin$_d$ and propose the following burial metamorphic sequence: halloysite/kaolin$_d$ → kaolinite → dickite/nacrite.

The crystal structure and stability relationships of chlorite polytypes has been elegantly treated by Bailey and Brown (1962). Hayes (1970) investigated chlorite polytypes present in sandstones and their use as diagenetic (metamorphic) indicators. From Hayes' data it can tentatively be concluded that (1) all type-I chlorites are pre-greenschist facies; (2) Ib$_d$ chlorites (Ib with disordered stacking) do not persist above 70°–80° C; and (3) the Ib → IIb conversion occurs at a metamorphic grade coincident with the lithologic change in pelitics, shale → slate, and the mineralogic change, illite → 2M dioctahedral mica (200° C).

Corrensite has a number of different types of occurrence. It occurs in dolomitic limestones (Peterson, 1961), associated with evaporites (Lucas, 1962; Kübler, 1963), and in volcanogenic sandstones that have undergone deep burial. Kübler (1973) has summarized the literature concerning these occurrences. Iijima and Utada (1971) investigated a burial metamorphic sequence in the Uetsu geosyncline of Japan. They found that the conversion of volcanic ferromagnesium minerals to corrensite takes place at about 95° C, by which temperature they also note the disappearance of noninterlayered smectites. Corrensite persists in this sequence to the bottom of the well at a measured temperature of 148° C.

TABLE 1.—TEMPERATURES FOR METAMORPHIC GRADE CHANGES INDICATED IN FIGURE 1. BECAUSE KINETICS ARE IMPORTANT IN THE ATTAINMENT OF GRADE, A SEPARATE SET OF TEMPERATURES IS GIVEN FOR VERY YOUNG (PLIOCENE-PLEISTOCENE) AND OLDER (LOWER TERTIARY—UPPER MESOZOIC) BURIAL METAMORPHIC SEQUENCES. SHALES WITH ASSEMBLAGES OF GRADE 3 AND ABOVE HAVE NOT BEEN OBSERVED IN PLIOCENE-PLEISTOCENE SEQUENCES.

Grade	Upper Mesozoic—Lower Tertiary Temperature (°C)	Pliocene-Pleistocene Temperature (°C)
1	60	60
2	100	140
3	120	—
4	175	—
5	200	—
6	—	—
7	300	—

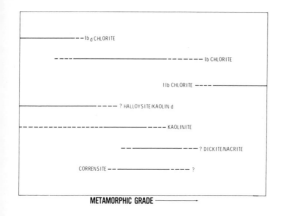

FIG. 3.—Metamorphic grade index minerals in sandstones.

Our estimates of the temperature dependence of the various metamorphic minerals in sandstones is shown in Figure 3. It should be emphasized that in contrast to the repetitive nature of mineral sequences in shales, the mineral assemblage in sandstones is at the mercy of the pore water composition and, in the case of corrensite, is dependent on the presence of detrital ferromagnesium minerals. Therefore, the absence of a given mineral does not indicate that the sandstone has not been subjected to the metamorphic grade that would produce that mineral. In sandstones it is the presence of indicator minerals that is of importance.

LOW GRADE REGIONAL METAMORPHISM IN THE
DISTURBED BELT AREA OF MONTANA

Introduction.—Mesozoic argillaceous sedimentary rocks and bentonite beds in the disturbed belt of Montana have been subjected to regional low grade metamorphic conditions. The mineral assemblages in the argillaceous rocks are those of the clay mineral-carbonate trend of "burial metamorphism" (Zen, 1974), discussed in this paper. Associated volcanic sands and tuffs contain

the zeolite laumontite and the mixed-layer clay mineral corrensite. All of the minerals used to estimate metamorphic grade in the Montana study are given in Table 2.

An estimation of temperatures attained in the strata of the disturbed belt can be made on the basis of the mineralogy and chemistry of the metamorphosed sediments. Shales in the disturbed belt have undergone mineralogic and chemical changes that occur in shale in response to deep burial in sedimentary basins and geosynclines. Paralleling these changes in the shale, bentonites in the disturbed belt have been converted to potash bentonites by an exchange of chemical constituents with adjacent sedimentary rocks. On the Sweetgrass Arch, the assemblages present indicate surface or near-surface conditions (e.g. $<<$ 100° C). The following sections outline the study area from a structural and stratigraphic standpoint; give the mineralogic and chemical evidence for low grade metamorphism, in conjunction with the probable source for the higher temperatures; and add what appears to us as conclusive proof for the origin of potash bentonites as burial metamorphic products of classical bentonites.

Study area.—The disturbed belt of Montana consists physiographically of the Front Ranges and the foothills of the northern Cordillera (Mudge, 1972b; Bally, Gordy, and Stewart, 1966). Principal structural features in the disturbed belt include the Lewis Thrust, the imbricate thrusts of the Sawtooth Range, and the associated thrusts of the Wolf Creek area (Figure 4). East of the disturbed belt is the Central Montana (Sweetgrass) Arch. The stratigraphy and the structure of both areas have been examined extensively (Childers, 1964; Cobban *et al.*, 1959a, b; Mudge, 1970, 1972a, b; McMannis, 1965). The units involved in thrusting and the style of thrusting change from north to south. In the northern part of the area a thick plate of Precambrian Belt Supergroup rocks (the Lewis Thrust) overlies Mesozoic strata. Farther to the south and west, these Precambrian rocks are in thrust contact with Paleozoic as well as

TABLE 2.—GRADE (TEMPERATURE) INDICATOR MINERALS FOR SHALES, VOLCANOGENIC ROCKS, AND BENTONITES FOR THE DISTURBED BELT AND SWEETGRASS ARCH.

	Sweetgrass Arch	Disturbed Belt
Shales	Highly expandable random illite/smectite	Ordered illite/smectite ± chlorite
Bentonites	Smectite	Ordered illite/smectite ± chlorite
Volcanogenic rocks	Heulandite	Laumontite
Volcanic sands	Ferromagnesium minerals	Corrensite
Temperature range	50–60° C	100–200° C

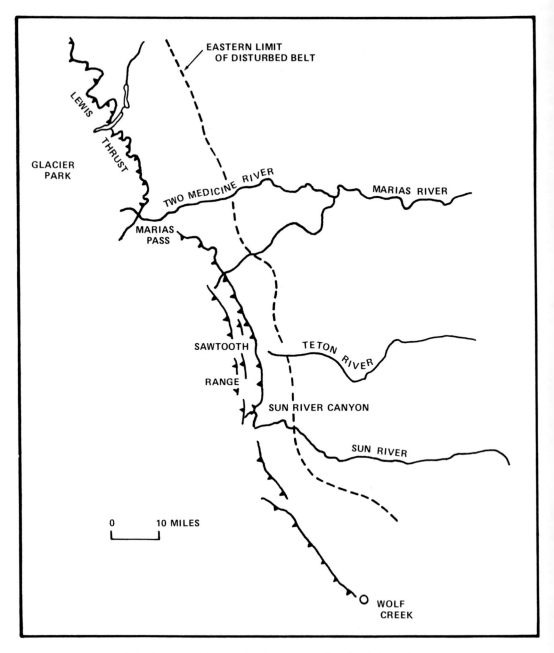

FIG. 4.—Principal structural features for the Montana disturbed belt and Sweetgrass Arch.

Mesozoic units. South of Marias Pass (cf. Fig. 4) the Lewis Thrust swings west and gives way to the imbricate style thrust faulting of the Sawtooth Range. Here, Paleozoic and older Mesozoic rocks are thrust over younger Mesozoic rocks. Southeast of the Sawtooth Range, the thrust sheets consist primarily of Mesozoic sedimentary rocks along with some flows and tuffs. The Mesozoic section in all these instances has been subjected to burial depths equal in thickness to the overlying plates. Further east the structure becomes more subdued; east of the disturbed belt on the Sweetgrass Arch, essentially flat-lying Mesozoic sedimentary rocks contain most of the stratigraphic units exposed in the disturbed belt.

Sampling.—Cretaceous argillaceous rocks, including some tuffs and volcanogenic rocks, and bentonite beds from the disturbed belt and the Sweetgrass Arch were sampled. A comparison was made of the mineralogy and chemistry of units from the same stratigraphic horizons in both areas. A total of 158 bentonite samples and 111 shale, mudstone, and tuffaceous samples were collected. Most of the tuffaceous sediments were collected in the Wolf Creek area (cf. Fig. 4). The remainder were collected throughout the study area with the majority from the Sun River Canyon area where structural and stratigraphic control were best.

Size separations.—Size separations were made for all samples at <1 μm by centrifugal sedimentation. For more detailed mineralogic and chemical work on the clay size fraction, an additional size separation was made at <0.5 μm. The 0.5 μm fraction was then separated at the <0.2 μm fraction using a continuous flow centrifuge. We also separated the >4 μm fraction from 20 shale samples in order to obtain material free of clay to examine feldspar types present.

X-ray diffraction analyses.—An aliquot of each sample for the <1 μm size fraction was dispersed in distilled water and allowed to settle and dry on a glass slide. Finer size fractions were dispersed and centrifuged onto porous ceramic tiles after the method of Kinter and Diamond (1956). X-ray diffractograms were run on all samples (air dried and ethylene glycol solvated) from 32° to 2° 2θ using CuK α radiation. These patterns were used to determine the expandability of the mixed-layer illite/smectite by methods described in Reynolds and Hower (1970) as well as to determine the presence or absence of chlorite, kaolin, and illite. A semiquantitative estimate of the relative percentages of smectite, illite/smectite, kaolin, and chlorite in all bentonite samples is reported in Hoffman (1976).

X-ray diffraction patterns of randomly oriented samples of the whole rock were run to make semiquantitative estimates of quartz, plagioclase

feldspar, potassium feldspar, calcite, dolomite, gypsum, and total clay, after the method of Schultz (1964). Summaries of the whole rock semiquantitative diffraction data are given in Table 3. The precision of any single analysis is ±10% of the amount present.

Chemical analyses.—The major element concentrations of 80 whole rock (shale, volcanic, and bentonite) and 12 bentonite samples (0.2 μm–0.5 μm) were determined. All elements except sodium were analyzed by x-ray spectroscopic techniques. Sodium was determined through flame photometry. Samples were fired at 950° C overnight, diluted 2:1 or 4:1 with $Li_2B_4O_7$ ($Li_2B_4O_7$/sample), fused, ground, and pelletized for analysis. The National Bureau of Standards plastic clay (no. 98) was used as a standard. Matrix differences were corrected using the computer iterative calculation program of Hower and others (1964). The precision of all constituents except magnesium is ±2% of the amount present. The precision of magnesium is ±5%. Sodium analyses by flame photometry were performed following methods described by Klar (personal commun.), Van Loon and Parissis (1969), and Boar and Ingram (1970). A summary of the whole rock chemical data for shales, volcanogenic sediments, and bentonites is given in Table 4. The chemical data are given on an ignited basis and an ignited CaO-free basis. The analyses were recalculated on a CaO-free basis to eliminate the effect of large variations in calcite.

EVIDENCE FOR METAMORPHISM: MINERALOGICAL AND CHEMICAL RESULTS

Shales.—The whole rock mineralogy for shales of the disturbed belt and Sweetgrass Arch is given in Table 3. For this analysis, the clay mineral species were not distinguished. At this level there is, in general, no distinction between the shales of the disturbed belt and arch for the major mineral species, except in the feldspar types present. Both feldspar types (plagioclase and potassium feld-

TABLE 3.—SUMMARY OF SEMIQUANTITATIVE X-RAY DIFFRACTION DATA FOR SHALES, BENTONITES, AND VOLCANIC SEDIMENTS FROM THE DISTURBED BELT AND SWEETGRASS ARCH.

	SHALES		BENTONITES		VOLCANICS
	Disturbed Belt	Sweetgrass Arch	Disturbed Belt	Sweetgrass Arch	Disturbed Belt
Total Layer Silicate	51	48	71	69	52
Quartz	33	37	14	7	30
Plagioclase Feldspar	9	6	11	5	11
Potassium Feldspar	<1	3	<1	3	—
Calcite	6	4	4	3	2
Dolomite	3	3	—	—	—
Zeolite	—	—	—	—	<5

TABLE 4.—SUMMARY OF WHOLE ROCK CHEMICAL DATA AS WEIGHT PERCENT OXIDE ON AN IGNITED AND ON AN IGNITED CaO-FREE BASIS FOR SHALES, BENTONITES, AND VOLCANIC SEDIMENTS FROM THE DISTURBED BELT AND SWEETGRASS ARCH.

Oxide	SHALES				BENTONITES				VOLCANIC SEDIMENTS
	Disturbed Belt[1]	Sweetgrass Arch[2]	Disturbed Belt CaO-free basis	Sweetgrass Arch CaO-free basis	Disturbed Belt[3]	Sweetgrass Arch[4]	Disturbed Belt CaO-free	Sweetgrass Arch CaO-free basis	Wolf Creek Area
SiO_2	65.51 ± 5.75	70.92 ± 2.08	67.66 ± 5.7	72.89 ± 2.78	54.62 ± 16.15	60.16 ± 11.55	60.46 ± 7.04	64.03 ± 5.63	65.26 ± 5.81
TiO_2	0.67 ± 0.12	0.61 ± 0.09	0.69 ± 0.11	0.65 ± 0.14	0.68 ± 0.35	0.42 ± 0.26	0.72 ± 0.32	0.45 ± 0.26	0.56 ± 0.29
Al_2O_3	18.00 ± 4.51	15.64 ± 2.24	18.53 ± 4.33	16.47 ± 1.96	25.39 ± 5.48	22.31 ± 6.77	26.46 ± 5.88	24.01 ± 5.50	17.88 ± 2.50
Fe_2O_3[5]	5.30 ± 2.68	4.14 ± 0.98	5.46 ± 2.96	4.23 ± 0.96	3.96 ± 2.27	4.04 ± 1.95	4.12 ± 2.34	4.69 ± 3.21	4.48 ± 2.83
MgO	2.71 ± 1.24	2.41 ± 0.75	2.82 ± 1.37	2.41 ± 0.86	2.60 ± 0.87	4.05 ± 1.90	2.69 ± 0.89	4.34 ± 1.84	17.88 ± 2.50
CaO	5.69 ± 12.84	2.31 ± 1.48	—	—	3.76 ± 5.26	6.26 ± 14.83	—	—	4.38 ± 4.58
Na_2O	0.67 ± 0.73	0.74 ± 0.55	0.70 ± 0.76	0.76 ± 0.58	0.74 ± 0.91	0.80 ± 0.69	0.79 ± 0.93	0.90 ± 0.78	0.56 ± 0.43
K_2O	3.39 ± 0.93	3.44 ± 0.83	3.49 ± 0.92	3.52 ± 0.85	3.51 ± 1.34	1.47 ± 0.92	3.65 ± 1.35	1.49 ± 0.97	3.69 ± 1.85
Total	99.23 ± 1.77	99.89 ± 1.76	99.19 ± 1.77	99.96 ± 1.70	98.92 ± 1.66	99.45 ± 1.68	98.92 ± 1.66	99.45 ± 1.68	99.28 ± 1.11

[1] Weight percent oxides given as the mean and first standard deviation of 26 chemical analyses.
[2] Mean values based on 11 chemical analyses.
[3] Mean values based on 29 chemical analyses.
[4] Mean values based on 12 chemical analyses.
[5] Total Fe as Fe_2O_3. FeO not determined.

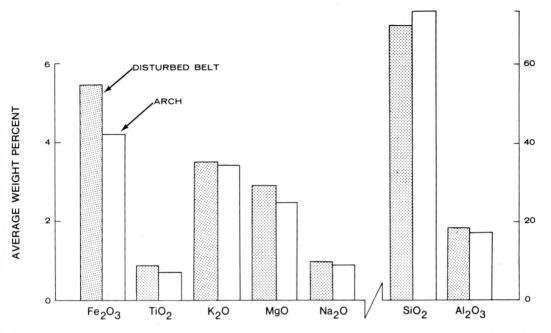

FIG. 5.—Comparison of the whole rock chemistry as weight percent oxide (ignited on a CaO-free basis) for shales from the Montana disturbed belt and the Sweetgrass Arch.

spar) are present on the arch; few samples in the disturbed belt contain potassium feldspar. The chemistry of whole rock samples is summarized in Figure 5, as weight percent oxides on a normal and a CaO-free basis. There is no significant difference between the two suites.

In the clay-size (<1 μm) fraction, the dominant mineral in the shales is a mixed-layer illite/smectite. On the Sweetgrass Arch the illite/smectite is randomly interstratified with a large proportion of smectite layers. On the basis of mineralogy and temperature relations observed in deeply buried shale, this mineralogy would not have persisted had burial metamorphic temperatures exceeded 50° or 60° C. In contrast, the Cretaceous shales involved in thrusting (disturbed belt) contain mineral assemblages indicating that they have been metamorphosed. Here the illite/smectite contains a high proportion of illite layers that exhibit ordered interstratification with smectite layers. Comparison with deeply buried shale sequences suggests that the shale mineralogy in the disturbed belt resulted from heating in the temperature range 100° to 200° C. Figure 6 is a comparison of the range in composition of the illite/smectite from the shales of the disturbed belt and from the arch. Figure 7 shows the geographic distribution of the illite/smectite compositions. Figure 8 shows x-ray diffraction patterns of the <1 μm fraction of shales from the disturbed belt and the arch.

The overall mineralogical reaction occurring in the shales appears to be the same as that which occurs in burial sequences of shales, that is:

$$Smectite + Potassium\ feldspar \rightarrow Illite$$

$$+ Quartz \pm Chlorite$$

Chemically, the potassium feldspar provides the

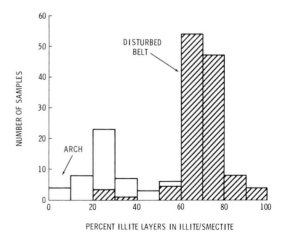

FIG. 6.—Composition of the illite/smectite as percent illite layers in mixed-layer illite/smectite as a function of frequency of occurrence for shales from the Montana disturbed belt and the Sweetgrass Arch.

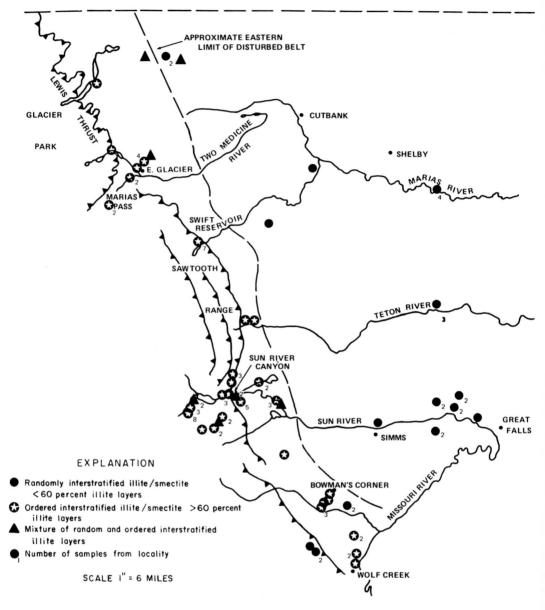

FIG. 7.—Geographic distribution of illite/smectite compositions in shales of the Montana disturbed belt and Sweetgrass Arch.

necessary aluminum and potassium for the conversion of smectite to illite layers in the mixed-layer clay. Excess silica forms quartz. Iron and magnesium lost by the smectite in the reaction probably forms chlorite (Hower et al., 1976). This is consistent with the observation that potassium feldspar is present in most shales of the arch and is absent from the disturbed belt. Further evidence that the source of potassium to form illite layers is by redistribution of potassium

already present in the shales can be seen in the whole rock chemistry—K_2O is essentially the same for both suites.

Volcanogenic sediments.—Tuffs and volcanogenic sediments are present in the southwestern portion of the disturbed belt, northwest of the town of Wolf Creek (cf. Fig. 4). The mineralogy and chemistry here yields additional evidence for a low-grade metamorphic environment in the disturbed belt. The upper Cretaceous Two Medi-

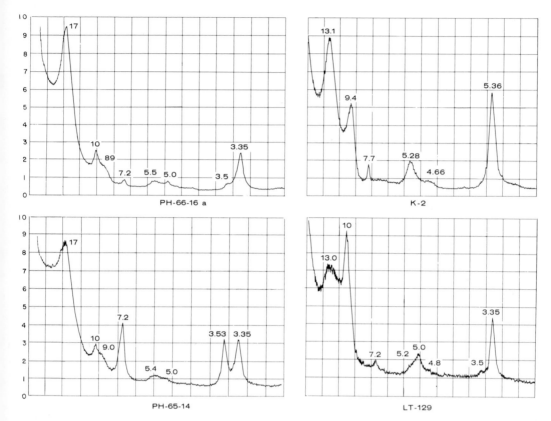

FIG. 8.—X-ray diffraction patterns representative of the clay-size fraction (<1 μm) of shales from the Montana disturbed belt (K-2, LT 129) and the Sweetgrass Arch (PH-66-18a, PH-65-14). All samples are solvated with ethylene glycol.

cine Formation shows a gradation of lithologies from units composed of volcanoclastic fragments to those containing varying amounts of "normal" sedimentary material. The mineral assemblages are therefore highly variable. Whole rock mineralogies (Table 3) include the zeolite laumontite, recognized by Coombs (1954, 1961) as being a burial metamorphic product of volcanogenic rocks. Tuffaceous rocks on the Sweetgrass Arch often contain heulandite, a zeolite indicating near surface conditions. The laumontite-bearing volcanogenic sediments are interbedded with shales and bentonite beds which contain an ordered interstratified illite/smectite. Therefore, the presence of laumontite is interpreted as indicating a metamorphic temperature in the range of 100°–175° C.

Also of significance petrologically is the higher feldspar content (almost always plagioclase) in many of the samples, as compared to non-volcanogenic sediments. Calcite is not present in the more volcanic-enriched units, even if these units have a high CaO content. Where this is the case,

laumontite is the dominant calcium-bearing pase, rather than calcite. It is apparent from the chemistry of these rocks that the role of calcium must be a dominant factor in controlling the mineralogy. As pointed out by Zen (1959) the partial pressure of CO_2 will control whether clay minerals or zeolites will form in silicate rocks containing a significant amount of calcium. His type reaction:

$$\text{Calcite + Smectite + Quartz}$$
$$= \text{Laumontite} + CO_2$$

demonstrates that the sequestering of calcium by CO_2 to form calcite permits clay minerals to form in place of zeolites. Zen also feels that the formation of zeolites in metamorphosed andesitic volcanics may be in part attributable to their more ready nucleation from pre-existing minerals.

In contrast to the persistent illite/smectite (ordered) found in other parts of the disturbed belt, these units also contain either corrensite, an ordered interstratified chlorite/smectite mineral, or another chlorite/expandable phase—both are

TABLE 5.—UNITS SAMPLED FROM THE DISTURBED BELT AND SWEETGRASS ARCH RELATING BENTONITES AND POTASH BENTONITES (NUMBER OF SAMPLES COLLECTED) TO DEPOSITIONAL ENVIRONMENT.

Formation	Depositional Environment	Bentonites	Potash Bentonites
Upper Cretaceous			
Two Medicine Formation (= Bearpaw Shale and Clagget Shale)	Nonmarine	12	26
Telegraph Creek Formation	Marine		5
Marias River Shale	Marine	9	60
Lower Cretaceous			
Blackleaf Formation	Marine/Nonmarine	16	30

most likely decomposition products of ferromagnesium minerals. This mineralogy would indicate burial metamorphic temperatures of at least 90° C (Kübler, 1973).

Bentonites.—Although bentonites make up only a minor part of the total stratigraphic section in northwest Montana, they provide the clearest evidence of low grade metamorphism in this area, as well as evidence as to the origin of potash bentonites. The units from which bentonites were sampled and the number of samples collected as well as the depositional environment of the enclosing sediments is given in Table 5. The mineralogical and chemical changes in the bentonite beds of the disturbed belt and arch parallel those of the shales and volcanogenic sediments, displaying a high temperature mineralogy (100–200° C) in the disturbed belt, and a low temperature mineralogy (<60° C) on the arch. The whole rock mineralogy is given in Table 3. Because clay mineral species are not distinguished, both suites appear quite similar except in the feldspar contents; potassium feldspar is more often present on the arch than in the disturbed belt. The difference is not so striking as in the shales, but it does indicate that potassium feldspar originally present in bentonites of the disturbed belt has decomposed.

There is a major difference in the clay mineralogy which, unlike the shales of the two suites, is reflected in a difference in bulk chemistry in the bentonites of the arch as compared to those of the disturbed belt (Fig. 9). The K_2O contents for the potash bentonites of the disturbed belt are significantly higher than those for bentonites from the arch. We feel that this major difference indicates the introduction of potassium into the

bentonite beds in the disturbed belt during metamorphism.

When all bentonites are considered, the clay-size fraction includes the following minerals: smectite, illite/smectite (randomly interstratified), illite/smectite (ordered interstratified), kaolin, chlorite, and illite. X-ray diffraction patterns for bentonites from the disturbed belt and from the arch are shown in Figures 10A and 10B.

Kaolin, present in many of the bentonite beds, is almost always formed during the initial conversion of the ash to a bentonite, the amount depending on the degree of leaching of silica during the conversion. Tonstein, found in coal deposits, forms from ash altered in swamp (acid) environments and is composed entirely of kaolin (Millot, 1970). As will be seen, kaolin can also be produced during the alteration of a bentonite to a potash bentonite, or in the decomposition of plagioclase feldspar. In the first case, the kaolin is a product of the decomposition of smectite layers in the bentonite bed. Although a high percentage of samples from the disturbed belt contain kaolin, the average kaolin content for samples from the disturbed belt is low (~6%). In the second case, plagioclase feldspar phenocrysts are frequently altered to a kaolin mineral. These feldspar pseudomorphs were separated from the bulk of the clay (when possible) in order to determine the kaolin polytype. The kaolin mineral present in bentonite beds from the arch is a disordered kaolinite (kaolin$_d$). Several potash bentonites from the disturbed belt contain dickite or an ordered kaolinite, both indicative of higher temperatures (Hay, 1966).

Chlorite is never present on the arch, but frequently occurs in the potash bentonites of the

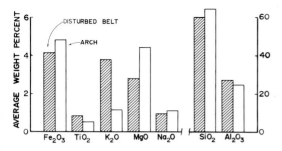

FIG. 9.—Comparison of the whole rock chemistry as weight percent oxide (ignited on a CaO-free basis) for bentonites from the Montana disturbed belt and the Sweetgrass Arch.

disturbed belt. Illite, when present, is in small amounts and is a contaminant due either to reworking of the beds or unclean sampling of very thin beds.

The most important variation in the clay mineral assemblages of the two suites is in the nature of the dioctahedral 2:1 mineral, the composition of which ranges from a pure smectite to an illite/smectite with 90% illite layers. Bentonite beds on the arch are the "classical" type; they contain a fully expandable smectite (or mixed-layer illite/smectite with only a few illite layers) as the dominant mineral, and have low potassium contents. In contrast, typical bentonites of the disturbed belt are potash rich, containing as much as 6% K_2O. Chemical analyses of the clay fraction for the two suites are given in Table 6. The excess potassium is present in the mixed-layer illite/smectite with a high proportion of illite layers. The mineralogy is identical to the well-known Ordovician meta-bentonites (Byström, 1956; Weaver, 1953, 1956). The compositional difference in the mixed-layer illite/smectite of the two suites is shown in Figure 11. The geographic distribution of the random and ordered illite/smectite is shown in Figure 12. By comparison with the mineralogy of the coexisting shales, this composition would indicate temperatures of from 100° to 200° C for the disturbed belt and less than 60° C for the arch.

It is apparent from the data presented here that the bentonites within the disturbed belt were originally normal bentonites like those on the Sweetgrass Arch and were converted to potash bentonites by a large influx of potassium from enclosing sediments, which were also undergoing low grade metamorphism in response to higher temperatures.

The reaction which converts a bentonite to a K-bentonite (i.e., smectite → illite/smectite) is

different from that which occurs in shales where the necessary components (both K^+ and Al^{+3}) are locally derived from within the shale itself. In the bentonite beds, decomposing potassium feldspar and perhaps, biotite, may contribute some of the K^+ and Al^{+3}, but they are not the dominating factors as in the shales. As evidenced by the K_2O contents in the whole rock analyses of the bentonites from the disturbed belt and arch, and even more obvious K_2O contents of the clay fraction of the two suites, one can see that an outside source for most of the potassium is necessary. No significant gains or losses of other components (except K_2O) occur, although the exchange ions Mg^{+2}, Na^+, and Ca^{+2} (not taken into account because of calcite) must leave the bentonite bed to balance the charge. Thus, the reaction must be of the nature: K^+ + Smectite → Illite/Smectite + Other Products. Several possibilities exist for a specific chemical reaction representing the above conversion of smectite or highly expandable illite/smectite to a less expandable (ordered) illite/smectite. These possible reactions and the conditions governing them are:

1. No K^+: no potassium available and smectite is unstable; X-Smectite → Kaolinite + Quartz + X^+.

2. Limited K^+: K = CEC (Eberl, 1971); K^+ + X-Smectite → Illite/Smectite + Kaolinite + Quartz + X^+.

3. Unlimited K^+: K^+ + X-Smectite → Illite/Smectite + Quartz + X^+.

One can use the mineralogic data for bentonites and K-bentonites to determine which of these reactions most clearly approximates the conversion of smectite to a mixed-layer illite/smectite. There is no mineralogic data to support reaction 1. Reactions 2 and 3 give the amount of products formed when a fully expandable smectite becomes converted to an illite/smectite with about 65% illite layers (Table 7). It must be remembered that both quartz and kaolinite, which are products of these two reactions, can be inherited from the conversion of an ash to a bentonite bed. However, the relatively low kaolin contents (average = 6%) for the disturbed belt samples, when compared to the minimum amount of kaolinite formed by reaction 2, would suggest that reaction 3, with unlimited potassium, most closely approximates the mineralogic changes occurring.

The reaction may be complicated even further for bentonites containing illite/smectite with high proportions of illite layers, for chlorite appears to be an additional reaction product. The chlorite probably forms from magnesium and iron lost from the smectite layers. Also ferric iron in the octahedral position of smectite may be reduced

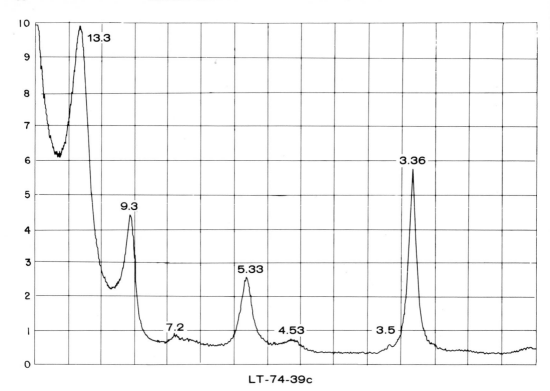

LT-74-39c

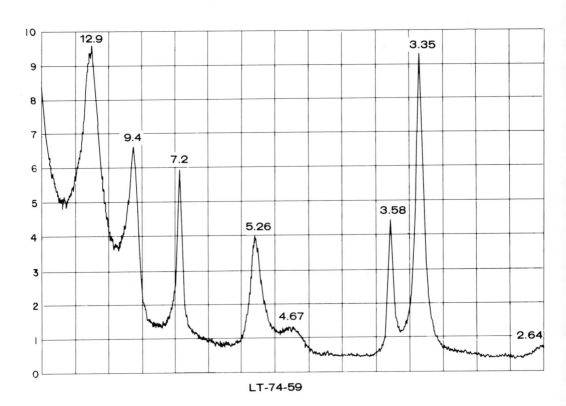

LT-74-59

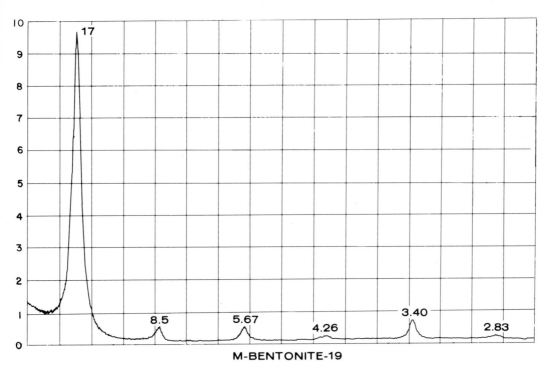

M-BENTONITE-19

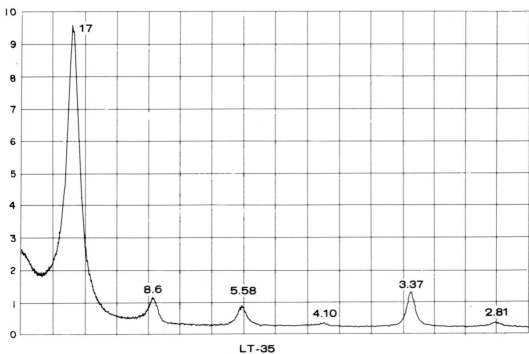

LT-35

Fig. 10.—*A*, X-ray diffraction patterns representative of the clay-size fraction (<1 μm) of bentonites from the Montana disturbed belt. All samples are solvated with ethylene glycol. *B*, X-ray diffraction patterns representative of the clay size fraction (<1 μm) of bentonites from the Sweetgrass Arch. All samples are solvated with ethylene glycol.

TABLE 6.—CHEMICAL ANALYSES OF THE 0.2–0.5 μM
FRACTION OF 10 POTASH BENTONITES FROM THE DISTURBED
BELT AND 2 "CLASSICAL" BENTONITES FROM THE
SWEETGRASS ARCH, GIVEN AS WEIGHT PERCENT OXIDE ON
AN IGNITED BASIS.

Oxide	Disturbed Belt	Sweetgrass Arch
SiO_2	54.95 ± 2.28	62.91 ± 2.84
TiO_2	0.76 ± 0.53	0.80 ± 0.32
Al_2O_3	31.28 ± 1.57	25.04 ± 3.33
Fe_2O_3*	3.44 ± 1.66	4.14 ± 2.02
MgO	2.35 ± 0.49	3.95 ± 2.03
CaO	0.46 ± 0.16	0.28 ± 0.11
Na_2O	0.36 ± 0.13	0.54 ± 0.30
K_2O	5.62 ± 1.35	0.67 ± 0.73
Total	99.12 ± 1.84	98.38 ± 1.93

*Total Fe as Fe_2O_3. FeO not determined.

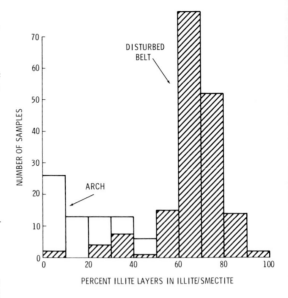

FIG. 11.—Composition of the illite/smectite as percent illite layers in mixed-layer illite/smectite as a function of frequency of occurrence for bentonites from the Montana disturbed belt and the Sweetgrass Arch.

to ferrous iron with the oxidation of organic material, leading to potassium fixation without substitution within the 2:1 layer of the smectite.

To further illustrate the reaction(s) occurring in the clay-size fraction of bentonites, structural formulas were calculated from the chemical analyses for the disturbed belt and arch samples. A comparison of the average illite/smectite compositions from the arch and from the disturbed belt, based on the chemical analyses given in Table 6, is shown below.

Disturbed Belt:

$$[(Al_{1.67} Fe^{+3}_{0.18} Mg_{0.21})(Si_{3.44} Al_{0.56}) O_{10} (OH)_2^{-0.59}]$$
$$[K^{+1}_{0.45} X^{+1}_{0.12} {}^{+0.57}].$$

Arch:

$$[(Al_{1.42} Fe^{+3}_{0.22} Mg_{0.40})(Si_{3.91} Al_{0.09}) O_{10} (OH)_2^{-0.37}]$$
$$[K^{+1}_{0.08} X^{+1}_{0.28} {}^{+0.36}].$$

It is easily seen that there is much greater substitution of aluminum for silicon in the tetrahedral layer of the illite/smectite in bentonites from the disturbed belt than from the arch. This results in an overall higher charge deficiency with the resultant much higher potassium content.

There is no correlation between the depositional environment and the mineralogy and/or chemistry of bentonites in the disturbed belt or on the arch (cf. Table 5). Potash bentonites occur only in the disturbed belt, in both marine and nonmarine environments; classical smectite bentonites, or highly-expandable illite/smectites, occur on the arch in both marine and nonmarine strata (Hower and Hoffman, 1976). A more detailed paper on the nature and origin of potash bentonites is in preparation (Hower and Hoffman).

SUMMARY OF MINERALOGIC AND CHEMICAL EVIDENCE
FOR LOW GRADE METAMORPHISM IN THE DISTURBED
BELT OF MONTANA

The mineralogy and chemistry of the shales, volcanogenic rocks, and bentonite beds present in the disturbed belt indicate exposure to low grade metamorphic conditions. The mineralogies show that the two trends of burial metamorphism described by Zen (1974) are present in rocks of the disturbed belt. Zeolites (and corrensite) form in the volcanic and volcanogenic rocks, while clay mineral-carbonate assemblages, ordered illite/smectite, chlorite, and the various kaolin polymorphs form in non-volcanogenic sediments. The interpretation from these mineralogies is that the probable metamorphic temperature range is between 100 and 200° C.

The occurrences of the mineral assemblages of shales and sandstones and volcanogenic rocks discussed in the early portions of this paper have been noted in many places as indicators of higher temperature regimes (below greenschist facies). However, the mineral assemblages of these three rock types have rarely, if ever, been investigated in any one metamorphic environment. Extending these temperature (grade)-composition relationships (cf. Figs. 2, 3) to the disturbed belt of Montana, we have shown that the mineralogy and chemistry of the shales are identical with those occurring in deeply buried shale sequences (tem-

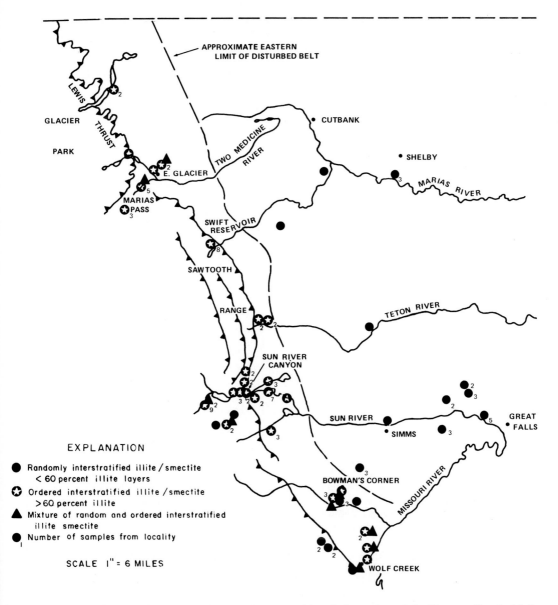

Fig. 12.—Geographic distribution of illite/smectite compositions in bentonites of the Montana disturbed belt and Sweetgrass Arch.

peratures in excess of 100° C). Most importantly, however, within the disturbed belt the shales are found in association with volcanogenic rocks, and potash bentonites—all containing mineral assemblages indicative of higher (100°–200° C) temperatures. Sandstone assemblages are correlated with those of shales on the basis of temperatures reported in the literature and on the basis of coexistence with shale metamorphic assemblages in the disturbed belt. Zeolite assemblages are correlated with shale and sandstone assemblages from the coexistence of laumontite-bearing volcanogenic rocks in the disturbed belt with ordered illite/smectite-bearing rocks and the correlation of the range of laumontite as compared to heulandite, analcite, prehnite, and pumpellyite as summarized by Zen (1974). Figure 13 summarizes these data, translating mineral assemblages in shales, sandstones, and volcanics into pre-greenschist facies metamorphic temperatures.

TABLE 7.—MINERALOGIC DATA FOR CONVERSION OF SMECTITE TO MIXED-LAYER ILLITE/SMECTITE.

Reaction 2

$$[Al_2(Si_{3.66}Al_{0.34})O_{10}(OH)_2][K^+_{0.34}] + 0.57H_2O \rightarrow 0.43\,[Al_2(Si_{3.2}Al_{0.8})O_{10}(OH)_2][K_{0.8}]$$
$$+ 0.57Al_2Si_2O_5(OH)_4 + 1.14SiO_2 + 0.85H_2O$$

K-Smectite (100% exp.) → Illite/Smectite (35% exp.) + Kaolinite + Quartz
(389 grams)   (218 grams)   (111 grams) (52 grams)
100% Smectite   →   57% I/S   +   29% Kaolinite + 13.5% Quartz

---

Reaction 3

$$0.6K^+ + [1.11Al_2Si_{3.66}Al_{0.34})O_{10}(OH)_2][X^+_{0.34}] \rightarrow [Al_2(Si_{3.4}Al_{0.6})O_{10}(OH)_2][K^+_{0.6}]$$
$$+ 0.67\ SiO_2 + 0.22\ H^+ + 0.34X$$

K$^+$ + X-Smectite (100% exp.) → Illite/Smectite (35% exp.) + Quartz + X$^+$
(423.1 grams)   (382.9 grams)   (40.2 grams)
100% Smectite   →   90.5% I/S   +   9.5% Quartz

These correlations are, of course, tentative, but we feel that they are fairly accurate for lower Tertiary and Mesozoic pre-greenschist facies metamorphic rocks.

THE GENERATION OF METAMORPHIC TEMPERATURES IN THE DISTURBED BELT

The metamorphic temperatures indicated by the mineral assemblages of the shales, bentonites, and volcanics of the disturbed belt, could have been produced in a variety of ways. Four possible heat sources that produced the metamorphic temperatures are (1) original deep burial of the sediments; (2) proximity to igneous bodies; (3) frictional heat produced along thrust planes; and (4) burial beneath major thrust plates. The first possibility, that of burial metamorphism in a sedimentary basin, can be discounted for the disturbed belt sediments on the basis of stratigraphic reconstructions. In the disturbed belt the original burial depths for the Upper Cretaceous Two Medicine Formation and the Lower Cretaceous Blackleaf Formation were from 350 to 1350 meters (Mudge, 1972b). Assuming that the geothermal gradient was 20° C/km—reasonable for a basin undergoing active sedimentation—this would indicate that the temperature of the most deeply buried sediments never exceeded 60° C—too low to produce any significant mineralogic reaction. The second possibility, that proximity to igneous bodies could produce these higher temperatures, can also be discounted, because the metamorphism observed in the disturbed belt is pervasive, having no spatial relationship to any intrusive or extrusive igneous body. A third possibility, frictional heat produced along thrust contacts, can be discounted again because the pervasiveness of the metamorphic mineral assemblages observed. Also, Oxburgh and Turcotte (1968) have calculated that, even assum-

ing the maximum shearing stress, the amount of heat available to rocks as close as a few tens of meters from the fault contact would be small in relation to the total heat content of the rocks necessary for regional metamorphism. The fourth possibility, and the one which we favor, is heat resulting from burial beneath thrust sheets superposed on the Cretaceous sediments during the Laramide orogeny. A structural model is as follows: Mudge (1972b) has estimated the thickness of strata above the zone of décollement in the eastern and western parts of the Sawtooth Range. According to Mudge's model, there was a series of thrust faults from east to west (imbricate style) with a thick piling up of strata at the front or eastern side of the Sawtooths and in the western Sawtooths. Between these areas, imbricate style thrusting also occurs, but the individual plates do not appear to have piled one atop another, creating the thick overburden as at the eastern and western sides (cf. Mudge, 1970, Figure 3). The mineralogic evidence from the disturbed belt supports this model, in that samples collected from the eastern and western portions of the Sawtooths reflect a higher grade mineralogy, whereas those collected from the middle zone have mineralogies similar to samples from the Sweetgrass Arch (cf. Hoffman, 1976). Mudge's estimates for thickness of burial by the overriding thrust plates are a minimum of 3700 meters in the western zone (which does not include the Cretaceous section in the thrust plate, and a minimum of 4100 meters in the east. The mineral assemblages, indicating temperatures between 100° and 200° C, support these data. The mechanism to raise temperatures in the overridden strata, i.e. superposition of thrust plates, is illustrated by a model proposed by Oxburgh and Turcotte (1974).

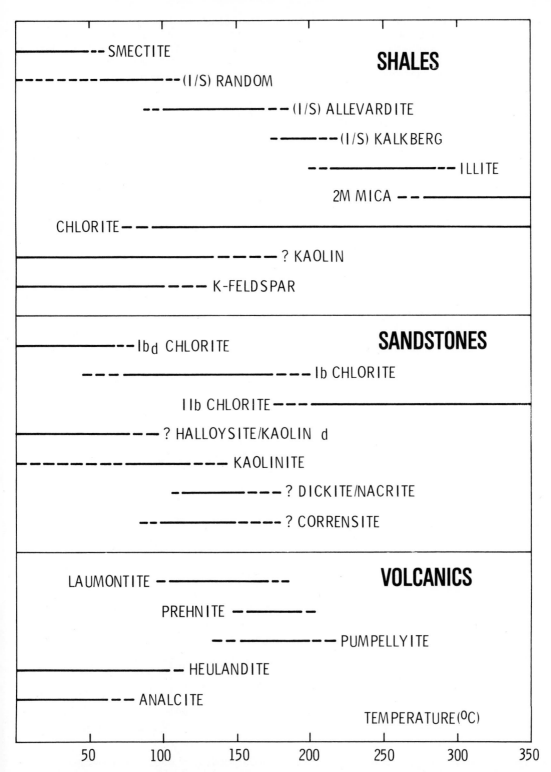

Fig. 13.—Correlation of the temperature-dependent mineral assemblages in shales, sandstones, and volcanogenic rocks. Temperatures do not represent equilibrium but are applicable (with caution) to lower Tertiary and Mesozoic pre-greenschist facies rocks.

Oxburgh and Turcotte (1974) have shown that at geologically reasonable rates of thrusting (3 cm/yr), one can calculate the temperature distribution as a function of time within a thrust plate and within the overridden strata. It is possible to determine, in a quantitative manner, the immediate and the long term effect of piling one block of strata atop another, the length of time necessary for temperatures in the strata beneath a thrust plate to rise sufficiently high to produce the metamorphic changes observed, and the length of time necessary to reestablish thermal equilibrium in a thrust-faulted area.

According to Oxburgh and Turcotte (1974), thrust-faulting is actually a kind of solid state thermal convection, and as long as thrusting continues, the temperature distribution is controlled by convection, conductive effects being of secondary importance. During thrusting, heat is transferred laterally by the moving thrust sheet at a far greater rate than it is lost to its surroundings, and therefore, the sheet acts, along with the normal heat flow from depths, as an important source of heat to produce higher temperatures in the overridden strata after movement has occurred.

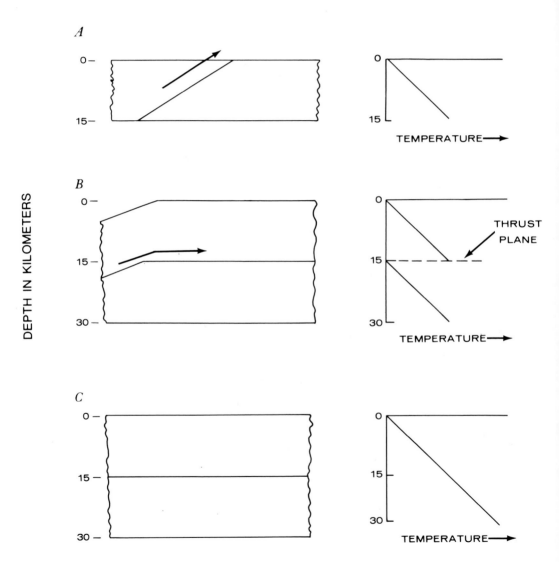

Fig. 14.—A schematic diagram of the thrust faulting model proposed by Oxburgh and Turcotte (1974): A, Before thrusting, normal geothermal gradient; B, after thrusting geothermal gradient with "sawtooth" form; C, reestablishment of thermal equilibrium (after Oxburgh and Turcotte, 1974).

Oxburgh and Turcotte have calculated the rates of temperature rise in the strata, following a single thrusting event, as a function of slab thickness and of time. They do this by considering separately: (1) temperatures along the interface of the slab and basement; (2) temperatures within the slab; and (3) temperatures within the basement. We refer you to Figures 3, 4, and 5, of Oxburgh and Turcotte (1974).

Figure 14 is a schematic representation of the qualitative aspects of the Oxburgh and Turcotte model. A thrust sheet, 15 kilometers thick is emplaced in a single phase of movement of short duration. The temperature, conductivity, and diffusivity of both the basement (overridden sheet) and the slab (overthrust sheet) are the same prior to thrusting. Surface temperature is considered to be 0° C. The temperature distribution with depth in the strata (slab and basement) immediately after thrusting is discontinuous, having a "sawtooth" form, which begins a gradual decay, because of conductive heat transfer, until equilibrium is reestablished and a uniform geothermal gradient exists in the total thickness of strata. The important points of the model are: (1) the interface (slab-basement boundary) temperatures rise immediately to one-half the value of the original temperature at that depth (15 kilometers in the example given) and (2) temperatures just below the interface (within about 3 kilometers) would initially rise rapidly to the temperature at the interface. The heat source for this temperature rise is the slab itself as well as the normal heat flux from greater depths. Temperatures above the interface would initially drop. Figure 15 is a plot of this relationship for the Oxburgh and Turcotte 15 km thick thrust sheet, showing the initial, intermediate, and final temperature profile as a function of time.

A restriction on the conditions chosen to apply this model to the disturbed belt is that based on the mineralogy present in the shales and bentonites, the temperatures never exceed 200° C. For thinner thrust sheets rates of equilibration would be faster, but, of course, the maximum temperature would be lower (for a given geothermal gradient). In the disturbed belt area the thrust plates of interest are the Lewis Thrust (7 km thick), the western Sawtooth or South Fork thrust zone (6 km thick), and the front or eastern Sawtooth thrust zone in Sun River Canyon (4 km thick). Using Oxburgh and Turcotte's data and assuming a more realistic surface temperature of 20° C, one can predict initial interface temperatures and final interface temperatures at different geothermal gradients (10°, 20°, 30° C/km) and different slab thicknesses (4, 6, 7 km thick). These data are given in Table 8. Interface temperatures as a function of time are given in Table 9.

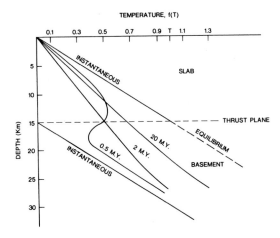

Fig. 15.—Temperature distribution and equilibrium profile as a function of time for a 15-km thick thrust sheet including interface temperatures, temperatures in the slab and temperatures in the basement (from Oxburgh and Turcotte, 1974). Note the rapid attainment of low grade metamorphic temperatures by overridden sediments within a few kilometers of the interface.

The area of most interest in applying this model to the disturbed belt is the temperature versus time distribution just below the interface of slab and basement strata. Figure 16 gives this plot at geothermal gradients of 10°, 20°, 30° C/km. It is evident from these values that rocks just below (within 200–300 meters) the South Fork and Lewis thrusts would have reached metamorphic temperatures in a short time (less than 1 million years). This is not true for the thrusts at the eastern end of the Sawtooths (Sun River Canyon), where the final temperature is 100° C (Table 7) and it might take on the order of 10 million years to reach metamorphic temperatures.

We conclude that, by application of this model,

TABLE 8.—INITIAL AND FINAL INTERFACE TEMPERATURES FOR THIN THRUST SHEETS ASSUMING A SURFACE TEMPERATURE OF 20° C (FROM OXBURGH AND TURCOTTE, 1974).

		Thickness of thrust sheet			
Geothermal gradient		4 km	6 km	7 km	10 km
10° C/km	I[1]	30	40	45	60
10° C/km	F	60	80	90	120
20° C/km	I	50	70	80	110
20° C/km	F	100	140	160	220
30° C/km	I	70	100	115	160
30° C/km	F	140	200	230	320

[1]I, interface temperature; F, final temperature at thermal equilibrium.

TABLE 9.—INTERFACE TEMPERATURES AS A FUNCTION OF TIME FOR A 4, 6, AND 7 KILOMETER THICK SLAB, A GEOTHERMAL GRADIENT OF 20° C/KM AND A SURFACE TEMPERATURE OF 20° C (FROM OXBURGH AND TURCOTTE, 1974, FIGURE 3: USING DATA FOR THE 5 AND 10 KILOMETER SLAB).

| | Temperature (°C) | | |
Time	4 Km	6 Km	7 Km
1 m.y.	63	88	82
2 m.y.	70	98	82
5 m.y.	78	109	102
10 m.y.	83	116	114
20 m.y.	88	123	125
30 m.y.	90	126	131
T_{Final}	100	140	160

the temperatures necessary to produce mineralogical assemblages observed in the disturbed belt could be attained by burial beneath thrust sheets. In addition, it is evident that these metamorphic temperatures would have been attained within a short time after superposition of the thrust sheets. Further verification can be seen in K-Ar radiometric dating results on the potash bentonites of the disturbed belt, which have been discussed briefly in an earlier paper (Hoffman, Hower, and Aronson, 1976).

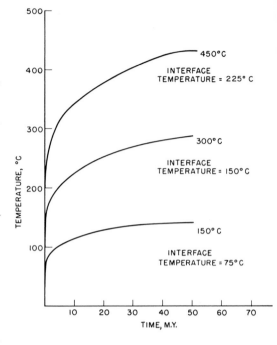

FIG. 16.—The temperature as a function of time (m.y.) for a three-kilometer depth below the interface of a 15-km-thick thrust sheet, at geothermal gradients of 10°, 20°, and 30° C/km.

SUMMARY AND CONCLUSIONS

An attempt has been made to correlate mineral assemblages indicative of metamorphic grade in shales, bentonite beds, sandstones, and volcanogenic rocks. Data used for this correlation come from studies of burial metamorphism, low grade Alpine metamorphism (Frey, 1974), and the metamorphism associated with the Laramide thrust belt in central Montana.

Metamorphic grade has been equated with temperature with the caveat that many assemblages are not at equilibrium. Therefore, the appearance (or disappearance) of an index mineral is often determined by reaction time. The kinetic aspects of the appearance of a given assemblage are most clearly shown by studies that have been carried out on burial metamorphism of shale. In the U.S. Gulf Coast the appearance of allevardite ordered illite/smectite takes place about 50° C higher in Pliocene-Pleistocene strata as compared to lower Tertiary-upper Mesozoic stratigraphic sections.

The clay mineral and zeolite assemblages considered are useful as geothermometers (and even more useful as indicators of grade) in the temperature range 60–200° C.

Detailed study of low grade metamorphic rocks in the Laramide disturbed belt of Montana shows that Mesozoic strata have been raised to temperatures approaching 200° C by burial beneath thrust plates. The heat source for this metamorphism seems to be admirably explained by the heat flow model devised by Oxburgh and Turcotte (1974) to describe temperature gradients in overthrust regions.

The Montana study is of particular interest because all the rock types being considered are present in the disturbed belt and allow a correlation of shale, sandstone, bentonite, and volcanogenic rock mineral assemblages. In addition, the study clearly shows that potash bentonites are metamorphic in origin.

ACKNOWLEDGEMENTS

Many people assisted in all phases of this study. Assisting in the collection of samples in the Montana disturbed belt were Eric Eslinger (West Georgia College), M. R. Mudge and R. W. Lemke (U.S. Geological Survey), James Helwig (Atlantic-Richfield Co.), and Graham R. Thompson (University of Montana). Assisting in laboratory portions of this study were Brigitt Hower, Mark Hower, and Dave Buchanan. Many discussions with our colleagues, James L. Aronson, Samuel M. Savin, and Eric Eslinger helped considerably in the direction of all phases of this study. Helpful suggestions also came from J. B. Hayes, D. G. McCubbin, and D. B. MacKenzie of the Marathon

Oil Research Center; John Obradovich, L. G. Shultz, and M. R. Mudge of the U.S. Geological Survey; B. E. Felber of Mobil Oil Company; and D. Turcotte of Cornell University. We wish to thank Ray Schneider, Tom Wright, and Roger Wolff of the U.S. Geological Survey for critically editing the final manuscript. The work was supported by National Science Foundation Grant DES 74-13574. Additional support came from Marathon Oil Company, Chevron Oil Company, the Petroleum Research Fund of the American Chemical Society, and a Geological Society of America Penrose Research Grant. Portions of this paper were submitted in partial fulfillment of the Ph.D. degree (Janet Hoffman) at Case Western Reserve University, Cleveland, Ohio.

REFERENCES

ARONSON, J. L., AND HOWER, JOHN, 1976, The mechanism of burial metamorphism of argillaceous sediments: 2. Radiogenic argon evidence: Geol. Soc. America Bull., v. 87, p. 738–744.

BAILEY, S. W., 1963, Polymorphism of kaolin minerals: Am. Mineralogist, v. 48, p. 1196–1209.

———, AND BROWN, B. E., 1962, Chlorite polytypism. I. Regular and semirandom one-layer structures: Am. Mineralogist, v. 47, p. 819–850.

BALLY, A. W., GORDY, P. L., AND STEWART, G. A., 1966, Structure, seismic data, and orogenic evolution of the southern Canadian Rocky Mountains: Bull. Canadian Petroleum Geology, v. 14, p. 337–381.

BERRY, F. A., AND HANSHAW, B. B., 1960, Geologic evidence suggesting membrane properties of shales [abs.]: 21st Internat. Geol. Congress (Copenhagen, 1960), Abs. Volume, p. 209.

BOAR, P. L., AND INGRAM, L. K., 1970, The comprehensive analysis of coal ash and silicate rocks by atomic absorption spectrophotometry by a fusion technique: The Analyst, v. 95, p. 124–130.

BURST, J. F., JR., 1959, Postdiagenetic clay mineral environmental relationships in the Gulf Coast Eocene, in A. Swineford (ed.), Clays and clay minerals, Proceedings of the 6th National Conference on Clays and Clay Minerals: Internat. Ser. Mon. Earth Sci., v. 2, p. 327–341.

BYSTRÖM, A. M., 1956, Mineralogy and petrology of the Ordovician bentonite beds at Kinnekulle, Sweden: Sveriges Geol. Undersökning Årsb., v. 48, no. 5, p. 62.

CARMICHAEL, I. S. E., TURNER, F. J., AND VERHOOGEN, JOHN, 1974, Igneous petrology: New York, McGraw-Hill, Ind., 739 p.

CARROLL, DOROTHY, 1970, Clay minerals: A guide to their x-ray identification: Geol. Soc. America Spec. Paper 126, 80 p.

CHILDERS, M. O., 1964, Structure and stratigraphy of the southwest Marias Pass area, Flathead County, Montana: Geol. Soc. America Bull., v. 74, p. 141–163.

COBBAN, W. A., ERDMANN, C. E., LEMKE, R. W., AND MAUGHN, E. K., 1959a, Colorado Group on Sweetgrass Arch, Montana: Billings Geol. Soc. Guidebook 10th Ann. Field Conf., p. 89—92.

———, ———, ——— AND ———, 1959b, Revision of Colorado Group on Sweetgrass Arch, Montana. Am. Assoc. Petroleum Geologists Bull., v. 43, p. 2786–2796.

COOMBS, D. S., 1954, The nature and alteration of some Triassic sediments from Southland, New Zealand: Royal Soc. New Zealand Trans., v. 82, p. 65–109.

———, 1961, Some recent work on the lower grades of metamorphism: Australian Jour. Sci., v. 24, p. 203–215.

———, ELLIS, A. J., FYFE, W. S., AND TAYLOR, A. M., 1959, The zeolite facies, with comments on the interpretation of hydrothermal syntheses: Geochim. et Cosmochim. Acta, v. 17, p. 53–107.

DUNOYER DE SEGONZAC, G., 1964, Les argiles du Crétace superieur dens le Bassin de Doula (Cameroun). Problèmes de diagenèse: Alsace-Lorraine Service Carte Géol. Bull., v. 17, p. 237–310.

———, 1970, The transformation of clay minerals during diagenesis and low-grade metamorphism: A review: Sedimentology, v. 15, p. 281–346.

EBERL, D. D., AND HOWER, JOHN, 1976, The kinetics of illite formation: Geol. Soc. America Bull., v. 87, p. 1326–1330.

EHINGER, R. F., GOERS, J. W., HALL, M. L., HARRIS, W. L., ILLICH, H. A., PETKEWICH, R. M., PEVEAR, D. R., STUART, C. J., AND THOMPSON, G. R., 1965, Clay mineralogy of Mesozoic sediments in the vicinity of Drummond, Montana: Billings Geol. Soc. Guidebook 16th Ann. Field Conf., p. 58–66.

FREY, MARTIN, 1974, Alpine metamorphism of pelitic rocks during Alpine orogenesis: Schweizer. Mineralog. u. Petrog. Mitt., v. 54, p. 489–503.

GRIM, R. E., 1968, Clay mineralogy: New York, McGraw-Hill Book Co., Inc., 596 p.

HAY, R. L., 1966, Zeolites and zeolite reactions in sedimentary rocks: Geol. Soc. America Spec. Paper 85, 130 p.

HAYES, J. B., 1970, Polytypism of chlorite in sedimentary rocks: Clays and Clay Minerals, v. 18, p. 285–306.

HOFFMAN, JANET, 1976, Regional metamorphism and K-Ar dating of clay minerals in Cretaceous sediments of the disturbed belt of Montana: PhD. Diss., Case Western Reserve Univ., 266 p.

HOWER, JOHN, ESLINGER, ERIC, HOWER, M. E., AND PERRY, E. A., 1976, Mechanism of burial metamorphism of argillaceous sediments: 1. Mineralogical and chemical evidence: Geol. Soc. America Bull., v. 87, p. 725–737.

——— AND HOFFMAN, JANET, 1976, The nature and origin of potash bentonites [abs.]: Clay Minerals Soc. Program 13th Ann. Meeting, Corvallis, Oregon, p. 39.

—— AND MOWATT, T. C., 1966, The mineralogy of illites and mixed-layer illite/montmorillonites: Am. Mineralogist, v. 51, p. 825–854.

——, SCHMITTROTH, L. A., PERRY, E. C., AND MOWATT, T. C., 1964, X-ray spectographic major constituent analysis of undiluted silicate rocks and minerals [abs.]: Geol. Soc. America Program 1964 Ann. Meeting, Miami, Florida, p. 96–97.

IIJIMA, A., AND UTADA, M., 1971, Present-day zeolite diagenesis of the Neogene geosynclinal deposits in the Niigata Oil Field, Japan: Advances in Chemistry Series, 101, Molecul. Sieve Zeolite. 1, p. 342–349.

KELLER, W. D., AND JOHNS, W. D., 1976, "Endellite" will reduce ambiguity and confusion in nomenclature of "halloysite": Clays and Clay Minerals, v. 24, p. 149.

KIERSCH, G. A., AND KELLER, W. D., 1955, Bleaching clay deposits, Defiance Plateau District, Arizona: Econ. Geology, v. 50, p. 469–494.

KINTER, E. B., AND DIAMOND, SIDNEY, 1956, A new method for preparation and treatment of oriented-aggregate specimens of soil clays for x-ray diffraction analysis: Soil Sci., v. 81, p. 111–120.

KÜBLER, BERNARD, 1963, Untersuchungen über die Tonfraktion der Trias der Sahara: Fortschr. Geologie Rheinland u. Westfalen, v. 10, p. 319–324.

——, 1973, La corrensite, indicateur possible de milieux de sédimentation et du degré de transformation d'un sédiment: Centre Recherches Pau Bull., v. 7, p. 543–556.

LONG, G., AND NEGLIA, S., 1968, Composition de l'eau interstielle des argiles et diagenèses de minéraux argileux: Inst. Francais Pétrole Rev., v. 23, p. 53–69.

LUCAS, J., 1962, La transformation des minéraux argileux dans la sedimentation. Études sur les argiles du Trias: Alsace-Lorraine Service Carte Geol. Bull., no. 23, 202 p.

McMANNIS, W. J., 1965, Resume of depositional and structural history of western Montana: Am. Assoc. Petroleum Geologists Bull., v. 49, p. 1801–1823.

MAXWELL, D. T., AND HOWER, JOHN, 1967, High-grade diagenesis and low-grade metamorphism of illite in the Precambrian Belt Series: Am. Mineralogist, v. 52, p. 843–857.

MILLOT, GEORGE, 1970, Geology of clays, weathering, sedimentology, geochemistry: New York, Springer-Verlag, 429 p.

MUDGE, M. R., 1970, Origin of the disturbed belt in northwest Montana: Geol. Soc. America Bull., v. 81, p. 377–392.

——, 1972a, Prequaternary rocks in the Sun River Canyon area, northwestern Montana: U.S. Geol. Survey Prof. Paper 663-A, 142 p.

——, 1972b, Structural geology of the Sun River Canyon and adjacent areas, northwestern Montana: U.S. Geol. Survey Prof. Paper 663-B, 51 p.

OXBURGH, E. R., AND TURCOTTE, D. L., 1968, Problem of high heat flow and volcanism associated with zones of descending mantle convective flow: Nature, v. 218, p. 1041–1043.

——, and ——, 1974, Thermal gradients and regional metamorphism in overthrust terrains withispecial reference to the eastern Alps: Schweizer Mineralog. u. Petrog. Mitt., v. 54, p. 641–662.

PARHAM, W. E., 1966, Lateral variations in clay mineral assemblages in modern and ancient sediments, *in* International Clay Conference, Jerusalem, 1966, Proceedings, v. 1: Jerusalem, Israel Prog. Sci. Translation, p. 135–145.

——, 1969, Formation of halloysite from feldspar: Low temperature, artificial weathering versus natural weathering: Clays and Clay Minerals, v. 17, p. 13–22.

PERRY, E. A., 1969, Burial diagenesis in Gulf Coast pelitic sediments: PhD. Diss., Case Western Reserve Univ., 121 p.

——, AND HOWER, JOHN, 1970, Burial diagenesis in Gulf Coast pelitic sediments: Clays and Clay Minerals, v. 18, p. 165–177.

PETERSON,, M.N.A., 1961, Expandable clay minerals from Upper Mississippian carbonate rocks of the Cumberland Plateau in Tennessee: Am. Mineralogist, v. 46, p. 1245–1269.

PETROV, V. P., 1958, Genetic types of white clays in the U.S.S.R. and laws governing their distribution: Clay Minerals Bull., v. 3, p. 287–297.

REYNOLDS, R. C., AND HOWER, JOHN, 1970, The nature of interlayering in mixed-layer illite/montmorillonites: Clays and Clay Minerals, v. 18, p. 25–36.

SCHULTZ, L. G., 1964, Quantitative interpretation of mineralogical composition from x-ray and chemical data for the Pierre Shale: U.S. Geol. Survey Prof. Paper 391-C, 31 p.

SHUTOV, V. D., ALEKSANDROVA, A. V., AND LOSIEVSKAYA, S. A., 1970, Genetic interpretation of the polymorphism of the kaolinite group in sedimentary rocks: Sedimentology, v. 15, p. 69–82.

SOMMER, F., 1975, Histoire diagenetique d'une serie gréseuse de Mer du Nord. Datation de l'introduction des hydrocarbures: Inst. Francais Pétrole Rev., v. 30, p. 729–741.

TRIPLEHORN, D. M., 1967, Occurrence of pure well crystallized 1M illite in Cambro-Ordovician sandstone from Rhourde el Baguel Field, Algeria: Jour. Sed. Petrology, v. 37, p. 879–884.

VAN HISE, C. R., 1904, A treatise on metamorphism: U.S. Geol. Survey Mon. 47, 1286 p.

VAN LOON, J. C., AND PARISSIS, C. M., 1966, Scheme of silicate analysis based on the lithium metaborate fusion followed by atomic-absorption spectrophotometry: The Analyst, v. 94, p. 1057–1062.

WEAVER, C. E., 1953, Mineralogy and petrology of some Ordovician K-bentonites and related limestones: Geol. Soc. America Bull., v. 64, p. 921–964.

——, 1956, Mineralogy of the Middle Devonian Tioga K-bentonite: Am. Mineralogist, v. 41, p. 359–363.

——, 1959, The clay petrology of sediments, *in* A. Swineford (ed.), Clays and clay minerals, Proceedings of the 6th National Conference on Clays and Clay Minerals: Internat. Ser. Mon. Earth Sci., v. 2, p. 154–187.

——, 1967, Potassium, illite, and the ocean: Geochim. et Cosmochim. Acta v. 31, p. 2181–2196.

—— AND BECK, K. C., 1971, Clay-water diagnesis during burial: How mud becomes gneiss: Geol. Soc. America Spec. Paper 134, 96 p.

YEH, HSUEH-WEN, AND SAVIN, S. M., 1977, Mechanism of burial metamorphism of argillaceous sediment: 3. Oxygen isotopic evidence: Geol. Soc. America, Bull., v. 88, p. 1321–1330.

ZEN, E-AN, 1959, Clay mineral-carbonate relations in sedimentary rocks: Am. Jour. Sci., v. 257, p. 29–53.

——, 1974, Burial metamorphism: Canadian Mineralogist, v. 12, p. 445–455.

SEPM Special Publication No. 26, p. 81–87, March 1979

PROBLEMS IN ZEOLITE FACIES GEOTHERMOMETRY, GEOBAROMETRY AND FLUID COMPOSITIONS

EDWARD D. GHENT

University of Calgary, Calgary, Alberta T2N 1N4, Canada

ABSTRACT

The zeolite facies was defined to "bridge the gap" between diagenesis and metamorphism and was largely based upon the studies of Coombs (1954) from Taringatura, New Zealand. The lack of zeolites in many stratigraphic sections which were presumably subjected to similar P_s-T conditions as zeolite-bearing rocks has led to the definition of a *clay-carbonate facies*. On theoretical grounds it can be shown that T and fluid composition exercise a strong control on the mineral assemblages and this has been verified for active geothermal areas such as Wairakei and Broadlands, New Zealand.

Estimates of P_s, T and fluid composition attending zeolite facies alteration can be made from correlation of mineral assemblages with those predicted from experimental and computed phase equilibria. Such estimates encounter several problems: (1) at low P_s and T growth and persistence of metastable phases are more important than at higher P_s, T; (2) for $P_{H_2O} < P_s$ equilibria involving zeolite dehydration are very strongly affected; (3) experimental studies often yield phases which differ chemically and structurally from the naturally occurring zeolites; (4) variables such as the activity of silica (a_{SiO_2}) may be important since volcanic glass is involved in the production of many zeolites; (5) in tectonically disturbed areas Zen and Oxburgh and Turcotte have shown that P_s-T conditions at the base of thrust sheets may place these rocks outside the stability field of many of the zeolites for significant periods of time; (6) factors such as distribution of porosity and permeability may strongly affect the mineralogy and these are often difficult to evaluate after the fact.

For a given area there is reasonable correlation between zeolite assemblages, coal rank and clay mineral assemblages and consideration of all of these types of evidence will lead to the best estimates of P_s, T and fluid composition.

INTRODUCTION

The theme of this symposium is the estimation of diagenetic paleotemperatures in sediments; however, as the title of this paper indicates, zeolitic assemblages are also a function of pressure and fluid composition. The purpose of this paper is to briefly outline some of the factors which should be considered in the interpretation of zeolitic assemblages in sedimentary rocks. This paper is intended for sedimentary geologists who are interested in the significance of zeolitic assemblages. The references in this paper should provide additional sources of information for those who wish to pursue these problems further. The complexity of these assemblages should not be considered a disadvantage, since it means that if we are clever enough, we can extract far more information than paleotemperatures.

The now classic paper on the zeolite facies is that of Coombs (1954) on the burial alteration sequence at Taringatura, New Zealand (Fig. 1). The zeolite mineral facies was subsequently defined by Fyfe, Turner and Verhoogen (1958) and by Coombs and others (1959) and was thought to "bridge the gap" between diagenesis and metamorphism. In fact, zeolitic assemblages can form under conditions ranging from those obtaining at the sea water-sediment interface (phillipsite, Hay,

1966) to contact metamorphic aureoles (wairakite, Seki and others, 1969). A mineral facies spanning such a range of physical conditions is too cosmopolitan to be useful. Coombs (1971) has recently restricted the zeolite mineral facies to include "a set of mineral assemblages that is characterized by the association calcium zeolite-chlorite-quartz in rocks of favorable bulk composition." A corollary would be the recognition of a separate *clay-carbonate facies* (Coombs and others, 1970, p. 152), which is stable under similar pressure-temperature conditions as the zeolite facies but is attended by different fluid compositions.

EFFECT OF TEMPERATURE AND $P_{H_2O} = P_s$ ON THE STABILITY OF ZEOLITES

On theoretical grounds it can be shown that temperature (T) exercises a strong control on zeolite mineral assemblages. For the condition H_2O pressure equal to load pressure ($P_{H_2O} = P_s$) at pressures of a few kilobars, zeolitic reactions show steep slopes on a $P_{H_2O} - T$ diagram (Fig. 2) and are thus very temperature dependent. It is for this reason that there is generally a reasonable correlation between zeolitic assemblages, and other assemblages which are thought to be temperature dependent, e.g., coal rank, clay mineral

Copyright ℗ 1979, The Society of Economic
Paleontologists and Mineralogists

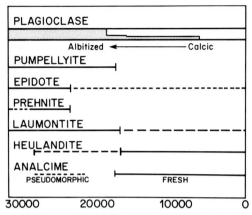

PRESENT STRATIGRAPHIC DEPTH (Feet)

Taringatura, N.Z., after Coombs (1954)

FIG. 1.—Burial alteration sequence at Taringatura, South Island, New Zealand, modified from Coombs (1954).

COMPLEXITIES IN ZEOLITIC ASSEMBLAGES

Compositions of zeolites.—One problem in the application of experimental studies on zeolite stability to the interpretation of the physical and chemical conditions of formation of natural zeolites is that the experimentally produced zeolites may not correspond chemically and structurally

assemblages (see other papers in this symposium volume).

Coombs (1954) suggested that the burial alteration sequence at Taringatura dominantly reflected a temperature increase with depth of burial (Fig. 1). The simplest model for zeolite equilibria in a burial metamorphic or diagenetic sequence is: a linear geothermal gradient (e.g., 30° C per km, with $P_s \sim 250$ bars/km); pure solid and fluid phases and $P_{H_2O} = P_s$. Such a model would suggest a regular increase in degree of dehydration of the mineral assemblages with depth and general lack of overlap of the reactant and product assemblages with depth. Rarely are natural zeolite assemblages this simple and it is obvious that a far more complex model of zeolite equilibria is necessary. Complexities include the overlap of apparent reactant and product assemblages over several meters of depth (Fig. 1, and Ghent and Miller, 1974), the occurrence of relatively dehydrated assemblages at relatively shallow depths, and the absence of zeolites in many sedimentary sequences together with the more common appearance of zeolites in sections rich in volcanic material. The remainder of this paper will discuss the reasons for these complexities.

to the natural zeolites. For example, Zen (1972) computed thermochemical properties of selected zeolites from experimental phase equilibria and suggested that some of the calculated inconsistencies are the result of variable water content of the experimental products.

Electron microprobe studies of natural zeolites, e.g., laumontite, from the Blairmore Group, Alberta, correspond closely with compositions based on ideal structural formulas (Table 1). Other zeolites, however, such as heulandite from the same area, show wide deviation from ideal compositions (Table 1). It should be emphasized that either electron microprobe analysis or very careful x-ray diffraction study may be necessary to document these deviations from ideal compositions. Extensive solid solution in one or more zeolites or other phases will cause overlap in the P-T stability fields of these phases with respect to those of the pure phases. For example, Ghent and Miller (1974) argued that partitioning of Ba and Sr in favor of heulandite with respect to laumontite may have permitted the stable co-existence of the two zeolites in the Blairmore Group rocks.

Equilibrium at low temperature and pressure.—

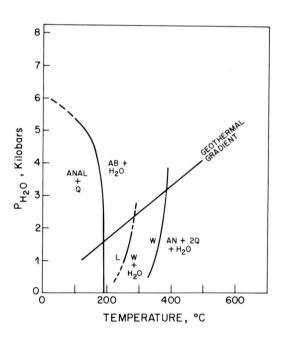

FIG. 2.—P_{H_2O}-T diagram showing typical reactions involving dehydration of zeolites. Symbols are: ANAL, analcime; Q, quartz; L, laumontite; W, wairakite; AN, anorthite. Geothermal gradient is drawn with T = 30° C per km and $P_s = 250$ bars/km. Dehydration curves are from Liou (1971c) for analcime + quartz and Liou (1971a) for laumontite and wairakite.

TABLE 1.—COMPARISON OF IDEAL COMPOSITIONS OF CA-ZEOLITES WITH ELECTRON MICROPROBE ANALYSES OF ZEOLITES FROM ALBERTA

	Laumontite		Heulandite	
	Ideal	MB-8	Ideal	MC-10
SiO_2	51.09	52.0	61.15	57.9
Al_2O_3	21.67	21.0	14.85	14.7
CaO	11.92	10.6	8.17	3.3
SrO	—	<0.2	—	1.5
BaO	—	<0.2	—	6.9
Na_2O	—	0.2	—	0.5
K_2O	—	0.8	—	0.4
H_2O	15.32	15.4[1]	15.74	14.8a

[1]H_2O by difference (calculated from sum of all other oxides subtracted from 100).

[a]Ideal composition of laumontite based on the formula: $CaAl_2Si_4O_{12}\cdot 4H_2O$ and ideal composition of heulandite based on the formula $CaAl_2Si_7O_{18}\cdot 6H_2O$. Electron microprobe analysis from Miller and Ghent (1973).

Hay (1966) questioned the validity of a zeolite mineral facies on the grounds that zeolitic mineral assemblages vary as a function of age and may represent incomplete replacement of one mineral by another, neither of these features being compatible with stable equilibrium in the zeolite facies. If the zeolite mineral facies does not generally represent a close approach to equilibrium, then use of zeolitic assemblages for accurate estimates of P_s, T and fluid compositions obtaining during authigenesis is not possible. Coombs (1971) reviewed geological and experimental evidence suggesting that certain quartz-analcime and laumontite assemblages are likely to represent stable mineral assemblages. Recently, Merino (1975a) studied diagenetic mineral assemblages from oil wells in the Kettleman North Dome area, California. Interstitial solutions in these rocks were also analyzed and Merino (1975b) showed that the aqueous species at 100° C could have equilibrated with the diagenetic minerals. Clearly, more detailed study of fluids from areas of active diagenetic reactions and fluid inclusions in diagenetic minerals would be rewarding. Numerous cases of disequilibrium at low temperatures could be cited (e.g., Barnes and O'Neil, 1969) and caution should be applied in the interpretation of specific zeolitic assemblages. All possible tests indicating lack of equilibrium crystallization (e.g., Zen, 1963) should be made.

The effect of $P_{H_2O} < P_s$ *on zeolite stability.*—The P_s-T stability fields for hydrated minerals such as zeolites are strongly affected when $P_{H_2O} < P_s$. We can distinguish two different cases: (1) H_2O can communicate with the surface so the P_{H_2O} approximates the hydrostatic value whereas the solid pressure (P_s) is due to the weight of the rock column; (2) the fluid is diluted with other

components which can react with zeolites and reduce their P_s-T stability field, e.g., CO_2 can react with laumontite, and/or the fluid is diluted with other components which do not necessarily react with zeolites but simply reduce the activity of H_2O (e.g., Greenwood, 1961). Although a given fluid phase can obviously show all of the effects simultaneously, we will discuss the effects separately.

At shallow depths of burial the pressure on an H_2O-rich fluid can be hydrostatic and will be approximately 1/2.6 the value of the pressure on the solids ($P_{H_2O} \sim 1/2.6\ P_s$). The effect of this condition can be illustrated for the reaction,

$$\text{laumontite} = \text{wairakite} + 2H_2O \qquad (1a)$$

The equilibrium constant equation for this reaction is

$$2 \log f_{H_2O} = \frac{-6452}{T} + 15.77 + \frac{0.0789\,(P-1)}{T}$$

$$(1b)$$

where f_{H_2O} is the fugacity of water (Liou, 1971a; Ghent and Miller, 1974). Equation (1b) is solved for different values of P_s which results in a set of $\log f_{H_2O} - 1/T$ curves. For pure H_2O at the value of $0.4\ P_s = P_{H_2O}$, a set of $\log f_{H_2O} - 1/T$ curves are constructed. Where the two $\log f_{H_2O} - 1/T$ curves for a given P_s cross, the reaction is in equilibrium with P(hydrostatic) at that T (Ghent and Miller, 1974). For reaction (1a), the equilibrium T is 255° C for $P_{H_2O} = P_s = 1000$ bars. When $P_{H_2O} = 0.4\ P_s$ the equilibrium T is reduced to near 200° C. This hydrostatic fluid pressure effect can produce variable P_{H_2O} in rocks of differing permeability and thus gross overlapping of mineral zones. For example, Coombs (1971), has pointed out that in Taringatura, New Zealand, tightly cemented impermeable beds preserve heulandite well within the laumontite zone (Fig. 1), whereas, in more permeable rocks, heulandite disappears at shallower depths of burial.

Zen (1961) suggested the calcium zeolites can be replaced by clay-carbonate assemblages by reactions such as

$$\text{laumontite} + CO_2 = \text{calcite} + \text{kaolinite}$$

$$+ \text{quartz} + H_2O \qquad (2)$$

Although active geothermal areas have geothermal gradients far exceeding those of most sedimentary basins, they provide a natural laboratory to evaluate the relative effects of T and fluid composition on zeolites. Studies on geothermal areas such as Broadlands, New Zealand, have shown that mod-

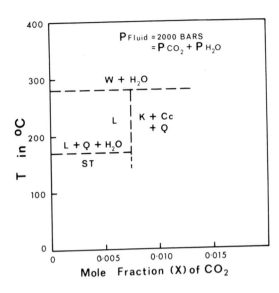

FIG. 3.—Plot of T against X_{CO_2} (mole fraction of CO_2) in coexisting fluid showing inferred phase relations among minerals in the CaO-Al$_2$O$_3$-SiO$_2$-H$_2$O-CO$_2$ system at P_f = 2000 bars = P_{CO_2} + P_{H_2O}, modified from Thompson (1971) and Liou (1971b). Note the extremely steep slope on the L + CO$_2$ → K + Cc + Q + H$_2$O boundary suggesting that modest values of X_{CO_2} would suppress laumontite formation. Symbols as in caption to Fig. 2; in addition, K, kaolinite; Cc, calcite; St, stilbite.

est values of P_{CO_2} in the aqueous fluids are sufficient to suppress Ca-zeolite assemblages and to stabilize a clay-carbonate assemblage (Mahon and Finlayson, 1972). Ghent and Miller (1974), in a study of Lower Cretaceous sedimentary rocks in Alberta, showed that the alternative authigenic assemblages calcite-kaolinite-quartz and laumontite occurred in the same stratigraphic section and this implied gradients in X_{CO_2} in the fluids attending metamorphism. Thompson (1971) using experimental and computed phase equilibria suggested that laumontite would be stable only in contact with fluids having X_{CO_2} < ~0.0075 (Fig. 3).

Greenwood (1961) demonstrated experimentally that the stability field of analcime was reduced by dilution of the aqueous fluid phase with another component. In sedimentary rocks undergoing burial, aqueous fluids expelled from the rocks are likely to have the activity of H$_2$O reduced by soluble salts such as NaCl.

The effect of reduction of a hydrate stability field by dilution of H$_2$O by another component can be illustrated by the reaction

$$\text{analcime} + \text{quartz} = \text{albite} + H_2O \qquad (3)$$

which is at equilibrium near 200° C and 1 bar (Campbell and Fyfe, 1965; Liou, 1971c).

For a 3M NaCl solution at 200° C and 1 bar, a_{H_2O} = 0.905 (Helgeson, 1969). Reduction in a_{H_2O} (activity of H$_2$O) by dilution with a soluble salt will reduce the stability field of analcime + quartz. The system is out of the equilibrium with respect to a system containing pure H$_2$O by RTln a_{H_2O} = −94 cal. This will displace equilibrium by about 3° C using $\Delta G = -\Delta S \cdot \Delta T$ and $\Delta S \sim 30$ cal/deg. Salts with divalent cations, e.g., CaCl$_2$, will have a more pronounced effect on reduction of a_{H_2O}. Some geothermal brines have a_{H_2O} near 0.7; however, even for this value of a_{H_2O} the T lowering of reaction (3) is only 11° C.

Effect of silica activity on zeolites.—In low temperature reactions where volcanic glasses are involved all zeolitic reactions involving SiO$_2$ will be affected by the activity of silica (a_{SiO_2}) which will generally be higher than that in equilibrium with alpha quartz.

This effect will be illustrated by order-of-magnitude calculations involving two different zeolitic reactions: (3) analcime + SiO$_2$ = albite + H$_2$O; (4) stilbite = laumontite + 3SiO$_2$ + 3H$_2$O.

In these calculations we have used silica (SiO$_2$) glass as the SiO$_2$ phase. These calculations should be regarded as order of magnitude since a_{SiO_2} produced by the solution of volcanic glass will differ from that of SiO$_2$ glass. If a metastable polymorph of SiO$_2$ such as cristobalite is considered, a_{SiO_2} would also be greater than that in equilibrium with alpha quartz.

For reaction (3) where alpha quartz is the SiO$_2$ phase, equilibrium is near 200° C at 1 bar (Campbell and Fyfe, 1965, Liou, 1971c). Using the free energy data for the reaction silica glass → quartz at 200° C (Robie and Waldbaum, 1968) and an estimated ΔS for the reaction (1) of about 30 cal/deg the reaction analcime + silica glass → albite + H$_2$O would be in equilibrium at a T near 160° C, a lowering of about 40° C. For reaction (4) with alpha quartz as the SiO$_2$ phase, equilibrium is near 170° C at P_{H_2O} = 2000 bars (Liou, 1971b). The entropies of stilbite and laumontite have not been measured by calorimetry. From experimental phase equilibria, Zen (1972) has estimated $S^0_{298.15}$ for laumontite at 118 cal deg^{-1} gfw^{-1}. He has pointed out that the entropies of zeolites tend to be high relative to the sum of the entropies of the oxides. The entropy contribution of H$_2$O to the entropy of a zeolite appears to be greater than the entropy contribution of H$_2$O to phases such as muscovite. It appears that in phases such as analcime and laumontite, the molecular H$_2$O exists in a very mobile state in the structure. Using an assumed entropy change for reaction (2) near 69 cal/deg and the free energy change for the alpha quartz-silica glass reaction, the reaction stilbite = laumontite +3 silica glass + 3H$_2$O would be in equilibrium near 185° C, an increase of about 15° C.

I again want to emphasize that these approximate calculations are intended to indicate the tendency for metastable solubility of silica to affect zeolite phase equilibria. They illustrate the importance of volcanic glass in the production of some zeolites at low temperatures.

Effect of thrusting on geothermal gradients.—In many areas estimates of temperature attending zeolite facies alteration can be made from consideration of the thickness of the former stratigraphic section and an estimate of the past geothermal gradient. In tectonically disturbed areas, however, the estimation of temperatures during loading of thrust sheets requires consideration of the thermal relaxation time after loading of the thrust sheets. This problem has recently been considered by

Zen (1974) and by Oxburgh and Turcotte (1974). One of the interesting points raised by Zen in his computations on the stability of laumontite beneath a tectonic load of 8 km was that conditions in the autochthon lie in the stability field of lawsonite rather than laumontite for at least hundreds of years. It is possible that lawsonite would not be produced at very low temperatures due to kinetic factors, but the occurrence of laumontite or other zeolites beneath thrust sheets sets constraints on the P_s-P_{H_2O}-T conditions imposed by the tectonic loading.

DISCUSSION AND SUGGESTIONS FOR FUTURE WORK

As pointed out by Kisch (1969), Zen and Thompson (1974) and several papers presented in this special publication, there is a reasonably

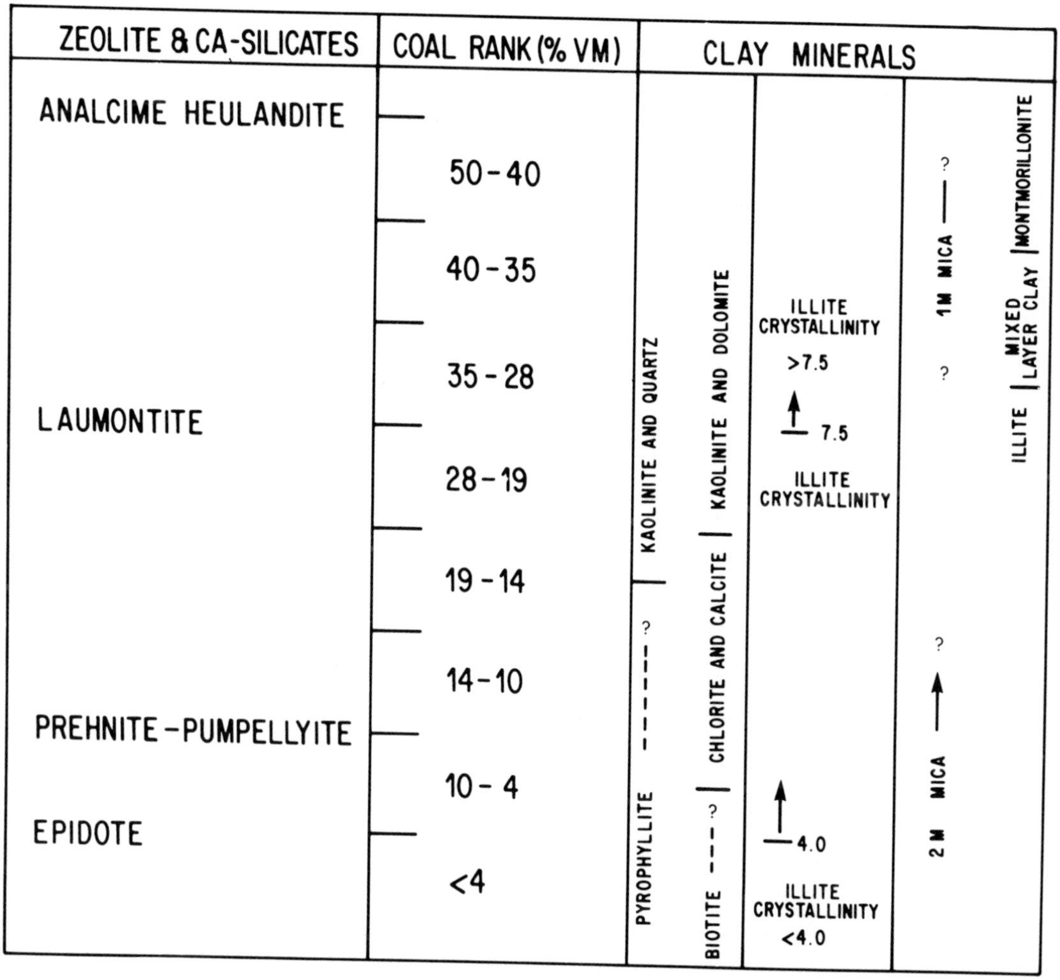

ZEOLITE & CA-SILICATES	COAL RANK (% VM)	CLAY MINERALS								
		KAOLINITE AND QUARTZ	PYROPHYLLITE	BIOTITE	CHLORITE AND CALCITE	KAOLINITE AND DOLOMITE	ILLITE CRYSTALLINITY	1M MICA	2M MICA	ILLITE | MIXED LAYER CLAY | MONTMORILLONITE
ANALCIME HEULANDITE	50–40							?		?
	40–35					ILLITE CRYSTALLINITY >7.5		?	
	35–28					— 7.5			
LAUMONTITE	28–19					ILLITE CRYSTALLINITY			
	19–14		?				?		
	14–10								
PREHNITE – PUMPELLYITE	10–4		?	?		— 4.0		2M MICA	
EPIDOTE	<4					ILLITE CRYSTALLINITY <4.0			

FIG. 4.—Diagram showing the approximate correlation of zeolite and Ca-silicate minerals, coal rank, and clay minerals plus other layer silicates. Modified and simplified from Zen and Thompson (1974).

good correlation between zeolite mineral assemblages, clay mineral assemblages, coal rank and other organic indicators of degree of diagenesis or metamorphism (Fig. 4). These various products of diagenesis-metamorphism can be roughly correlated with temperature, although there are still some problems in the precise calibration of geothermometers at low temperatures. In particular, the effect of time is difficult to evaluate in processes that result in elimination of metastable phases e.g., the change from metastable, poorly crystallized and disordered graphitic material to well-crystalized and ordered graphite. The best approach to estimation of paleotemperatures in sedimentary rocks is to use all components of the rocks. The various geothermometers should be properly evaluated against one another, particularly in areas undergoing active thermal alteration. In addition to estimates of temperature, other parameters such as load pressure and fluid composition can be derived from comparison of zeolitic assemblages with experimental and computed phase equilibria.

ACKNOWLEDGEMENTS

I wish to thank Peter Scholle and the SEPM for inviting me to participate in the symposium. Derrill Kerrick, Janet Hoffman and two anonymous reviewers made some very helpful critical comments on the manuscript. I wish to thank the Department of Geosciences at The Pennsylvania State University for providing me with workspace and secretarial help during the completion of the manuscript. The research was supported by National Research Council of Canada Operating Grant A-4379.

REFERENCES

BARNES, I., AND O'NEIL, J. R., 1969, The relationship between fluids in some fresh alpine-type ultramafics and possible modern serpentinization, western United States: Geol. Soc. America Bull., v. 80, p. 1947–1960.

CAMPBELL, A. S., AND FYFE, W. S., 1965, Analcime-albite equilibria: Am. Jour. Sci., v. 263, p. 729–804.

COOMBS, D. S., 1954, The nature and alteration of some Triassic sediments from Southland, New Zealand: Roy. Soc. New Zealand Trans., v. 82, p. 65–109.

——, 1971, Present status of the zeolite facies: Advances in Chemistry Ser. 101 (Molecular sieve zeolites, Am. Chem. Soc.-I), p. 317–327.

——, ELLIS, A. J., FYFE, W. S., AND TAYLOR, A. M., 1959, The zeolite facies, with comments on the interpretation of hydrothermal synthesis: Geochim. et Cosmochim. Acta, v. 17, p. 53–107.

——, HORODYSKI, R. J., AND NAYLOR, R. S., 1970, Occurrence of prehnite-pumpellyite facies metamorphism in northern Maine: Am. Jour. Sci., v. 268, p. 142–156.

FYFE, W. S., TURNER, F. J., AND VERHOOGEN, J., 1958, Metamorphic reactions and metamorphic facies: Geol. Soc. America Mem. 73, 259 p.

GHENT, E. D., AND MILLER, B. E., 1974, Zeolite and clay-carbonate assemblages in the Blairmore Group (Cretaceous), southern Alberta foothills, Canada: Contr. Mineralogy and Petrology, v. 44, p. 313–329.

GREENWOOD, H. J., 1961, The system NaAlSi$_2$O$_6$-H$_2$O-argon: Total pressure and water pressure in metamorphism: Jour. Geophys. Research, v. 66, p. 2923–2946.

HAY, R. L., 1966, Zeolites and zeolitic reactions in sedimentary rocks: Geol. Soc. America Spec. Paper 85, 130 p.

HELGESON, H. G., 1969, Thermodynamics of hydrothermal systems at elevated temperatures and pressures: Am. Jour. Sci., v. 267, p. 729–804.

KISCH, H. L., 1969, Coal rank and burial metamorphic mineral facies, in Advances in organic geochemistry 1968: Oxford, England, Pergamon Press, p. 407–425.

LIOU, J. G., 1971a, Pressure-temperature stabilities of laumontite, wairakite, lawsonite, and related minerals in the system CaAl$_2$Si$_2$O$_8$-H$_2$O: Jour. Petrology, v. 12, p. 379–411.

——, 1971b, Stilbite-laumontite equilibrium: Contr. Mineralogy and Petrology, v. 31, p. 171–177.

——, 1971c, Analcime equilibria: Lithos, v. 4, p. 389–402.

MAHON, W. A., AND FINLAYSON, J. B., 1972, The chemistry of the Broadlands geothermal area, New Zealand: Am. Jour. Sci., v. 272, p. 48–68.

MERINO, E., 1975a, Diagenesis in Tertiary sandstones from Kettleman North Dome, California—I. Diagenetic mineralogy: Jour. Sed. Petrology, v. 45, p. 320–336.

——, 1975b, Diagenesis in Tertiary sandstones from Kettleman North Dome, California—II. Interstitial solutions: Distribution of aqueous species at 100° C and chemical relation to the diagenetic mineralogy: Geochim. et Cosmochim. Acta, v. 39, p. 1629–1645.

MILLER, B. E., AND GHENT, E. D., 1973, Laumontite and barian-strontian heulandite from Blairmore Group (Cretaceous), Alberta: Canadian Mineralogist, v. 12, p. 188–192.

OXBURGH, E. R., AND TURCOTTE, D. L., 1974, Thermal gradients and regional metamorphism in overthrust terrains with special reference to the eastern Alps: Schweizer. Mineralog. u. Petrog. Mitt., v. 54, p. 641–662.

ROBIE, R. A., AND WALDBAUM, D. R., 1968, Thermodynamic properties of minerals and related substances at 298.15° K (25.0° C) and one atmosphere (1.013 bars) pressure and at higher temperatures: U.S. Geol. Survey Bull. 1259, 256 p.

SEKI, Y., OKI, Y., MASUDA, T., MIKAMI, K., AND OKUMURA, K., 1969, Metamorphism in the Tanzawa Mountains, central Japan: Japan. Assoc. Mineral., Petrol., Econ. Geol., v. 61, p. 1–75.

THOMPSON, A. G., 1971, P_{CO_2} in low-grade metamorphism; zeolite, carbonate, clay mineral, prehnite relations in the system $CaO-Al_2O_3-SiO_2-CO_2-H_2O$: Contr. Mineralogy and Petrology, v. 33, p. 145–161.

ZEN, E-AN, 1961, The zeolite facies: An interpretation. Am. Jour. Sci., v. 259, p. 401–409.

——, 1963, Components, phases, and criteria of chemical equilibrium in rocks: Am. Jour. Sci., v. 261, p. 929–942.

——, 1972, Gibbs free energy, enthalpy and entropy of ten rock-forming minerals: Calculations, discrepancies, implications: Am. Mineralogist, v. 57, p. 524–553.

——, 1974, Burial metamorphism: Canadian Mineralogist, v. 12, p. 445–455.

—— AND THOMPSON, A. B., 1974, Low-grade regional metamorphism: Mineral equilibrium relations: Ann. Rev. Earth Planet. Sci., v. 2, p. 179–212.

SEPM Special Publication No. 26, p. 89–107, March 1979

FLUID INCLUSION EVIDENCE ON THE ENVIRONMENTS OF SEDIMENTARY DIAGENESIS, A REVIEW

EDWIN ROEDDER

U.S. Geological Survey, M.S. 959, Reston, Virginia 22092

ABSTRACT

Most sedimentary diagenesis involves recrystallization or overgrowths on original minerals, or the growth of new phases. This new growth may trap fluid as inclusions that provide data not only on the nature, composition, pressure, and density of the fluids present during diagenesis, but particularly on the temperature at which the host crystals grew. As most optical methods of study require inclusions >1–2 μm in diameter, fine-grained products of diagenesis, in the 10–20 μm range, seldom provide useful material. The possibilities of finding inclusions of useful size increase as the size of the host crystal increases. In spite of this limitation, reasonably valid quantitative or qualitative physical and chemical data, both new and from the literature, have been obtained on inclusions from the following specific diagenetic environments: (1) crystal-lined geodes, vugs, and veins in sediments; (2) Mississippi Valley-type ore deposits; (3) carbonate and quartz cements in detrital rocks; (4) saline and sulfur deposits; (5) petroleum reservoir rocks; (6) sphalerite in bituminous coal beds.

Most inclusion temperatures in these and other similar environments range from 25 to 150° C, and most of the fluids are moderately to strongly saline brines which commonly contain petroleum and as much as tens of atmospheres of methane-rich gas. Homogenization temperatures of inclusions in some Mississippi Valley-type ore deposits are higher than 150° C but seldom more than 200° C. It is concluded that hot, strongly saline fluids have moved through many, if not most, sediments at some time in their history, and that at least part of the diagenetic changes seen have been caused by such fluids.

INTRODUCTION

The environments of diagenesis, when one uses the term in a broad sense, determine the nature of deposits of coal, oil, and inorganic minerals in sediments, and thus are of considerable economic significance in the search for such deposits. Hence all possible sources of potentially useful data on these various environments should be explored. The fluid inclusions that are formed in some minerals during diagenesis provide one such source of data that has not been explored as diligently as it merits. Determination of the origin of the inclusions studied is essential, as many minerals contain several generations, formed at different stages in the history of the sample. For discussions of the origin and significance of fluid inclusions, and the techniques of studying them, see Roedder (1962b, 1972, 1976).

In this review the published literature is summarized,[1] with some previously unpublished data from the author, on six types of samples covering a large part of the spectrum of environments normally included in the term diagenesis. Most of the available data on fluid inclusions from diagenetic environments fall in one of these categories, mainly because these six provide the best

sample material, but suitable material may eventually be found in samples from other environments.

CRYSTAL-LINED GEODES, VUGS AND VEINS IN SEDIMENTS

In many areas throughout the world, what were originally soft and porous Paleozoic and younger carbonate sediments have been strongly modified postdepositionally to yield hard, dense crystalline limestones and dolomites. Although the individual sample porosity may be low, such rocks commonly contain open vugs of varying size, sometimes lined with crystals of calcite, dolomite, quartz, fluorite, barite, and celestite. Some also contain sulfides, particularly very coarse sphalerite, and less often galena, pyrite, marcasite, chalcopyrite, wurtzite, millerite, etc. Such localities as Clay Center, Ohio, and Herkimer, New York, have provided spectacular mineral specimens for many collections.

In many of these geodes, vugs, and veins in carbonate rocks, one or more minerals may be relatively rare, so that a mineral collector may consider himself lucky to find one crystal on a given visit, yet this crystal may be well formed, clear, and sometimes several centimeters on an edge. The nucleation and growth of such a sparse distribution of large, perfect, crystals of a given mineral, particularly relatively insoluble phases such as sphalerite, requires that both nucleation and growth take place exceedingly slowly, from

---

[1] Much of the literature on inclusions is in Russian; English abstracts (and some translations) of the post-1968 literature cited here will be found in Roedder (1968-onward).

Copyright © 1979, The Society of Economic Paleontologists and Mineralogists

solutions having a very low degree of supersaturation, under essentially static conditions.

In the laboratory, even very slow precipitation of ZnS from solution usually results in a milky solution that contains many millions of sub-micrometer crystals per milliliter. Yet the distribution of nuclei formed in the fluid in the rocks may have been about one per cubic meter, 9 orders of magnitude less. Furthermore, growth was so slow that there was time for diffusion to occur to these few nuclei through the rock pores, instead of forming new nuclei. Even where the nuclei were more abundant, the degree of perfection of the crystals is sometimes phenomenal, e.g., the Herkimer quartz crystals ("Herkimer diamonds"). There is generally no solid evidence on the specific time at which this slow crystallization took place, except that it was post-lithification, but the widespread occurrence of such crystal-lined vugs indicates the process to be relatively common.

Some indication of the elapsed time involved in the growth may be provided by celestite (Fig. 1A). Crystals from several localities show a microscopic, very regular compositional banding, which has been interpreted as annual "varves," representing variations in the Ba content due to annual variations in the salinity (Roedder, 1969; see also Scherp and Strübel, 1974). If this interpretation is correct, these celestite crystals grew in $\sim 10^4$ years. The solutions from which they grew were hot ($\sim 100°$ C) and moderately to strongly saline ($\sim 25\%$ NaCl equivalent). Leach (1973a) has found similar banding in the central Missouri barite district, but reversed, i.e., regular bands of high Sr content in barite.

Some of the more recent studies on inclusions from geodes, vugs, and veins are summarized in Table 1, but many of the entries show special features too complex to tabulate. For example, Touray and Barlier (1975) have been able to correlate the map distribution of the phase composition of multiphase organic-rich inclusions in quartz with the degree of metamorphism of clays and of opaque organic matter in the enclosing rocks (as measured by its reflectivity; see also Barlier, Ragot, and Touray, 1974). Kvenvolden and Roedder (1971) report that gas chromatographic and mass spectrometric studies of the organic materials in quartz from calcite veins of unknown age in Precambrian metasedimentary rocks of southwest Africa suggest biological precursors for these components, particularly for the isoprenoid hydrocarbons. The inclusion composition and phase data neither prove nor preclude the inclusion fluids originating during diagenesis of formerly overlying Paleozoic or Mesozoic sediments.

The quartz crystals from Herkimer and adjacent Montgomery County, New York, are in vugs in a crystalline petroliferous dolomite. Inclusions in them contain, in addition to brine, several types of organic matter: high-pressure supercritical mixtures of organic gases (Roedder, 1972, Plate 5); colorless to yellow, highly fluorescent oils; and broken fragments of anthraxolite, a black, organic material with conchoidal fracture that is also found in the vugs with the quartz (Dunn and Fisher, 1954). Individual inclusions may have one or more of these phases, in any ratio, suggesting that all were separate phases at the time of trapping. Small fragments of anthraxolite sometimes are found adhering to the vapor bubble, on the surface of which they move rapidly when minute thermal gradients, caused by asymmetric illumination, result in surface tension differences. The oily liquids show a variety of colors and freezing temperatures (Roedder, 1963, p. 201), and hence presumably indicate a variety of source materials or histories. The physical properties of the gas inclusions show that they also have a variety of compositions, although the major constituents are probably methane and ethane (Roedder, 1963, p. 202; Roedder, 1972, Plate 5, figs. 6 and 7; Rosasco, Roedder and Simmons, 1975). Good compositional data on these, along with homogenization temperatures of cogenetic aqueous inclusions, might permit a valid estimate of the depth at the time of trapping, as it is evident from their occurrence that these were trapped as actual bubbles of gas in the brines from which the crystals grew. Hence these gas inclusions should record the ambient hydrostatic pressure. On warming after being solidly frozen at low temperatures, the water solutions in many of these crystals showed a first melting temperature in the range -23 to $-27°$ C, and had a NaCl $\cdot$ 2H$_2$O liquidus; these data indicate near saturation with NaCl, and very little other material in solution (Roedder, 1963). The host rock in the area, the Little Falls Dolomite (Upper Cambrian), is overlain by halite-bearing Silurian formations; hence saturation of the fluids with NaCl is expectable.

Sphalerite, quartz, and fluorite from geodes, vugs, and clay seams in some Paleozoic limestones and dolomites of Indiana were also examined (Table 1; Fig. 1B). The inclusions in these samples contain brines, with freezing temperatures in the range -10 to $-16°$ C (3-5 molar NaCl equiv.), that have been trapped at $\sim 100°$ C. These salinities are even greater than modern oil field brines in the state and may represent mixing of strong brines from the adjacent Illinois or Michigan basins with more dilute fluids or ground water (N. R. Shaffer, written commun., 1976). The data on inclusions in fluorite and celestite from similar occurrences

TABLE 1.—INCLUSION DATA FROM CRYSTAL-LINED GEODES, VUGS AND VEINS IN SEDIMENTS

Reference	Mineral and locality	T_H' (°C) Min.	T_H' (°C) Max.	T_F' (°C) Min.	T_F' (°C) Max.	Notes
	Quartz, various localities					
Voznyak, Kvasnitsa, and Galaburda, 1974	Quartz, ("Marmarosh diamonds"), Ukraine, USSR			−0.2	−0.1	Large P incs., some with Hc L and Hc G.
Lazarenko et al, 1974	Quartz, ("Marmarosh diamonds"), Carpathians, USSR	100	200			Large P incs, some with Hc L and Hc G.
Cameron, A., 1977	Quartz, veins in Paleozoic Jacksonburg limestone, PA	130	160			Formation includes carbonaceous material, and authigenic albite and 2M muscovite.
Touray, and Barlier, 1975	Quartz, single xls from septaria and veins, French Alps	115	230			L and G Hc incs. used for T_H.
Karwowski, and Kozlowski, 1973	Quartz, authigenic smoky xls from bituminous ls, Poland; also brown-black calcite	48	190			Yellow L and dark brown bitumen incs. IR spectra show saturated and aromatic Hcs, and possibly oxidized derivatives.
Roedder, 1963	Quartz, Montgomery County, N.Y. USNM R1433			+2.2	+3.2 (15)	First melting <−13°C; data on Hc L.
Kvenvolden and Roedder, 1971	Quartz, from calcite veins of unknown age in Precambrian metasediments, South-West Africa	120	160(73)	−2.1	0.0	First melting −28.5 to −20.8°C, L and G Hc incs. also present.
Roedder, 1963	Quartz in Paleozoic crystalline dolo.; quarry just east of Catasauqua, Northampton County, Pa. (Sample H-Pa-1)			−15.4	−13.4 (26)	First melting −24.7°C.
Roedder, 1963	Quartz, Herkimer County, N.Y. (Sample ER61-26)			−20.1	0.0 (~250)	First melting −23°C; some have $NaCl \cdot 2H_2O$ liquidus and some contain yellow oil.
Roedder, 1963	Quartz, Herkimer County, N.Y. (Sample ER61-30)				−8.7 (1)	First melting −26.7°C; contains some CO_2
	Ohio localities					
Roedder, 1969	Celestite, Bascom, Ohio (USNM 94965)	68	114	−8	−7	
Roedder, 1969	Celestite, from vug in Paleozoic limestone, Clay Center, Ohio	~100		~−25		Crystals show annual(?) "varves." (see Fig. 1A).

TABLE 1.—CONTINUED

Reference	Mineral and locality	T_H^1 (°C) Min.	Max.	T_F^1 (°C) Min.	Max.	Notes
Roedder, 1967a	Fluorite, associated with red sphalerite, celestite, and calcite, from vug in Paleozoic limestone, Clay Center, Ohio (Sample ER65-69)	~100		−24.5	−23 (7)	
Roedder, unpub. data	Celestite, Basic, Inc., quarry, Clay Center, Ohio (Sample ER65-71)	68	76 (4)			
Roedder, unpub. data	Sphalerite, same locality	68	76 (2)	−16.0	−15.3 (3) −8.5 (1)	
Roedder, unpub. data	Calcite, Pugh quarry, Custar, Ohio, in Dundee Formation (Sample ER65-74)	68	76 (5)	−5.6 −22 −12.1	−4.8 (3) −14.1 (17) −7.0 (5) −0.17(2)	In part (or all?) metastable.
Indiana localities						
Roedder, unpub. data	Sphalerite, coarse xls in clay seam in Silurian reefal dolo. (Wabash Fm); quarry at SE¼NE¼ Sec. 19, T. 25 N., R. 2 W., near Delphi, Carroll County, Ind.	82 86(4) 84 97(1) 119(1)	83 (6) 88(15)	−12.4	−14.1 (6) −14.1 (4) −12.3 −15.5 −16.6	First melting <−25.1 to <<−26.5°C. (See Fig. 1B).
Roedder, unpub. data	Barite, occurring with sphalerite as nodules in Sanders Group (Mississippian), quarry at SW¼NE¼ Sec. 5, T. 17 N., R. 6 W., near Waveland, Parke County, Indiana	97	99 (2)	−5.7	−5.6	First melting <−27.6°C.
Roedder, unpub. data	Sphalerite, geode with quartz and dolomite in Harrodsburg Limestone (Mississippian); railroad cut at SW¼NE¼ Sec. 8, T. 9 N., R. 1 E., near Bloomington, Monroe County, Ind.	120(1)		−11.7 −12.2		First melting <−26.6°C Inc. necked down, T_H probably high.
Roedder, unpub. data	Quartz, same geode as above. Other geodes here have fluorite, millerite, chalcopyrite, barite.	83		−10.1		First melting <−26°C.

Miscellaneous occurrences

Reference	Occurrence	T_H	T_F	Remarks
Roedder, unpub. data	Sphalerite, coarse xls in clay seam in Silurian reefal dolo. (Wabash Fm); quarry at SE¼NE¼ Sec. 19, T. 25 N., R. 2 W., near Delphi, Carroll County, Ind.	69 (2) 108(11) 102 109	−14.2 / −14.1 −14.1 −15.1	First melting <−25.1 to <<−26.5°C.
Roedder, unpub. data	Fluorite, associated with dolomite, from vug in Ste. Genevieve Limestone (Mississippian); road cut at SE¼SE¼ Sec. 33, T. 5 S., R. 3 E., near Corydon, Harrison County, Ind.	101 104	−10.9	First melting <−23°C.
Roedder, unpub. data	Celestite, U.S. Gypsum Co. mine, Sperry, Iowa (Sample ER69-61)	<40		Inclusions full at room temperature.
Roedder, 1967a	Fluorite from vug, Volga, Iowa (Sample ER65-97)		−27.5 −26 (8) −12 −2 (3)	
Jepsen, 1964	Quartz and calcite lining mineralized dinosaur bone, Cleveland-Lloyd quarry, central Utah	43		

Geodes, Iowa

Reference	Occurrence	T_H	T_F	Remarks
Roedder, unpub. data	Quartz, geode, 11 miles NW of Keokuk, Iowa (ER64-24)	100?	−6.55 −1.71 (9) −0.37 −0.03 (4)	Not including nine with metastable ice.
Roedder, unpub. data	Calcite, geode with millerite, Keokuk, Iowa (Sample ER71-5)	<40		Most inclusions full at room temperature.

Geodes, Kentucky

Reference	Occurrence	T_H	T_F	Remarks
Roedder, unpub. data	Quartz, geode, Salem Limestone, Boone Hollow, Ky. (Sample ER65-38)	~60?	−19.5 −18 (3)	Not including two with metastable ice.
Roedder, unpub. data	Quartz, geode, Salem Limestone, Boone Hollow, Ky. (Sample ER62-23)	~60?	−22.8 (1)	Not including six with metastable ice.
Roedder, unpub. data	Quartz, probably from weathering of geodes, Douglas Lake, Knoxville, Tenn., just south of dam. (Sample ER65-5)		−2.5 <−1.7	Also contains Hc L and G; <−1.7 refers to metastable ice.

[1] Number of inclusions given in parentheses. Range or average given for temperature of homogenization (T_H) and temperature of freezing (T_F) (of water phase except as noted); both types of data on same line where data are on same line.
Abbreviations: P—primary; L—liquid; G—gas; Hc—hydrocarbon; incs.—inclusions; ls.—limestone; dolo.—dolomite; USNM—United States National Museum; Fm—formation; xls—crystals.

in Ohio, and on inclusions in fluorite from vugs at Volga, Iowa, about 100 km west of the Upper Mississippi Valley zinc-lead district, are similar to the Indiana samples (Table 1). Sphalerite is also widespread in the Lockport Dolomite (Middle Silurian) of New York (e.g., see Bassett and Kinsland, 1973), and celestite is common in vugs in dolomite beds of the Pennington Formation (Upper Mississippian) of central Tennessee (Frazier, 1973).

Often the inclusions in barite are the most dilute. Barite is known to dissolve and reprecipitate with surprising ease, and hence inclusions in it commonly represent the latest fluids. Furthermore, barite inclusions tend to leak and to neck down; both phenomena yield erroneous homogenization temperatures. The data reported on barite in Table 1 seem to be based on carefully selected inclusions and hence are believed to be valid.

There have been many suggestions that these scattered occurrences of sphalerite, etc., have formed from the same kind of fluids as the Mississippi Valley ores. The general geological environments and mineralogy are very similar; only the volumes of ore minerals are different. Although the fluid inclusions in these minerals are similar to those in the Mississippi Valley deposits (see following section), in that they were formed from hot, strongly saline brines, with much organic matter, the temperature range and salinity are both a little lower. Many have suggested dilution of hot brines as a mechanism for the formation of the Mississippi Valley-type ore bodies; the present inclusions may reflect more such dilution, but detailed studies of the chemical and isotopic composition of the fluids in inclusions are required to prove such an interpretation.

In addition to the above, numerous geodes in shales and limestones are lined with quartz or calcite and rarely have any sulfides other than pyrite or marcasite. The writer has examined many of these geode minerals, generally with disappointing results, as they are remarkably free of recognizable primary inclusions. In addition, many of the inclusions exhibit metastable superheated ice on freezing (Roedder, 1967b), and hence the true freezing temperature is some unknown amount below the temperature found. Calcite in such geodes, e.g., from the famous Keokuk, Iowa, locality, is commonly the last stage of deposition, and is found to have inclusions filled with only liquid, indicating that it probably grew at $<40°$ C.

The quartz of the geodes from Kentucky has many gypsum crystals embedded in it, and according to C. F. Withington (personal commun., 1965) these geodes started as gypsum-anhydrite nodules and have been replaced, presumably by strongly saline warm brines (Table 1). Fisher (1976) has suggested that these geodes formed during at least two periods of mineralization, and that the distribution patterns are related to the source of the ore fluids of the Central Kentucky Mineral District. The fluid inclusion data on the geodes (Table 1) are compatible with this concept, as the available data on the inclusions from Central Kentucky Mineral District (Roedder, 1967a, 1976) show these deposits to have formed from strongly saline solutions ranging from 60 to 140° C, but mainly ~110° C. Data on carbon and oxygen isotopes in such concretions (e.g., see Hudson and Friedman, 1976) might provide corroboration.

One aspect of inclusions in geodes that is frequently asked about pertains to the very large "fluid inclusions" visible or audible in unopened geodes from various localities. The amplified sloshing sounds made as these natural containers are shaken has attracted the attention of many visitors to mineral shows (Sutton, 1964). Agate geodes containing visible liquid water constitute a collector's item called enhydros, and are found particularly in the soil from the decomposition of basalt in Brazil. Because such geodes have polycrystalline walls, it is expected that they will leak with time, and most museum specimens are either kept in water or coated with impervious coatings to keep them from drying out. The rate of leakage may be very slow; one 10-cm enhydro in the possession of the writer has been steadily losing a few milligrams a year to the laboratory air. As a result of such leakage, the fluid in these geodes has probably been replaced by passing fluids many times since the geodes were first formed, and the present water in them is probably moderately recent ground water. This has been verified by studies of the isotopic composition of the waters (Matsui, Salati, and Marini, 1974).

MISSISSIPPI VALLEY-TYPE ORE DEPOSITS

Dunham (1970, p. B133) has pointed out that "ore formation is a minor and specialized process in comparison with the far reaching mineralogical changes brought about in sediments in the course of diagenesis by their formation waters or migratory brines." But fluid inclusions have been studied in more Mississippi Valley-type ore deposits than probably any other type of deposit, largely because such deposits frequently provide excellent sample material, and because the ambiguities in interpretation of the inclusion data are minimum. These many studies are discussed in a recent publication (Roedder, 1976),[2] and need

---

[2] Some additional published studies that are not in this summary include the Viburnum Trend, Missouri (Roedder, 1977a); northern Arkansas (Bennett, 1974; Leach, Nelson, and Williams, 1975); Central Missouri

not be discussed in detail here, but some generalizations are appropriate.

Perhaps the most striking aspect of the Mississippi Valley-type deposits is the great uniformity of environmental conditions in these various deposits that is evident in the data from fluid inclusions. The data are consistent even though the deposits cover a wide range of elemental composition (e.g., from almost pure lead at Laisvall, Sweden, and southeast Missouri, to almost pure zinc at Friedensville, Pennsylvania, to almost pure fluorite in some deposits in southern Illinois), isotopic make-up (normal lead, B-type lead, or J-type lead), structural setting, geological age, host rock type, etc. All deposits that have been studied, from many places in the world and with almost no exceptions, show that the ore-forming fluids had the following characteristics (Roedder, 1976).

Density.—Always >1.0 and frequently >1.1 g/cm^3 at the time of trapping, so they are always more dense than surface waters. These densities are based on measurements of the volumes of liquid and gas at room temperature, and of the salinity of the liquid (from freezing data); with these and the data on the density of similar brines, the present density of the liquid can be calculated and hence the density when the liquid just fills the cavity (Roedder, 1976).

Rate of movement.—Very slow, perhaps in the range of a few m/yr.

Total pressure.—Low but always greater than the vapor pressure of the brines (i.e., no boiling has occurred), although there may have been gases in solution at pressures as much as 20 bars.

Temperature.—Generally 100°–150° C, and seldom as high as 200° C (Fig. 1D). (Some of the highest reported numbers later shown to be invalid; see Larsen et al., 1973.)

Gross salinity.—Usually >15 wt. % salts and frequently >20%, yet daughter crystals of NaCl are almost never found, implying appreciable amounts of ions other than Na and Cl.

Organic matter.—Frequently but not always present, as gases such as methane in solution, immiscible oil-like droplets, and in solution in the brines (Fig. 1E).

Nonvolatile ions (i.e., "salts") in solution.—Highly concentrated solution of mainly sodium and calcium chlorides, with very minor potassium, magnesium, boron, and extremely low sulfur (Rosasco, Roedder, and Simmons, 1975). Heavy

metals (Zn and Cu) may be high (Czamanske, Roedder and Burns, 1963).

The source of the brines themselves is not at all clear, although individual brines have been assumed to represent connate, oil-field, compaction, or formation waters. As an example, the Pine Point deposit in Canada has generally been related to the salines of the Elk Point Group (Roedder, 1968). Thiede and Cameron (1975) have shown that three different types of metal-bearing brines might be generated during the history of such a basin: (1) brines residual from evaporation, (2) diagenetic brines released by dehydration of gypsum to anhydrite, and (3) postdepositional brines generated when evaporites are dissolved and leached by circulating ground water. He favors (2) or (3) for Pine Point. In many basins semipermeable membrane filtration may be the main cause for the high salinities. The ratio K/Na is one of the easiest to determine in the laboratory, and the one on which the precision is highest. When inclusions from Mississippi Valley-type deposits are compared with oil field brines, they are found to be similar except for K/Na. The K/Na ratios are all higher (Roedder *et al.*, 1963) than the *highest* value in the range given for oil field waters by White (1957).

The time of formation of the ore minerals in these deposits is usually not known precisely, but it was generally postlithification and hence certainly should be considered a part of the diagenesis of the enclosing rocks. This view is supported by paleomagnetic evidence placing the time of formation of the ore relatively close to that of the host rock (Beales, Carracedo, and Strangway, 1974). The view that the inclusions in such deposits merely represent fluid present during recrystallization of a preexisting syngenetic deposit is discussed and rejected by Roedder (1976, p. 73–76).

An important aspect of the inclusion evidence concerning the environment of diagenesis has yet to be explored. This is the specific nature of the organic material so common in these inclusions. In theory, at least, these materials can provide considerable detail on the thermal and oxidation history that might be read from the variety of specific compounds present (MacQueen, 1976), but care must be taken in such interpretations, as some of the organic inclusions show clear evidence of major chemical reorganization of the compounds present *after* trapping (Roedder, 1962b, p. 40; 1976, p. 96). Almost no study has been made of the bitumens that occur in some inclusions, yet bitumen can be formed in several ways, and the results commonly can be differentiated (MacQueen, 1976). Still another aspect that may merit further work is the presence and specific nature of any amino acids in inclusions.

(Leach, 1973b,c); Upper Mississippi Valley (McLimans, 1975); North Wales (Smith, 1973); Durham, England, barite (Hirst and Smith, 1974); and possibly south-central New Mexico (Allmendinger, 1974; Beane, 1974).

Mueller (1972) reports finding them among the organic inclusions in the Derbyshire fluorite-lead-zinc deposits. As the various amino acids vary widely in their susceptibility to thermal degradation (Hare and Mitterer, 1969), the assemblage present may provide valuable data on the thermal limits. Fatty acids have also been found in fetid sedimentary barite deposits (Miller, Brobst and Beck, 1972) and may occur, along with H_2S, in minute fluid inclusions.

Although many Mississippi Valley-type deposits are believed to have formed at only a few hundred meters depth, some, such as those at East Tennessee, may have formed at much greater depths, and mineralization of this type has been found in midwest oil wells at depths of nearly 2 km.

Although generally considered to be a variant on the normal Mississippi Valley deposit, the barite deposits that are sometimes associated with them are frequently quite different in terms of fluid inclusion data. Necking down and leakage are common problems with barite, but in most deposits, those few inclusions that do look valid (Roedder, 1976) generally have much lower salinities and/or homogenization temperatures than the sphalerite or fluorite in possibly related mineral deposits. As an example, barite from mines and prospects in the Sweetwater barite district of East Tennessee was examined (Roedder, unpub. data). Barite from the Nuns Cove prospect in Sevier County, Tennessee (ER 63-82) showed freezing temperatures of -0.47 to $-0.32°$ C, and some inclusions of organic liquid and gas, and that from the Click Creek prospect, Hawkins County, Tennessee (ER 63-81), showed $-0.15°$ C freezing temperatures, corresponding to nearly fresh water. Barite from the Ballard mine contained too many inclusions ($\sim20\%$ by volume), and hence was porous and no inclusion could be trusted; white barite from many localities is similar in this respect. The associated earlier green and blue fluorite in samples from the Ballard mine (ER 65-103, -106, and -108) had 14 good primary inclusions with freezing temperatures of -5.6 to $-10.6°$ (Roedder, 1967a) and homogenization temperatures of 53 to $128°$ C (Roedder, unpub. data).

Fig. 1.—*A*, Two planes of secondary inclusions, formed by the healing of fractures in a celestite crystal from a vug in Paleozoic dolomite from Clay Center, Ohio (sample ER 65–72). The periodicity of the spacing of the inclusions reflects a regularly spaced alternation in the Sr/Ba ratio with a 7.4 μm thickness per cycle, visible here as faint vertical bars, parallel to {210} of the host crystal. This banding is believed to be a result of annual variations in the salinity of the depositing brines (i.e., they are equivalent to varves; Roedder, 1969). Taken with transmitted, strongly collimated light. Bar = 100 μm.

B, Inclusion in sphalerite from vug in Wabash Formation near Delphi in Carroll County, Indiana (sample no. 1, courtesy N. R. Shaffer). This inclusion, and many others in this material, homogenized at 82–83° C and froze at $-14.1°$ C. Bar = 10 μm.

C, Inclusion in sphalerite from cleats in bituminous coal from the Herrin no. 6 Coal, Knox County, Illinois (sample ER 75-6, L00041, courtesy Illinois Geol. Survey). This inclusion, and others in these samples, homogenized at 94° C and froze at $-17.2°$ C. Bar = 10 μm.

D, Primary negative crystal inclusion in fluorite from the fluorite-zinc-lead deposit at Cave-in-Rock, Illinois (sample courtesy P. B. Barton, Jr.). Most inclusions of this type from this deposit have homogenization temperatures of $\sim145°$ C and salinities of 15–20 wt. % salts. Bar = 100 μm.

E, Oil inclusion in yellow fluorite from Ozark-Mahoning's West Green mine, southern Illinois fluorite-Pb-Zn deposits (sample ER 59-57e; F330 from Illinois Geol. Survey, courtesy R. Grogan). This inclusion originally formed as a spherical, immiscible globule of oil that stuck to the growing surface of the host fluorite cube at the bottom surface (see arrow). As the fluorite grew up around it, additional oil droplets in the surrounding brine adhered to the exposed top of the droplet, causing it to develop the neck of the "bottle." Subsequent cooling from the temperature of trapping ($\sim150°$ C) formed the shrinkage bubble (V), and the degradation of the oil precipitated a black asphaltic material that preferentially wet only certain crystallographic planes on the host fluorite wall, yielding black spots with fourfold symmetry (see illustration in Roedder, 1962b, for plan view of such inclusions). The balance of the inclusion fluid is enriched in lighter hydrocarbons; some such inclusions vaporize instantly on opening at room temperature. Bar = 100 μm.

F, Remnant of corner of hopper crystal of halite, embedded in large, single (mainly recrystallized?) halite crystal from ERDA no. 9 borehole, Carlsbad, New Mexico, 2065 foot depth. The hopper growth is outlined by dense, almost opaque, masses of mostly very minute primary inclusions. These contain a strong bittern, not just saturated NaCl. Bar = 100 μm.

G, Three large primary inclusions in recrystallized halite from ERDA no. 9 borehole, Carlsbad, New Mexico, 2569 foot depth. Bar = 100 μm. These contain a strong bittern with a composition similar to that present in the original, unrecrystallized salt. The two larger inclusions have nucleated a vapor bubble on cooling from the recrystallization temperature (other similar inclusions in this sample homogenized at 43–45 C). The vapor bubble in the larger inclusion (arrow) has a minute (3 μm) spherical globule sticking to it (see inset photo; bar = 10 μm); this is possibly an immiscible hydrocarbon, precipitated on cooling (see Price, 1973).

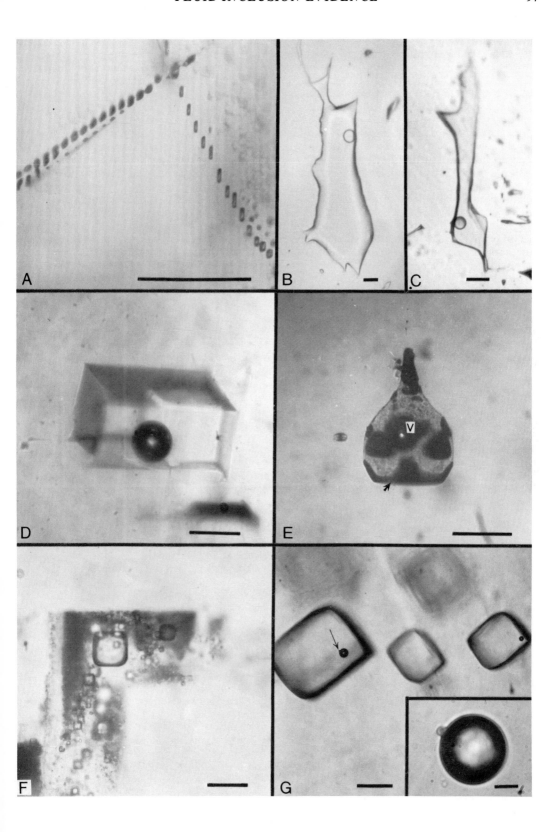

Another aspect of the study of fluid inclusions in Mississippi Valley-type deposits concerns the help they may provide for exploration programs. Every exploration program must be based somewhat on a model of the mode of formation of the type of deposit being explored. If this model is valid, it can greatly enhance the possibility of success by concentrating the exploration effort on the most likely ground (Roedder, 1977b). Fluid inclusion evidence on the Mississippi Valley-type deposits does not suffice by itself to pinpoint which of many suggested models is correct in any given deposit, but it does suffice to eliminate some suggested models and hence help the explorationist. Thus the high salinities and the high temperatures exclude cold surface waters and shallow ocean lagoon waters, both of which have been seriously proposed as the ore-forming fluids for some of these deposits.

CARBONATE AND QUARTZ CEMENTS IN DETRITAL ROCKS

Anyone who has looked at detrital carbonate rocks in thin section is aware of carbonate overgrowths on the grains that commonly act as a cement in these rocks. The small size of these overgrowths is such, however, that they would seem to be a very unlikely place to find usable fluid inclusions. But a study by Nelson (1973) has shown that small but usable primary fluid inclusions can indeed be found in such cements. In a crinoidal biosparite, the Fernvale Limestone (Upper Ordovician), from samples across northern Arkansas, such inclusions show a homogenization temperature range from 85–170° C, with a distinct mode in the range 110–150° C. The salinity ranged from 5–25 wt. % NaCl equivalent. These data are very similar to those found for inclusions in the barite-lead-zinc deposits of central and northern Missouri (Leach, 1973a, b), and it is presumed that the cementation fluids and the ore-forming fluids may represent a single episode of fluid flow through these rocks. The possibility of multiple periods of circulation (and cementation) must always be considered (Blatt, 1978).

Another similar application of inclusion data to carbonate rocks is found in the "dolomite problem," i.e., when did what dolomite form? In some mining areas there are several stages of dolomitization, e.g., Pine Point, Canada (Dunsmore, 1973; MacQueen and Taylor, 1974), and East Tennessee (Wedow, 1974). Freeman (1973) has reported that the fluid inclusions in some epigenetic dolomite-calcite cements show that the fluids forming the dolomite were both hotter and saltier than those forming the associated calcite cements.

Quartz cements may provide similar opportunities for finding inclusions that can delineate the environment of sandstone diagenesis. R. C. Nelson (personal commun., 1975) has studied quartz overgrowths in the Blakely and Crystal Mountain Sandstones (Lower Ordovician) from central Arkansas. Most of the inclusions are trapped at the original grain boundaries of the detrital quartz grains, but some occur within the overgrowth, and considerable care must be used to avoid confusion with the inclusions of the original detrital grains. Homogenization temperatures for inclusions in the overgrowths ranged 97.5–> 152° C (possibly as high as 175° C). More recently, Pagel (1977) has made use of the inclusions in quartz cements in a study of uranium deposits.

Studies such as these show that fluid inclusions can provide useful quantitative data on problems that heretofore have been plagued by ambiguous, qualitative data. They will generally require extensive and careful microscopy, but the possibilities of getting answers to otherwise rather intractable problems make the effort worthwhile.

SALINE AND SULFUR DEPOSITS

Saline formations can be very sensitive indicators of diagenesis, as they recrystallize rather readily. Much bedded salt has recrystallized, but it is not uncommon to find within bedded halites single crystals which have very clear multiple chevron-like patterns (Fig. 1F), corresponding to growth zoning parallel to the faces of original hopper crystal cube corners. As these hopper crystals grew on the surface of the brine, and then sank, their orientation is random. When these patterns are examined in detail (e.g., those from the Salina beds at Goderich, Ontario; Roedder, 1963), they are found to be composed of planes of very tiny, liquid-filled inclusions, generally 3–30μm, but many are <1 μm in diameter and a very few are as large as 300 μm. Some samples have as many as 2×10^{10} inclusions per cm^3 (Roedder, 1972, p. 43). The wide range of sizes making up a pattern that has remained intact since Salina times places an interesting constraint on the rate of movement of inclusions in the geothermal gradient. Any inclusion in a thermal gradient should move, generally toward the heat source, because of solution on one side and deposition on the other, and large inclusions should move fastest. Unfortunately, numerous factors are involved (e.g., see Anthony and Cline, 1974), but as the original growth pattern has not been lost or even visibly distorted in millions of years in a geothermal gradient, this movement must be exceedingly slow or have a threshold.

When inclusions in halite are studied on the freezing stage, they are frequently found to contain a wide range of compositions, from bitterns with high concentrations of calcium and magnesium to essentially pure solutions of NaCl (Roedder,

1963, p. 182; Roedder and Belkin (1978) have shown that the Carlsbad area of New Mexico provides a notable exception). Such a range is expectable from the normal events in the history of such salt beds. During the original crystallization, evaporation continuously concentrates the more soluble ions such as Ca and Mg into the residual liquids, and unless refluxing is effective, inclusions will be trapped representing various stages in this process. Under diagenesis, formation waters penetrating the recrystallizing halite bed will dissolve the more soluble minerals and gradually flush out residual and grain boundary fluids, until only NaCl (and $CaSO_4$) remain. Any fluids trapped during subsequent recrystallization or upon the healing of fractures will contain only NaCl (plus any salts originally in the waters passing through).

Analyses of the fluid in inclusions in halite have been reported by several workers (see Tables 4 and 6 in Roedder, 1972; Derevyagin, 1973; Kovalevich, 1975; Petrichenko, 1973; Petrichenko, Kovalevich, and Chalyi, 1974; Petrichenko and Shaydetskaya, 1973; Petrichenko and Slivko, 1973; Sedletskii, Trufanov, and Maiskii, 1973). Several of these studies show large differences in the composition of inclusions in primary salt and in recrystallized material. Although several thousand analyses of inclusions are reported in the literature, for all types of material, the only actual determinations of Eh (-400 to $+515$ mV) of the fluids have been on inclusions in halite, by Petrichenko and coworkers (see above). He also reports what are probably some of the most valid pH determinations made on inclusions (4.5–6.4), as the inclusions available were huge, and hence minimized the otherwise very serious experimental problems in measurement.

In addition to the major ions Na, Cl, K, Mg, and Ca, several of the minor constituents are useful in understanding the environment of formation. Thus Sabouraud-Rosset (1973, 1974) has found that the Cl/Br ratio in fluid inclusions in gypsum crystals from various types of saline environments varies from 150 to more than 1000, and she has been able to recognize leaching by later waters in some of these environments on the basis of neutron activation analyses for Cl and Br. This ratio is particularly suitable, as it is not apt to be affected seriously by reactions with clays, etc., that can seriously influence other minor elements (Petrichenko and Slivko, 1974). Such reactions particularly affect the ratio K/Mg, and the content of SO_4 ions. Organic matter is also present in the inclusions in many saline deposits, as bitumen (e.g., Kul'chitskaya, 1974), as liquid and/or liquified hydrocarbons, under pressure (e.g., Fig. 1G; also Roedder, 1972, p. 43), and as gas (mainly either CO_2 or methane)

under pressures up to many atmospheres (e.g., Bol'shakov, 1972; Petrichenko and Slivko, 1973; Petrichenko, Kovalevich, and Chalyi, 1974). Sometimes the pressure of the gases in the inclusions is enough to make the salt decrepitate either spontaneously or under minor relief of stress, yielding "popping salt" that can become a major hazard in mining (Roedder, 1972, p. 43). There is no consensus concerning the origin of these gases, and they have been termed both syngenetic and epigenetic. As the composition varies widely from one occurrence of popping salt to another, probably several different processes are involved.

As a result of the rather common occurrence of leakage, necking down, and metastable stretched liquid under negative pressure in inclusions in halite (center inclusion in Fig. 1G; see also Roedder, 1967b, 1971b), temperature measurements by the homogenization method are generally suspect and frequently impossible. Such processes may explain some of the reports of exceedingly high homogenization temperatures (e.g., 240–360° C, Panov, 1975). Gypsum also may give unreliable results (Kul'chitskaya, 1974). However, a few halite deposits have yielded seemingly valid values. Kovalevich (1975) found that homogenization of sylvite daughter crystals in some primary inclusions in halite from Stebnik in the USSR took place at 38–60° C, whereas secondary gas/liquid inclusions in recrystallized halite homogenized in the range 56–86° C, with the average of 80 determinations 71° C. Petrichenko and Slivko (1973) established that diagenetic alteration of Permian salt in the Donbass took place at ~60° C, and Roedder and Belkin (1978) showed that inclusions in both primary and recrystallized salt in a core from the Delaware Basin (Carlsbad area, New Mexico) homogenized in the range 25–45° C.

For determination of homogenization temperatures with a minimum of ambiguity, other minerals that have formed in the halite beds are generally more tractable. Thus Sedletskii, Trufanov, and Mel'nikova (1971) measured homogenization temperatures of 40–110° C [3] for inclusions in authigenic quartz crystals from Upper Jurassic saline deposits in the Hissar Range, USSR.

One of the most interesting minerals that acts as a recorder of diagenetic conditions in saline deposits is sulfur. Sulfur is found in many saline deposits, where it generally is assumed to have formed as a consequence of bacterial oxidation of organic matter and reduction of sulfate from anhydrite or in the water. There is frequently

---

[3] These authors erroneously subtracted 15–20° from these values as a "correction for salinity" to obtain trapping temperatures.

a problem concerning the time at which this action took place, and the fluid inclusions in the sulfur may provide useful input. These inclusions are frequently large, and as there is no reported evidence of inclusions in sulfur leaking, these should provide good material for analysis. The inclusions in sulfur and associated gypsum in the famous Sicilian deposits were so large that they were some of the first inclusions to be analyzed quantitatively and reasonably completely (Silvestri, 1882; Sjögren, 1893). Sjögren found the gypsum to contain a sodium-chloride-rich solution containing 4% salts, but the fluid inclusion in sulfur analyzed by Silvestri contained only 0.1% salts. The latter may be an unfortunate example of an inclusion in sulfur that did actually leak, in view of the very low salinity and the very large size (6 cm^3), as large inclusions are much more apt to leak than small ones (Roedder and Skinner, 1968, p. 723).

Yushkin and Srebrodol'skii (1965) studied large inclusions in sulfur from the Rozdol and Shorsui deposits in carbonate-sulfate rocks in Uzbekistan, USSR. The inclusions are single phase (i.e., full of liquid) except for a film of bitumen in some. The presence of large single-phase inclusions indicates that the sulfur grew at low temperatures, as even cooling from 40° C will cause a bubble to form in most large inclusions. The fluid released some H_2S when the crystals were crushed, and had a pH of 7–7.5, as determined by the use of various organic indicators. It contained about 6% salts, mainly (Na, K) and Ca chloride, bicarbonate and sulfate. Merlich and Datsenko (1972) found that the fluid in inclusions in sulfur deposits from the Little Carpathians in southern USSR were NaCl solutions, similar to seawater.

Beskrovnyi and Lebedev (1971) studied various minerals from the Gaurdak sulfur deposit which is in a sequence of gypsum-anhydrite-halite rocks in limestone in southeastern Turkmenia. This must be a different type of sulfur deposit, however, as it contains also celestite, fluorite, barite, danburite, hematite, gypsum, calcite, solid bitumens, quartz, sphalerite (high in Hg and Pb), oil, and gas. Early fluorite inclusions homogenized at 130–160° C, but those in late gypsum and calcite homogenized at <50° C.

PETROLEUM RESERVOIR ROCKS

Organic matter in contact with fluids moving through a sediment is subject to a continuous series of changes with time, depth, and temperature (Barker, 1972; Macqueen, 1976), as well as surficial weathering (Clayton and Swetland, 1976). However, when the growth of a crystal causes the trapping of an inclusion containing such organic matter, it effectively isolates it from reactions with subsequent external environments. Isochemical changes may still take place, but for reasons that are not clear, they do so only in *some* inclusions (e.g., some southern Illinois oil inclusions in fluorite; Fig. 1E; Roedder, 1962a, p. 40; 1972, Plate 9, Fig. 2; see also Kvenvolden and Roedder, 1971, p. 1214). Insofar as the environment of trapping can be estimated, or at least delimited, by data on the organic compounds present, these oil inclusions can be useful. Thus, in theory at least, the many changes that take place during the migration and maturation of petroleum should be recorded in oil inclusions trapped at various stages along the way. Very little has been done in this respect, but with the recent tremendous improvement in appropriate analytical techniques, such as microgaschromatography, mass spectrometry, and particularly the combination of the two, the approach has considerable potential.

Organic gases, liquids, and solids have been recognized in inclusions in many samples, and these materials have been characterized to various degrees. The extensive literature is listed or abstracted elsewhere (Table 1; see also Roedder, 1968-onward, 1972) and only a few items can be reviewed here. A pioneering effort in this direction was made by Murray (1957), who reported a detailed mass spectrometric analysis of the molecular constituents in organic liquid-gas inclusions in quartz crystals from vugs in a dolomite core from a gas-productive interval in Mississippian rocks in Alberta. The inclusions contained mainly methane and ethane under pressure, and also included small amounts of many other constituents, but no water. On heating, the two phases homogenized in the gas phase at about 100° C. The problem is how such inclusions can become trapped, as it would seem to require growth of quartz from the hydrocarbon fluid. The fluids trapped in some very thin wedge-like planes of secondary inclusions suggest that oil inclusions are trapped because of preferential wetting of the quartz surface with the oil phase, and growth of the exposed quartz surfaces from the immiscible water phase, so that the cavity full of oil can be enclosed completely, without any of the water phase (Kvenvolden and Roedder, 1971).

In North Derbyshire, England, organic materials of several types have been found associated with lead-zinc-fluorite deposits in Carboniferous limestones. Although these various materials are found there as inclusions, particularly in fluorite, they are also found free, in larger masses, and have been studied extensively in an attempt to determine their origins (e.g., Nooner et al., 1973; Pering, 1973). There have evidently been several stages of selective leaching, transport, and deposition, and possibly recent partial microbial oxidation. This is only one of many lead-zinc-fluorite deposits in carbonate rocks that contain organic matter (see also Table 1). Although some mines have oil or tar actually dripping from the back, others that seem to be free of it have been found to contain measurable amounts (≤ 100 ppm) in certain minerals, such as sphalerite (Rickard *et al.*, 1975).

Even if no organic phase in the aqueous fluid inclusions is visible, a growing body of evidence shows that very significant amounts of a wide variety of hydrocarbons can dissolve in water or brine (Price, 1973; 1976); these compounds should be looked for. Possibly the "hydrocarbon peaks" frequently seen in mass spectrometric studies of inclusions, that are usually passed off as normal atmospheric contamination, may be in part real. Other compounds, such as amino acids (K. Kvenvolden, personal commun., 1975), should also be searched for that might define better the maximum temperatures to which a sample has been subjected in the past.

Still another application of inclusions in connection with the history of oil-bearing rocks is their use to date the formation of fracture porosity at depth. Currie and Nwachukwu (1974) studied inclusions in mineral fillings of fractures in oil-field formations in Canada. They found that there were ranges of homogenization temperatures, from 45–120° C, which they interpreted as indicating that opening of fractures developed progressively as an accompaniment to tectonism, regional uplift and erosional unloading. They also suggest on this basis that incipient fracture porosity at depth can develop gradually into a network of open fractures under conditions of continued uplift and erosional unloading. The presence of organic coatings on some of the minerals studied suggests the possibility of establishing the time relationship between fracture-porosity formation and oil migration.

One of the most striking convergences of scientific lines of thought has been the rather recent recognition of the similarity of the problems of the petroleum geologist and the minerals exploration geologist in looking for deposits in sediments around the margins of basins. This aspect has been discussed by many (e.g., Dunham, 1970; Macqueen, 1976) and places additional importance on the full characterization of the organic compounds found in inclusions from each of these environments.

SPHALERITE IN BITUMINOUS COAL BEDS

All coals contain at least some sulfides, and because of the environmental significance there has been considerable interest in the nature and origin of these sulfides. Iron sulfides are by far the most abundant and are mainly of authigenic

origin (Boctor, Kullerud, and Sweany, 1975). In some coals, however, sphalerite is a significant constituent, and as it is a transparent mineral, fluid-inclusion studies on it may yield information concerning the conditions of origin. Leach (1973a) studied inclusions in sphalerite from coal mines in central Missouri and found homogenization temperatures of 80–110° C, and strongly saline brines (>22% NaCl equivalent). As the sphalerite from the adjacent northern Arkansas zinc district had similar fluid inclusions (83–132° C and >22% NaCl equivalent), Leach suggests that these two mineralizations formed from a single episode of fluid flow.

In the northwest part of the Illinois Basin some bituminous coals have very coarsely crystalline banded yellow and purple sphalerite both as vertical veins ("cleats") and as crystals in clay dikes cutting the coal seams (Hatch, Gluskoter, and Lindahl, 1976; Cobb and Russell, 1976). Fragments of coal are found embedded in the sphalerite. The sequence of color banding is regular throughout a large part of the basin (Hatch, Gluskoter, and Lindahl, 1976). Samples of these sphalerites show many secondary or pseudosecondary aqueous inclusions, and only a very few inclusions that might be primary (Fig. 1C). A group of 25 inclusions from the cleat sphalerite and 19 from the clay dike sphalerite, all from Knox, Peoria, Montgomery and Fulton Counties, Illinois, were selected on the basis of maximum likelihood of a primary or at least pseudosecondary origin, and homogenization and freezing temperatures determined (Roedder, unpub. data). Homogenization temperatures ranged from 90–102° C for the cleat samples (average: 95.7° C) and 82–96° C for the clay dike samples (average: 89.5° C). The freezing temperatures of all samples ranged from −15.6 to −18.9° C and averaged −16.9° C, and all showed first melting at <−26.5° C. The freezing temperature corresponds to about 21% NaCl solutions, but the first melting temperature requires the presence of ions other than Na and Cl (Roedder, 1962a). Although Hatch, Gluskoter and Lindahl (1976) report five generations of sphalerite deposition, no recognizable difference could be detected between the inclusions in the various colors in the present work. However, the distribution of the selected inclusions among the various samples and color zones in them was adequate to detect only gross differences.

The interpretation of these results is not at all clear. Bituminous coal itself is a sensitive indicator of "diagenetic" (low-grade metamorphic) conditions (Walenczak, 1974). Bostick (1973, and personal comm., 1976) has shown from coal petrography that the high-sphalerite coals of the Illinois Basin were never subjected to long-continued burial temperatures above 40–65° C, and any anomalous temperature events on the order of 100° C could have lasted only 1–3 million years. Thus the maximum temperatures from the inclusion data and the coal petrography data may not be in conflict.

There is an interesting possibility of a connection between the fluids depositing this sphalerite and those forming the sphalerite in the Upper Mississippi Valley zinc deposits ~150 km to the north. The homogenization temperatures found in the Upper Mississippi Valley zinc deposits by earlier workers (see Roedder, 1976, Table IV) range from 75–121° C, and freezing temperatures of −20° C (Roedder, 1967a). These fluids were thus in the same temperature range but somewhat more saline than those in the coal beds. But recent studies by McLimans (1975) showed homogenization temperatures for inclusions in early sphalerite in the zinc deposits higher than those in any other recorded Mississippi Valley-type ore deposit in the world (150–210° C). Even this large a difference does not preclude a genetic connection, however, as it is expected that the zinc-depositing brines eventually would cool and become more dilute from flowing through cooler rocks and the addition of ground water. As pointed out by

Hatch, Gluskoter and Lindahl (1976) from the color banding, the deposition of this sphalerite was a basin-wide event, making it evident that large-scale fluid movements must be involved.

SUMMARY

From all the above data on six seemingly very different environments, it is apparent that most environments of sedimentary diagenesis, at least those recorded by fluid inclusions, involved the presence of hot, saline brines. Although many deep basins now contain hot saline brines, particularly below 3 km, some geologists are reluctant to accept such an environment for the thinner piles of cratonic sediments. Admittedly, little evidence of such brines may be visible in the usual outcrop, once the brines have been replaced with surface water, as most of the minerals present are relatively inert. But the inclusions present in the minerals can and do preserve evidence of these hot brines for geologic time. The presence of such hot fluids under pressure in present-day sedimentary piles, and their migration, whether it be due to compaction or other gradients (Magara, 1973; Price, 1975), is exceedingly important to an understanding of both ore and oil deposits.

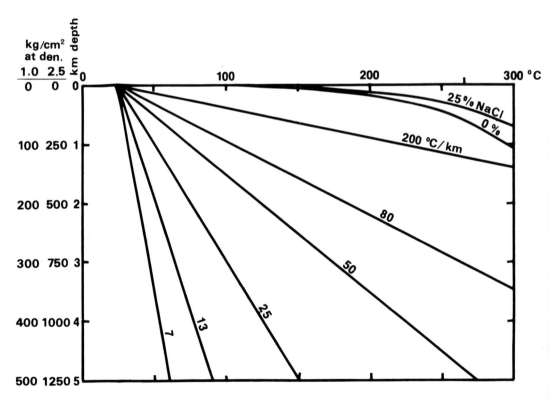

FIG. 2.—Temperature-depth relations with various geotherms. For comparison, the boiling curves for water (0%) and 25 wt. % NaCl solution are given.

As the maximum depth of cover of many of the formations from which the samples were obtained is generally low, this raises the question, what was the geothermal gradient at the time of deposition? Figure 2 shows a series of linear geothermal gradients. From this figure, and the available estimates of depth of cover for the various samples described above on which homogenization data have been obtained, it is evident that those in the upper temperature ranges, particularly those over 150° C, must represent very high gradients at the time of trapping.

The heat capacity of brine is so high relative to that of rock that movement of the brine is of great importance in any thermal calculations. Thus a sediment having 10% porosity (Clark, 1966) has less than six times the total heat capacity of the much lighter brines (assuming 20% NaCl) filling the 10% pores. Hence relatively few recharges of the fluids in the pores could bring the rock to the temperature of the entering fluids, and with higher porosities the process would be even more effective. Diment *et al.* (1975) show that over much of the interior of the United States, the present vertical heat flow is $\sim 1.5 \times 10^{-6}$ cal/cm^{2}s. This rate of heat flow (from conductivity) is about the same magnitude as would be obtained from vertical fluid flow rates, assuming normal porosities, in the range of 30 cm/yr (A. H. Lachenbruch, personal commun., 1976). Thus even a very slow upwelling of hot brines can be effective in increasing the thermal gradient of the region, as long as it continues. It may be that the minerals sampled for fluid inclusions are a biased sample, enriched in those from higher gradient areas, perhaps for the very reason that such rising, cooling fluids have caused the precipitation of the host (ore) minerals. Even such slow flow rates can cause the transport of surprisingly vast amounts of material in the available time (Roedder, 1976, p. 70).

The magnitude of the homogenization temperatures found for some Mississippi Valley-type deposits and the high geothermal gradients they require have caused some to look for novel sources of heat, in particular exothermic reactions. Thus Bush (1970), Dhannoun and Fyfe (1972), and Dunsmore (1973), among others, have suggested the reduction of SO_4^{2-} by petroleum (either bacteriologically or direct chemical) as a source of heat as well as the sulfide ion for precipitation of the ores. This is seemingly a very happy solution to the dilemma of simultaneous transport of sulfur and metal in a single solution, as well as the high thermal gradients, as the reaction is admittedly exothermic. However, even with a very liberal choice of chemical and geological parameters, the possible temperature rise of the passing fluids from this reaction can only be small fraction of one degree—several orders of magnitude too low (Roedder, 1971a). Significant temperature rise could be achieved only if solid anhydrite and hydrocarbons were permitted to react in place, i.e., neither carried by the brines, but then the disposal of the resulting H_2S becomes a problem, particularly as this will retard further bacterial action.

The salinity of the fluids in most deep sedimentary basins generally increases with depth, frequently at such a rate that the effect of salinity on the density is just sufficient to counteract the opposite effect of increasing temperature (Hanor, 1973). The densities of the fluids trapped in the fluid inclusions in these materials, when corrected for expansion up to the temperature of homogenization of these inclusions, are also found to be usually a little more than 1.0 g/cm^3. Thus the fluid column is gravitationally stable, but subject to possible turnover if perturbed, as by erosion or by additional heat from a deep intrusive. It is tempting to suggest that the Mississippi Valley-type deposits may represent exactly those areas where such disturbance and convective turnover occurred in the past.

ACKNOWLEDGEMENTS

The writer is indebted to many people for discussions that have contributed to this paper. Samples on which new data are presented here were supplied by H. Wedow, Jr., N. R. Shaffer, C. F. Withington, R. C. Kepferle, R. L. Sutton, Jr., M.D., R. W. Lanhann, J. S. Branham, Jr., and R. F. Strogonoff. Numerous other samples supplied by these individuals and others were found to have no usable inclusions and hence are not recorded here. Many of the previously unpublished freezing and heating runs reported, some of which were exceedingly difficult, were made by H. E. Belkin and the late J. P. Creel. The manuscript was improved as a result of reviews by R. Potter II, and J. J. Hemley.

REFERENCES[4]

ALLMENDINGER, R. J., 1974, Source of ore-forming fluids at the Hansonburg Mining District, central New Mexico: Econ. Geology, v. 69, p. 1176.

ANTHONY, T. R., AND CLINE, H. E., 1974, Thermomigration of liquid droplets in salt, *in* A. H. Coogan (ed.), Fourth symposium on salt: Cleveland, Ohio, Northern Ohio Geol. Soc., p. 313–321.

[4] English abstracts of many of the Russian references will be found in Roedder (1968-onward).

BARKER, C., 1972, Pyrolysis techniques for source rock evaluation [abs.]. Geol. Soc. America Abs. with Programs, v. 4, p. 443.

BARLIER, J., RAGOT, J. -P., AND TOURAY, J. -C., 1974, L'évolution des Terres Noires subalpines méridionales d'après l'analyse minéralogique des argiles et la réflectométrie des particules carbonées: Bur. Recherches Géol. et Minières Bull., ser. 2, v. 2, p. 533–548.

BASSETT, W. A., AND KINSLAND, G. L., 1973, Trip H—Mineral collecting at Penfield Quarry, in P. C. Hewitt (ed.), Guidebook to field trips. New York State Geol. Assoc., 45th Ann. Meeting, p. H1–H9.

BEALES, F. W., CARRACEDO, J. C., AND STRANGWAY, D. W., 1974, Paleomagnetism and the origin of Mississippi Valley-type ore deposits: Canadian Jour. Earth Sci., v. 11, p. 211–223.

BEANE, R. E., 1974, Barite-fluorite-galena deposits in south-central New Mexico: A product of shallow intrusions, groundwater and epicontinental sediments. Econ. Geology, v. 69, p. 1176.

BENNETT, R. E., JR., 1974, Fluid inclusion study of sphalerite from the northern Arkansas zinc-lead district: M.S. Thesis, Univ. Michigan, 157 p.

BESKROVNYI, N. S., AND LEVEDEV, B. A., 1971, O proyavleniyakh sfalerita i drugikh gidrotermal'nykh mineralov na Gaurdakskom sernom mestorozhdenii (Yugo-Vostochnaya Turkmeniya) [Occurrences of sphalerite and other hydrothermal minerals in the Gaurdak sulfur deposit, southeastern Turkmenia]: Akad. Nauk SSSR Doklady, v. 200, p. 185–188.

BOCTOR, N. Z., KULLERUD, G., AND SWEANY, J. L., 1975, Sulfide minerals in coal bed III, Chinook mine, Indiana [abs]: Geol. Soc. America Abs. with Programs, v. 7, p. 1003.

BOL'SHAKOV, YU. YA., 1972, Osobennosti gasonakopleniya v galogennoy formatsii Solikamskoy vpadiny [Gas accumulation in the evaporite formation of the Solikamsk Basin]: Akad. Nauk SSSR Doklady, v. 204, p. 1222–1224.

BOSTICK, N. H., 1973, Time as a factor in thermal metamorphism of phytoclasts (coaly particles): Congr. Internat. de Stratig. et de Géol. du Carbonifère, Septième, Krefeld, Aug. 23–28, 1971, Compte Rendu, v. 2, p. 183–193.

BUSH, P. R., 1970, Chloride-rich brines from sabkha sediments and their possible role in ore formation: Inst. Mining and Metallurgy Trans., v. 79(B), p. B137–B144.

CAMERON, AUBREY, 1977, Physical conditions of low grade metamorphism of the Jacksonburg Formation, Northampton County, Pennsylvania: M.S. Thesis, Lehigh Univ., Bethlehem, Pennsylvania, 86 p.

CLARK, S. P., JR. (ed.), 1966, Handbook of physical constants: Geol. Soc. America, Mem. 97, 583 p.

CLAYTON, J. L., AND SWETLAND, P. J., 1976, Subaerial weathering of sedimentary organic matter [abs]: Geol. Soc. America Abs. with Programs, v. 8, p. 815.

COBB, J. C., AND RUSSELL, S. J., 1976, Sphalerite mineralization in coal seams of the Illinois Basin [abs.]: Geol. Soc. America Abs. with Programs, v. 8, p. 816.

CURRIE, J. B., AND NWACHUKWU, S. O., 1974, Evidence on incipient fracture porosity in reservoir rocks at depth: Bull. Canadian Petroleum Geology, v. 22, p. 42–58.

CZAMANSKE, G. K., ROEDDER, E., AND BURNS, F. C., 1963, Neutron activation analysis of fluid inclusions for copper, manganeze and zinc: Science, v. 140, p. 401–403.

DEREVYAGIN, V. S., 1973, Investigations of some microelements in liquid inclusions of rock salt from south of middle Asia [abs.]: Rostov, Rostov. Univ. Press, Abs. of papers at Fourth Reg. Conf. on Thermobaro-geochemistry of Mineral-Forming Processes [in Russian], p. 167–168.

DHANNOUN, H. Y., AND FYFE, W. S., 1972, Reaction rates of hydrocarbons with anhydrite. Natl. Envir. Res. Council, Pub. Ser. D, Progress in Experimental Petrology, v. 2, p. 69–71.

DIMENT, W. H., URBAN, T. C., SASS, J. H., MARSHALL, B. V., MUNROE, R. J., AND LACHENBRUCH, A. H., 1975, Temperatures and heat contents based on conductive transport of heat: U.S. Geol. Survey Circ. 726, p. 84–103.

DUNHAM, K. C., 1970, Mineralization by deep formation waters: A review: Inst. Mining and Metallurgy Trans, v. 79(B), p. B127–B136.

DUNN, J. R., AND FISHER, D. W., 1954, Occurrence, properties, and paragenesis of anthraxolite in the Mohawk Valley: Am. Jour. Sci., v. 252, p. 489–501.

DUNSMORE, H. E., 1973, Diagenetic processes of lead-zinc emplacement in carbonates: Inst. Mining and Metallurgy Trans., v. 82(B), p. B168–B173.

FISHER, I. S., 1976, Distribution, composition and source of geodal minerals in Kentucky [abs.]: Geol. Soc. America Abs. with Programs, v. 8, p. 173.

FRAZIER, W. J., 1973, Origin of celestite-bearing vugs in the Pennington Formation of central Tennessee [abs.]: Geol. Soc. America Abs. with Programs, v. 5, p. 397.

FREEMAN, T., 1973, Temporal dolomite-calcite sequence and its environmental implications [abs.]: Am Assoc. Petroleum Geologists Bull., v. 57, p. 780.

HANOR, J. S., 1973, The role of in situ densities in the migration of subsurface brines [abs.]: Geol. Soc. America Abs. with Programs, v. 5, p. 651–652.

HARE, P. E., AND MITTERER, R. M., 1969, Laboratory simulation of amino-acid diagenesis in fossils: Carnegie Inst. Washington Year Book 67, 1967–1968, p. 205–208.

HATCH, J. R., GLUSKOTER, H. J., AND LINDAHL, P. C., 1976, Sphalerite in coals from the Illinois Basin: Econ. Geology, v. 72, p. 613–624.

HIRST, D. M., AND SMITH, F. W., 1974, Controls of barite mineralization in the Lower Magnesian Limestone of the Ferryhill area, County Durham. Inst. Mining and Metallurgy Trans., v. 83(B), p. B49–B55.

HUDSON, J. D., AND FRIEDMAN, I., 1976, Carbon and oxygen isotopes in concretions: Relationship to pore-water changes during diagenesis: Prague, Geol. Survey, Proc. Internat. Symp. on Water-Rock Interaction, Czechoslovakia, 1974, p. 331–339.

JEPSEN, G. L., 1964, Riddles of the terrible lizards. Am. Scientist, v. 52, p. 227–246.

KARWOWSKI, L., AND KOZLOWSKI, A., 1973, Authigenic smoky quartz from the Famennian Limestones at Lagow in the Holy Cross Mts. Acta Geol. Polonica, v. 23, p. 171–178.

KOVALEVICH, V. M., 1975, Usloviya obrazobaniya Verkhnevorotyshchenskikh galogennykh otlozhenii v raione Stebnika (Po vklyucheniyam v galite) [Conditions of forming of Verkhnevorotyshchenskiye saline deposits in the region of Stebnik (based on inclusions in halite)]: Kiev, Geol. and Geochem. of Fuels, v. 44, p. 42–50.

KUL'CHITSKAYA, A. A., 1974, Vklyucheniya mineraloobrazuyushchei sredy v gipsakh i vozmozhnosti ikh izucheniya [Inclusions of mineral-forming solution in gypsum and their significance], in Ye. K. Lazarenko (ed.), Mineralogy of sedimentary deposits: Kiev, Nauk. Dumka, p. 34–38.

KVENVOLDEN, K. A., AND ROEDDER, E., 1971, Fluid inclusions in quartz crystals from Southwest Africa: Geochim, et Cosmochim. Acta, v. 35, p. 1209–1229.

LARSON, L. T., MILLER, J. D., NADEAU, J. E., AND ROEDDER, E., 1973, Two sources of error in low temperature inclusion homogenization determination, and corrections on published temperatures for the East Tennessee and Laisvall deposits: Econ. Geology, v. 68, p. 113–116.

LAZARENKO, E. K., LAZARENKO, E. A., ZAYTSEVA, V. N., AND MALYGINA, O. A., 1974, Zonal'nost' al'piiskikh magmatieskikh formatsii i orudenediya v Karpatakh [Zoning of alpine igneous associations and mineralizations in the Carpathians]: Akad. Nauk SSSR Doklady, v. 218, p. 913–915.

LEACH, D. L., 1973a, A study of the barite-lead-zinc deposits of central Missouri and related mineral deposits in the Ozark region: PhD. Diss., Univ. Missouri-Columbia, 186 p.

——, 1973b, Possible relationship of Pb-Zn mineralization in the Ozarks to Ouachita orogeny [abs.]: Geol. Soc. America Abs. with Programs, v. 5, p. 269.

——, 1973c, Possible two-stage mineralization in the central Missouri barite district [abs.]: Geol. Soc. America Abs. with Programs, v. 5, p. 331.

——, NELSON, R. C., AND WILLIAMS, D., 1975, Fluid inclusion studies in the northern Arkansas zinc district: Econ. Geology, v. 70, p. 1084–1091.

McLIMANS, R. K., 1975, Systematic fluid inclusion and sulfur isotope studies of the Upper Mississippi Valley Pb-Zn deposits [abs.]: Geol. Soc. America Abs. with Programs, v. 7, p. 1197.

MACQUEEN, R. W., 1976, Sediments, zinc and lead, Rocky Mountain Belt, Canadian Cordillera: Geoscience Canada, v. 3, p. 71–81.

—— AND TAYLOR, G. C., 1974, Facies changes, dolomitization, and zinc-lead mineralization in Devonian rocks of Peace River area, Rocky Mountains, northeastern British Columbia: Geol. Assoc. Canada-Mineral. Assoc. Canada Meeting, Newfoundland, p. 57–58.

MAGARA, K., 1973, Compaction and fluid migration in Cretaceous shales of western Canada: Canada Geol. Survey Paper 72-18, 81 p.

MATSUI, E., SALATI, E., AND MARINI, O. J., 1974, D/H and $^{18}O/^{16}O$ ratios in waters contained in geodes from the basaltic province of Rio Grande do Sul, Brazil: Geol. Soc. America Bull., v. 85, p. 577–580.

MERLICH, B. V., AND DATSENKO, N. M., 1972, Sostav vodnykh vytyazhck iz zhidkikh vklyuchenii v sere i autigennykh mineralakh sernykh mestorozhdenii Predkarpat'ya [The composition of aqueous extracts of liquid inclusions in sulphur and authigenic minerals of sulphur deposits of the Precarpathians]: L'vov Gos. Univ. Mineralog. Sbornik, v. 26, p. 73–88.

MILLER, R. E., BROBST, D. A., AND BECK, P. C., 1972, Fatty acids as a key to the genesis and economic potential of black bedded barites in Arkansas and Nevada [abs.]: Geol. Soc. America Abs. with Programs, v. 4, p. 596.

MUELLER, G., 1972, Organic microspheres from the Precambrian of Southwest Africa: Nature, v. 235(5333), p. 90–95.

MURRAY, R. C., 1957, Hydrocarbon fluid inclusions in quartz: Am. Assoc. Petroleum Geologists Bull., v. 41, p. 950–956.

NELSON, R. C., 1973, Fluid inclusions as a clue to diagenesis of carbonate rocks [abs.]: Geol. Soc. America Abs. with Programs, v. 5, p. 748.

NOONER, D. W., UPDEGROVE, W. S., FLORY, D. A., ORO', J., AND MUELLER, G., 1973, Isotopic and chemical data of bitumens associated with hydrothermal veins from Windy Knoll, Derbyshire, England: Chem. Geology, v. 11, p. 189–202.

PAGEL, M., 1977, Microthermometry and chemical analysis of fluid inclusions from the Rabbit Lake uranium deposit, Saskatchewan, Canada [abs.]: Inst. Mining and Metallurgy Trans., v. 86(B), p. B157–B158.

PANOV, V. V., 1975, Paleotemperaturye issledovaniya po gazovozhidkim vklucheniyam v galite [Paleo-temperature studies on gas-liquid inclusions in halite]: Akad. Nauk BSSR Doklady, v. 19, p. 257–260.

PERING, K. L., 1973, Bitumens associated with lead, zinc and fluorite ore minerals in North Derbyshire, England: Geochim. et Cosmochim. Acta, v. 37, p. 401–417.

PETRICHENKO, O. I., 1973, Metody doslidzhennya vklyuchen' u mineralakh halogennikh porid [Methods of investigating inclusions in halide minerals]: Kiev, Nauk. Dumka, 92 p.

——, KOVALEVICH, V. M., AND CHALYI, V. N., 1974, Geokhimicheskaya obstanovka soleobr ovaniya v Tortonskom evaporitovom basseine Severo-Zapadnogo Predkarpat'ya [Geochemical conditions of salt origin in Tortonian evaporite basin of the northwest Precarpathians]: Geologiya i geokhimiya goryuchikh iskopaemykh, v. 41, p. 74–80.

RICKARD, D. T., WILLDEN, M., MARDE, Y., AND RYHAGE, R., 1975, Hydrocarbons associated with lead-zinc ores at Laisvall, Sweden: Nature, v. 255, p. 131–133.

ROEDDER, E., 1962a, Studies of fluid inclusions I: Low temperature application of a dual-purpose freezing and heating stage: Econ. Geology, v. 57, p. 1045–1061.

——, 1962b, Ancient fluids in crystals: Scientific American, v. 207, p. 38–47.

——, 1963, Studies of fluid inclusions II: Freezing data and their interpretation: Econ. Geology, v. 58, p. 167–211.

——, 1967a, Environment of deposition of stratiform (Mississippi Valley-type) ore deposits, from studies of fluid inclusions: Econ. Geology Mon., v. 3, p. 349–362.

——, 1967b, Metastable superheated ice in liquid-water inclusions under high negative pressure: Science, v. 155, p. 1413–1417.

——, 1968, Temperature, salinity, and origin of the ore-forming fluids at Pine Point, Northwest Territories, Canada, from fluid inclusion studies: Econ. Geology, v. 63, p. 439–450.

—— (ed.), 1968-onward, Fluid inclusion research—Proceedings of COFFI: An annual summary of world literature; volumes 1–5 (1968–1972) privately printed and available from the editor; volume 6 (1973-onward) printed and available from the University of Michigan Press.

——, 1969, Varvelike banding of possible annual origin in celestite crystals from Clay Center, Ohio, and in other minerals: Am. Mineralogist, v. 54, p. 796–810.

——, 1971a, Discussion of "Chloride-rich brines from sabkha sediments and their possible role in ore formation," by P. R. Bush: Inst. Mining and Metallurgy Trans., v. 80(B), p. B61.

——, 1971b, Metastability in fluid inclusions: Japan Soc. Mining Geology Spec. Issue (Proc. IMA-IAGOD Meetings 1970, IAGOD Vol.), v. 3, p. 327–334.

——, 1972, The composition of fluid inclusions: U.S. Geol. Survey Prof. Paper 440 JJ, 164 p.

——, 1976, Fluid-inclusion evidence on the genesis of ores in sedimentary and volcanic rocks, *in* K. H. Wolf (ed.), Handbook of strata-bound and stratiform ore deposits: Amsterdam, Elsevier Pub. Co., v. 4(2), p. 67–110.

——, 1977a, Fluid inclusion studies of ore deposits in the Viburnum Trend, southeast Missouri: Econ. Geology, v. 72, 474–479.

——, 1977b, Fluid inclusions as tools in mineral exploration: Econ. Geology, v. 72, p. 503–525.

—— AND BELKIN, H. E., 1978, Fluids present during the diagenetic history of the Salado Formation, Delaware Basin, southeastern New Mexico, as recorded by fluid inclusions [abs.]: Am. Geophys. Union Trans., v. 59, p. 226.

——, INGRAM, B., AND HALL, W. E., 1963, Studies of fluid inclusions III: Extraction and quantitative analysis of inclusions in the milligram range: Econ. Geology, v. 58, p. 353–374.

—— AND SKINNER, B. J., 1968, Experimental evidence that fluid inclusions do not leak: Econ. Geology, v. 63, p. 715–730.

ROSASCO, G. J., ROEDDER, E., AND SIMMONS, J. H., 1975, Laser-excited Raman spectroscopy for nondestructive partial analysis of individual phases in fluid inclusions in minerals: Science, v. 190, p. 557–560.

SABOURAUD-ROSSET, C., 1973, Rapports Cl/Br des inclusions liquides des cristaux de gypse de divers gisements; Corrélations avec les données de la microcryoscopie et interprétations génétiques [abs.]: Paris, Réunion Ann. des Sci. de la Terre, p. 375.

——, 1974, Determination par activation neutronique des rapports Cl/Br des inclusions fluides de divers gypses. Correlation avec les données de la microcryoscopie et interprétations génétiques: Sedimentology, v. 21, p. 415–431.

SCHERP, A., AND STRÜBEL, G., 1974, Hydrothermal investigation of the system $BaSO_4$-$SrSO_4$-NaCl-H_2O and its bearing on Ba-Sr mineralizations: Internat. Assoc. on the Genesis of Ore Deposits, Fourth Symp., Varna, Abstracts of Papers: Sofia, IAGOD, p. 464.

SEDLETSKII, V. I., TRUFANOV, V. N., AND MAISKII, YU. G., 1973, Mechanism of mobilization and the nature of highly-mineralized brines in halogenide formations [abs., in Russian]: Rostov, Rostov Univ. Press, Abstracts of papers at Fourth Regional Conf. on Thermobarogeochemistry of Mineral-Forming Processes, p. 42–44.

——, ——, AND MEL'NIKOVA, YE. M., 1971, Nekotoryye osobennosti obrazovaniya autigennogo kvartsa v solerdonykh basseynakh [Origins of authigenic quartz in salt basins]: Akad. Nauk SSSR Sibirsk. Otdeleniye Geologiya i Geofizika, v. 5, p. 72–77.

SILVESTRI, O., 1882. Sulla natura chimica di alcune inclusioni liquide contenute in cristalli naturali di solfo della Sicilia: I Gazzetta Chimica Italiana, v. 12, p. 7–9.

SJÖGREN, JH., 1893, On large fluid inclusions in gypsum from Sicily: Uppsala Univ. Geol. Inst. Bull., v. 1, p. 277–281.

SMITH, F. W., 1973, Fluid inclusion studies on fluorite from the North Wales ore field: Inst. Mining and Metallurgy Trans., v. 82(B), p. B174–B176.

SUTTON, R. L., JR., 1964, Bubble crystals and notes on enhydros: Lapidary Jour., v. 18, p. 924–935.

THIEDE, D. S., AND CAMERON, E. N., 1975, Concentration of heavy metals in the Elk Point evaporite sequence, Saskatchewan [abs.]: Geol. Soc. America Abs. with Programs, v. 7, p. 1297.

TOURAY, J.-C., AND BARLIER, J., 1975, Liquid and gaseous hydrocarbon inclusions in quartz monocrystals from

"Terres Noires" and "Flysch à Helminthoides" (French Alps): Fortschr. Mineralogie, Spec. Issue to v. 52, p. 419–426.

VOZNYAK, D. K., KVASNITSA, V. N., AND GALABURDA, YU. A., 1974, Typomorphic peculiarities of "Marmarosh diamonds," *in* Ye. K. Lazarenko (ed.), Typomorphism of Ukrainian quartz [in Russian]: Kiev, Nauk. Dumka, p. 29–82.

WALENCZAK, Z., 1974, Investigation of degree of metamorphism of coal substances in sedimentary rocks, *in* Wydawnictwa Geologiczne (ed.), Geochemical investigations of bitumens, Results of LXIX Scientific Session of Geological Institute [in Polish]: Warsaw, p. 49–51.

WEDOW, H., 1974, Two-stage dolomite in East Tennessee zinc district: U.S. Geol. Survey Prof. Paper 900, p. 3–4.

WHITE, D. E., 1957, Magmatic, connate, and metamorphic waters: Geol. Soc. America Bull., v. 68, p. 1659–1682.

YUSHKIN, N. P., AND SREBRODOL'SKII, B. I., 1965, K izucheniyu sostava zhidkhikh vklyuchenii v kristallakh samorodonoi sery [Study of the composition of liquid inclusions in crystals of native sulfur]: L'vov Gos. Univ. Mineralog. Sbornik, v. 19, p. 229–236 [translated in Fluid Inclusion Research—Proceedings of COFFI, v. 2, p. 153–160].

SEPM SPECIAL PUBLICATION No. 26, p. 109–112, MARCH 1979

THERMAL HISTORY OF SEDIMENTARY BASINS: FISSION-TRACK DATING OF SUBSURFACE ROCKS

C. W. NAESER

U.S. Geological Survey, Denver, Colorado 80225

ABSTRACT

Fission tracks that are present in apatite crystals recovered from sedimentary and crystalline basement rocks can be used to determine the thermal (tectonic) history of a sedimentary basin. Because fission tracks in apatite usually record the time when the rock temperature cooled below 100° C, one can use the apparent apatite fission-track ages as a function of depth, to determine the amount and duration of an uplift event.

INTRODUCTION

Fission-track dating is a relatively new geochronological method. In the early 1960's three physicists at the General Electric Company's Research Laboratory established the theoretical and practical groundwork (Fleischer and others, 1975) for the method as it is now known. Fission tracks form from the spontaneous fission of ^{238}U. The damage traces left by the fission fragments accumulate throughout the history of a glass or mineral, provided that the glass or mineral remains below a certain temperature. A number of different minerals can be used for fission-track dating, but the three most common minerals are apatite, zircon, and sphene.

Fission tracks are very small damage zones in the structure (≈ 50Å $\times \approx 10$ μm). After the material has been etched, the tracks are enlarged so that they can be seen and counted in an optical microscope. Single crystals ranging in size from larger than 1 cm to as small as about 50 μm can be dated using this method.

Very early in their work, Fleischer, Price, and Walker (1965) discovered that the apparent fission-track age of a mineral or glass was occasionally younger than the age determined by geologic associations or another isotopic age method. This relationship led to their discovery of fission-track annealing (Fleischer and others, 1965). They found that when a uranium-bearing mineral or glass was heated above a certain temperature the fission tracks disappeared. This fading of fission tracks occurs at different temperatures for different minerals. Of the three common minerals used for fission-track dating, apatite is the most temperature sensitive, zircons is less, and sphene is the least sensitive.

In the late 1960's and early 1970's, several detailed geochronologic studies were done using fission tracks (Naeser and Faul, 1969; Naeser and

Dodge, 1969; Wagner and Reimer, 1972; and Wagner and others, 1977). These studies involved dating igneous and metamorphic rocks and showed that apparent fission-track ages of apatite were generally very much younger than the fission-track, K-Ar, or Rb-Sr ages of co-existing minerals. These young apatite fission-track ages were correlated with cooling of the rocks during uplift. For example, Naeser and Faul (1969) reported apatite fission-track ages of 60–70 m.y. in the Precambrian rocks of the Colorado Front Range; co-existing sphene fission-track ages were greater than 1000 m.y. These apatite ages reflected the time of cooling due to uplift during the Laramide orogeny. Wagner, Reimer, and Jager (1977) showed that young apatite fission-track ages could be related to the cooling history of the Central Swiss Alps following uplift during the Alpine orogeny. They were also able to demonstrate a change in fission-track age as a function of altitude. The higher the elevation at which a sample was collected, the older the apatite. Naeser and Forbes (1976) reported apatite fission-track ages relative to depths in two deep drill holes in igneous and metamorphic rocks. In one drill hole (Eielson Air Force Base, Alaska) apatite fission-track ages decreased from 100 m.y. at the surface to 12 m.y. at 3.0-km depth (95° C present temperature). In the second hole (GT-1, 2 Los Alamos, New Mexico), apatite fission-track ages decreased from 70 m.y. to 0 m.y. (135° C, 1.9 km deep). In the deep holes, as the temperature approaches 100° C, the fission-track age of the apatite approaches 0 fission-track years. These changes in fission-track age with depth are in reasonable agreement with extrapolated laboratory annealing data of Naeser and Faul (1969). By dating apatite grains present in a rock, you can often determine when it last cooled to a temperature below 100° C, provided an independent age of formation of the rock is known.

Copyright © 1979, The Society of Economics Paleontologists and Mineralogists

THERMAL HISTORY OF A BASIN

An approach to determining the thermal history of a basin would be to separate apatite crystals from samples of crystalline basement rocks taken from drill holes. If ages could be determined for a number of samples, it would be possible to construct an apparent apatite fission-track-age map. Variations in the ages should indicate where the basin floor had been heated, and the ages would date the last cooling. The older the apparent age, the less heating has occurred. This heating probably occurred during the time of maximum burial, but it is possible that it happened at some later time owing to igneous or hydrothermal activity. Samples collected from the margins of the basin would provide age control. An example of the age variation that might be expected is provided by apparent apatite ages determined in the Front Range of Colorado. Most of the apatite ages in the Precambrian rocks are between 60 m.y. and 100 m.y. These ages reflect the deep burial of this region prior to the Laramide uplift. However, older apatite fission-track ages are found on top of Pikes Peak and Mt. Evans, 400 m.y. and 135 m.y. respectively.

Another approach would be to separate apatite crystals present in sedimentary rocks within the basin through outcrop and drilling. These apatites would record the thermal history of the sediments themselves. Apatite from rocks that were not deeply buried (less than about 2 km) would give an average age of the source terrain of the sediment. A Precambrian age for apatite in unheated Paleozoic or Mesozoic sedimentary rocks is quite possible. As heating (burial) increases, the apparent age will become younger, even younger than the age of the sediment. Apatite from a Permian sandstone could give a Cretaceous age if it were deeply buried and then uplifted in Cretaceous time. Figures 1 and 2 are schematic representations of the variations in apatite age with depth at two times during the history of a basin. Figure 1 represents the time of maximum heating (maximum burial), and Figure 2 represents the present conditions after uplift of the basin.

In Figure 1, three different apatite age groupings are possible. In those rocks that were never heated above about 70° C, the ages will reflect the ages of the source rocks. The deeper rocks, between

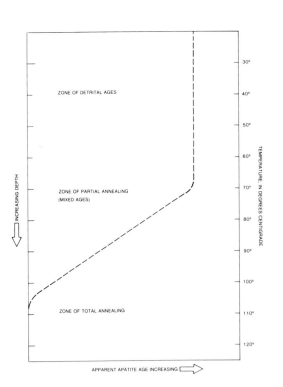

FIG. 1.—The distribution of apparent apatite ages with depth at the time of maximum paleotemperature.

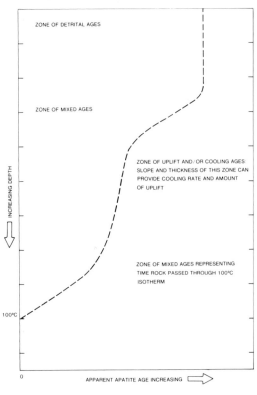

FIG. 2.—Apparent apatite ages with depth after uplift and/or cooling.

70 and 110° C, will have apparent ages that become younger with depth. When the temperature reaches about 110° C, total track annealing (0 apparent age) will occur. Any tracks present before burial as well as any tracks forming from a fission event during burial will be annealed. As long as the apatite remains at a temperature of 110° C or greater, it will have a 0 apparent age.

Figure 2 shows diagramatically what the apatite fission-track ages in the basin, relative to depth, should look like after uplift. Here, there is the possibility of five or more groupings of apatite fission-track ages are possible. Assuming that erosion has not been too extensive, the first grouping will reflect the source-rock ages. The next grouping will be the zone of mixed ages, younger than the source rock-ages but not as young as the uplift ages. The third grouping, probably the most important, is the zone in which the fission tracks in apatite were totally annealed prior to uplift. Below the orogenic uplift zone will be another zone, which represents the eustatic uplift which has continued to the present; each age represents the time that an apatite crystal passed through the 100° C isotherm. The last grouping is again the zone of total fission-track annealing. If the basin has been subjected to two or more periods of rapid uplift, it would be possible to see this, with more of the zones described above being preserved.

Figure 3 is a composite of two sample profiles, one in Utah and the other in Colorado, which illustrate apatite fission-track age zones. The profiles depict the apatite ages as a function of elevation for uplift involving Precambrian metamorphic-igneous rocks: (1) the Farmington Canyon Complex, in the Wasatch Mountains of Utah, just east of Salt Lake City; and (2) the basement rocks of the Mt. Evans area of the Front Range, Colorado, west of Denver. Both areas show a change of apparent apatite fission-track age with altitude. The ages from Mt. Evans simulate the profile for the second and third groupings of Figure 2; the two highest samples were not completely annealed during the Cretaceous burial prior to the Laramide orogeny. The two lower samples were totally annealed prior to the Laramide uplift; they date the cooling at 65 m.y. and, therefore, related to the rapid regional uplift. The ages from the rocks east of Salt Lake city duplicate the profile for zones 3 and 4 from Figure 2. The higher samples from the Farmington Canyon Complex have apparent fission-track ages of about 65 m.y., but the ages decrease with descending altitude to about 10 m.y. at the base of the mountains near the Wasatch fault. Apparently the top of the Laramide uplift can be recorded on Mt. Evans and the base of the Laramide uplift in the Wasatch Mountains.

If zircon and sphene are also dated using fission tracks, higher temperature histories can be documented. Zircon will record the cooling at temperatures between 150° and 200° C, and sphene between 200° and 250° C.

CONCLUSIONS

The apparent fission-track ages of apatite crystals separated from sedimentary and basement crystalline rocks can be used to study the thermal (tectonic) history of a basin or uplifted block. Apatite fission-track ages usually record the last time the rock cooled below 100° C. If fission-track ages of zircon and sphene from the same rock are available, the higher temperature histories can be reconstructed as well.

ACKNOWLEDGEMENTS

The results presented in Figure 3 are preliminary and are a part of a larger study involving the following geologists of the U.S. Geological Survey: B. Bryant (Mt. Evans), M. Crittenden, and M. Sorenson (Wasatch Mts.).

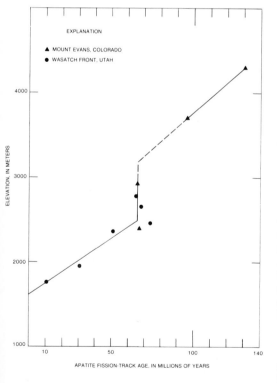

EXPLANATION

▲ MOUNT EVANS, COLORADO
● WASATCH FRONT, UTAH

ELEVATION, IN METERS

APATITE FISSION-TRACK AGE, IN MILLIONS OF YEARS

Fig. 3.—Apatite ages versus elevation on two mountain blocks.

REFERENCES

FLEISCHER, R. L., PRICE, P. B., AND WALKER, R. M., 1965, Effects of temperature, pressure, and ionization on the formation and stability of fission tracks in minerals and glasses: Jour. Geophys. Research, v. 70, p. 1497–1502.

——, ——, AND ——, 1975, Nuclear tracks in solids: Principles and applications: Berkeley, Univ. California Press, 605 p.

NAESER, C. W., AND DODGE, F. C. W., 1969, Fission-track ages of accessory minerals from granitic rocks of the central Sierra Nevada Batholith, California: Geol. Soc. America Bull., v. 80, p. 2201–2212.

—— AND FAUL, H. L., 1969, Fission track annealing in apatite and sphene: Journ. Geophys. Research, v. 74, p. 705–710.

—— AND FORBES, R. B., 1976, Variations of fission-track ages with depth in two deep drill holes: EOS (Am. Geophys. Union Trans.), v. 57, p. 353.

WAGNER, G. A., AND REIMER, G. M., 1972, Fission-track tectonics: The tectonic interpretation of fission track apatite ages: Earth and Planetary Sci. Letters, v. 14, p. 263–268.

——, —— AND JAGER, E., 1977, Cooling ages derived by apatite fission-track, mica Rb-Sr and K-Ar dating: The uplift and cooling history of the central Alps: Memorie Clegli Instituti Geologia e Mineralogia dell Universita di Padova, v. 30, p. 1–28.

SEPM Special Publication No. 26, p. 113–124, March 1979

OXYGEN ISOTOPE GEOTHERMOMETRY OF DIAGENETICALLY ALTERED SHALES[1]

ERIC V. ESLINGER, SAMUEL M. SAVIN, AND HSUEH-WEN YEH
West Georgia College, Carrollton, Georgia 30118;
Case Western Reserve University, Cleveland, Ohio 44106;
and California Institute of Technology, Pasadena, California 91125

ABSTRACT

The maximum temperature to which a shale has been heated as a result of burial can, in some instances, be estimated using oxygen isotope geothermometry. The isotopic fractionation, or difference between O^{18}/O^{16} ratios of two coexisting minerals which have reached isotopic equilibrium with one another, is temperature dependent. Hence, if two coexisting minerals, which have isotopically equilibrated with one another, can be separated from a shale, and if the variation of the equilibrium isotopic fractionation between these minerals is known, the temperature of equilibration can be estimated.

Quartz and coexisting illite or mixed layer illite/smectite is a promising pair for isotope geothermometry of shales. A preliminary equilibrium fractionation curve for this pair is given by:

$$1000 \, ln \, \frac{(O^{18}/O^{16})_{quartz}}{(O^{18}/O^{16})_{illite/smectite}} = [0.95 - 0.24 \, (exp)] \, 10^6 \, T \, (°K)^{-2} + 1.42$$

where *exp* refers to the fraction of layers in the mixed-layer clay which are expandable.

The results of three isotope geothermometry studies are summarized. Mineralogic and O^{18}/O^{16} data for coexisting quartz and illite from the altered volcanic rocks of the active hydrothermal region at Broadlands, New Zealand were used to investigate isotopic equilibration and to serve as a basis for calibration of the quartz-clay isotope geothermometer.

Mineralogic and O^{18}/O^{16} data for coexisting clay-sized quartz and illite/smectite from one of three deep wells in the Gulf Coast indicate that isotopic equilibrium is approached between these two minerals at a well temperature above about 100° C. The illite/smectite apparently exchanges oxygen with pore waters in an approach toward isotopic equilibrium during the reaction: smectite + Al + K → illite + Si. The released Si forms quartz which dominates the finest quartz fractions and forms overgrowths on detrital grains. This quartz apparently forms in isotopic equilibrium with pore waters.

Isotopic temperatures derived from coexisting quartz and illite from the Precambrian Belt argillites range from 225° C to 310° C and generally increase down-section. This temperature range is compatible with the bulk mineralogy and probable depth to which the rocks have been buried.

Oxygen isotope geothermometry can not yet be used routinely. However, it may be more possible to do so after additional information is obtained on factors such as chemical alteration and mineralogic reactions that control isotopic exchange.

INTRODUCTION

Temperatures at which rock formation or alteration occurred can often be estimated from the isotopic compositions of oxygen in coexisting minerals (or a mineral and water). Oxygen isotope geothermometry has been most successfully and frequently used in the study of igneous rocks, middle and high grade metamorphic rocks, and carbonates formed in sedimentary environments.

In this paper, we review progress on the development of techniques of oxygen isotope geothermometry applicable to sediments (especially shales) which have been diagenetically altered at temperatures above those of the depositional environment and below those of biotite grade metamorphism. This temperature range includes those temperatures generally thought to prevail during the maturation of organic matter and the generation of liquid and gaseous hydrocarbons. It is not yet possible to estimate routinely, from oxygen isotopic compositions, the maximum temperatures to which sediments have been heated. However, the results obtained so far are promising and, in addition to providing information about burial temperatures, they have provided insight

[1]Contribution No. 123, Department of Earth Sciences, Case Western Reserve University, and Contribution No. 2964, Division of Geological and Planetary Sciences, California Institute of Technology.

Copyright © 1979, The Society of Economic Paleontologists and Mineralogists

into mineralogical reactions which occur during shale diagenesis.

The application of oxygen isotope measurements in geothermometry is based on the fact that when oxygen-containing phases are in complete thermodynamic equilibrium with one another, the relative proportions of the oxygen isotopes (i.e., O^{18}/O^{16} ratios) in the different phases differ. The magnitude of the isotopic fractionation, or difference between the O^{18}/O^{16} ratios of the two phases[2] in equilibrium, is a function of the nature of the phases and of the temperature of equilibration. For example, isotopic fractionation in the quartz-calcite system can be considered in terms of an exchange reaction between the isotopically pure end members:

$$1/2\ SiO_2^{16} + 1/3\ CaCO_3^{18} \rightleftharpoons 1/2\ SiO_2^{18}$$
$$+ 1/3\ CaCO_3^{16}$$

$$K = \frac{[SiO_2^{18}]^{1/2}\ [CaCO_3^{16}]^{1/3}}{[SiO_2^{16}]^{1/2}\ [CaCO_3^{18}]^{1/3}}$$

K varies with temperature as do all equilibrium constants. The *fractionation factor*, α, is defined as:

$$\alpha_{A\text{-}B} = \frac{(O^{18}/O^{16})_A}{(O^{18}/O^{16})_B}$$

where the subscripts A and B denote two oxygen-containing compounds. For the isotopic exchange reaction in the quartz-calcite system, as written above, making straightforward assumptions concerning the distribution of the isotopes within each phase,

$$\alpha_{SiO_2 - CaCO_3} = K$$

In general, for a reaction written so that n atoms of the isotope are being exchanged, $\alpha = K^{1/n}$. α may be calculated from analytical data using the relationship:

[2] O^{18}/O^{16} ratios are expressed in the usual δ (delta) notation as per mil deviations from the O^{18}/O^{16} ratio of the SMOW standard.

$$\delta = \left[\frac{(O^{18}/O^{16})_{sample} - (O^{18}/O^{16})_{SMOW}}{(O^{18}/O^{16})_{SMOW}}\right] \times 1000$$

$$\alpha_{A\text{-}B} = \frac{1 + \dfrac{\delta_A}{1000}}{1 + \dfrac{\delta_B}{1000}} \approx 1 + \frac{\delta_A - \delta_B}{1000}$$

A useful approximation is:

$$1000\ \ln \alpha_{A\text{-}B} \approx \delta_A - \delta_B$$

If $\alpha_{A\text{-}C}$ and $\alpha_{B\text{-}C}$ are known, it is a simple matter to calculate $\alpha_{A\text{-}B}$:

$$\alpha_{A\text{-}B} = \frac{\alpha_{A\text{-}C}}{\alpha_{B\text{-}C}}$$

Four requirements must be satisfied if meaningful temperatures of diagenesis (or maximum temperatures reached during burial) are to be obtained from isotopic study of a shale:

1. It must be possible to separate at least two coexisting minerals from the rock for isotopic analysis.

2. The magnitude of the isotopic fractionation between the minerals and the manner in which it varies with temperature must be known.

3. The minerals analyzed must have reached isotopic equilibrium with one another at the maximum temperature reached (or at some other identifiable point in the history of the rock).

4. Once isotopic equilibrium between minerals has been achieved, the minerals must not have undergone subsequent (retrograde) isotopic exchange.

These requirements and the extent to which they may be satisfied will be discussed in the sections which follow. Temperatures determined using isotopic geothermometers are referred to as *isotopic temperatures*.

Mixtures of quartz and feldspar can be isolated from shales using the pyrosulfate fusion technique of Syers et al. (1968). Quartz can be isolated from quartz-feldspar mixtures by leaching with hydrofluorosilic acid (Syers et al., 1968).

The isotopic composition of feldspar can be estimated if the isotopic compositions of quartz and the quartz-feldspar mixture as well as the relative proportions of quartz and feldspar in the mixture are known. However, the errors in the $\delta\ O^{18}$ values of feldspars estimated in this way are frequently so large as to render them of little use for isotope geothermometry (Eslinger, 1971).

Illite or mixed-layer illite/smectite is the dominant mineral in the finest size fractions (finer than 0.1 μm) of many shales. Therefore, it can frequently be concentrated by size-separation following standard treatments (Jackson, 1969) to remove carbonates, organic matter, and oxides of iron and manganese. Associated clay-size chlorite can often be destroyed chemically. None of the chemical treatments affect the isotopic composition of the remaining clay minerals (Eslinger, 1971; Yeh, 1974).

Carbonates need not be separated prior to isotopic analysis. The extraction of CO_2 from carbonates by reaction with phosphoric acid (McCrea, 1950) is not affected by the presence of silicates.

Oxygen is liberated from silicates by reaction with hot F_2 (Taylor and Epstein, 1962) or BrF_5 (Clayton and Mayeda, 1963). The oxygen is converted to CO_2 by reaction with hot carbon. The isotopic composition of the CO_2 is measured by comparison with a standard on a Nier-type dual collector mass spectrometer (Nier, 1947; McKinney *et al.*, 1950).

CALIBRATION OF ISOTOPE GEOTHERMOMETERS

Three approaches have been used in the determination of the magnitude and temperature dependence of isotopic fractionations between phases: (1) calculation using statistical mechanical theory; (2) isotopic equilibration or exchange of phases (commonly a mineral and water) in the laboratory under controlled conditions; and (3) estimation based on the isotopic compositions of naturally occurring phases which formed or exchanged under known or inferred conditions. The results of estimates obtained for the same system using the different techniques are not always in agreement, and the calibration curves of many geothermometers are subject to revision as new data are obtained.

Theoretical considerations of systems of ideal gases indicate that in the temperature ranges normally encountered in geologic systems ln α should vary linearly with T^{-2} where T is the temperature in degrees Kelvin. Laboratory investigations indicate that in many real mineral or mineral-water systems isotopic fractionations over fairly large temperature ranges can be expressed by equations of the form

$$1000 \ln \alpha = A + BT^{-2}$$

Isotopic fractionation data are therefore commonly plotted on graphs of 1000 ln α vs. T^{-2}, and in many instances linear extrapolations have been made to temperatures below or above those for which data are available.

Quartz is one of the minerals which has proven most useful in isotopic studies of diagenetically altered shales, and accurate knowledge of its isotopic behavior is most desirable. Unfortunately, slow reaction rates make isotopic exchange experiments involving quartz at low temperatures difficult or impractical. The lowest temperature for which experimental isotopic data are available in the quartz-water system is 195° C (Clayton *et al.*, 1972). The accuracy of the isotopic fractionation curve of Clayton *et al.* (1972) has been discussed by Bottinga and Javoy (1973) and Taylor (1974) who have proposed other curves. Published estimates of the quartz-water fractionation disagree by less than 1 or 2 per mil throughout most of the diagenetic temperature range. In that temperature range this could cause isotopic temperatures to be in error by as much as 50° C. Quartz-calcite and quartz-feldspar isotopic temperatures of shales published by Eslinger and Savin (1973b) and Yeh and Savin (1977) have been based in part on extrapolation to low temperatures of the quartz-water fractionation curve of Clayton *et al.* (1972). However, the isotopic geothermometers which have been applied most successfully to diagenetically altered shales are the quartz-clay geothermometers. While the calibration curves of these geothermometers are not inconsistent with the quartz-water calibration curve of Clayton *et al.* (1972), they can be derived largely independently of that curve.

Isotopic fractionations between calcite and water have been determined experimentally by O'Neil *et al.* (1969) in the temperature range 0° to 500° C. Isotopic fractionations between feldspars of different compositions and water between 350° and 800° C have been measured by O'Neil and Taylor (1967). These calcite-water fractionations and feldspar-water fractionations extrapolated to low temperatures have been combined with the quartz-water fractionation of Clayton *et al.* (1972) to yield quartz-calcite and feldspar-calcite fractionation curves.

Empirical calibration of the quartz-illite fractionation: Ohaki-Broadlands, New Zealand.—A quartz-illite isotopic fractionation curve was determined using data obtained in an isotopic and mineralogic study of hydrothermally altered volcanic rock from a borehole in the Ohaki-Broadlands geothermal area of New Zealand (Eslinger and Savin, 1973a). In Figure 1 are shown the temperature and the oxygen isotopic compositions of the mineral phases plotted against sample depth. Primary igneous rocks of the kind found in the region have δ O[18] values between +6 and +9 per mil (Taylor, 1968). The trend toward lower δ O[18] values of the minerals with depth reflects isotopic exchange with the hydrothermal waters at temperatures which increase with depth. The geothermal water originates as meteoric water which in that region has a δ O[18] value of about −6.0 per mil.

In Figure 2 are shown the fractionations between co-existing quartz and illite from seven

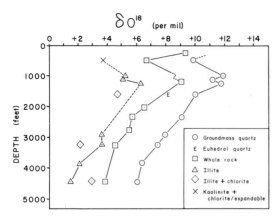

$\delta\, O^{18}$ (per mil)

FIG. 1.—Oxygen isotope ratios of whole rock samples and mineral separates from borehole Br 16 plotted versus depth within the hole. Ohaki-Broadlands, New Zealand geothermal area (Eslinger and Savin, 1973a).

samples plotted against measured borehole temperatures. The solid line through the points is a regression line with the equation

$$1000\,\ln\alpha_{\text{quartz-illite}} = 0.95\,(10^6\,T^{-2}) + 0.88$$

This equation describes the fractionation between quartz and illite in the temperature range 160° to 270° C provided three conditions have been satisfied for each sample: (1) both quartz and illite in each sample must have equilibrated isotopically with water of the same isotopic composition; (2) the two minerals must have equilibrated at the same temperature; and (3) the temperature of equilibration must be that which prevailed when borehole temperatures were measured and must be accurately known.

The quartz-muscovite fractionation curve calculated from the higher temperature quartz-water fractionations of Clayton *et al.* (1972) and muscovite-water fractionation of O'Neil and Taylor (1969) has the equation

$$1000\,\ln\alpha_{\text{quartz-muscovite}} = 1.00\,(10^6\,T^{-2}) + 0.49$$

This curve is shown as the dashed line of Figure 2. The similarity of the quartz-illite curve to the quartz-muscovite curve determined in this way is apparent. This similarity may be fortuitous in view of the uncertainty, discussed above, in the magnitude of quartz-water isotopic fractionations, the large temperature range over which the muscovite-water curve was extrapolated, and the small chemical and structural differences between illite and muscovite. However, the similarity between the two curves does suggest that isotopic equilibrium was closely approached in the samples

from Broadlands, New Zealand. Eslinger and Savin (1973b) and Yeh and Savin (1977) used the quartz-illite fractionation curve derived from the Broadlands, New Zealand, study in the work on diagenetically altered shales discussed below.

Only two of the samples from the Broadlands, New Zealand, borehole contained calcite detectable by X-ray diffraction. The calcite of the sample from a depth of 1000 feet (t = 160° C) was not in isotopic equilibrium with coexisting quartz and illite. Oxygen isotopic equilibrium among all three phases was closely approached in the sample from 4450 feet (t = 270° C). These results are similar to those found by Clayton and Steiner (1975) in a study of the Wairakei, New Zealand, geothermal area. They found that the calcite from the shallower, cooler regions tended to be out of isotopic equilibrium with the modern environment while isotopic equilibrium between calcite and geothermal fluid did exist in deeper, hotter regions. They interpreted the disequilibrium between calcite and the geothermal fluids of shallow regions as reflecting formation of the calcite under temperature conditions different from those which now prevail, and lack of subsequent isotopic re-equilibration.

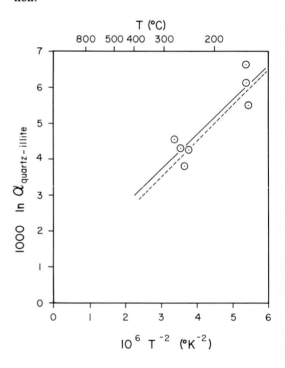

FIG. 2.—$1000\,\ln\alpha_{\text{quartz-illite}}$ versus $10^6 T^{-2}$. Temperatures are measured borehole temperatures. Solid line is a regression line through the date. Ohaki-Broadlands, New Zealand geothermal area (Eslinger and Savin, 1973a). Dashed line is extrapolation of high temperature experimental data for quartz and muscovite.

Estimation of oxygen isotope fractionations between quartz and mixed-layer illite/smectites.— Many diagenetically altered shales contain mixed-layer illite/smectite rather than illite as their dominant clay mineral. The isotopic behavior of the mixed-layer phase might be expected to be similar but not identical to that of illite. Using extrapolated values of the quartz-illite (Eslinger and Savin, 1973a) and quartz-water (Clayton *et al.*, 1972) fractionations and the isotopic composition of an authigenic marine smectite, Yeh (1974) derived the following preliminary equation for the quartz-illite/smectite geothermometer:

$$1000 \ln \alpha_{quartz-illite/smectite} = [0.95$$
$$- 0.24(\text{expandability})] \, 10^6 \, T^{-2} + 1.42$$

where "expandability" is the fraction of layers in the mixed-layer clay which are expandable.

ISOTOPE GEOTHERMOMETRY OF DIAGENETICALLY ALTERED GULF COAST SHALES

Oxygen isotope geothermometry has been attempted on samples from three wells drilled through sediments of the Gulf Coast (Yeh and Savin, 1977). Of these wells (CWRU Gulf Coast Wells No. 6, 9, and 10), one (Well No. 6) also has been the object of detailed mineralogical, chemical and geochronological study (Hower *et al.*, 1976; Aronson and Hower, 1976).

Samples were collected from Well No. 6 at depths from 1300 to 5500 meters. Logged temperatures increased with depth from about 44° C at 1300 meters to a maximum of about 170° C at 5500 meters. Samples were Late Oligocene to Early Miocene in age. The main mineralogic trends with depths, interpreted by Hower *et al.* (1976) from X-ray diffraction studies of the finer-than-0.5 μm fraction, are:

1. Progressive conversion of a mixed-layer illite/smectite with a high percentage of expandable (smectite) layers to a mixed-layer illite/smectite with a low percentage of expandable layers.
2. The decomposition of potassium feldspar and coarse-grained mica.
3. The decomposition of calcite.
4. The formation of chlorite.

Although whole-rock chemistry does not change appreciably with depth, chemical redistribution among the different phases is apparent. Fine grained fractions exhibit an increase in K and Al and a decrease in Si. This reflects an overall chemical process which can be summarized

$$\text{Smectite} + Al^{+3} + K^+ \rightleftharpoons \text{illite} + Si^{+4}$$

The Al and K are supplied by the breakdown of mica and K-feldspar (Hower *et al.*, 1976).

Oxygen isotopic compositions of different size fractions of clay (predominantly mixed-layer illite/smectite) and quartz are shown plotted vs. well depth in Figures 3 and 4. The expandability of the illite/smectite of the different size fractions (from Hower *et al.*, 1976) is shown in Figure 5. The interpretation of the isotopic data (Yeh and Savin, 1977) may be summarized as follows:

1. The scatter of isotopic compositions among the clays in the upper portions of the well indicates isotopic disequilibrium within individual samples reflecting the diverse origins of different detrital grains. The departure from isotopic equilibrium decreases with increasing depth, presumably as the clays exchange with pore waters. The finest size fractions are probably closest to isotope equilibrium with the pore water. The rate of isotopic exchange of clays with pore water appears to be accelerated during the conversion of smectite layers to illite layers.

2. The quartz in each sample is isotopically heterogeneous. There is no evidence for isotopic exchange between detrital quartz and pore water at any depth in this well. However, quartz formed during the conversion of smectite to illite layers undoubtedly forms in equilibrium with pore water. This newly formed quartz dominates the finest quartz fractions and forms overgrowths on detrital grains.

Isotopic temperatures were calculated from the isotopic compositions of the finest quartz (0.1 to 0.5 μm) and clay (finer-than-0.1 μm) separated from the rocks (Yeh and Savin, 1977). Logged well temperatures are shown plotted vs. the calculated isotopic temperatures in Figure 6. At logged temperatures above about 85° C there is good agreement between the isotopic temperatures and the temperatures measured in the well. These results suggest that isotope geothermometry is a promising method for the determination of diagenetic temperatures when those temperatures are above about 85° C.

The results of less detailed studies of CWRU Gulf Coast Wells 9 and 10 are similar to those for Well 6. In both wells, isotopic temperatures approached logged temperatures more closely with increasing depth (Figs. 7, 8). However, in neither well was satisfactory agreement achieved between the isotopic and logged temperatures even at the maximum logged temperatures (111° and 120° C). The cause of the discordancy between logged and measured temperatures is not known, although it is suspected that some of the quartz analyzed may have been detrital rather than diagenetic (Yeh and Savin, 1977). Better results from studies of this type may be achieved by analyzing even finer size fractions of quartz which may necessitate the processing of larger rock samples.

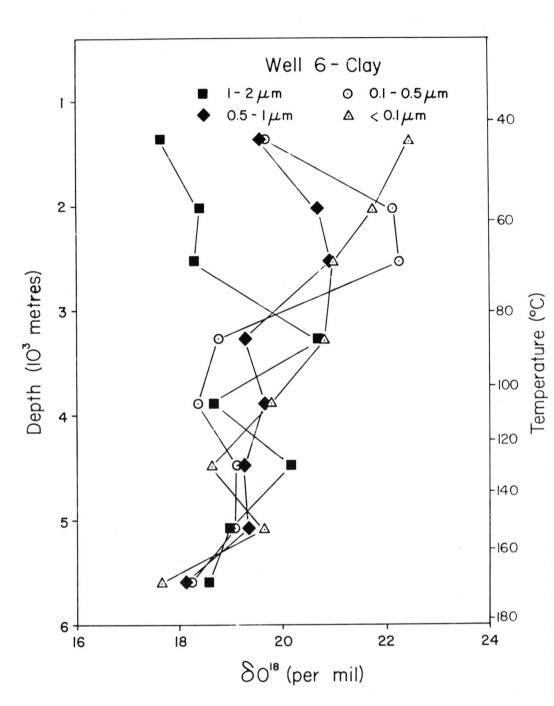

Fig. 3.—Oxygen isotope ratios of different size fractions of clay (predominantly mixed-layer illite/smectite) plotted versus depth. CWRU Gulf Coast Well No. 6 (Yeh and Savin, 1977).

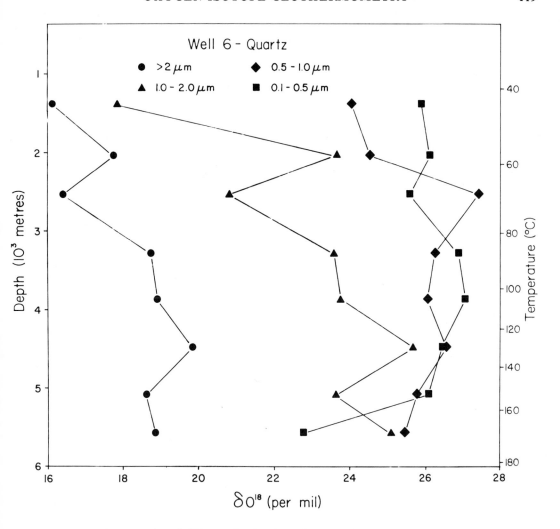

Fig. 4.—Oxygen isotope ratios of different size fractions of quartz plotted versus depth. CWRU Gulf Coast Well No. 6 (Yeh and Savin, 1977).

Quartz-calcite isotopic temperatures that were calculated for all three Gulf Coast Wells were unreasonable. In shale sequences similar to those of the Gulf Coast, calcite apparently cannot be used for isotopic geothermometry. Yeh (1974) suggested that calcite may have continued to undergo isotopic exchange with pore waters of different isotopic compositions after the isotopic compositions of quartz and clay had ceased to change.

Some uncertainty in quartz-illite/smectite isotopic temperatures results from errors in the determination of the expandability of the mixed-layer clay. An error of about 10 percent in the expandability would lead to an error in isotopic temperature of about 10° C in the temperature range 40° to 150° C. This uncertainty must be added to that due to the error in the isotopic measurements. As may be seen in Figure 2, a result of the T^{-2} dependence of the quartz-illite isotopic fractionation factor is that isotopic temperatures are subject to greater uncertainty the higher the temperature of equilibration. Probably the best accuracy which can be expected with the quartz-illite/smectite geothermometer is $\pm 15°$ C when temperatures of equilibration are 40° C and $\pm 30°$ C when temperatures of equilibration are 150° C (Yeh, 1974).

ISOTOPE GEOTHERMOMETRY OF ROCKS FROM THE BELT SUPERGROUP

The Gulf Coast shales were, when sampled, at the maximum temperatures to which they had been heated. A useful geothermometric technique

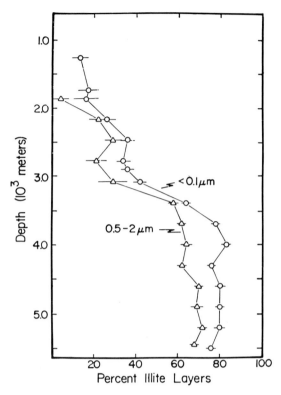

FIG. 5.—Proportion of illite layers in mixed-layer illite/smectities plotted versus depth in the finest and coarsest clay fractions, CWRU Gulf Coast Well No. 6 (Hower *et al.*, 1976).

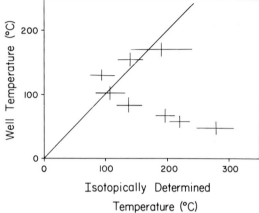

FIG. 6.—Logged well temperatures versus calculated isotopic temperatures. CWRU Gulf Coast Well No. 6 (Yeh and Savin, 1977).

requires that the isotopic compositions acquired at the maximum temperature be retained if the temperature of the rock should subsequently be lowered. Some indication that retrograde isotopic exchange is not a serious problem in geothermometric studies of shales is provided by the results of Eslinger and Savin (1973b) on outcrop samples from the Precambrian Belt Supergroup.

The Belt Supergroup is a sequence of relatively undeformed argillites, carbonates and quartzites formed about 1325 to 760 million years ago. It crops out mostly in Idaho, Montana, and British Columbia (Smith and Barnes, 1966; Obradovich and Peterman, 1968; Goldich *et al.*, 1959). The thickness of the unit ranges from about 1400 meters near Great Falls, Montana (Weed, 1900) to at least 11,000 meters at Pend Oreille Lake, Idaho (Harrison and Jobin, 1963). The thickness of the section is such that burial metamorphism is likely to have occurred within the rocks. Maxwell and Hower (1967) found evidence of such diagenesis in a detailed study of the dioctahedral micas in the less-than-2.0 μm size fraction of the rocks. With increasing depth (increasing tempera-

ture) in the section, the 1Md polytype of illite is converted into the higher temperature 2M polytype. This mineralogic trend is accompanied by textural changes and in the samples from the bottom of the thick section in Idaho the biotite isograd was reached.

Samples for isotopic study were collected over a 2000 m thick section of the Belt Supergroup, Glacier National Park, Montana. The rocks are composed of quartz, feldspar, illite, chlorite and sometimes calcite and/or dolomite. No kaolinite or mixed-layer phases were detected. An increase in the ratio 1Md/1Md + 2M illite with depth was found, similar to that observed by Maxwell and Hower (1967).

Isotopic compositions of the whole rock, quartz (bulk), clay (<0.5 μm size fraction; mostly illite; corrected for quartz contamination), and feldspar (mass balance calculation from analyses of quartz and quartz-feldspar mixtures) are plotted in Figure 9 versus stratigraphic position. In most samples, the minerals ranked in order of decreasing O^{18}/O^{16} ratio are: quartz, feldspar, and clay. This is consistent with the ranking observed in igneous and metamorphic rocks and also that expected on the basis of the experimental isotopic-equilibration studies discussed previously.

Isotopic temperatures were calculated for five samples using the quartz-illite geothermometer (Eslinger and Savin, 1973b). These temperatures are plotted in Figure 10 versus stratigraphic position. The isotopic temperatures range from 225° C to 310° C. These temperatures are consistent with the mineralogy and the regression line through the points in Figure 10 indicates a not unreasonable geothermal gradient of about 36° C/km. Also, an

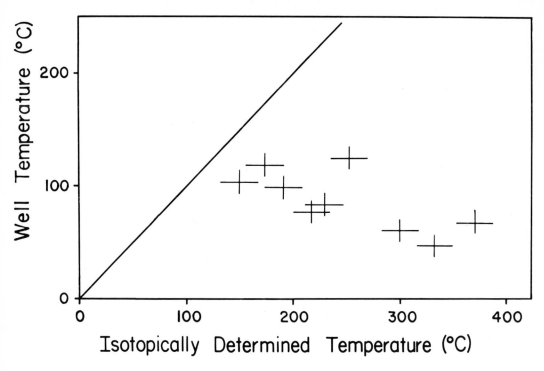

FIG. 7.—Logged well temperatures versus calculated isotopic temperatures. CWRU Gulf Coast Well No. 9, (Yeh and Savin, 1977).

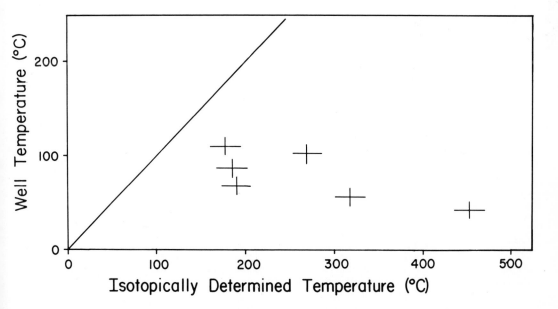

FIG. 8.—Logged well temperatures versus calculated isotopic temperatures. CWRU Gulf Coast Well No. 10 (Yeh and Savin, 1977).

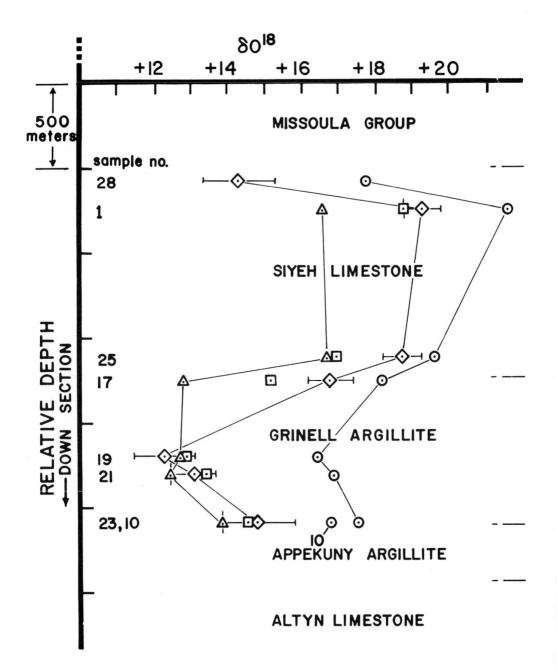

Fig. 9.—Oxygen isotope ratios of whole rock, quartz, feldspar, and clay plotted versus relative stratigraphic position. *Squares,* whole rock; *circles,* quartz; *diamonds,* feldspar; *triangles,* clay (mostly illite). Belt Supergroup, Glacier National Park, Montana (Eslinger and Savin, 1973b).

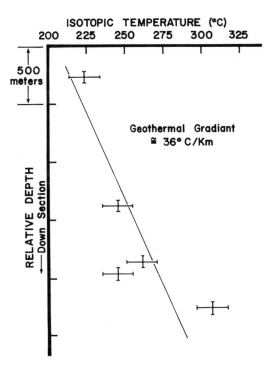

FIG. 10.—Correlation between quartz-illite isotopic temperatures and relative stratigraphic position. Belt Supergroup, Glacier National Park, Montana (Eslinger and Savin, 1973b).

extrapolation of this regression line to surface temperatures indicates that there was about 5500 meters of overburden on top of the section at the time of isotopic quenching. This overburden thickness compares with a thickness of 3000 to 6000 meters for the Missoula Group which is the uppermost unit of the Belt Supergroup and which immediately overlies the stratigraphically highest sample used in this study. Much more work would be necessary to firmly establish the ambient geothermal gradient extant during burial. The main conclusions of this study are that isotopic temperatures generally increase down-section, that the temperature range is very reasonable, and that there is no evidence of retrograde isotopic exchange.

DISCUSSION

Work done to date gives promise that oxygen isotope geothermometry may become a useful technique for determining maximum temperatures of burial of diagenetically altered shales. However, it is not yet possible to routinely apply the technique to shales.

It must still be demonstrated that the technique can give consistently useful results in shale sequences which are now at their maximum temperatures, such as the Gulf Coast shales. It remains to be seen whether better results can be obtained from samples such as those from Gulf Coast Wells 9 and 10 by analyzing finer size fractions of quartz as was proposed by Yeh and Savin (1977). More information is also required on the mechanisms by which minerals undergo isotopic exchange. Since isotopic exchange between quartz or clay and water is negligibly slow at temperatures less than about 150° C, isotopic geothermometry in the lower temperature ranges may be applicable only for rocks in which minerals have become chemically altered or have been newly formed at the maximum temperature reached. Chemical alteration would require the breaking of chemical bonds which would in turn open up the structure to isotopic exchange with pore water. Rocks such as those of the Gulf Coast, in which smectite layers are converted to illite layers with concommitant crystallization of quartz, would satisfy this criteria over a wide range of temperatures. Shales in which the original detritus was composed primarily of illite would not. However, there is indication (Savin, unpublished data) that at temperatures above 150° or 160° C, in at least some shales, oxygen isotope exchange between fine-grained quartz or clay and pore water may proceed sufficiently rapidly to permit isotopic equilibration in the absence of obvious chemical or mineralogical reaction.

Finally, the importance of retrograde exchange in modifying the isotopic record needs further study.

ACKNOWLEDGEMENTS

This work was supported by the National Science Foundation under Grants DES 75-20431 and OCE 76-01457.

REFERENCES

ARONSON, J., AND HOWER, J., 1976, Mechanism of burial metamorphism of argillaceous sediment: 2. Radiogenic argon evidence: Geol. Soc. America Bull., v. 87, p. 738–744.

BOTTINGA, Y., AND JAVOY, M., 1973, Comments on oxygen isotope geothermometry: Earth and Planetary Sci. Letters, v. 20, p. 250–265.

CLAYTON, R. N., AND MAYEDA, T. K., 1963, The use of bromine pentafluoride in the extraction of oxygen from oxides and silicates for isotopic analysis: Geochim. et Cosmochim. Acta, v. 27, p. 43–52.

——, O'NEIL, J. R., AND MAYEDA, T. K., 1972, Oxygen isotope exchange between quartz and water: Jour. Geophys. Research, v. 77, p. 3057–3067.

—— AND STEINER, A., 1975, Oxygen isotope studies of the geothermal system at Wairakei, New Zealand: Geochim. et Cosmochim. Acta, v. 39, p. 1179–1186.

ESLINGER, E. V., 1971, Mineralogy and oxygen isotope ratios of hydrothermal and low-grade metamorphic argillaceous rocks: PhD. Diss., Case Western Reserve Univ., 205 p.

—— AND SAVIN, S., 1973a, Mineralogy and oxygen isotope geochemistry of the hydrothermally altered rocks of the Ohaki-Broadlands, New Zealand geothermal area: Am. Jour. Sci., v. 273, p. 240–267.

—— AND ——, 1973b, Oxygen isotope geothermometry of the burial metamorphic rocks of the Precambrian Belt Supergroup, Glacier National Park, Montana: Geol. Soc. America Bull., v. 84, p. 2549–2560.

GOLDICH, S. S., BAADSGAARD, H., EDWARDS, G., AND WEAVER, C. E., 1959, Investigations in radioactivity-dating of sediments: Am. Assoc. Petroleum Geologists Bull., v. 43, p. 654–662.

HARRISON, J. E., AND JOBIN, D. A., 1963, Geology of the Clark Fork Quadrangle, Idaho-Montana: U. S. Geol. Survey Bull. 1141-K, 38 p.

HOWER, J., ESLINGER, E., HOWER, M., AND PERRY, E., 1976, Mechanism of burial metamorphism of argillaceous sediment: 1. Mineralogic and chemical evidence: Geol. Soc. America Bull., v. 87, p. 725–737.

JACKSON, M. L., 1969, Soil chemical analysis—Advanced course: Univ. Wisconsin-Madison College of Agriculture, Dept. Soils, 894 p.

MAXWELL, D. T., AND HOWER, J., 1967, High-grade diagenesis and low-grade metamorphism of illite in the Precambrian Belt Series: Am. Mineralogist, v. 52, p. 843–857.

McCREA, J. M., 1950, On the isotopic chemistry of carbonates and a paleotemperature scale: Jour. Chem. Physics, v. 18, p. 849–857.

McKINNEY, C. R., McCREA, J. M., EPSTEIN, S., ALLEN, H. A., AND UREY, H. C., 1950, Improvements in mass spectrometers for the measurement of small differences in isotopic abundance ratios: Rev. Sci. Instruments, v. 21, p. 724–730.

NIER, A. O. C., 1947, A mass spectrometer for isotope and gas analysis: Rev. Sci. Instruments, v. 18, p. 398–411.

OBRADOVICH, J. D., AND PETERMAN, Z. D., 1968, Geochronology of the Belt Series, Montana: Canadian Jour. Earth Sci., v. 5, p. 737–747.

O'NEIL, J. R., CLAYTON, R. N., AND MAYEDA, T. K., 1969, Oxygen isotope fractionation in divalent metal carbonates: Jour. Chem. Physics, v. 51, p. 5547–5558.

—— AND TAYLOR, H. P., JR., 1967, The oxygen isotope and cation exchange chemistry of feldspars: Am. Mineralogist, v. 52, p. 1414–1437.

—— AND ——, 1969, Oxygen isotope equilibrium between muscovite and water: Jour. Geophys. Research, v. 25, p. 6012–6022.

SMITH, A. G., AND BARNES, W. C., 1966, Correlation of and facies changes in the carbonaceous, calcareous, and dolomitic formations of the Precambrian Belt-Purcell Supergroup: Geol. Soc. America Bull., v. 77, p. 1399–1426.

SYERS, J. K., CHAPMAN, S. L., JACKSON, M. L., REX, R. W., AND CLAYTON, R. N., 1968, Quartz isolation from rocks, sediments, and soils for determination of oxygen isotopic composition: Geochim. et Cosmochim. Acta, v. 32, p. 1022–1025.

TAYLOR, H. P., JR., 1968, The oxygen isotope geochemistry of igneous rocks: Contr. Mineralogy and Petrology, v. 19, p. 1–71.

——, 1974, The application of oxygen and hydrogen isotope studies to problems of hydrothermal alteration and ore deposition: Econ. Geology, v. 69, p. 843–883.

—— AND EPSTEIN, S., 1962, Relationship between O^{18}/O^{16} ratios of coexisting minerals of igneous and metamorphic rocks. Pt. I. Principles and experimental results: Geol. Soc. America Bull., v. 73, p. 461–480.

WEED, W. H., 1900, Geology of the Little Belt Mountains, Montana: U. S. Geol. Survey Ann. Rep., v. 20, pt. 3, p. 257–461.

YEH, H., 1974, Oxygen isotope studies of ocean sediments during sedimentation and burial diagenesis: PhD. Diss., Case Western Reserve Univ.

—— AND SAVIN, S., 1977, The mechanism of burial diagenetic reactions in argillaceous sediments: 3. Oxygen isotope evidence: Geol. Soc. America Bull., v. 88. 1321–1330.

SEPM Special Publication No. 26, p. 125–126, March 1979

PART 2. DIAGENESIS AS IT AFFECTS CLASTIC RESERVOIRS—INTRODUCTION

PAUL R. SCHLUGER
General Crude Oil Co., Denver, Colorado 80202

This collection of papers is the outgrowth of a symposium entitled "Diagenesis as it affects clastic reservoirs"; a symposium presented in Denver, Colorado, April 2–6, 1977, as part of the Rocky Mountain Section AAPG-SEPM, 26th Annual Meeting. The symposium was organized and chaired by Paul R. Schluger and was presented during a day and a half of meetings. The idea for a special symposium originated with the Rocky Mountain Section of the Society of Economic Paleontologists and Mineralogists and was particularly encouraged by its president (1975–1976), Thomas S. Ahlbrandt.

The Rocky Mountain Section of the Society of Economic Paleontologists and Mineralogists wishes to dedicate this volume to furthering the study and recognition of diagenesis in clastic rocks and to belatedly honor the 50th anniversary of SEPM.

Diagenesis has been attracting an ever increasing amount of attention in recent years, especially in the petroleum industry. The obvious oil and gas seeps, which helped launch the petroleum industry as initiated by E. L. Drake in 1859, and the less obvious subsurface structural traps and reservoirs are becoming increasingly difficult to find. The subtle stratigraphic traps and reservoirs will increasingly become the prospects of the future. They frequently are controlled by both depositional and diagenetic processes, processes which have often been ignored or neglected when considering the play and seem to be found more frequently by accident than by design.

It is still relatively easy to find numerous publications and dissertations concerned with clastic rocks which ignore or barely mention diagenesis. Perhaps diagenesis has been neglected because the geologist has been examining the forest in such detail that he or she often fails to observe the leaves. Sometimes diagenesis is foreceably ignored in industry because all too many influential petroleum geologists still maintain that not a drop of oil has been found with a microscope. In any case, it is apparent that geologists are going to be forced to look at some of the finer details of diagenesis in order to find the oil and gas held in the subtle diagenetically controlled stratigraphic traps.

The papers presented in this volume should be used as a guidebook of general principles governing diagenesis in clastic rocks with special emphasis on petroleum reservoirs. Three subdivisions of the papers are noticeable. The first group of papers deals with major principles. John B. Hayes and Harvey Blatt in two separate papers examine the generation and destruction of porosity from physical and geochemical viewpoints. Emphasis is placed on the tectonic settings, the composition and weathering regime and the environments of deposition of the sediments. Edward Pittman examines the basics of porosity type and associated permeabilities and relates them to diagenetic modifications. Volkmar Schmidt and David McDonald further examine the diagenetic modifications of porosity, especially secondary porosity, and in a second shorter paper give criteria for the recognition of secondary porosity. Chemical considerations are examined in some detail in two papers, one by Ronald Surdam and James Boles, and the other by James Wood and Ronald Surdam.

The second group of papers deals with major geographic areas of interest and includes William Galloway's paper on arc-derived sandstones and their implications for petroleum exploration. Robert C. Morris et al. examine the deep-water sandstones of the Ouachita Mountains, and David K. Davies et al. present a study of Tertiary volcaniclastics in Guatemala.

The final group of papers deals with specific, smaller scale (formations or fields), problems of diagenesis and includes Larry K. Burns and Frank Ethridge's study of the Umpqua Formation, David Mankiewicz and James Steidtmann's paper on the Tensleep Sandstone, Roderick Tillman and William Almon's study of the Frontier Formation of the Spearhead Ranch Field, William Almon and David K. Davies' examination of the Muddy Sandstone, Kenneth O. Stanley and L. V. Benson's inspection of the High Plains Sequence, and finally the study by I. E. Odom et al. of the St. Peter Sandstone.

I believe the reader will find this collection of papers only a starting point for what will probably be a burst of interest in diagenesis. It became abundantly clear to those of us attending the symposium in Denver that we have focused our attention on diagenesis as a response to a given set of physical and chemical parameters. What we have not attempted, what we have

Copyright © 1979, The Society of Economic
Paleontologists and Mineralogists

alluded to, and what we leave for a future symposium is the delineation of the models and the tectonic styles which are the driving mechanisms behind the response.

Far too many people were of great help in assisting with the organization of the symposium, as critical reviewers and manuscript editors to be listed here, but their aid is greatly appreciated. Mobil Oil Corporation is to be thanked for having been so supportive of my early organizational efforts. Finally, the authors are to be specially thanked for their patience, endurance and persistence.

. SEPM Special Publication No. 26, p. 127–139, March 1979

SANDSTONE DIAGENESIS—THE HOLE TRUTH

JOHN B. HAYES

Marathon Oil Company, Littleton, Colorado 80160

ABSTRACT

Four truths about holes in sandstone underlie current research and unsolved problems of sandstone diagenesis. First, primary intergranular porosity and permeability of sand are greatly reduced and subject to total destruction in the early stages of burial diagenesis. Compaction, cementation, recrystallization, and replacement are widely recognized porosity-reducing mechanisms. Rate of porosity loss with depth is related mainly to original sand composition.

Second, at later stages of diagenesis, secondary porosity can be produced by dissolution of detrital and authigenic minerals. Porosity can be restored and enhanced at depth. Porosity of many major hydrocarbon reservoirs is mainly secondary, a fact just recently documented in the literature. Secondary porosity must be formed before hydrocarbon migration if it is to serve as reservoir porosity. Secondary porosity can be destroyed diagenetically, but it will persist to greater depths than will primary porosity.

Third, chemical diagenesis of sandstones is a kinetic process; mineral matter is dissolved, transferred, and precipitated by aqueous solutions moving through sandstones. The main source of water is from dewatering of shales interbedded with sandstones. Reconstruction of the chemical evolution of moving water, of its flow paths through a basin, and of the time of migration are the keys to predicting subsurface distribution of sandstone porosity. Mathematical modeling of hydrodynamics and mineral reactions by means of computer simulation is a promising approach to porosity prediction.

Fourth, the course of sandstone diagenesis in a given basin is programmed by the preburial, prediagenetic factors of provenance, depositional environments, and tectonic setting. These interrelated factors influence sand composition and texture, which in turn govern mineral reactions and fluid-flow rates.

Diagenetic processes determine porosity in terms of origin, amount, subsurface distribution, pore-size distribution, pore shape, surface area, and attendant permeability. Thus, diagenetic history must be taken into account by geologists and engineers in the petroleum industry. Rewards from studies of diagenesis will be sharper porosity prediction in exploration and more efficient management of rock-fluid interactions in producing reservoirs.

INTRODUCTION

Current studies of sandstone diagenesis and applications thereof in the petroleum industry are based on several related themes.

1. Adequate reservoir porosity and permeability, among other requirements, are essential for hydrocarbon accumulations.

2. Present-day porosity and permeability of a potential reservoir are the products of diagenetic modification of original porosity.

3. Other than compaction, the important porosity-modifying diagenetic processes are chemical reactions between minerals and migrating pore fluids.

4. The course of sandstone diagenesis is determined to a degree by preburial, prediagenetic tectonic setting, provenance, and depositional environments.

Each paper given for the SEPM symposium[1] on sandstone diagenesis embraced one or more of these themes. This paper is based on the lead-off talk of the symposium, and is a brief overview of recent progress and remaining problems. It is drawn from my struggle with sandstone diagenesis since 1969 at the Denver Research Center of Marathon Oil Company. The title does not imply that the entire truth will be revealed, but rather that some truths about holes in sandstone will be presented.

POROSITY REDUCTION

The first of these truths is that sand, when deposited by water or wind, has initial porosity on the order of 35 to 40 percent and permeability of several darcys, which are considered very high values. However, typical oil- or gas-reservoir sandstones have porosities ranging between 10 and 25 percent, and permeabilities of a few to a few hundred millidarcys. So, during diagenesis, considerable primary porosity and permeability must be destroyed. Virtually every paper given for the symposium considers porosity-reducing processes in specific sandstones. Taken together, the examples published in this volume represent a wide range of initial compositions, from the quartzose (Odom and others; Mankiewicz and

[1]AAPG-SEPM Rocky Mountain Section Meeting, April 2–6, 1977, Denver, Colorado: SEPM Special Symposium entitled, "Diagenesis as it affects clastic reservoirs".

Copyright © 1979, The Society of Economic Paleontologists and Mineralogists

Steidtmann), to the arkosic (Stanley and Benson), to the lithic and volcanogenic (Surdam and Boles; Galloway; Davies and others; Burns and Ethridge).

Porosity-reducing processes can be classified as: (1) chemical (cementation, replacement, recrystallization); (2) mechanical (compaction by plastic deformation and fracture of detrital grains); (3) combination (alteration of a detrital grain accompanied by compaction). Table 1 is a list of authigenic, void-filling and replacement minerals I have observed in sandstones. Other minerals could be added to this list by examining the literature. These minerals are the products of chemical processes, mainly precipitation from aqueous solutions. Silica and carbonate cements are abundant, widely recognized, and well documented in the literature. However, as more studies are published about the quartz-poor, arkosic and lithic sandstones of the volumetrically dominant clastic wedges at continental margins, the importance of authigenic clay minerals and zeolite cements will become more apparent (e.g., this volume; Surdam and Boles; Galloway). Pettijohn and others (1972, p. 419) expressed the generalization that, ". . . .carbonate and silica, account for the overwhelming bulk of cement of all sandstones." This view is biased by earlier studies of thin, blanket-like, cratonic, quartz-rich, mainly Paleozoic sandstones.

Compaction due to overburden pressure reduces original porosity by plastic deformation of ductile sand grains and, to a lesser extent, by fracture or cleavage of brittle grains. Soft sand grains are squeezed and penetrated by adjacent rigid grains; in some cases the soft material

"flames" out as thin lamellae among a great many neighboring rigid grains. The results are destruction of intergranular pores and creation of diagenetic, fine-grained matrix (Cummins, 1962). Papers in this volume by Burns and Ethridge and by Galloway consider sandstone compaction. Rittenhouse (1971) demonstrated, using ideal packing models, the relationships between porosity loss and content of labile grains. Grain squeezing alone can reduce porosity to nearly zero in lithic sandstones, such as the sandstones of the Beluga Formation of Cook Inlet Basin in Alaska (Hayes and others, 1976).

Combination chemical-mechanical processes which destroy original porosity are typified by the usual diagenetic history of detrital biotite. Biotite is abundant in many quartz-poor, arkosic and volcanogenic, lithic sandstones. Biotite is very unstable chemically in the diagenetic environment; early in diagenesis, or perhaps even before burial, detrital flakes will alter to a mixture of fine-grained carbonates and hydrous clay minerals. The alteration process causes enormous volume expansion, resulting in opaque, fine-grained masses several times the size of the original detrital flakes. These clay-carbonate globs are then squeezed among the rigid grains, reducing porosity (e.g., Hayes, 1973, Fig. 3). The fact that volume expansion can take place before compaction suggests that biotite alteration is a very early diagenetic process. Any chemical replacement of detrital grains which renders them ductile can be regarded as a combination process, such as replacement of feldspars, pyroxenes, or amphiboles by clay minerals.

Another porosity-destroying process, which might be regarded as combination chemical-mechanical, is cementation of quartzose sandstones by pressure solution. In this process, quartz is presumed to be dissolved at points of grain contact because the overburden pressure increases quartz solubility at those points. The dissolved silica moves into the fluid-filled pores where pressure is lower, and the silica precipitates as overgrowths on surfaces of detrital quartz grains adjacent to the pores. The literature on this subject is venerable and voluminous. However, Sippel (1968) showed with cathodeluminescence petrography that sutured, interpenetrating grain contacts, a classical criterion for pressure solution, are commonly the result of interfering quartz overgrowth instead. Sibley and Blatt (1976) demonstrated by luminescence petrography that pressure solution was less important for reducing porosity than had been classically supposed in the Silurian Tuscarora quartzitic sandstones. It seems that the volumetric importance of pressure solution as a source of silica cement needs to be reassessed, and that

TABLE 1.—AUTHIGENIC, PREMETAMORPHIC, VOID-FILLING AND REPLACEMENT MINERALS IN SANDSTONES

SILICA	ZEOLITES	SULFATES
Quartz overgrowths	Analcime	Anhydrite
Chalcedony	Clinoptilolite	Barite
Opal-A and -CT	Laumontite	Celestite
	Stilbite	
	Wairakite	
CLAY MINERALS	FELDSPARS	HALIDES
Kaolinite	K-feldspar	Halite
Dickite	Plagioclase	Fluorite
Chlorite		
Mica	CARBONATES	Fe-O-(OH)[1]
Smectite		
Mixed-layer clays	Calcite	PYRITE
	Dolomite	
	Siderite	

[1] Numerous iron oxides and hydroxides, of which hematite and goethite are most common.

additional sources of silica must be invoked to explain widespread silica cementation of quartz-rich sandstones. Silica cementation (and pressure solution) are not very important in quartz-poor sandstones, because alkali and alkali-earth cations from the breakdown of feldspars, mafic minerals, and volcanic grains combine with dissolved silica to form authigenic clays and zeolites, not quartz overgrowths.

Porosity reduction, especially compaction, begins soon after deposition and initial burial. The rate of reduction with increasing depth depends on many factors, with initial composition being perhaps the most important (Fig. 1). Sand with considerable mechanically and chemically unstable grains, such as volcanic rock fragments, will be compacted and cemented faster than will sand composed mainly of mechanically and chemically stable quartz grains. Some early diagenetic reactions, such as zeolitization of glass and feldspars, are hydration reactions (Surdam and Boles, this volume). Thus, cementing and replacing zeolites occupy more volume than the reactants, and that extra volume is provided by destruction of pore space. Cementation and compaction actually are competing in the race to destroy original inter-granular porosity. If a fairly rigid mineral is precipitated very early in the pores, compaction is forestalled, and the "floating" sand texture commonly seen in early calcite concretions is produced. On the other hand, if compaction of ductile grains proceeds rapidly during initial burial, not only is porosity reduced, which might otherwise be filled with cement, but also permeability is greatly reduced, which retards circulation of fluids from which intergranular cements are precipitated.

Considering the numerous processes which can so effectively destroy original porosity, we should marvel at the amount of subsurface sandstone porosity available for aquifers and hydrocarbon reservoirs. Actually, a very large percentage of such porosity is not original intergranular porosity which escaped destruction, but rather is secondary or solution porosity, created by the dissolution of detrital grains and authigenic cements and replacements. The porosity of many major hydrocarbon reservoirs is almost totally secondary. That is the second truth about holes in sandstones, a fact which is being recognized increasingly, and significantly so at this symposium. Table 2 is a list of detrital and authigenic components I have observed to have been dissolved in sandstones of a wide variety of compositions, ages, and geographic locations.

Secondary, solution pores generally do not look like primary pores. In thin section, secondary pores are distinguished by their size, shape, and relations to grains, as well as undissolved remnants of the original grains or cements. Table 3 is a list of petrographic characteristics of solution pores. The technique of impregnating sandstone chips with colored epoxy resin or similar material before the thin section is made has led to ever-increasing recognition of secondary porosity. The blue plastic widely used in the petroleum industry distinguishes between large secondary pores and plucked grains, shows pore geometry clearly in plain light, and greatly enhances color photography of porous rocks. Traditional petrographic studies emphasized the mineral content of sandstones and not the fluid-bearing holes, but new techniques and concepts are changing that.

Based on examination of many thick sandstone-shale sequences in outcrop and subsurface, mainly from the east and west coasts of North America, I conclude that if secondary porosity develops, it will be while the sandstones are quite deeply buried, and after the initial burial period during which primary porosity is greatly reduced. This is especially true for marine rocks. Most marine sandstones with secondary porosity show in thin section abundant evidence of earlier compaction and cementation, even where the cement is the dissolved component. On the other hand, nonmarine sandstones, which may have been exposed to meteoric waters shortly after deposition and before deep burial, may have had considerable secondary porosity created early in diagenesis before primary porosity was destroyed. Such was the case in the Sterling Formation of

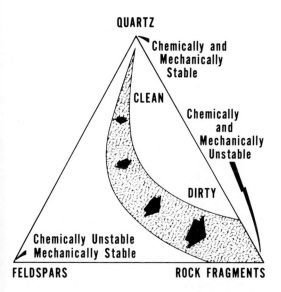

Fɪɢ. 1.—Sandstone diagenesis: the pathway to porosity destruction as a function of detrital sand composition.

TABLE 2.—SANDSTONE CONSTITUENTS DISSOLVED TO PRODUCE SOLUTION PORES

DETRITAL	AUTHIGENIC
Feldspar (mainly plagioclase)	Void-filling cement, especially:
Biotite[1]	Carbonates
Amphibole	Chlorite
Pyroxene	Smectite
Other heavy minerals	Zeolites
Chert	Anhydrite
Carbonate rock fragments	Replacement minerals, especially:
Calcareous and siliceous fossil fragments	Carbonates
Volcanic glass and fine-grained volcanic	Chlorite
rock fragments	Mixed-layer clays
	Zeolites

[1]Detrital biotite typically is altered diagenetically to clay-carbonate mixtures, which in turn are dissolved.

Cook Inlet Basin, Alaska (Hayes and others, 1976) or in the redbeds of the desert southwest (Walker and others, 1978).

Some might argue that observed secondary porosity is the product of modern outcrop weathering. If so, this could lead to incorrect prediction of solution porosity in the subsurface based on its presence in outcrop samples around the margin of a basin, and minimize the value of outcrop samples. To evaluate the weathering problem, I made comparisons between subsurface samples and surface samples of the same sandstone unit from nearby outcrops in several basins (e.g., the Sterling Formation of Cook Inlet Basin, Hayes and others, 1976). These comparisons show similar kinds and amounts of solution porosity in subsurface and outcrop samples, demonstrating that solution porosity in these outcrop samples predated modern weathering. I have seen solution pores produced by leaching on outcrop, but these are usually restricted to a highly weathered, oxidized rind only a few centimeters thick. Such weathering porosity is distinguishable from solution porosity formed at substantial burial depth.

As one accepts by experience the fact that secondary, solution porosity is very important in hydrocarbon reservoirs, several implications necessarily follow. First, secondary porosity must be created diagenetically; it is not inherently available as is primary porosity. The explorationist cannot automatically assume that secondary porosity will exist in a given potential reservoir interval, any more than he should assume that primary porosity will have escaped diagenetic reduction. The second implication of secondary porosity has to do with the time of its formation. Reservoir porosity is one of several essential ingredients for a commercial hydrocarbon accumulation. Hence, to be the principal reservoir porosity, secondary porosity must be created before hydrocarbon migration through the sandstone, just as the trap must be created before migration. In basins where source rocks and reservoir rocks are interbedded and about the same age, such as parts of the Gulf Coast, secondary porosity must be created during burial at about the same time and in about the same physiochemical environment as the hydrocarbons themselves. In basins where source beds are younger than reservoir rocks and separated from them by major unconformities (e.g., some Rocky Mountain basins), secondary porosity could have formed at several different times, such as during the initial burial of the reservoir section, during uplift and erosion of the reservoir section, or during its reburial under the source section. In areas where hydrocarbons have migrated from considerably older source beds into younger reservoir beds, it is possible that the younger reservoir beds might retain some primary porosity, and have not evolved to the point of secondary-porosity creation.

TABLE 3.—PETROGRAPHIC CRITERIA FOR SOLUTION PORES IN SANDSTONES

Scattered patches of undissolved, corroded authigenic cements

Large pores the size and shape of detrital grains, including fossil fragments

Partially dissolved, "skeletal" detrital grains

Undissolved authigenic coatings and overgrowths on dissolved detrital grains

Insoluble residue or reaction products in large pores

Alternating areas of open and close packing of detrital grains

Detrital grains bent and broken by collapse into adjacent large solution pores

A third implication of secondary porosity, if one accepts what has been said so far, is that there is a normal progression of sandstone-porosity modification during the initial burial diagenesis of a basin fill, before interruption by uplift and erosion. This progression is shown schematically in Figure 2, which exaggerates the best possible case of sandstone porosity versus depth. For the first several thousand feet of burial, primary porosity is reduced by the mechanisms described previously, and at a rate which is determined mainly by initial sand composition (Fig. 1). This process may take effective porosity to zero, or if not, the depth to zero porosity can be extrapolated. However, as temperature and the rate of hydrocarbon generation increase, chemically active aqueous solutions moving from the mudstones into the sandstones dissolve and flush away certain sandstone minerals, creating secondary porosity (Table 2). In the most favorable case, porosity may actually increase with depth (Fig. 2), or more likely, the slope of the porosity-depth curve may simply steepen, but continue to decline. At even greater depths, secondary porosity will be destroyed by compaction and cementation, but probably not at as high a rate as primary porosity was destroyed, because most of the chemically and mechanically unstable grains already reacted during earlier diagenesis, and

because of bridging and keystone relations between rigid grains developed during initial compaction. Not all sandstones will have traveled the full evolutionary pathway of Figure 2. We can intercept them at most any point along the way. Also, original porosity may go to nearly zero, and no secondary porosity ever develops at depth, the worst possible case.

A fourth implication of solution porosity is apparent on Figure 2; that is, secondary porosity can exist at greater depths than one would expect by extrapolation of the primary porosity versus depth curve. Published scatter plots of depth versus porosity are typically fitted to a straight line, based on the assumption that porosity should decrease monotonically with depth (e.g., Maxwell, 1964; Atwater and Miller, 1965). As a result, it becomes accepted exploration lore in certain regions that reservoir porosity in a given formation simply cannot exist below a certain depth. This kind of thinking can handicap the nimble imagination required for modern exploration. Recent oil discoveries in the Tensleep Sandstone of western Wyoming in secondary porosity at much greater depth than previous Tensleep production testify to the need for recognition of primary versus secondary porosity in predicting subsurface distribution of porosity.

Secondary porosity in sandstones has been described previously in the literature (e.g., Phipps, 1969; Morgan and Gordon, 1970; Hayes, 1973; Heald and Larese, 1973), but I think many readers regarded it only as a geological curiosity. Only very recently have papers appeared which demonstrate the common occurrence and volumetric importance of secondary, solution porosity in potential hydrocarbon reservoirs (Hayes and others, 1976; Lindquist, 1976; Stanton and McBride, 1976; Schmidt and others, 1977). A case of parallel but independent investigations, begun about 1969–1970 and leading to nearly identical conclusions, can be found in this volume in this paper and the papers by Schmidt and McDonald. The examples and illustrations used for the oral presentations of both papers at the symposium were very similar. For that reason, and because the Schmidt and McDonald papers deal solely with solution porosity, I have elected not to offer more documentation in this paper. Both studies stressed that solution porosity of reservoir grade is typically formed while the rocks are buried and hydrocarbons are being generated and migrating, a concept of great significance to exploration. Schmidt and McDonald emphasized that early-diagenetic carbonate cements and replacements are the main constituents dissolved from sandstones, and that the necessary acidic solutions are by-products of organic reactions in mudstones.

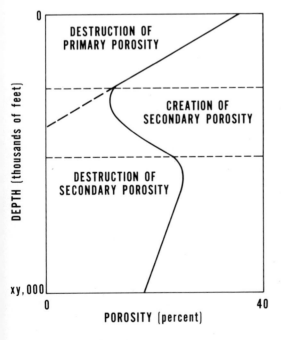

FIG. 2.—Depth distribution and evolutionary sequence of primary and secondary porosity.

I, too, recognized the importance of carbonate dissolution early in my studies; but subsequent work with mineralogically immature "dirty" sandstones (Fig. 1) has shown direct dissolution of detrital and authigenic silicates to be equally significant (Table 2). Such is the case in the Sterling Formation of Cook Inlet Basin, Alaska (Hayes and others, 1976). Also, the paper by Pittman in this volume describes the influence of secondary porosity on reservoir properties of sandstones, demonstrating that recognition of secondary porosity is as important for production activities as it is for exploration.

MIGRATING PORE FLUIDS

Up to this point the discussion has been based mainly on petrographic observations and has dealt with the distribution of primary and secondary porosity with depth. Now let us consider the more difficult and largely unsolved problem of predicting how sandstone porosity has been modified in space and time throughout a sedimentary basin. I have no ready answers on how to do that, but some purpose will be served by defining the problem, describing approaches, and asking some specific questions.

First, it should be apparent that a lot of dissolved mineral matter is moved around in a sedimentary basin to account for the observed precipitation and dissolution of minerals in sandstones. Also, much of this movement of dissolved material must take place during the initial period of burial diagenesis, before the basin fill is uplifted and subject to erosion. As pointed out earlier, secondary porosity commonly serves as hydrocarbon reservoirs; because hydrocarbons typically are produced during the initial burial episode, porosity modification must be active then, also. And, during this first burial episode of a basin fill, mud with up to 80 percent pore water is dewatered by compaction until porosity is about 15 percent at depths of several thousand feet (Burst, 1976). Figure 3 shows the decrease of shale porosity with depth, and also shows that water squeezed from the mud enters the much more permeable, interbedded sands and flows laterally through the sands toward the surface (Magara, 1976). Putting all these ideas together, it is easy to conclude that sandstones have water moving through them sometime during diagenesis, and that water is the dynamic agent redistributing mineral matter around the basin by dissolution and precipitation.

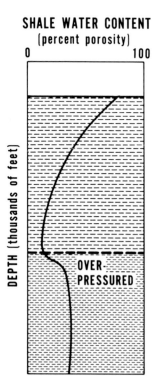

SHALE WATER CONTENT
(percent porosity)

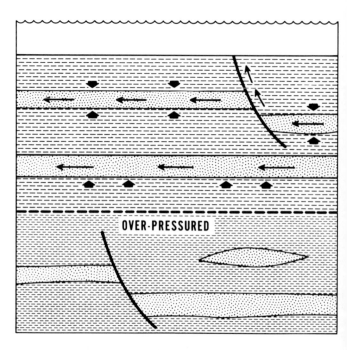

SHALE DEWATERING

FIG. 3.—Shale porosity versus depth, and flow paths of shale water during compaction and diagenesis.

By these mental gymnastics we arrive at the third truth about holes in sandstone; porosity-modifying sandstone diagenesis is a hydrodynamic as well as a chemical phenomenon. This was implied earlier in the paper. Also, I suggest that transfer of ions by bulk fluid flow is a competing and perhaps dominant mechanism to diffusion of ions through static pore fluids. The literature on diffusion of ions and ionic filtration through porous media is voluminous. I do not intend to open the field to discussion in this paper. The mathematical modeling studies being initiated by Wood and Surdam (this volume) are intended to assess, among other things, the relative importance of diffusion versus dynamic transfer of ionic solutions under a variety of diagenetic conditions. My intuitive feeling is that fluid-flow transfer will be shown to be much more effective than diffusion in sandstones where permeability is more than a few millidarcys. In the terminology of Wood and Surdam, most of the precipitation, dissolution, and transfer processes of dissolved mineral matter in sandstones are described by a large Peclet number (Pe).

So, to understand and predict sandstone-porosity distribution in a basin is to reconstruct how and when water moved through the shales and sandstones of the basin fill, where the water came from, what its chemical composition was when it entered the sandstone, how its chemical composition evolved while flowing through sandstone, and what its flow paths were through the basin. This is no simple task. It is difficult to obtain uncontaminated, unmodified samples of deep subsurface water for analysis from sandstones, and particularly from shales. Even if it were easy, the present-day water composition may not be representative of water composition earlier in diagenesis when porosity was actively being modified. The waters which accomplished the most important cementation and dissolution early in diagenesis may be long gone from the basin or a stratigraphic zone of interest. About the only hope for directly analyzing and tracking water would be in a young, thick basin fill which was still undergoing initial shale dewatering and traveling the diagenetic pathway shown in Figure 2. Even there, adequate well coverage and good water-sampling techniques would be required for success.

So, if direct study of subsurface water movement and chemistry is difficult or impossible, we are left with trying to decipher the character of water from minerals precipitated and dissolved in its wake. Because porosity modification is essentially a series of chemical reactions between minerals and migrating pore fluids, the compositions of authigenic and dissolved minerals should

be clues to the compositions of the reactive fluids. This is the approach used out of necessity by most present-day students of diagenesis. It is an observational, empirical approach, the success of which is enhanced by adequate subsurface sampling and skillful, detailed mineralogic and petrographic analysis. One has to take into account not just the mineral species, but also polymorphism, crystal size, morphology, surface area, crystal perfection, and compositional variations due to ionic substitution as clues to chemical environments in which the minerals formed. For example, what is the significance in terms of fluid source, movement, and chemistry of the Fe/Mg or Si/Al ratio of authigenic chlorite, of the kaolin polytypes, dickite and kaolinite, as authigenic pore fillings in sandstone beds only a few feet apart vertically, or of coexisting clinoptilolite, laumontite, and analcime as pore-filling cements in a given sandstone hand specimen?

This approach of reconstructing fluid chemistry and movement from the nature of the minerals is constrained by our lack of knowledge of solubility and stability relations of many of the complex silicates involved in sandstone diagenesis. What information we have is for minerals in equilibrium with the solutions surrounding them, the "closed beaker" model. But to what degree is equilibrium achieved between solids and dissolved ions in a hydrodynamic system, where the minerals encrust the pipes of the subterranean sandstone plumbing? At times during diagenesis of a particular sandstone, the rate of fluid flow past a given point was too great and the composition of the fluid changed too quickly for equilibrium to be achieved for very long between minerals and solution at that point. Indeed, large-scale dissolution in some areas of a basin and large-scale precipitation elsewhere, or precipitation alternating with dissolution at a given point, are clear indications that equilibrium is continually thwarted by the dynamic transfer of dissolved material around a basin by bulk fluid flow.

So, the geologically traditional, Sherlock Holmes approach of piecing together fragmentary clues after the fact is beset by difficulties when applied to sandstone diagenesis. Yet this will remain the main approach. The problems will have to be overcome gradually if we are to understand the kinetics of sandstone diagenesis and predict porosity distribution. Hope for some rapid progress is offered by the mathematical and geochemical modeling techniques described by Wood and Surdam (this volume), based on concepts reviewed by Domenico (1977). This approach allows computer simulation of simultaneous mass transfer and chemical reactions and tracking of reaction zones in time and space. Diagenetic systems and basin models can be constructed to take into account the size and shape of the basin, geometry of sandstone bodies, sand-shale ratios, rate of inflow of shale water, flow rates in sandstones, sandstone porosity, permeability, and mineralogy, solution chemistry, temperature, pressure, etc. The models can be based on data from real basins or on hypothetical situations. Boundary conditions are set at time zero, and the computer simulates diagenesis through time. The possible sets of conditions which could be modeled are many, and the ramifications are endless. However, modeling results should constantly be checked against real rocks in real basins to avoid ludicrous conclusions. At the very least, the mathematical modeling approach will show us which parameters are more important than others, and will guide future data gathering from real rocks. At best, we may learn to recognize and measure the critical parameters of a particular real basin, and by plugging these into the model, determine in which areas and stratigraphic intervals of the basin to expect the best primary and secondary porosity today.

Figure 4 is an example of a model which could be treated mathematically. It is based on reality, is very simple, is fragmentary, but would be difficult to investigate except by computer simulation. The model considers just one continuous flow path updip in a basin, shown as a single sandstone bed of unspecified thickness embraced in thick shales. The sandstone bed is the same age throughout. Because of the dip, which is assumed to be part sedimentary and part structural, the bed spans a considerable depth, temperature, and pressure range. Fluid pressure is assumed to be hydrostatic. Water is squeezed by compaction from the underlying shale (in reality some water must enter from the overlying shale also) and flows laterally updip through the much more permeable sandstone along a declining pressure gradient. Assume that the sandstone and contained pore water are of uniform composition throughout and in chemical equilibrium. Also, assume that the sandstone has undergone no previous chemical diagenesis, a necessary simplification at this point. Now, start the water flowing updip by introducing at point A, shale water which

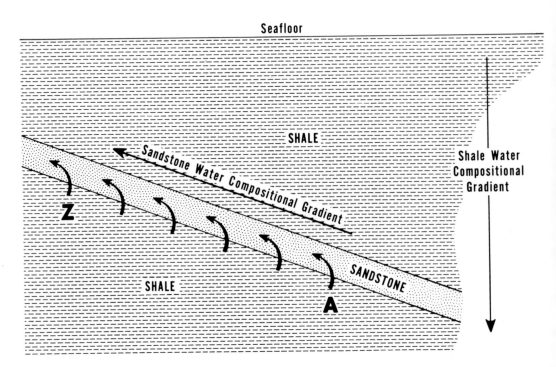

Fig. 4.—Simple kinetic model of sandstone diagenesis, amenable to computer simulation (read text for explanation).

is not in chemical equilibrium with the sandstone minerals or sandstone water, and which will displace the sandstone water. Given these conditions, one could begin with simple composition and realistic flow rate and track the progress of reaction fronts or zones upward through the sandstone. Using an analogy from analytical chemistry, I would anticipate a "chromatographic" separation or zonation of dissolved and precipitated minerals throughout the sandstone "column", which would have the effect of creating zones of reduced and enhanced porosity.

Still with reference to Figure 4, assume that the shale water can dissolve detrital potash feldspar in the sandstones. Potassium ions and silicon and aluminum ionic complexes will be released into solution, thus changing composition of the first unit of introduced shale water. As this unit of water moves updip, the rate at which it can dissolve potassium feldspar will decrease, because it will be approaching saturation with respect to one or more of the feldspar components. In fact, at some point further updip, a new, potassium-deficient phase (kaolinite?) may begin to precipitate, but the dissolved potassium keeps on going. So, the "chromatographic" separation begins. The distance updip from point A at which a new phase begins to precipitate and the distance that the dissolved potassium travels beyond the locus of new-phase deposition before reacting are functions of the fluid-flow rate. So far, we have considered only the first slug of introduced shale water, but actually a steady stream of shale water of uniform composition can be introduced at point A. This will have the effect over time of shifting the locus of precipitation of new phases updip and of increasing the separation distance between segregated constituents. The water in the sandstone will not be of uniform composition throughout, but will change systematically updip as dissolved material is added and removed. A given unit of water will evolve chemically as it moves along. Eventually, at point A all the detrital feldspar will be dissolved (creating solution porosity); but updip from there, the amount of feldspar remaining will gradually increase. This dissolution gradient will move updip and stretch out with time.

Now let us add another level of complexity. Instead of shale water entering only at point A, let it enter the base of the sand bed everywhere between point A and point Z, but let the shale water have the same composition everywhere as at point A. Water traveling in the sand between point A and point Z will evolve chemically, as noted before, but all along the way, water of "unevolved" composition will be added. What will be the effect of this constant disturbance of the "chromatograph" on the distribution of

dissolved and precipitated minerals? Computer simulation has a chance of answering that question. Going one step further, we can be more realistic by saying that shale-water composition is not uniform between point A and point Z. Rather, there is a chemical-composition gradient in shale water with depth, caused by diagenetic reactions and ionic filtration within the shale. So, what is the effect of superimposing shale-water and sandstone-water compositional gradients (Fig. 4)? By adding only a few complexities, we very quickly have asked questions which even the computer may have difficulty answering. The dynamic modeling approach will be challenging. Students of diagenesis with the necessary mathematical and geochemical skills are encouraged to follow the lead of Wood and Surdam (this volume).

As noted before, compaction and cementation early in diagenesis can reduce porosity and permeability to nearly zero at depths of several thousand feet (Fig. 2). Some persons then ask how fluids can continue to move through tight sandstones to dissolve and flush away cements and detrital minerals, and create secondary porosity. Even though sand permeability can be very low at that stage in diagenesis, shale permeability probably will be even lower. In other words, if fluid can move laterally at all along a declining pressure gradient, it will move more readily through tight sand than through tight shale. Once dissolution begins, removal of minerals should enlarge the flow channels, increase permeability, increase the flow rate, which in turn will increase dissolution rates, and the process becomes self-accelerating. The dissolution process in tight sandstones can be hastened if the rocks are fractured by tectonic deformation of the basin fill. Fractures can act as avenues for either dissolving or cementing fluids. Hayes (1973) described secondary, solution porosity grading outward symmetrically from tiny hairline fractures in folded, faulted Pliocene sandstones from Hole 177A of the Deep Sea Drilling Project near Vancouver Island. Folding and faulting of the basin fill create traps for hydrocarbons. Because these traps must exist before hydrocarbon migration if they are to hold oil, and because secondary porosity must also, it is reasonable to expect that tectonic deformation may have accompanied and aided creation of secondary, solution porosity in some cases. Tectonic squeezing of the basin fill also can add impetus to moving fluids.

An important consequence of the hydrodynamic model of sandstone diagenesis is chemical evolution of water moving past a given point; at some time the change may be great enough to dissolve minerals which were precipitated earlier. For example, dissolution of early diagenetic carbonate cement is one very important cause of secondary porosity. If compacting shale is the only source of water moving through sandstone, the water must be reversed chemically without reversing flow direction. The downstream (updip) migration of reaction zones described for the simple model of Figure 4 could accomplish this for certain minerals, given enough time. Another way to effect a chemical reversal is to change the composition of shale water entering the sand at a given point. This would most likely be caused by some depth- and temperature-related reaction in the shales as the basin continues to subside and the basin fill becomes thicker. For example, Schmidt and McDonald (this volume) called upon hydrogen ions produced in shales as by-products of temperature-controlled kerogen diagenesis to dissolve carbonates in sandstone and to flush the carbonates updip to be precipitated as early diagenetic cement. As these cemented sandstones become more deeply buried, shale water entering them becomes more acidic because of progressive organic diagenesis, and carbonate is dissolved, creating secondary porosity. Thus, carbonate minerals (and presumably silicates also) are continually cycled upward in the basin fill. As mentioned before, my studies and those of Schmidt and McDonald, though conducted independently, have arrived at similar conclusions about sandstone diagenesis. Both studies recognize the kinetic, evolutionary, and cyclical consequences of hydrodynamic diagenesis, and are grappling with the problem of porosity prediction.

PREBURIAL INFLUENCES ON SANDSTONE DIAGENESIS

The main message of the preceding section is that chemical diagenesis of sandstones is accomplished by many complex chemical reactions between minerals and aqueous solutions migrating through the pore system of sandstones. In other words, the compositions, amounts, and distribution of precipitated and dissolved minerals are governed by detrital mineralogy and fluid flow. Detrital mineralogy and fluid flow, in turn, are influenced by several interrelated factors. Figure 5 can be read from top to bottom, or from bottom to top, to show the relationships. This leads to the fourth truth about holes in sandstone; the course of porosity-modifying diagenesis is programmed by prediagenetic, preburial tectonic setting of the basin, by compositions of rocks being eroded in sediment source areas (provenance), and by depositional environments within the basin.

The control of detrital mineralogy by provenance and in turn the control of provenance by tectonic setting are most dramatically displayed along converging plate boundaries. These elongate zones of collision between lithospheric plates are

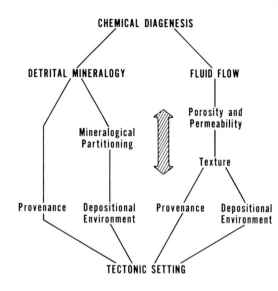

FIG. 5.—Flow chart of relationships between chemical diagenesis and prediagenetic conditions.

marked by volcanic arcs, deep oceanic trenches, and by marine shelves, slopes, and trough-like deep basins in the arc-trench gap (Dickinson, 1970b). Andesitic magma derived from melting of the descending lithospheric slab moves upward to create the arc. Volcanic and plutonic rocks of the arc have intermediate composition, poor in quartz and potassium feldspar and rich in plagioclase and mafic minerals. Older sediments deposited on the descending slab, as well as chunks of oceanic crust, may be implaced into the arc-trench gap, and will be greatly deformed, metamorphosed, and perhaps elevated in the process. The principal provenance for sediment deposited in the arc-trench gap is the arc, but in some cases rocks exposed in the arc-trench gap are recycled to contribute sediment, also. Hence, the provenance of sandstones deposited along converging plate margins is quartz-poor and yields sand rich in feldspar, mafic minerals, metasedimentary, volcanic, and pyroclastic rock fragments, all of which are very susceptible to rapid diagenetic alteration (Fig. 1). Furthermore, high relief in the provenance, maintained by volcanism and tectonism, makes erosion rates so rapid that chemical weathering cannot remove very effectively the chemically unstable components before deposition. Relatively short distance between sediment source and site of deposition means that mechanically unstable grains will not be greatly reduced during transportation into and within the basin. All of these cause-and-effect, tectonic and provenance factors result in converging plate boundaries being the prime habitat of mineralogically immature, lithic and feldspathic sandstones (Fig. 1), to the virtual exclusion of quartz-rich sandstones. Galloway (this volume) explored origin and diagenesis of arc-derived sandstones in some detail.

In contrast, quartz-rich sandstones are found mainly in cratonic settings, where provenance is dominated by sialic, quartz-rich, plutonic and metamorphic rocks and by old sediments derived therefrom. The relative tectonic stability of cratons permits chemical and mechanical weathering to reduce feldspars and mafic minerals to fines, thus enriching the sand fraction in quartz. Diagenesis further eliminates non-quartz minerals from the sand-size fraction, and when such sandstones are uplifted and eroded, they provide even more quartz-rich sand. Odom and others (this volume) described diagenesis of the quartzose St. Peter Sandstone.

Detrital mineralogy is controlled not only by provenance and tectonic setting, but also by mineralogical partitioning within the depositional environment (Fig. 5). Water and wind, the principal agents whereby sand is transported and deposited, separate particles according to size, shape, and density. If certain minerals tend to be concentrated in certain size fractions for whatever reason, sands of different composition can be deposited simultaneously within different parts of the basin. Furthermore, processes within the basin can influence sand mineralogy, particularly homogenization of alternating sand and mud layers by burrowing organisms. The range of depositional environments within a basin, their extent, distribution, and mutual relations are governed largely by rates and patterns of subsidence and uplift. That is, depositional environments are influenced by tectonic setting (Fig. 5).

Fluid flow is the other critical influence on sandstone diagenesis (Fig. 5). The amount of water and the rate at which it moves will govern the amounts and kinds of minerals dissolved and precipitated and the spatial distribution of mineral reactants and products. Fluid flow is determined by sandstone permeability and porosity. Generally, sand when deposited has quite high porosity and permeability; but not all sands have the same values. Initial porosity and permeability are very much controlled by the textural parameters of grain size, grain shape, grain-size distribution or sorting, and by efficiency of grain packing. Sand texture, in turn, is related to the texture of rocks in the sediment source area (provenance) and to the sorting action of waves and currents in various depositional environments. As noted before, provenance and depositional environments are influenced by tectonic setting.

So, all paths of reasoning, from top to bottom of Figure 5, lead to tectonic setting as a funda-mental influence on the eventual course of sandstone diagenesis, with depositional environment and provenance as second-order controls. The paper by Hayes and others (1976) is a case history of such from the Tertiary rocks of Cook Inlet Basin, Alaska. The paper shows why sand derived from the volcanic arc has secondary, solution porosity suitable as gas reservoir, whereas sand derived from a subaerially exposed forearc ridge has very poor reservoir properties.

In summary, the main point of this section is that initial mineralogy and texture of a sand profoundly influence its diagenetic history. Pre-diagenetic controls on initial mineralogy and texture are shown in Figure 5. To understand diagenetic history of a sandstone, one must know what the starting materials were. This is not easy to do, because diagenetic processes have altered the initial texture and mineralogy considerably, to the point where important detrital components have been dissolved, replaced, or deformed beyond recognition. Very thoughtful petrographic examination is required to peer through the veil of diagenetic alteration and reconstruct original, prediagenetic sand composition (e.g. Dickinson, 1970a). An example of an attempt to do this is given by Hayes (1973).

Because original composition and texture are influenced by tectonics, provenance, and depositional environment, sandstone petrographers traditionally have made inferences about these preburial factors from sandstone composition and texture, but many have been led astray by failing to take diagenetic alteration into account. I would suggest the opposite approach: let us learn all we can about tectonics, provenance, and depositional environment by methods other than petrography, and use these clues to help reconstruct original sand composition and texture to aid studies of diagenesis.

DISCUSSION

Recent progress and problems related to sandstone diagenesis revolve around four main points.

1. Primary intergranular porosity and permeability of sand are subject to almost total destruction by several mechanical and chemical processes early in diagenesis.

2. Later in diagenesis, secondary porosity can be produced by dissolution of detrital and authigenic minerals; porosity of many major hydrocarbon reservoirs is mainly secondary.

3. Chemical diagenesis of sandstones is a kinetic process involving reactions between minerals and moving aqueous solutions; the main source of water is from dewatering of shales interbedded with sandstones.

4. The course of sandstone diagenesis in a given basin is programmed by the preburial, predia-

genetic factors of provenance, depositional environments, and tectonic setting.

Significant advancements in the last decade include: widespread documentation of mechanical compaction and diagenetic origin of fine-grained matrix in immature sandstones; recognition principally with the scanning electron microscope of clay minerals and zeolites as abundant authigenic cements in unmetamorphosed sandstones; common use of cathode-luminescence petrography to study sandstone cements, particularly silica and carbonates; recognition of secondary, solution porosity, not only for what it is, but for how abundant it is and what its implications are for hydrocarbon exploration; initial attempts to integrate the principles of thermodynamics, fluid dynamics, and energy and mass transfer as a way of modeling and predicting the diagenetic transformation and translocation of initial components of a basin fill; viewing sandstone diagenesis in terms of the pervasive principles of new global tectonics.

Remaining problems have the common theme of understanding the diagenetic evolution of a basin fill. Specifically, we need to: improve our ability to reconstruct initial materials and conditions at the depositional interface at any time in the history of basin filling; verify and modify the concept of porosity evolution in the vertical sense (Fig. 2); employ the principles governing mass and energy transfer as a means of predicting distribution of diagenetic minerals and porosity in space through time; understand and reconstruct the temperature and pressure history of basins; incorporate in our models the fact that subsidence and diagenesis are simultaneous, not mutually exclusive; recognize that sandstone diagenesis is greatly influenced by diagenesis of associated shales, limestones, evaporites, and organic matter; learn to predict the delicate interdependence and relative timing of hydrocarbon generation and migration, secondary porosity development, and trap formation.

Problem solving will continue to rely heavily on traditional geologic methods and reasoning. Thin-section petrography and X-ray diffraction, supplemented by other ways of directly analyzing rocks, will provide the main data base. Basin-wide studies of stratigraphy, sedimentology, and structural evolution will be necessary. A principal new approach will be computer simulation of kinetic models of diagenesis. Because diagenesis is wholly a subsurface process, geologists should be increasingly diligent and innovative in their efforts to obtain relevant subsurface information. More thought should be given to the potential value of subsurface water samples to diagenetic studies, and methods for obtaining meaningful samples. Geologists and geophysicists, once acknowledging the differences between primary and secondary porosity, should reexamine the fundamental responses of borehole logging tools to see if porosity types can be distinguished and mapped. Geologists should encourage geophysicists in their efforts to obtain elemental and mineralogical information by direct downhole measurement, such as with the neutron-activated, gamma-ray spectrometer now being developed. Recent experiments in seismic processing suggest that sandstone porosity can be recognized and mapped by analysis of velocity data in basins where stratigraphy is well known. Information derived in this way should be evaluated for its usefulness to diagenetic studies.

As stated before, the main practical application of all this is prediction of suitable porosity in potential hydrocarbon reservoirs, though there may also be spinoff related to mineral deposits and geothermal energy. Because secondary porosity differs from primary porosity in terms of origin, subsurface distribution, pore-size distribution, pore shape, surface area, and attendant permeability, explorationists and reservoir managers must correctly identify porosity type in order to make sound decisions. In frontier areas of hydrocarbon exploration, diagenetic concepts can narrow the areal and stratigraphic range of potential reservoirs by eliminating from consideration those judged to be tight for reasons of composition, age, depth, temperature, or whatever. Negative recommendations can save time and money. In partially explored basins, diagenetic studies can offer encouragement to drill deeper to horizons which are productive at shallower depths elsewhere, to reconsider horizons previously condemned by a few dry holes, or to test traps which conventional thinking dismissed as nonprospective. Fluid-flow properties and rock-fluid interactions in sandstones are governed mainly by pore geometry and authigenic minerals in pores. These diagenetically controlled rock properties must be taken into account for efficient management of producing reservoirs, particularly in drilling, completion, and stimulation of wells, and in enhanced-recovery projects where exotic fluids are pumped into sandstones.

REFERENCES

ATWATER, G. I., AND MILLER, E. E., 1965, The effect of decrease in porosity with depth on future development of oil and gas reservoirs in southern Louisiana [abs.]: Am. Assoc. Petroleum Geologists Bull., v. 49, p. 344.

BURST, J. F., 1976, Argillaceous sediment dewatering: Ann. Rev. Earth Planetary Sci., v. 4, p. 293–318.

CUMMINS, W. A., 1962, The greywacke problem: Liverpool-Manchester Geol. Jour., v. 3, p. 51–72.

DICKINSON, W. R., 1970a, Interpreting detrital modes of graywacke and arkose: Jour. Sed. Petrology, v. 40, p. 695–707.

——, 1970b, Relations of andesites, granites, and derivative sandstones to arc-trench tectonics: Rev. Geophys. Space Phys., v. 8, p. 813–860.

DOMENICO, P. A., 1977, Transport phenomena in chemical rate processes in sediments: Ann. Rev. Earth Planetary Sci., v. 5, p. 287–317.

HAYES, J. B., 1973, Petrology of indurated sandstones, Leg 18, Deep Sea Drilling Project, *in* L. D. Kulm, R. von Huene, and others, Initial Reports of the Deep Sea Drilling Project, Leg 18: Washington, D. C., U. S. Government Printing Office, p. 915–924.

——, HARMS, J. C., AND WILSON, T., JR., 1976, Contrasts between braided and meandering stream deposits, Beluga and Sterling Formations (Tertiary), Cook Inlet, Alaska, *in* T. P. Miller (ed.), Recent and ancient sedimentary environments in Alaska: Anchorage, Alaska, Alaska Geol. Soc., p. J1–J27.

HEALD, M. T., AND LARESE, R. E., 1973, The significance of the solution of feldspar in porosity development: Jour. Sed. Petrology, v. 43, p. 458–460.

LINDQUIST, S., 1976, Leached porosity in overpressured sandstones—Frio Formation (Oligocene), south Texas [abs.]: Am. Assoc. Petroleum Geologists Bull., v. 60, p. 1612–1613.

MAGARA, K., 1976, Water expulsion from clastic sediments during compaction—Directions and volumes: Am. Assoc. Petroleum Geologists Bull., v. 60, p. 543–553.

MAXWELL, J. C., 1964, Influence of depth, temperature, and geologic age on porosity of quartzose sandstone: Am. Assoc. Petroleum Geologists Bull., v. 48, p. 697–709.

MORGAN, J. T., AND GORDON, D. T., 1970, Influence of pore geometry on water-oil relative permeability: Jour. Petroleum Technology, October 1970, p. 1199–1208.

PETTIJOHN, F. J., POTTER, P. E., AND SIEVER, R., 1972, Sand and sandstone: New York, Springer-Verlag, 618 p.

PHIPPS, C. B., 1969, Post-burial sideritisation of calcite in Eocene beds from the Maracaibo Basin, Venezuela: Geol. Mag., v. 106, p. 485–495.

RITTENHOUSE, G., 1971, Mechanical compaction of sands containing different percentages of ductile grains: A theoretical approach: Am. Assoc. Petroleum Geologists Bull., v. 55, p. 92–96.

SCHMIDT, V., McDONALD, D. A., AND PLATT, R. L., 1977, Pore geometry and reservoir aspects of secondary porosity in sandstones: Bull. Canadian Pet. Geol., v. 25, p. 271–290.

SIBLEY, D. F., AND BLATT, H., 1976, Intergranular pressure solution and cementation of the Tuscarora orthoquartzite: Jour. Sed. Petrology, v. 46, p. 881–896.

SIPPEL, R. F., 1968, Sandstone petrology, evidence from luminescence petrography: Jour. Sed. Petrology, v. 38, p. 530–554.

STANTON, G. D., AND McBRIDE, E. F., 1976, Factors influencing porosity and permeability of lower Wilcox (Eocene) sandstone, Karnes County, Texas [abs.]: Am. Assoc. Petroleum Geologists and Soc. Econ. Paleontologists and Mineralogists Ann. Meeting Abstracts, v. 3, p. 118–119.

WALKER, T. R., WAUGH, B., AND CRONE, A. J., 1978, Diagenesis in first-cycle desert alluvium of Cenozoic age, southwestern United States and northwestern Mexico: Geol. Soc. America Bull., v. 89, p. 19–32.

SEPM Special Publication No. 26, p. 141–157, March 1979

DIAGENETIC PROCESSES IN SANDSTONES

HARVEY BLATT

University of Oklahoma, Norman, 73019

ABSTRACT

The range of physical and chemical conditions included in diagenesis is 0–200° C, 1–2000 kg/cm^2, and water salinities from fresh to brines twice as concentrated as the Dead Sea. Numerical values of these parameters vary not only with depth, but areally at any single depth. In addition, gross differences in heat flow in different tectonic settings can cause the average temperature at a given depth in a eugeocline to be double that in a miogeocline.

Despite the large variation in physical and chemical conditions during diagenesis, it is striking that calcite and quartz are the dominant chemical precipitates in pore spaces of sandstones. To a first approximation, this reflects two facts. (1) Most preserved sands were deposited in shallow marine environments and sea water is at least saturated with respect to calcium carbonate. (2) The average sand contains about 65% quartz and rates of flow of subsurface waters are so slow that quartz is the main buffer for the silica content of these waters.

The slow rate of movement of subsurface waters places important restrictions on when cementation of a sand can occur. To lithify a sand, the circulating water must be supersaturated with respect to the solid to be precipitated in the pore space and the number of pore volumes of water that must flow through the sand must be very large. If the sand is areally widespread, calculations for well-sorted pure quartz sand indicate that cementation of the unit by quartz by horizontal flow of subsurface water is impossible within geologically reasonable periods of time. Plugging of pore spaces by quartz must result from vertical circulation, probably when the depth of sand burial does not exceed a few hundred meters. This cementation can occur either soon after deposition of the sediment or at any subsequent time when tectonic forces elevate the sediment to a shallow depth.

INTRODUCTION

Diagenetic reactions are defined as those that occur in a rock from the time the crystals or grains are deposited until the time the texture or mineralogy of the ensuing sedimentary rock is markedly changed. The range of temperature, pressure, and chemical variation encompassed by this definition is great. It includes about 20% of the temperature and pressure variation present in the earth's crust, from 0–200° C, 1–2000 kg/cm^2 (bars), and water compositions from fresh to hypersaline brine.

These variations are imposed on a heterogeneous assemblage of sedimentary detritus containing various amounts of quartz, feldspars, rock fragments of diverse kinds, carbonate minerals, hematite, clay minerals, and other inorganic and organic debris. The complexity of the interactions between the detrital particles and changing physicochemical conditions is perhaps rivaled only by organic interactions in the primeval oceanic "soup." Nevertheless, the resource geologist is called on daily to predict reservoir conditions at a specific moment in space and time. The petroleum-intensive American economy stands as a tribute to his success.

Our purpose in this paper is to consider the physics and chemistry of diagenesis, discuss the present state of understanding of the interactions involved, and to point out some areas in which additional data are needed.

VARIATION IN TEMPERATURE

Geothermal gradients for the upper ten kilometers or so of the earth's crust are determined almost entirely from measurements made in bore holes drilled in search of petroleum and natural gas. Some of these down-hole temperature measurements are made immediately after cessation of drilling but before equilibrium has been reestablished by the formation pore waters, and these temperatures tend to be significantly lower (10–20° C) than those measured days, weeks, or months after active mud circulation has stopped. There are many measurements that have been made after equilibrium has been reestablished, however, and these have been collated for the Texas-Louisiana Gulf Coast region (Fig. 1) by Maxwell (1964). Also shown is the range of equilibrium temperature values for part of a currently active continental shelf-volcanic island arc-oceanic trench tectonic system in Indonesia. Several important observations may be made from Figure 1.

1. The range of temperatures in either region is large at any depth chosen; for example, from 65° C to 145° C at a depth of 3000 m in the NW Gulf Coast. The fact that the two temperature

Copyright © 1979, The Society of Economic Paleontologists and Mineralogists

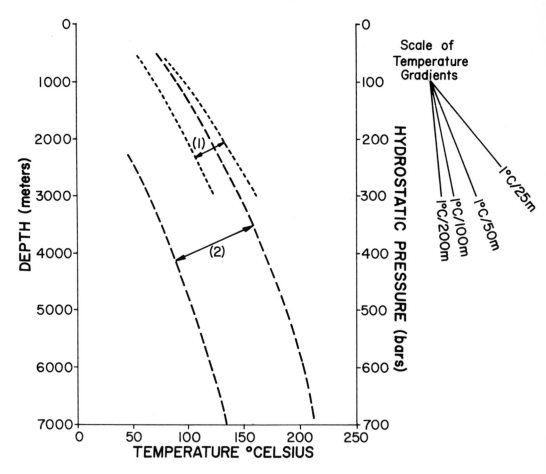

Fɪɢ. 1.—Boundaries of measured geothermal gradients in (1) the northwest Java Basin, Indonesia, and in (2) the northwestern Gulf of Mexico (from Fletcher and Bay, 1975; Maxwell, 1964).

bands are curved suggests that the gradient in any single well is also curved, but this may not be apparent in shallow wells. Thus, contour maps of geothermal gradient are limited in their accuracy unless there are at least three maps at different depth levels.

2. Temperatures at any depth are, on the average, greater in the island arc by 30–40° C than in the miogeoclinal Gulf Coast. This seems reasonable in view of the high heat flows measured along volcanic arcs. These higher temperatures are one reason for the extensive diagenetic alteration of detrital fragments in sandstones deposited in eugeoclinal settings.

Jam L. *et al.* (1969) collated subsurface well temperatures in South Louisiana and constructed a contour map for the area showing isotherms at a depth of 3050 m (Fig. 2), illustrating a hot belt slightly south of the present coastline with temperatures 10 to 15° C hotter than the surrounding area. Extrapolating their geothermobaric

curve to a depth of 15,240 m, the thickness of the sedimentary pile under the hot belt, they concluded that the base of the section was undergoing albite-epidote hornfels facies metamorphism.

As before, these data from the Gulf Coast may be compared with analogous data from the Indonesian island arc (Fig. 3) and, as before, the contrast is marked. The Indonesian data are on a surface only half the depth of those in the Gulf Coast yet the temperature values are very similar because of the higher heat flow associated with the Javanese volcanoes. In general, sources of underground heat are of varied origin and include convection currents in the mantle, radioactive disintegration of elements in basement crystalline rocks, and release of heat during crystallization of magma.

Superimposed on the fundamental irregularity in space and time of these heat sources are variations in conductivities of rocks and fluids

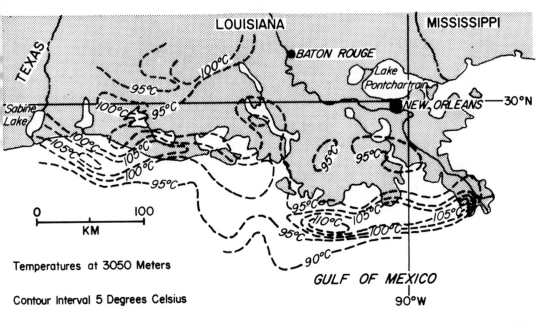

Temperatures at 3050 Meters

Contour Interval 5 Degrees Celsius

FIG. 2.—Temperatures in south Louisiana at a depth of 3050 m illustrating the irregular isotherms characteristic of this type of map (from Jam L. *et al.*, 1969).

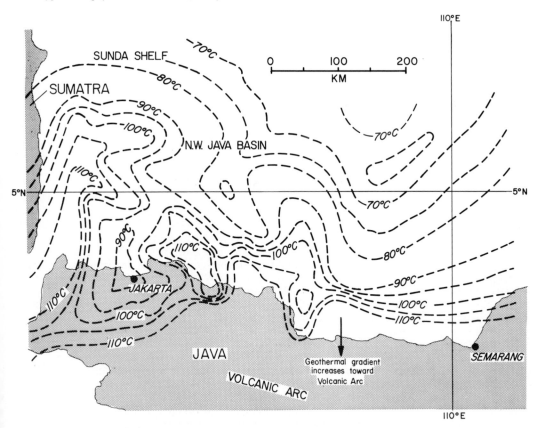

FIG. 3.—Temperatures in northwestern Java Basin, Indonesia, at a depth of 1525 m illustrating the effect of volcanism on geothermal gradient (modified from Fletcher and Bay, 1975).

in sedimentary columns. Water has a low conductivity compared to rocks, so that very porous rocks and mudrocks containing water structurally bound to clay minerals are better insulators than non-porous sandstones. Overpressured or under-consolidated mudrocks, like those common in modern geoclinal regions such as the Gulf Coast, are particularly poor conductors of heat. At the other extreme of conductivity are salt domes, which serve as heat funnels in Gulf Coast rocks and are the cause of some of the ovoid areas of high temperature (Fig. 2). The existence of ovoid positive heat anomalies in the Indonesian sediments requires a different explanation, perhaps related to the presence of shallow bodies of magma.

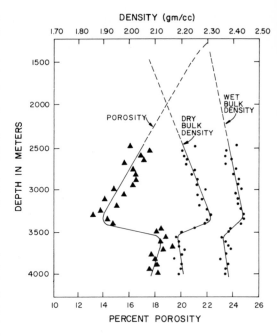

FIG. 4.—Sharp increases in porosity and decrease in bulk density of shale at the top of an overpressured zone in the Manchester Field, Calcasieu Parish, Louisiana (from Schmidt, 1973).

VARIATION IN STRESS

Stresses in the subsurface can be either hydrostatic or non-hydrostatic, with the hydrostatic gradient approximating 10 bars/100 meters. Very few quantitative data are available concerning the magnitude of non-hydrostatic stress in compacting sediments. Published work tends to treat "lithostatic pressure" as hydrostatic multiplied by 2.65 although the vertical pressure on a compacting mass of sediments is certainly greater than the confining pressure in a horizontal plane. This difference may be significant during compaction as sand in a lenticular unit is forced laterally into easily deformable muddy units.

Of considerable importance in the development of subsurface stress fields in sediments is the existence of undercompacted or overpressured zones in muds and associated lenticular sands in geoclinal sediments (Hower et al., 1976; Burst, 1976; Bradley, 1975). Many muds are composed initially of large percentages of interlayered smectite-illite among their clay minerals and, at temperatures approximating 100° C, the smectite-illite reacts with potassium in associated potassic feldspars and interstitial waters to increase the proportion of illite layers. The conversion of smectite to illite releases large amounts of water from the clay structure in several discontinuous stages (Burst, 1976) whose timing varies with rate of change of temperature and pressure; i.e., rate of burial. These changes can result in volumetric expansion of the muddy unit and decrease in mudrock density so often found at depths below about 3000 m in thick Tertiary deltaic sequences such as the Gulf Coast (Fig. 4). The "new" water can be forced into adjoining permeable sands so that they, too, become undercompacted. Powers (1967) has shown that the volume of water produced by alteration of montmorillonite to illite is equal to approximately one-half the volume of the original montmorillonite. Additional stress leading to sediment expansion and undercompac-

tion is generated by the normal expansion of water with the increased temperature that accompanies increased burial depth (Magura, 1975).

Abnormal pressures can also originate when sand and mud are deposited faster than the included fluids can adjust to the added weight. The rapidly increasing load must be partly supported by the fluid that is trapped as a result of the decrease in porosity and permeability during compaction. Other causes of overpressuring include faulting, tectonic activity, and many other factors. Fertl and Chilingarian (1977) provide a complete list of possible causes.

The existence of abnormal ("excess") fluid pressures requires that an impermeable seal be present. When the seal is broken by the development of joints, faults, or other conduits for fluids, normal compaction pressures develop rapidly so that most overpressured units are of Tertiary age.

COMPACTION

Many investigators have compacted quartz sands in laboratory experiments with the result that the thickness of the aggregate is decreased about 10–15% as a result of rearrangement and chipping of grains. The amount of compaction increases significantly, however, with the proportion of ductile rock fragments such as mud clasts,

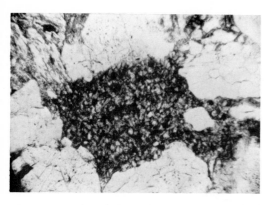

FIG. 5.—Medium sand size mud fragment after compaction between more rigid quartz and feldspar grains. Original porosity and permeability are practically eliminated.

schist fragments, or books of mica (Fig. 5). These grains deform easily under relatively light load, thinning the stratigraphic section and decreasing porosity. In her classic study, Taylor (1950) recognized four types of grain-to-grain contacts in thin sections: tangential, long, concavo-convex, and sutured. Tangential contacts decreased rapidly in abundance with depth, from 52% of all contacts at 900 m to zero at 2200 m (Fig. 6). Sutured contacts increased from zero at 1700 m to 32% at 2700 m. Concavo-convex and long contacts, however, increased in abundance with increasing depth but then declined. Taylor was aware of the factors influencing the relative abundances of different types of contacts, but her petrographic work was not sufficiently detailed to determine how much of the increased closeness of grains was due to plastic deformation of elongate ductile fragments and how much resulted from either an increase in percentage of elongate rock fragments with depth or increases in clay content of the sandstones.

Increased compaction of sand is inversely correlated with the porosity of the sand, so that decrease in porosity with depth in uncemented Tertiary sands is a measure of the degree of compaction. Atwater and Miller (1965) collated porosity vs. depth data from more than 17,000 cores of subsurface sands in south Louisiana (Fig. 7) and found that below a depth of 350 m porosity decreases linearly with depth, from 38% to about 18% at 6000 m. Presumably the decrease results from increased plastic deformation of ductile rock fragments with depth, but Atwater and Miller made no petrographic studies of their core samples.

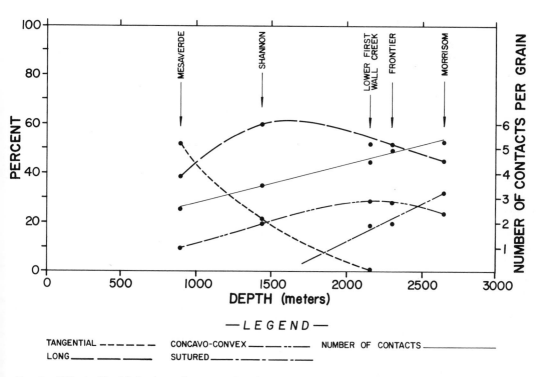

FIG. 6.—Effect of burial depth on the types of grain-to-grain contacts in Jurassic and Cretaceous sandstones in two wells in Fremont County, Wyoming (from Taylor, 1950).

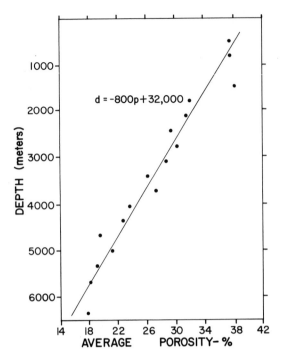

$$d = -800p + 32,000$$

FIG. 7.—Relationship between depth of burial and porosity of 17,367 bottom-hole cores of late Tertiary sandstones in southern Louisiana. Data points were averaged for each 1000 feet to obtain the 17 data points shown (from an unpublished manuscript by G. I. Atwater and E. E. Miller, 1965).

Hsü (1977) studied the effect of compaction on Pliocene oil sands in the Ventura Basin of California using both thin section observations and permeability measurements. He determined that the decrease of three orders of magnitude in permeability with three thousand meters of burial did not result from either precipitation of authigenic cement or variation in grain size. The sole cause was compaction and increased closeness of packing.

In eugeoclinal sections the ductility of many fragments may be greatly increased by the chemical changes associated with production of a phyllosilicate "mush" from originally non-ductile fragments. This diagenetic matrix may be produced largely from existing fragments in a porous sand (Whetten and Hawkins, 1970), with a resulting "second generation" of compaction and loss of porosity. The quantitative importance of this effect has not been evaluated.

AUTHIGENESIS

Geologic problems are posed initially by relationships seen in rocks, both in the field and in the laboratory. Based on these studies, a useful subdivision of diagenetic phenomena can be made

on the basis of lithology. Sands containing only unyielding grains such as quartz and feldspar do not compact as much as sands containing appreciable amounts of clay or ductile rock fragments such as phyllite or schist. Further, this latter group of sands commonly is lithified by compaction alone, without noticeable introduction of chemical precipitates such as calcite or quartz.

Often this subdivision based on sand composition can be correlated with tectonic setting. Cratonic sands usually lack ductile rock fragments and clay and, therefore, must have a precipitate in their pore spaces to be lithified. Quartz, calcite, and hematite are most common. Quantitatively minor authigenesis of clay minerals also may occur, but normally is not the main lithifying agent in the sands. Eugeoclinal sands typically are lithified by clays and micas produced by diagenetic alteration of chemically unstable lithic fragments of volcanic origin ("graywackes").

The precipitation of minerals from subsurface solutions in sandstones was first recognized in thin sections about 100 years ago when Sorby (1880) identified secondary growths on detrital quartz grains. His observations have been extended by a host of subsequent sandstone petrographers and the number of minerals known to be formed during diagenesis now numbers more than 20. Most of these are volumetrically unimportant, however; and although no reliable data are available, it seems clear that calcite and quartz form the bulk of the solids precipitated in sands after burial. In many sandstones authigenic clays and other micaceous minerals have formed, as emphasized by the recently intensified use of scanning electron microscopy in petrologic studies. A variety of authigenic zeolites has been reported in Cenozoic volcanoclastic sandstones. Other secondary minerals reported to have formed in sandstones during diagenesis include hematite, feldspars, dolomite, siderite, anhydrite and gypsum, barite, several titanium oxide minerals, zircon, tourmaline, and most recently, garnet.

The large variety of secondary minerals in sandstones is to be expected because of the large range in physical and chemical conditions included in "diagenesis." Equally expectable is the replacement of one secondary mineral by another or the dissolution of a mineral to produce secondary porosity. Such changes are a consequence of subsidence, uplift, and changing flow patterns of underground fluids. Descriptions of the replacement of one cement by another are common in published petrographic studies of sandstones (e.g., Levandowski *et al.*, 1973; Glover, 1963).

QUARTZ

Studies of sandstones that include units partially or completely cemented by secondary silica (orthoquartzites) are common features of many

FIG. 8.—SEM of authigenic quartz growing into pore space, with authigenic illite coating the secondary quartz; Niton sand (Cretaceous), Canada (Courtesy J. B. Thomas, Amoco Production Co.).

petrographic investigations. From these studies and relevant geochemical data several generalizations can be made.

1. Those sands composed almost entirely of detrital quartz almost always contain at least a small amount of petrographically visible secondary silica. The silica occurs as overgrowths (Fig. 8) in optical continuity with the detrital nuclei and usually as rhombohedra because rhombohedral faces grow faster than prism faces on quartz. Secondary quartz not in optical continuity with any surrounding quartz grains is rare or absent because thermodynamic considerations favor extension of an existing crystal structure rather than *de novo* nucleation in a void space. The initial rhomb or prism faces are lost as overgrowths from adjacent detrital grains abut to form crystallographically irrational compromise boundary surfaces that are easily mistaken for pressure solution features (Pittman, 1972).

2. It is uncommon to find an appreciable volume of secondary quartz in mineralogically less mature sandstones such as arkoses and lithic arenites. The cementing agent in these rocks normally is calcite, hematite, or diagenetically produced clay minerals. This observation is consistent with the hypothesis that the detrital grains themselves serve as a partial source of dissolved silica for precipitation in an adjacent part of the rock unit. The fewer detrital quartz grains, the less secondary quartz. The detrital quartz grains serve both as a source of dissolved silica and as a substrate for precipitated silica.

3. The equilibrium solubility of quartz in water at 25° C is 6 ppm and it rises relatively slowly with increasing temperature (21 ppm at 50° C; 62 ppm at 100° C; 140 ppm at 150° C). Solubility is increased also by increasing hydrostatic pressure; at 1 kb the increase is about 35% (Willey, 1974, p. 242). These solubilities are comparable to the dissolved silica contents of underground waters (oil-field brines), in which values range up to at least 100 ppm (White *et al.*, 1963), suggesting that the equilibrium solubility of quartz is the major buffer for the silica content of underground waters in sandstones. The most recent confirmation of this control of silica content by the solubility of quartz is the work of McMurtry *et al.* (1977) who successfully used dissolved silica as a geothermometer for groundwater in Hawaii.

Shallow nearshore sea water contains an average of less than 1 ppm dissolved silica. Hence, connate waters in marine quartz sands have a content of dissolved silica at least an order of magnitude less than the amounts typical of sub-surface waters. Even at the surface, large amounts of silica are required simply to raise the silica content from less than 1 ppm to the 6 ppm needed to saturate the pore solution. Then additional amounts of dissolved silica are needed to make possible the precipitation of sufficient quartz to fill the pores of the original sand. For the average well sorted quartz sand, the porosity is about 40%.

Fluvial or surface waters average 13 ppm dissolved silica, adequate to initiate precipitation of quartz in pore spaces but only an infinitesimally small volume of quartz can be produced from a single pore volume of connate waters. For fluvial connate waters, as well as for marine connate waters, we are faced with the hydraulic problem of moving a sufficient number of pore volumes of water through the quartz sand unit.

Assuming a dissolved silica content of 32.5 ppm in a pore water and a precipitable silica of 26.5 ppm (6 ppm must remain in the solution to keep it saturated with respect to quartz), $1/10^5$ of the volume of each pore can be filled with quartz by each pore volume of water (Sibley and Blatt, 1976). The number of pore volumes of water required to reduce the porosity to half its original volume is then

$$V_{1/2} = \frac{1}{k} \ln 2 = \frac{.693}{10^{-5}}$$

$$= 7 \times 10^4 \text{ pore volumes of water.}$$

This number of pore volumes is not greatly changed by doubling or tripling the amount of silica in solution.

How much time is required to move this much water through a well-sorted quartz sand to convert it into an orthoquartzite? If we assume a homogeneous sheet of quartz sand only 6.4×10^4 m (40 miles) in length and width and 20 meters in thickness, and assume a high velocity of flow of pore water of 20 m/yr., then one pore volume of water would pass through the sand every 3,200 years (6.4×10^4 m/20m/yr.). If the unit has 16% pore space to be filled with quartz derived from a source outside the boundaries of the unit, to reduce the porosity to only 2% requires 6.7×10^8 years, clearly a geologically unacceptable answer. Evidence from structural geology indicates that quartz sands much more extensive than that used in our example are lithified by secondary quartz within a few tens of millions of years.

Something must be wrong with the initial assumptions. There are adequate data to support the assumptions concerning the amount of dissolved silica in pore waters; and approximately 20 m/yr is the rate of flow of some of the nation's major buried aquifers. The width of the sand unit in our example is quite small; for example, the Tuscarora Formation is 7–8× the width of the unit in our example. The only assumption for which there is no firm support is the assumption of a horizontal flow path for the circulating pore waters. Suppose cementation is caused by vertically circulating surface waters at a time when the sand unit is relatively close to the surface, say 100 meters. This might occur either soon after burial or at any subsequent time that tectonic forces raise the unit to a near-surface position. The distance of flow is reduced from 6.4×10^4 meters to 120 meters, allowing one pore volume of water to pass through in only six years and reduction of porosity to 2% in 1.3×10^6 years. Decrease in flow velocity by an order of magnitude to only 2.0 m/yr. increases cementation time to 1.3×10^7 years, still a geologically reasonable answer. These considerations strongly suggest that the bulk of the quartz cement in orthoquartzites is precipitated at very shallow depths. Flow rates of underground water are simply too slow to do the job once the sand is buried to depths greater than a few hundred meters.

This inference based on hydraulic and geochemical considerations is consistent with petrographic observations of orthoquartzitic sandstones (Greensmith, 1957; Sibley and Blatt, 1976). Greensmith examined Upper Carboniferous sandstones in England and noted no evidence of interpenetration of detrital quartz grains and few grains in grain-to-grain contact. Sibley and Blatt (1976) examined the Tuscarora orthoquartzite in detail and made a reconnaisance examination of numerous other orthoquartzites using luminescence petrography. They found few interpenetrating grains and many "floating" grains (Fig. 9). This implies that precipitation of secondary quartz occurred rather soon after deposition and at a shallow depth, before a great deal of compaction of the detrital grains took place. Folk (1960, p. 19) observed that although there was no direct evidence of the time of origin of the quartz cement

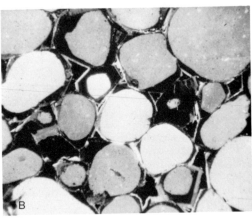

Fig. 9.—Medium sand size quartz grains in the Tuscarora Orthoquartzite (Silurian, West Virginia) in uncrossed nicols (*A*) and under cathodoluminescence (*B*). Apparent pressure solution contacts are clearly seen to be formed of secondary quartz abutting in original pore space.

in the Tuscarora, "the full-bodied slate fragments in the red Tuscarora indicate probable quartz cementation prior to much compaction." Petrographic evidence of very early cementation of sands by quartz also has been reported by numerous other workers (e.g., Dapples, 1959; Siever, 1959; Bucke and Mankin, 1971; Blanche and Whitaker, 1978). Millot (1970, p. 277–301) has emphasized that the formation of macrocrystalline quartz rather than chert or chalcedony from saturated solution is favored by a lack of other ions in solution; i.e., meteoric rather than saline waters.

An important question remains unanswered, however. In some areas there exist Cenozoic quartz sands that have had surface waters circulating through them for tens of millions of years. Yet these sands are still unlithified. What are the kinetic factors that have prevented the excess silica in solution from nucleating on detrital quartz surfaces and cementing the sand? To date, there have been few experimental studies of the kinetic factors involved in quartz nucleation and we can only speculate about the part played by factors such as organic matter, pH, fluorine ion activity, salinity, or other variables (Harder and Flehmig, 1970; Mackenzie and Gees, 1971; Stein and Kirkpatrick, 1976; Kastner *et al.*, 1977).

Possible sources of silica.—Throughout this discussion we have assumed that the solubility of quartz is 6 ppm and, as surface waters average 13 ppm, sufficient dissolved silica is present from this source to cause cementation (Friedman, 1954; Riezebos, 1974). Meteoric waters are known to circulate to depths of many hundreds of meters so that the source of silica was not a problem. However, the solubility of quartz increases with depth and, as noted previously, the content of dissolved silica in many subsurface waters is several tens of ppm. Although surface water contains sufficient silica in solution to promote quartz cementation at shallow depth (the solubility of quartz rises to 13 ppm at a depth of a few hundred meters), it is clear that additional sources of dissolved silica are required to account for the concentrations present in oil field brines at depths of several thousand meters.

Only two sources seem sufficiently general in distribution to raise the silica content of subsurface brines from the amount in the connate water (less than 1 ppm for marine waters and 13 ppm for nonmarine waters) to the values in the brines. These are pressure solution and the silica released during diagenesis of clay minerals.

The realization that the diagenetic conversion of smectite or interlayered smectite-illite to pure illite might be an important source of silica to pore solutions occurred in 1962 (Siever; Towe). In calculating the amount of free silica that might be produced, Siever assumed a pure sodium montmorillonite, dissolved it, and precipitated pure illite from the solution. Towe, on the other hand, assumed that the structural state of the starting material is conserved and that smectitic layers are converted to illitic layers by substitution of magnesium and iron for aluminum in the octahedral layers; and substitution of aluminum for silicon in tetrahedral layers. Towe's proposed mechanism is much more likely than Siever's from the viewpoint of chemical energetics, and has been discussed in some detail by Weaver and Beck (1971) from the viewpoint of sequential changes in the clay structure. The free silica released by this mechanism was estimated by Towe to equal 2.2 grams of quartz or chert per 100 grams of clay transformed. Mudrocks average only 60% clay minerals so that even if all the original clay

were interlayered smectite-illite and all the dissolved silica released were to crystallize within the mudrock, only 1.3% of quartz or chert would be added to the mineral composition of the mudrock. It would be nearly impossible to detect so small an addition using standard petrographic techniques because of the variable amounts of detrital quartz and chert in mudrocks (Blatt and Schultz, 1976).

It is clear, therefore, that although dissolved silica is produced by clay mineral diagenesis, it is possible that the silica might remain in the shale and be undetected. We can not simply assume that diagenesis of clay minerals is an important source of silica for cementation of quartz sands. Field observations are required to support such a hypothesis. Phillip *et al.* (1963) and Füchtbauer (1967) reported that cementation by quartz in the Dogger Sandstone increases toward the shaley margin of the bed, presumably as a result of "leakage" of dissolved silica from the shale. The decrease in porosity was small, however, and Füchtbauer noted that "a minor addition of silica suffices to explain the increased marginal quartz diagenesis . . . ." Similar observations have been made in the United States, although they apparently have not been published. It is significant that the presence of the secondary quartz is confined to the margins of the sand rather than occurring throughout the unit, suggesting that the amount of silica released from the shales is small, even when it does occur.

Hower *et al.* (1976) conducted a detailed mineralogic, sedimentologic, and geochemical study of two cores from late Tertiary sediments in the Gulf Coast. Their results indicated to them that the mudrocks acted as a closed system with respect to silica migration during clay mineral diagenesis. Because of difficulties inherent in the interpretation of analyses of ancient rocks, it is uncertain whether the data of Hower *et al.* are adequate to preclude all leakage of silica or simply large-scale leakage.

In summary, it seems possible that a small amount of soluble silica can sometimes be exported from mudrocks during their diagenesis, but there is no evidence of wholesale migration of silica.

Pressure solution.—The phenomenon known as pressure solution was first seen in thin section soon after the development of the polarizing microscope more than 100 years ago and, since that time, an extensive literature has developed concerning it (Trurnit, 1968; de Boer, 1977; Robin, 1978). During the past 20 years it has become the most generally accepted mechanism for increasing the amount of dissolved silica in pore solutions and stimulating the growth of secondary quartz. The standard criterion for recognizing the presence of pressure solution in orthoquartzites has been the existence of sutured contacts between apparently detrital parts of adjacent quartz grains. Sippel (1968), however, showed that standard petrographic techniques often can not distinguish between the detrital grain and its overgrowth. Using luminescence petrography, Sippel demonstrated that many of the interdigitations between adjacent grains were in fact either compromise boundaries between overgrowths or pressure solution between overgrowths (Fig. 9). As overgrowth-overgrowth contacts they could not be a source of silica to pore solutions. More recently, Sibley and Blatt (1976) made a quantitative study of cementation of the Tuscarora orthoquartzite using luminescence petrography. They determined that pressure solution between the detrital parts of the orthoquartzite could not have supplied more than one-third of the silica present as secondary quartz in the formation. Reconnaissance examination by them of other orthoquartzites yielded similar results; published qualitative observations by other petrographers studying other units are consistent with the data of Sibley and Blatt (1976). Pressure solution is an important source of dissolved silica but not the major one for cementation of orthoquartzites. It adds silica to pore waters, perhaps enough to account for the concentrations typical of oil field brines.

Other sources of silica.—Other sources of silica for pore waters are known but currently are thought to be either important only locally or else quantitatively trivial. Volcanic rock fragments are altered diagenetically and yield dissolved silica. But such fragments normally are not produced in the cratonic and shelf environments where most orthoquartzites occur. Dissolution of feldspars and accessory minerals during diagenesis has been reported frequently and Fothergill (1955) and Hawkins (1978) reported a statistical correlation between the occurrence of diagenetically kaolinized feldspar and secondary quartz overgrowths. These phenomena are generally believed to be quantitatively unimportant as sources of silica. Diatoms and radiolaria are mostly of silt size and are deposited with muds or carbonate sediments rather than in river sand bars or on beaches and barrier bars. The question of whether dissolved silica from siliceous skeletons in muds is exported into adjacent sands is unanswerable at present. The same is true of carbonate sediments. Is all the silica in modern carbonates used in the formation of chert in these rocks?

CALCITE

Although the petrography and geochemistry of limestone formation have been studied extensively, there have been few investigations concerned with the origin of calcium carbonate cement in sandstones. Some useful generalizations can be made.

1. Calcareous cement in Pleistocene or Holocene quartz sands usually is calcite rather than aragonite, and occurs in fibrous, drusy, or granular forms. Aragonite cement is totally absent from pre-Pleistocene sands. Most commonly the calcium carbonate for the cement is produced by dissolution of shell material, with precipitation induced either by downward flow of meteoric water or evaporation of marine waters forced upward through the quartz sand beach or bar. Davies (1967) made a detailed stratigraphic and petrographic analysis of thin interbedded friable sandstones and calcite-cemented sandstones in Liassic sediments in England and concluded that the calcite cement precipitated before the deposition of 15 cm of overlying sediments. He believes that cementation was accomplished within about 150 years.

2. There is no direct petrologic evidence concerning the timing of calcite cementation in ancient sandstones but inferences are often made based on the absence of compaction phenomena in thin sections, tectonic considerations, and the hydraulic gradients produced by uplifts whose dates are known (Todd, 1963; Wright, 1964; Warner, 1965; Phipps, 1969; Flesch and Wilson, 1974; Stalder, 1975, Morgan *et al.*, 1976).

Each of these authors either stated or implied that cementation of the sandstone occurred during a time when the unit was at or near the surface. This conclusion for calcite cement is consistent with that arrived at for quartz cement using different types of data. The impression one obtains is that a great deal of cementation (or decementation) occurs at very shallow depths and will frequently be related to the presence of unconformities in the stratigraphic column.

3. The geochemistry of calcium carbonate is considerably more complex than that of silica. Recent summaries of the problems involved are provided by Blatt *et al.* (1972), Berner (1971), Krauskopf (1967) and Garrels and Christ (1965). The explanation of the increased complexity is that (1) the relevant equilibria for calcite precipitation involve a gas phase; (2) nearly all of the chemical species involved are ions rather than neutral molecules such as H_4SiO_4; (3) Calcite solubility is extremely sensitive to pH change, unlike quartz, which is unaffected by pH change within the range found in the subsurface; (4) Calcite is much more soluble than quartz and thus more susceptible to pressure solution. Each of these facts has numerous implications for carbonate cementation.

At atmospheric P_{CO_2}, sea water is saturated to slightly supersaturated with respect to either aragonite or calcite but the water becomes undersaturated if P_{CO_2} is increased. This may occur because of organic decay or respiration of animals, or because of metamorphic decarbonation reactions occurring at depth. Carbon dioxide gas is also exolved by an increase in total salinity.

The important chemical species into which calcite dissolves are H_2CO_3, HCO_3^-, CO_3^{-2}, and Ca^{+2}. All of these, excepting undissociated carbonic acid, are charged species, which means that they have a high tendency to form ion pairs with other charged species in the pore waters. As a result, their thermodynamic activities are often at least an order of magnitude less than their concentrations. Among abundant cations in sea water, the neutral magnesium carbonate pair is probably the most common in subsurface waters.

Because carbonate and calcium in water are ions, changes in their concentrations (and activities) are effected by the process of salt sieving. The process of salt sieving occurs during compac-tion, as clay flakes in mudrocks act as semiper-meable membranes. Essentially fresh water escapes upward toward the surface but dissolved salts remain below the clay membrane. The effec-tiveness of this process is reflected in the general trend in subsurface waters toward increasing salinity with depth (Fig. 10). Salt sieving can continue to be effective after compaction has largely ceased. Near the center of a basin, the water can move upward through confining strata as the result of the hydrostatic pressure of me-teoric waters in the updip parts of the aquifer.

The significance of the ionic character of a dissolved species lies in the fact that not all species are held with equal ease below the clay membrane. Most strongly held are ions of large size and charge; for example, calcium > magne-sium > potassium > sodium. Divalent ions are held more strongly below the membrane because their bond with the clay flake is more directional

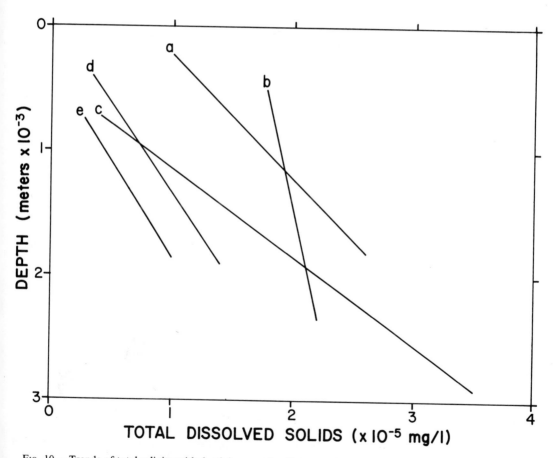

FIG. 10.—Trends of total salinity with depth in several sedimentary basins and formations; (a) Cherokee Group, Pennsylvanian, Oklahoma; (b) Wilcox and Simpson sands, Ordovician, Oklahoma; (c) Rodessa, Hosston, Cotton Valley, and Smackover Formations, Jurassic-Cretaceous, Arkansas and Louisiana; (d) Wilcox sands, Eocene, Louisiana; (e) Woodbine and Eagle Ford Formations, Cretaceous, Texas. (From Dickey, 1969).

(covalent) than that of a monovalent ion. Large ions are held more strongly because their electrostatic charge is distributed over a larger surface, is correspondingly weaker, and attracts a thinner coating of water molecules. Hence, the bond between the ion and the clay flake is stronger. Electrical neutrality is maintained below the membrane by diffusion of the hydrated hydrogen proton downward as other cations diffuse upward. This concept of selective diffusion of cations is supported by several field studies (White, 1965; Billings *et al.*, 1969). Anions are rejected by the negatively charged clay structure and remain below the membrane, but the addition of the hydrogen ions causes increased acidity and a corresponding decrease in the CO_3^{-2}/HCO_3^- ratio below the membrane. Thus, the tendency in subsurface waters is to increase the concentration of calcium ions, decrease the concentration of carbonate ions, and increase total salinity, which has the effect of decreasing the activities of all ions. One can only speculate concerning the net effect on the precipitation of carbonate cements.

The ease of precipitating calcite cement in sandstones increases with burial depth because calcite solubility decreases with increasing temperature (because of the escape of carbon dioxide gas). Solubility increases somewhat with increasing hydrostatic pressure, but the net effect is to decrease the solubility of calcite with increasing burial depth. This contrasts sharply with the solubility of quartz, which increases with burial depth. Although the solubilities of both minerals increase with pressure; the effect is greater for calcite, suggesting that pressure solution (non-hydrostatic stress) may be a more important source of calcium and carbonate ions to pore waters than it was for monosilicic acid molecules. This possibility is supported by Hudson (1975) who points out that the carbon isotopic ratio in the average ancient limestone is identical to the ratio in modern marine carbonate sediments with no apparent influence of isotopically light carbon from vadose or phreatic meteoric waters. He proposes to explain this identity by the derivation of most calcite cement in limestones by pressure solution of the clastic sediment during burial diagenesis. Isotopically "light" carbon formed during initial lithification under surface and near-surface conditions would be removed or diluted beyond recognition by pressure solution. It is conceivable that excess ions from pressure solution of limestones at depth can be supplied to adjacent sandstones for precipitation in sandstones.

Dunnington (1967) examined several petroliferous limestones in which stylolites were prominent and inferred from structural considerations that they were formed at depths between 700 m and 900 m. He concluded that "Many markedly stylolitic limestones have suffered a thickness reduction of 20–25% since induration, and reductions of the order of 40% have been recorded." (p. 341). He further noted (p. 342) that in the average limestone the volume of rock dissolved is greater than the pore space to be filled so that "some material must have passed out of the system, to precipitate elsewhere."

The possibility of export of calcium carbonate from limestones has been further supported by Mimran (1977) in his study of Upper Cretaceous English chalks. He concluded that pervasive pressure solution occurred at a depth of 500 m, removing approximately 90% of the original carbonate sediment over a time period of 15–20 million years. The subsequent fate of this carbonate "juice" is unknown but the potential of such a source for calcite cementation of adjacent sandstones is obvious.

Dissolution of carbonate rocks (or previously formed calcite cement in sandstones) can also result from the maturation of organic matter in rocks. Organic matter contains an abundance of fatty acids and esters which release carbon dioxide gas as they are broken down to simpler compounds. These processes occur as a result of microbial activities near the surface and thermal maturation during deeper burial but the relative amounts of decarboxylation and deesterification that occur at different depths is uncertain. As a result, the quantitative importance of these processes as a means of increasing the P_{CO_2} and acidity of subsurface waters is unknown.

INTERACTION BETWEEN QUARTZ AND CALCITE

There are no adequate data from which to determine whether quartz or calcite is a more abundant pore filling in sandstones, and the subjective impressions of individual petrographers can be easily biased. However, there is a general consensus that quartz predominates over calcite (Füchtbauer and Müller, 1970; Pettijohn, 1975). In the one study that tried to collect relevant data (Tallman, 1949) it was noted that the type of cement seems to be a function of geologic age, calcite predominating in younger sandstones, quartz in older ones. Calcite is an order of magnitude more soluble than quartz in sea water and Tallman's data can be interpreted to indicate that this relationship holds under most diagenetic conditions as well. If calcite is more easily dissolved there will be a statistical tendency for quartz cement to become more abundant in older sandstones. This may occur either through simple void filling after all the calcite has been removed or may occur in the presence of calcite. In the latter case, undigested shreds of the carbonate can be present within the secondary quartz and this observation is often reported. The reasons why calcite remains more soluble than quartz during diagenesis are unknown. Given the many variables that affect the solubility of calcium carbonate this is hardly surprising.

CLAY MINERALS

Clay minerals in sandstones are both detrital and diagenetic in origin and usually the relative proportions of each can not be determined. The exceptions are the clay-bearing but otherwise well-sorted and rounded sandstones in which the clay can be seen either in thin section or in the scanning electron microscope to be euhedral and/or in growth position normal to sand grain surfaces (Fig. 11A, B, C). The SEM has proven to be a powerful tool in the recognition of authigenic clay minerals but is untested on sandstones containing mixtures of detrital and authigenic clay, such as many graywackes.

In pure quartz sandstones the volume of pore space that is filled by authigenic clay is very small and kaolinite (or its polymorph, dickite) predominates. The required alumina is brought in by circulating waters. Because the volume of authigenic clay is so limited in quartz sands, the number of pore volumes of water that must pass through the sand is much less than was required to fill the pores with quartz or calcite. Hence, the kaolinite may have formed at a greater depth. However, it is required that the circulating waters be of meteoric origin, for montmorillonite or illite will precipitate rather than kaolinite unless they are sufficiently dilute. Calculations indicate the

value of $\log \left[\dfrac{Na^+}{H^+} \right]^2$ cannot exceed 13 and the

value of $\log \left[\dfrac{K^+}{H^+} \right]^2$ cannot exceed 20. In sea

water these values are 10^8 and 10^6, respectively, but in average river water they are only 8 and 5. As was the case for the precipitation of quartz and calcite cements, flushing at shallow depth by meteoric waters can be inferred.

Some quartz sands contain authigenic montmorillonite, illite, or chlorite (Wilson and Pittman, 1977). Clearly, they can not be produced by

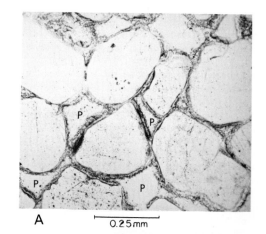

A 0.25 mm

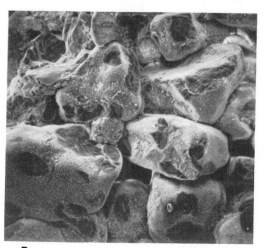

B 0.25 mm

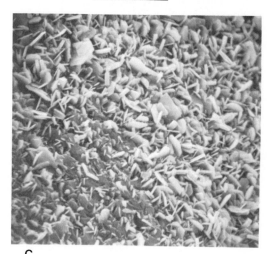

C 10 μ

FIG. 11.—*A*, Thin section showing authigenic chlorite coating quartz grains in the Spiro sand (Pennsylvanian), McAlester Basin, Oklahoma; P = pore. *B*, SEM at low magnification illustrating the absence of the authigenic clay at points of contact of adjacent quartz grains (dark areas). *C*, SEM at high magnification showing bladed character of the chlorite. (Photos courtesy E. D. Pittman, Amoco Production Co.)

meteoric flushing, and they are very unlikely to have been produced by flushing with sea water because of the difficulty of maintaining a suitable hydraulic gradient between the sea floor and the land surface. The source of the required metallic cations for these clay minerals must be either from subjacent mudrocks or dirty sands during their diagenesis or from sources internal to the sandstone. If the light mineral fraction is entirely quartz and chert, heavy minerals can provide the cations and the nature of this process as it pertains to the release of iron from heavy minerals has been discussed by Walker (1967; Walker *et al.,* 1967). Intrastratal dissolution of ferromagnesian minerals during diagenesis of porous sands has often been documented.

The formation of authigenic clay minerals in less mineralogically mature sands such as arkoses, lithic sands, graywackes, etc., can be understood almost entirely in terms of internal sources of ions. Only enough transport of pore water is required to maintain diagenetic alteration of the detrital grains and release of ions to the water. Thus, shallow depth to enhance the volume of circulated water is not critical. Indeed, greater depth and resulting higher temperature is the preferred condition to stimulate authigenesis, with illite being favored in arkoses and montmorillonite in volcanoclastic sandstones. Whetten and Hawkins (1970) have produced montmorillonitic clay matrix from Columbia River sand in laboratory experiments with non-circulating water at 250° C. Galloway (1974) and Merino (1975a,b) have recently discussed the close relationship between detrital and authigenic mineralogy in sands of different composition.

In many volcanoclastic sandstones authigenic clays are accompanied by zeolites of similar composition. The factors favoring growth of zeolites rather than clays in these rocks are unknown because of the variable compositions of the minerals in both groups and the small differences in free energy among the zeolites.

HEMATITE

Because of the high P_{O_2} at the earth's surface, iron released during weathering of ferromagnesian minerals from crystalline rocks is nearly always precipitated as ferric hydroxide or oxide. During the past 10 years, Walker (1974) and Walker *et al.* (1978) have studied the origin of the red pigment in mineralogically immature sands of late Tertiary and Quaternary age and have documented the method by which it accumulates to form red sandstones. The formation of hematite apparently can occur through intrastratal solution as well as in association with changes in the elevation of the ground water table during weathering. The only requirements for the authigenesis of hematite in pore spaces are a source of iron atoms and sufficient circulation of meteoric water to maintain oxidizing conditions in the pores. The rarity of minerals such as siderite and pyrite in sandstones indicates circulation is usually sufficient. Time periods on the order of 10^6 years are adequate to form the bulk of the red pigment.

SUMMARY

Quartz and calcite form the bulk of the diagenetically produced pore filling in sandstones, a circumstance directly related to conditions at the site of deposition. The normal preponderance of quartz among detrital fragments keeps pore waters enriched in dissolved silica during diagenesis, and this enrichment is supplemented by pressure solution and probably also by silica released during diagenesis of clay minerals. Subsurface alteration of feldspars and accessory minerals also may be locally important as a silica source.

The abundance of calcite cement in sandstones results from the fact that connate sea water in shallow marine sediments is oversaturated with respect to calcium carbonate. Additional calcium and carbonate ions may result from dissolution of fossils, clay membrane filtration, or pressure solution of adjacent limestone units during diagenesis.

Calculations reveal that sandstones are difficult or impossible to lithify by precipitation of cement from laterally migrating pore waters because of their slow rate of flow. There is the strong implication that the precipitation of both calcite and quartz is accomplished by vertically circulating groundwaters. This process of cementation is most efficient when the sands are located close to the surface so that flow distance is minimized; depths less than a few hundred meters are required. For calcite, the depth may be greater because an adequate amount of carbonate-rich pore water is available from underground sources. Cementation may occur either soon after burial or at any subsequent time when structural deformation elevates buried sands to a near-surface position. With respect to pure quartz sands, almost the only sands that are lithified by secondary quartz, this implies cementation within a few tens of millions of years after deposition because of the cratonic and shallow shelf environments in which these sands occur. Sands cemented by calcite are common in a wide variety of tectonic settings and consequently are, on the average, buried more deeply and undergo more structural uplift than pure quartz sands. Hence, initial cementation by calcite may occur later in time, on the average, than cementation by quartz.

REFERENCES

ATWATER, G. I., AND MILLER, E. E., 1965, The effect of decrease in porosity with depth on future development of oil and gas reserves in south Louisiana [abs.]: Am. Assoc. Petroleum Geologists Bull., v. 49, p. 334.

BERNER, R. A., 1971, Principles of chemical sedimentology: New York, McGraw-Hill Book Co., Inc., 240 p.

BILLINGS, G. B., HITCHON, B., AND SHAW, D. R., 1969, Geochemistry and origin of formation waters in the western Canada sedimentary basin, 2. Alkali metals: Chem. Geology, v. 4, p. 211–223.

BLANCHE, J. B. AND WHITAKER, J. H. McD., 1978, Diagenesis of part of the Brent Sand Formation (Middle Jurassic) of the northern North Sea Basin: Jour. Geol. Soc., v. 135, p. 73–82.

BLATT, HARVEY, MIDDLETON, G. V., AND MURRAY, R. C., 1972, Origin of sedimentary rocks: Englewood Cliffs, New Jersey, Prentice-Hall, 634 p.

—— AND SCHULTZ, D. J., 1976, Size distribution of quartz in mudrocks: Sedimentology, v. 23, p. 857–866.

BRADLEY, J. S., 1975, Abnormal formation pressure: Am. Assoc. Petroleum Geologists Bull., v. 59, p. 957–973 [also discussion in v. 60, p. 1124–1128].

BUCKE, D. P. AND MANKIN, C. J., 1971, Clay-mineral diagenesis within interlaminated shales and sandstones: Jour. Sed. Petrology, v. 41, p. 971–981.

BURST, J. F., 1976, Argillaceous sediment dewatering: Ann. Rev. Earth Planetary Sci., v. 4, p. 293–318.

DAPPLES, E. C., 1959, The behavior of silica in diagenesis: *in* Silica in sediments, Soc. Econ. Paleon. Miner. Spec. Pub. No. 7, p. 36–54.

DAVIES, D. K., 1961, Origin of friable sandstone-calcareous sandstone rhythms in the Upper Lias of England: Jour. Sed. Petrology, v. 37, p. 1179–1188.

DEBOER, R. B., 1977, On the thermodynamics of pressure solution-interaction between chemical and mechanical forces: Geochim. et Cosmochim. Acta, v. 41, p. 249–256.

DICKEY, P. A., 1969, Increasing concentration of subsurface brines with depth: Chem. Geol., v. 4, p. 361–370.

DUNNINGTON, H. V., 1967, Aspects of diagenesis and shape change in stylolitic limestone reservoirs: 7th World Petroleum Congr. Proc., v. 2, p. 339–352.

FERTL, W. H., AND CHILINGARIAN, G. V., 1977, Importance of abnormal fluid pressures: Jour. Petroleum Technology, v. 29, p. 347–354.

FLEHMIG, WERNER, 1977, The synthesis of feldspars at temperatures between 0–80 C, their ordering behaviour and twinning: Contr. Miner. Petrology, v. 65, p. 1–9.

FLESCH, G. A., AND WILSON, M. D., 1974, Petrography of Morrison Formation (Jurassic) sandstone of the Ojito Quadrangle, Sandoval County, New Mexico: New Mexico Geol. Soc. Guidebook 25th Field Conf., p. 197–210.

FLETCHER, G. L., AND BAY, K. W., 1975, Geochemical evaluation—N.W. Java Basin: Indonesian Petroleum Assoc. 4th Ann. Conv., Jakarta, p. 211–241.

FOLK, R. L., 1960, Petrography of the Tuscarora, Rose Hill, and Keefer Formations, Lower and Middle Silurian of eastern West Virginia: Jour. Sed. Petrology, v. 30, p. 1–58.

FOTHERGILL, C. A., 1955, The cementation of oil reservoir sands and its origin: 4th World Petroleum Conf., Rome, Proc., Sec. 1, p. 301–314.

FRIEDMAN, MELVIN, 1954, Miocene orthoquartzite from New Jersey: Jour. Sed. Petrology, v. 24, p. 235–241.

FÜCHTBAUER, HANS, 1967, Influence of different types of diagenesis on sandstone porosity: 7th World Petroleum Congr. Proc., v. 2, p. 353–369.

—— AND MÜLLER, G., 1970, Sedimente und Sedimentgesteine: Stuttgart, E. Schweitzerbart'sche Verlagsbuchhandlung, 726 p.

GALLOWAY, W. E., 1974, Deposition and diagenetic alteration of sandstone in northeast Pacific arc-related basins: Implications for graywacke genesis: Geol. Soc. America Bull., v. 85, p. 379–390.

GARRELS, R. M., AND CHRIST, C. L., 1965, Solutions, minerals, and equilibria: New York, Harper & Row, Inc., 450 p.

GLOVER, J. E., 1963, Studies in the diagenesis of some western Australian sedimentary rocks: Jour. Royal Soc. Western Australia, v. 46, p. 33–56.

GREENSMITH, J. T., 1957, Lithology, with particular reference to cementation of Upper Carboniferous sandstones in northern Derbyshire, England: Jour. Sed. Petrology, v. 27, p. 405–416.

HARDER, H., AND FLEHMIG, W., 1970, Quartzsynthese bei tiefen Temperaturen: Geochim. et Cosmochim. Acta, v. 34, p. 295–305.

HAWKINS, P. J., 1978, Relationship between diagenesis, porosity reduction, and oil emplacement in late Carboniferous sandstone reservoirs, Bothamsall oilfield, E. Midlands: Jour. Geol. Soc., v. 135, p. 7–24.

HOLLAND, H. D., 1972, The geologic history of sea water—An attempt to solve the problem: Geochim. et Cosmochim. Acta, v. 36, p. 637–651.

HOWER, JOHN, ESLINGER, E. V., HOWER, M. E., AND PERRY, E. A., 1976, The mechanism of burial metamorphism of argillaceous sediments: 1. Mineralogical and chemical evidence: Geol. Soc. America Bull., v. 87, p. 725–737.

HSÜ, K. J., 1977, Studies of Ventura Field, California: II: Lithology, compaction, and permeability of sands: Am. Assoc. Petroleum Geologists Bull., v. 61, p. 169–191.

HUDSON, J. D., 1975, Carbon isotopes and limestone cement: Geology, v. 3, p. 19–22.

JAM L., PEDRO, DICKEY, P. A., AND TRYGGVASON, E., 1969, Subsurface temperature in south Louisiana: Am. Assoc. Petroleum Geologists Bull., v. 53, p. 2141–2149.

KASTNER, M., KEENE, J. B., AND GIESKES, J. M., 1977, Diagenesis of siliceous oozes—I. Chemical controls on the rate of opal-A to opal-CT transformation—An experimental study: Geochim. et Cosmochim. Acta, v. 41, p. 1041–1060.

KRAUSKOPF, K. B., 1967, Introduction to geochemistry: New York, McGraw-Hill Book Co., Inc., 721 p.

LEVANDOWSKI, D. W., KALEY, M. E., SILVERMAN, S. R., AND SMALLEY, R. G., 1973, Cementation in Lyons Sandstone and its role in oil accumulation, Denver Basin, Colorado: Am. Assoc. Petroleum Geologists Bull., v. 57, p. 2217–2244.

MACKENZIE, F. T., AND GEES, R., 1971, Quartz synthesis at Earth-surface conditions: Science, v. 173, p. 533–534.

MAGARA, KINJI, 1975, Importance of aquathermal pressuring effect in Gulf Coast: Am. Assoc. Petroleum Geologists Bull., v. 59, p. 2037–2045.

MAXWELL, J. C., 1964, Influence of depth, temperature, and geologic age on porosity of quartzose sandstone: Am. Assoc. Petroleum Geologists Bull., v. 48, p. 697–709.

McMURTRY, G. M., FAN, P-F., AND COPLEN, T. B., 1977, Chemical and isotopic investigations of groundwater in potential geothermal areas in Hawaii: Am. Jour. Sci., v. 277, p. 438–458.

MERINO, ENRIQUE, 1975a, Diagenesis in Tertiary sandstones from Kettleman North Dome, California. I. Interstitial solutions: Distribution of aqueous species at 100° C and chemical relation to diagenetic mineralogy: Geochim. et Cosmochim. Acta, v. 39, p. 1629–1645.

——, 1975b, Diagenesis in Tertiary sandstones from Kettleman North Dome, California, II. Diagenetic mineralogy: Jour. Sed. Petrology, v. 45, p. 320–336.

MILLOT, GEORGES, 1970, Geology of clays, New York, Springer Verlag, 429 p.

MIMRAN, Y., 1977, Chalk deformation and large-scale migration of calcium carbonate: Sedimentology, v. 24, p. 333–360.

MORGAN, J. T., CORDINER, F. S., AND LIVINGSTON, A. R., 1976, Tensleep reservoir study, Oregon Basin Field, Wyoming—Reservoir characteristics: Soc. Petroleum Engineers, AIME, Paper SPE 6141, 12 p.

PETTIJOHN, F. J., 1975, Sedimentary rocks, 3d ed.: New York, Harper & Bros., 628 p.

PHILIPP, W., DRONG, H. J., FÜCHTBAUER, H., HADDENHORST, H. G., AND JANKOWSKY, W., 1963, The history of migration in the Gifhorn Trough (NW-Germany): 6th World Petroleum Congr. Proc., Sec. 1, Paper 19, PD 2, p. 457–481.

PHIPPS, C. B., 1969, Post-burial sideritization of calcite in Eocene beds from the Maracaibo Basin, Venezuela: Geol. Mag., v. 100, p. 485–495.

PITTMAN, E. D., 1972, Diagenesis of quartz in sandstones as revealed by scanning electron microscopy: Jour. Sed. Petrology, v. 42, p. 507–519.

POWERS, M. C., 1967, Fluid-release mechanisms in compacting marine mudrocks and their importance in oil exploration: Amer. Assoc. Pet. Geol. Bull., v. 51, p. 1240–1254.

RIEZEBOS, P. A., 1974, Scanning electron microscopical observations on weakly cemented Miocene sands: Geologie en Mijnbouw, v. 53, p. 109–122.

ROBIN, P-Y. F., 1978, Pressure solution at grain-to-grain contacts: Geochim. et Cosmochim. Acta, v. 42, p. 1383–1389.

SCHMIDT, G. W., 1973, Interstitial water composition and geochemistry of deep Gulf Coast shales and sandstones: Am. Assoc. Petroleum Geologists Bull., v. 57, p. 321–331.

SIBLEY, D. F., AND BLATT, H., 1976, Intergranular pressure solution and cementation of the Tuscarora Orthoquartzite: Jour. Sed. Petrology, v. 46, p. 881–896.

SIEVER, RAYMOND, 1959, Petrology and geochemistry of silica cementation in some Pennsylvanian sandstones: in Silica in sediments, Soc. Econ. Paleon. Miner. Spec. Pub. No. 7, p. 55–79.

——, 1962, Silica solubility, 0–200° C, and the diagenesis of siliceous sediments: Jour. Geology, v. 70, p. 127–150.

SIPPEL, R. F., 1968, Sandstone petrology, evidence from luminescence petrography: Jour. Sed. Petrology, v. 38, p. 530–554.

SORBY, H. C., 1880, On the structure and origin of non-calcareous stratified rocks: Geol. Soc. London Proc., v. 36, p. 46–92.

STALDER, P. J., 1975, Cementation of Pliocene-Quaternary fluviatile clastic deposits in and along the Oman Mountains: Geologie en Mijnbouw, v. 54, p. 148–156.

STEIN, C. L., AND KIRKPATRICK, R. J., 1976, Experimental porcellanite recrystallization kinetics: A nucleation and growth model: Jour. Sed. Petrology, v. 46, p. 430–435.

TALLMAN, S. L., 1949, Sandstone types, their abundance and cementing agents: Jour. Geology, v. 57, p. 582–591.

TAYLOR, J. M., 1950, Pore-space reduction in sandstones: Am. Assoc. Petroleum Geologists Bull., v. 34, p. 701–716.

TODD, T. W., 1963, Post-depositional history of Tensleep Sandstone (Pennsylvanian), Big Horn Basin, Wyoming: Am. Assoc. Petroleum Geologists Bull., v. 47, p. 599–616.

TOWE, K. M., 1962, Clay mineral diagenesis as a possible source of silica cement in sedimentary rocks: Jour. Sed. Petrology, v. 32, p. 26–28.

TRURNIT, PETER, 1968, Pressure solution phenomena in detrital rocks: Sed. Geology, v. 2, p. 89–114.

WALKER, T. R., 1967, Formation of red beds in modern and ancient deserts: Geol. Soc. America Bull., v. 78, p. 353–368.

——, 1974, Formation of red beds in moist tropical climates: A hypothesis: Geol. Soc. America Bull., v. 85, p. 633–638.

——, RIBBE, P. H., AND HONEA, R. M., 1967, Geochemistry of hornblende alteration in Pliocene red beds, Baja

California, Mexico: Geol. Soc. America Bull., v. 78, p. 1055–1060.

——, WAUGH, B., AND CRONE, A. J., 1978, Diagenesis in first-cycle desert alluvium of Cenozoic age, southwestern United States and northwestern Mexico: Geol. Soc. America Bull., v. 89, p. 19–32.

WARNER, N. M., 1965, Cementation as a clue to structure, drainage patterns, permeability, and other factors: Jour. Sed. Petrology, v. 35, p. 797–804.

WEAVER, C. E., AND BECK, K. C., 1971, Clay water diagenesis during burial: How mud becomes gneiss: Geol. Soc. America Spec. Paper 134, 96 p.

WHETTEN, J. T., AND HAWKINS, J. W., JR., 1970, Diagenetic origin of graywacke minerals: Sedimentology, v. 15, p. 347–361.

WHITE, D. E., 1965, Saline waters of sedimentary rocks, *in* Fluids in subsurface environments: Am. Assoc. Petroleum Geologists Mem. 4, p. 342–366.

——, HEM, J. D., AND WARING, G. A., 1963, Data of geochemistry, Chapter F, Chemical composition of subsurface waters: U.S. Geol. Survey Prof. Paper 440-F, 67 p.

WILLEY, J. D., 1974, The effect of pressure on the solubility of amorphous silica in seawater at $0°$ C: Marine Chemistry, v. 2, p. 239–250.

WILSON, M. D., AND PITTMAN, E. D., 1977, Authigenic clays in sandstones: Recognition and influence on reservoir properties and paleoenvironmental analysis: Jour. Sed. Petrology, v. 47, p. 3–31.

WRIGHT, M. D., 1964, Cementation and compaction of the Millstone Grit of the central Pennines, England: Jour. Sed. Petrology, v. 34, p. 756–760.

SEPM Special Publication No. 26, p. 159–173, March 1979

POROSITY, DIAGENESIS AND PRODUCTIVE CAPABILITY
OF SANDSTONE RESERVOIRS

EDWARD D. PITTMAN
Amoco Production Co., Research Center, Tulsa, Oklahoma 74102

ABSTRACT

Four basic types of porosity occur in sandstones: intergranular, dissolution, micro and fracture. The first three types are related to rock texture and can be considered end members of a ternary classification diagram. Fracture porosity may be associated with any other porosity type.

All sandstones initially have intergranular porosity, which, if not destroyed, often is associated with good permeability, large pore apertures, and prolific hydrocarbon production. Dissolution porosity results from leaching of carbonate, feldspar, sulfate, or other soluble material. Sandstone reservoirs with dissolution porosity range from excellent to poor, depending on amount of porosity and interconnection of pores. Isolated dissolution pores result in low permeability. Sandstones with significant amounts of clay minerals have abundant microporosity, high surface area, small pore apertures, low permeability, high irreducible water saturation, and an increased sensitivity to fresh water. Fracture porosity, which contributes no more than a few percent voids to storage space, will enhance the deliverability of any reservoir. Open fractures, either natural or induced, are essential for economic deliverability rates from reservoirs with essentially only micropores or isolated dissolution pores.

Porosity type and/or pore geometry change with diagenesis: macropores become micropores, minerals dissolve to create voids, and pores are partly to completely occluded by precipitation of minerals. It is important to have an understanding of pore geometry, that is the size, shape, and distribution of pores in a reservoir. Pore geometry influences the type, amount, and rate of fluid produced.

Porosity type seldom is homogeneous in rocks. As a result, log interpretation problems may occur in sandstones containing significant micropores and interconnected macropores. Micropores may hold irreducible water while macropores may hold producible oil, gas, or water, depending on height above the oil- or gas-water contact. Log calculations may indicate high water saturation and a nonproductive interval, although the reservoir may be capable of water-free hydrocarbon production because the water is not producible.

INTRODUCTION

The success of massive hydraulic fracture treatments and the scramble for new hydrocarbon reserves has enabled the oil industry to complete wells in sandstone reservoirs that a few years ago were considered uneconomic. When dealing with these low-quality reservoirs, it is important to have an understanding of pore geometry, that is the size, shape, and distribution of pores. In other words, a three-dimensional representation of interconnected void space in the rock. Pore geometry influences the type, amount, and rate of fluid produced. Fluid factors, such as viscosity, also play a role but will not be covered in this paper.

Purpose of this paper is to discuss the basic types of porosity that occur in sandstones and to show examples that illustrate the importance of understanding pore geometry.

RESERVOIR CHARACTERISTICS OF POROSITY TYPES

Three types of porosity, excluding fractures, occur in sandstones: intergranular, dissolution and micro. These three types of porosity can be considered end members of a ternary diagram representing total matrix porosity (Fig. 1). Fracture porosity will be considered later as a secon-

dary feature that enhances other porosity types. Any of the porosity end members may be hydrocarbon reservoirs under certain conditions. Generally, permeability and pore aperture size increase toward the intergranular porosity pole. Irreducible water, i.e., water held in the rock by the physical attraction of the rock for the liquid (capillary pressure), increases toward the microporosity pole.

Diagenesis may cause a change of porosity types. For example, precipitation of authigenic clay minerals in pores and pore throats increases surface area, creates microporosity, decreases effective intergranular macroporosity and lowers permeability. Of course, any porosity type may be partly to completely occluded by precipitation of mineral cements. Diagenesis may also create void space through dissolution of soluble components of the rock.

Intergranular porosity.—Intergranular pores occur among detrital sand grains. The best sandstone reservoirs from viewpoint of storage porosity and deliverability have predominantly intergranular porosity. Sandstone reservoirs with intergranular porosity range from a bottom cutoff for pay of about 5% to totally unconsolidated sand with porosities exceeding 40%.

Copyright © 1979, The Society of Economic Paleontologists and Mineralogists

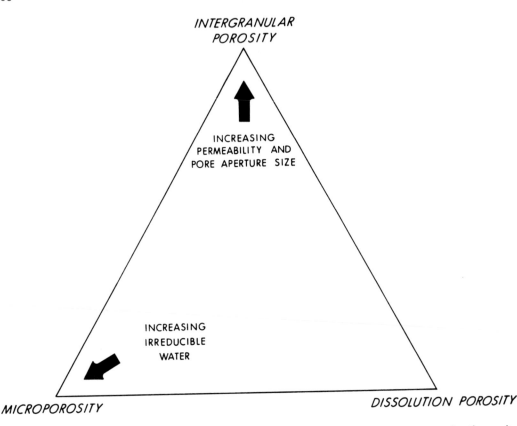

INTERGRANULAR
POROSITY

INCREASING
PERMEABILITY AND
PORE APERTURE SIZE

INCREASING
IRREDUCIBLE
WATER

MICROPOROSITY   DISSOLUTION POROSITY

Fig. 1.—Ternary classification diagram of matrix related porosity. Fracture porosity represents a fourth porosity type.

All sands start with primary intergranular pores that are modified in size and shape, or even destroyed by diagenetic processes. Secondary intergranular porosity can form through dissolution of carbonate cement (see Schmidt and Mc-Donald, this publication).

The Pennsylvanian Tensleep Sandstone of Wyoming is an example of a quartz arenite with intergranular porosity (photomicrograph, Fig. 2). This example has 15.3% porosity and 280 md permeability. A mercury injection curve reveals large, well-sorted pore apertures (approximately 20 μm breakthrough): desirable characteristics for a reservoir rock (Fig.2).

The Tensleep sample has quartz overgrowths and dolomite cement (Figs. 2, 3A). A scanning electron micrograph of a pore cast, which is an epoxy resin replica of the pore space (Pittman and Duschatko, 1970), for this reservoir shows that the intergranular voids are interconnected in a three-dimensional network (Fig. 3B).

Dissolution porosity.—Dissolution pores result from removal of carbonates, feldspars, sulfates, or other soluble materials (Rowsell and DeSwardt,

1975; Schmidt, *et al.*, 1976; Lindquist, 1976; Stanton and McBride, 1976). Soluble components may be: (1) detrital grains; (2) authigenic mineral cement; or (3) replacement minerals. Individual sandstones may contain dissolution pores of single or multiple origins.

Sandstone reservoirs with only dissolution porosity range from poor to excellent, depending on amount of porosity and interconnection of pores. Sandstones with only dissolution porosity may have essentially no measurable matrix permeability if the soluble grains are disseminated because upon leaching they form isolated pores with microporous interconnections. Good permeability exists if the soluble material is abundant enough to be in contact because of grain packing or interconnection of mineral cement. Excellent reservoirs develop where carbonate cement has been dissolved to form secondary intergranular porosity (see Schmidt and McDonald, this publication).

In my opinion, porosity created by the dissolution of feldspar (or dissolution of carbonate that has replaced feldspar) is common worldwide in

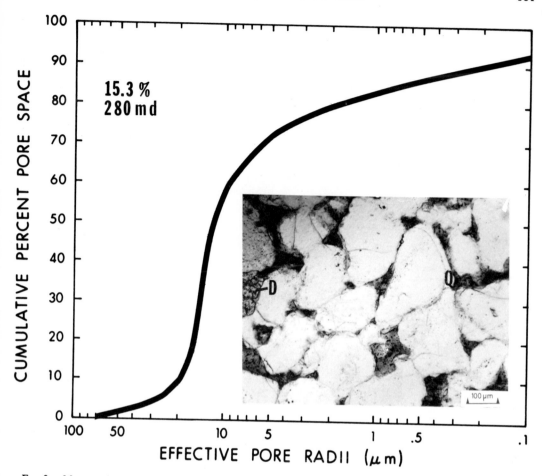

Fɪɢ. 2.—Mercury injection curve and photomicrograph of Tensleep Sandstone (Pennsylvanian), Wyoming. Dark gray areas among grains represent void space occupied by epoxy resin. Grains are cemented by quartz overgrowths (Q) and dolomite (D). Mercury injection curve reveals relatively coarse and well-sorted pore apertures indicative of a good reservoir.

sandstones of all ages. Dissolution may affect portions of feldspar grains (Fig. 4A–C), or essentially the entire grain (Fig. 4D–E). If feldspar is abundant in the sandstone, considerable porosity can originate in this manner.

Morgan and Gordon (1970) appear to have first discussed the importance of feldspar dissolution on reservoir rock performance. Mineralogy of dissolved feldspar and impact of dissolution pores on reservoirs were described by Shenhav (1971), Heald and Larese (1973), and Larese (1974). Feldspars commonly affected by dissolution are sanidine, orthoclase, and plagioclase. Leached feldspars are often turbid, due to incipient sericite or vacuoles. In contrast, microcline, which often coexists in sandstone with partly dissolved other feldspar, is usually clear and lacks any sign of dissolution. Presumably, this is explainable

through the relative temperature of formation-stability series for the potash feldspar group (Deer *et al.,* 1962). Sanidine and orthoclase form at higher temperatures and possess more disordered structures than microcline. Thus, they are not as stable under diagenetic conditions. Plagioclase feldspar also forms at higher temperatures than microcline.

When the soluble material has been totally removed, identification is a matter of conjecture based on mold size and shape. For example, in Figure 4F, a pore filling material has been removed to create a pore in an otherwise tightly quartz-cemented sandstone. A carbonate mineral is a likely choice, perhaps as cement around a fossil fragment.

An example of a sandstone with isolated dissolution porosity is the Silurian Tuscarora from

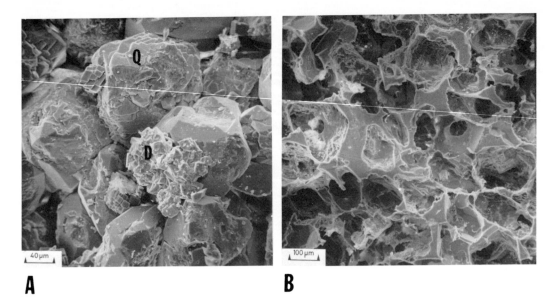

FIG. 3.—Scanning electron micrographs of Tensleep Sandstone. *A*, Rock has obvious pores despite some quartz overgrowths (Q) and dolomite cement (D). *B*, Pore cast of specimen in "A" reveals that the pores are interconnected three dimensionally and that the apparent pore apertures are many times smaller than the large intergranular pores.

the Appalachian Province (photomicrograph, Fig. 5). This example has 10.0% porosity but only 0.05 md permeability. The mercury injection curve reveals small pore throats (breakthrough of mercury at about 0.5 μm) caused by abundant quartz overgrowths and possibly pressure solution (Fig. 5). In this example, there is no remnant material to provide a clue as to what was dissolved to produce the pores. Scanning electron microscope examination of the rock and particularly the pore cast confirms that the rock has small pore apertures (Figs. 6A, B). Pore interconnections are sparse and thin compared to the Tensleep example discussed earlier.

Microporosity.—Generalizing, microporosity —as distinguished from macroporosity—may be defined as pores with pore-aperture radii less than 0.5 μm. Pores with very small pore apertures usually are associated with small pores, but relatively large pores with very small pore apertures are not uncommon.

Micropores occur among clay minerals or at pore-throat restrictions in sandstone. Argillaceous sandstones commonly have significant microporosity, regardless of whether the clay is authigenic or allogenic in origin. Based on my observations, authigenic clay minerals and associated microporosity are common in sandstone reservoirs.

An argillaceous sandstone with only microporosity has essentially no measurable matrix permeability. A rock of this type with small pore apertures and high surface area will also have high irreducible water saturation.

In a water-wet system, it is possible for hydrocarbons to displace water in micropores. To do this, the height of the hydrocarbon column must be sufficient to provide adequate buoyancy pressure to overcome capillary pressure, which tends to hold water in the rock. I do not know of a totally microporous sandstone reservoir where this has happened. However, the Ekofisk chalk

FIG. 4.—Dissolution porosity in sandstones. *A–C*, Partial dissolution of detrital feldspar grains in sandstones. Medium to dark gray area in photomicrographs represents blue epoxy in pores. *D, E*, Nearly complete dissolution of feldspar grains. Only small scraps of feldspar remain in "D". In "E", the authigenic feldspar rim is conspicuous despite the near absence of a rounded detrital core. *F*, A small cavity or vug in a sandstone. The size and shape suggests that something larger than the quartz sand grains was removed. A calcareous fossil, perhaps surrounded by calcite cement, is a likely possibility.

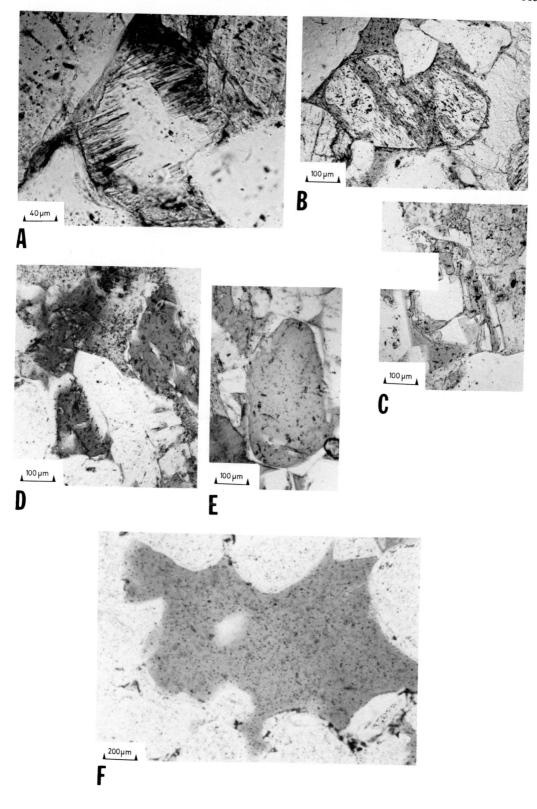

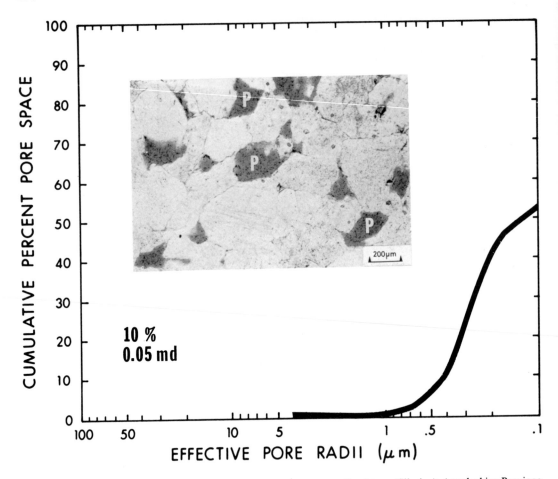

FIG. 5.—Mercury injection curve and photomicrograph of Tuscarora Sandstone (Silurian), Appalachian Province. Pores (P) are dark colored and appear to be isolated, but are actually interconnected by micropores. The mercury injection curve indicates the rock has small pore apertures because mercury did not break through until about 0.5 μm. A reservoir with these characteristics needs fractures, either natural or induced, to provide an economic deliverability rate.

reservoir in the North Sea, which has over 600 feet of oil column, is an example of this principle in carbonates.

The Mesaverde Sandstone, shown in the photomicrograph of Figure 7, has 11.1% porosity (all microporosity) and less than 0.05 md permeability. In this example, allogenic and authigenic clay minerals fill intergranular pore space. Micropores occur among the clay particles. Ninety-eight percent of the pore-aperture radii are less than 0.5 μm and 69% are less than 0.1 μm (Fig. 7). Breakthrough of mercury occurs at approximately 0.2 μm. Examination of scanning electron micrographs of this sandstone and its pore cast confirm the small pore apertures (Figs. 8A, B). This type of rock would be expected to have high water

saturation due to irreducible water. In order for this particular sandstone to become a reservoir, irreducible water would have to be displaced by hydrocarbon and the rock fractured either naturally or artificially.

ROLE OF FRACTURES

Fracture porosity, which contributes no more than a few percent voids to storage space, will enhance the deliverability of any sandstone reservoir. Intergranular porosity, unless of poor quality, does not need associated fractures to be a suitable reservoir because the pores are interconnected. A sandstone reservoir with significant micropores or isolated dissolution pores typically needs fractures, either natural or induced, to

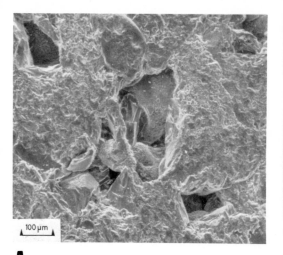
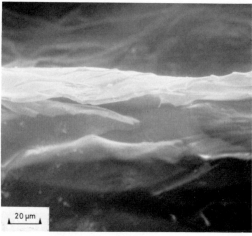

A   **B**

Fig. 6.—Scanning electron micrographs of Tuscarora Sandstone. *A,* Relatively large dissolution pore in the center has no obvious interconnections to other pores. *B,* Pore cast showing apparent pore aperture represented by curved plastic sheet, which is less that 1 μm thick in places.

provide permeability and economic deliverability rates.

Natural fractures may represent the entire storage porosity and permeability of a reservoir. Porosity due only to fractures is rarely greater than a few percent and usually is less than one percent. Reservoirs of this type characteristically have a high initial flow rate followed by rapid depletion.

Natural fractures may provide the necessary permeability to make productivity more attractive for a reservoir with low matrix permeability. A reservoir with a well-developed natural fracture system would be expected to yield a strong initial flow of hydrocarbons with a gradual decline as matrix porosity is depleted.

Sometimes natural fractures occur in reservoirs with good matrix porosity and permeability. In this situation, the fractures improve the productive capability and recovery efficiency of the reservoir (assuming coning of water is not a problem).

Induced fractures can provide the necessary permeability when matrix porosity is present but matrix permeability and effective natural fractures are absent. A hydraulically fractured reservoir of this type yields high initial hydrocarbon production with a rapid early decline followed by a slower later decline as the matrix yields fluid to the fracture.

ESTIMATION OF POROSITY TYPES

By combining study of thin sections prepared from rocks impregnated with colored epoxy and scanning electron microscopy, it is possible to make reliable estimates of the different porosity types. Intergranular pores can be readily identified in thin section by their position among detrital grains. Dissolution pores are recognizable in thin section by their location, size, and shape outline with respect to the rock framework and in some cases by the presence of a soluble precursor. Micropores are best recognized in scanning electron micrographs.

EXAMPLES OF SANDSTONE RESERVOIRS WITH MIXED POROSITY TYPES

Second Wall Creek Sandstone.—The Second Wall Creek Sandstone, Wyoming, has significant amounts of intergranular and dissolution porosity, but only minor microporosity. Data for a selected suite of samples from four wells plot along the intergranular-dissolution side of the ternary diagram (Fig. 9). Porosity ranges from 15.4 to 23.3% and permeability from 3.98 to 115 md. Higher permeability samples have a tendency to plot nearer to the intergranular pole, which illustrates the generalization expressed earlier. Intergranular pores interconnect dissolution pores to provide an effective macroporous network (photomicrograph, Fig. 10). Micropores occur among authi-

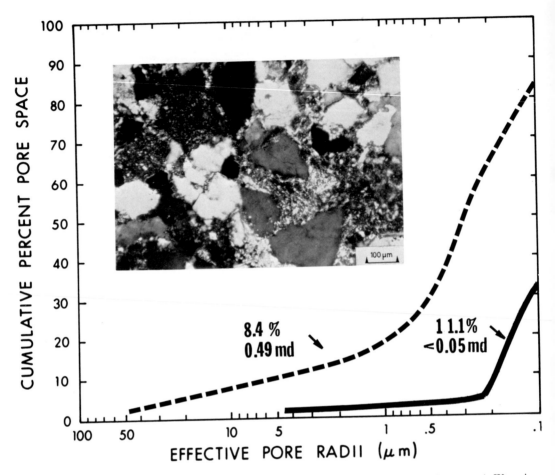

Fig. 7.—Mercury injection curves and photomicrograph of sandstone from Mesaverde (Cretaceous), Wyoming. Intergranular porosity is filled by clay, which has reduced pore apertures. The mercury injection curve (solid line) for the sample corresponding to the photomicrograph indicates that the break in the curve is at about 0.2 μm. This particular rock did not yield hydrocarbons. The dashed curve is for a Mesaverde sandstone that was productive. Note the coarser pore apertures and higher permeability although the porosity is even lower than for the other samples.

genic clays, but are not abundant enough to hold significant amounts of irreducible water. This is reflected in the mercury injection curve, which shows relatively large pore apertures (breakthrough at approximately 5 μm; Fig. 10).

Dissolution porosity in the Second Wall Creek Sandstone apparently originated from leaching of potash feldspar and plagioclase or from leaching of carbonate that replaced the feldspars. Detrital feldspar grains are partially to completely removed, but authigenic feldspar overgrowths are essentially unaltered (Figs. 10, 11). Based on scanning electron microprobe analyses, a compositional difference exists between authigenic rims and detrital cores of feldspars in the

Second Wall Creek Sandstone (Fig. 12). In all cases, the rims are essentially K-rich potassium feldspar or Na-rich plagioclase compared to the cores. This compositional difference between rim and core may explain why the authigenic rim composed of more stable feldspar is preserved, while the detrital nuclei composed of less stable feldspar have been dissolved.

Permian Sandstone, South Africa.—Permian sandstones from South Africa have intergranular, dissolution, and microporosity (Fig. 13). These data plot slightly to the left and below data for the Second Wall Creek (Fig. 9). Samples of Permian Sandstone with significant amounts of microporosity and dissolution porosity have lower

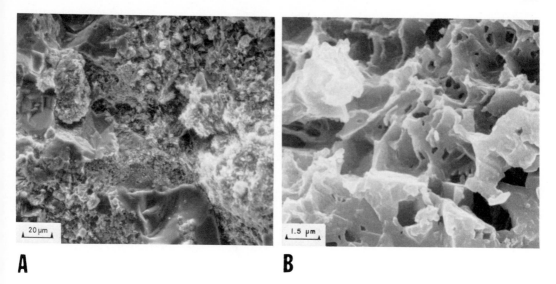

Fig. 8.—Scanning electron micrographs of Mesaverde Sandstone. *A*, Rock contains so much clay that individual sand grains are indistinct. *B*, Pore cast of this rock reveals an extremely fine pore network among the clay particles. Some pore apertures are only about 0.1 μm across.

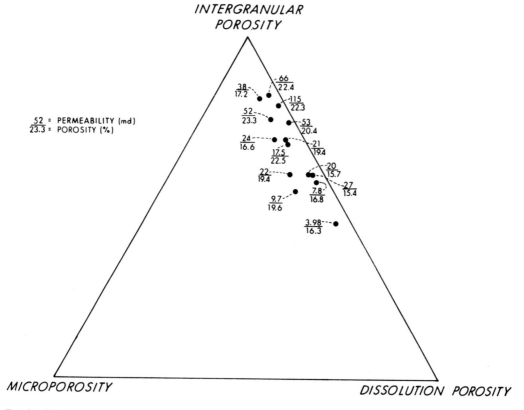

Fig. 9.—Triangular plot of porosity types from four wells in the Second Wall Creek Sandstone (Cretaceous), Wyoming. Note the tendency for permeability to increase towards the intergranular pole.

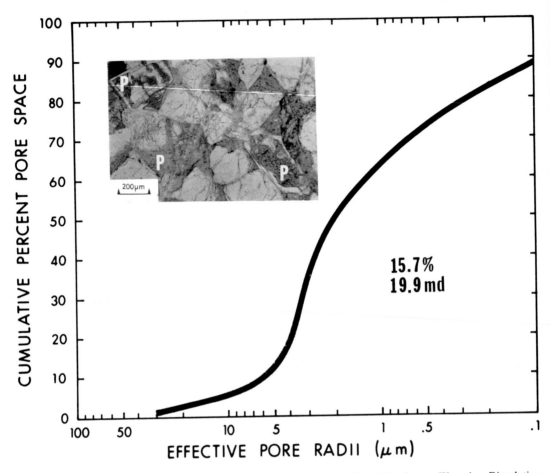

FIG. 10.—Mercury injection curve and photomicrograph of Second Wall Creek Sandstone, Wyoming. Dissolution pores (P) caused by dissolution of feldspar, and intergranular pores are visible in the micrograph. The pore system is well interconnected in contrast to the Tuscarora example (Fig. 5). The mercury injection curve indicates a relatively coarse pore system with breakthrough at about 5 μm.

permeabilities than samples containing predominantly intergranular porosity. In this case, dissolution porosity, which is more variable than microporosity, appears to have a pronounced influence on permeability. Note the significant increase in permeability moving in the direction of the intergranular pole of the diagram.

Muddy Formation.—Sandstones of the Cretaceous Muddy Formation, Denver-Julesburg

FIG. 11.—Scanning electron micrograph showing pore formed by dissolution of feldspar. Authigenic feldspar rim is well preserved. Kaolinite (K) occurs within the pore and as coating on detrital grain in foreground; Second Wall Creek Sandstone, Wyoming.

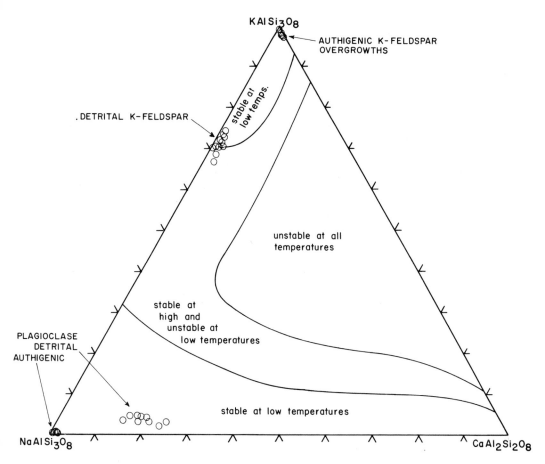

KAlSi$_3$O$_8$

AUTHIGENIC K-FELDSPAR
OVERGROWTHS

stable at low temps.

.DETRITAL K-FELDSPAR

unstable at all
temperatures

stable at
high and
unstable at
low temperatures

PLAGIOCLASE
DETRITAL
AUTHIGENIC

stable at low temperatures

NaAlSi$_3$O$_8$ CaAl$_2$Si$_2$O$_8$

Fig. 12.—Composition of feldspars shown as mean values for each grain or component of grain (detrital nucleus and authigenic overgrowth), based on 127 analyses of 27 grains in 2 thin sections of Second Wall Creek Sandstone. Stability fields from Winchell and Winchell (1951, p. 264).

Basin, often have a mixture of porosity types. Figure 14 shows two groups of data: one near the microporosity pole and the other towards the intergranular pole. All but one sample contains the three porosity end members; however, dissolution porosity is less abundant than intergranular or microporosity. Samples plotting near the microporosity pole have low permeability (generally less than 1 md) caused by small pore apertures associated with abundant authigenic clay minerals. Porosity, however, is adequate for a reservoir (5.6 to 23.6%). For comparison, samples grouped in the upper part of the diagram have significantly better permeability (3.31 to 161 md) although the porosity is about the same (7 to 24.3%). This reflects the larger and better interconnected pores associated with the intergranular porosity.

The photomicrographs of Figure 15 illustrate the differences between the two groups of sand-

stones in Figure 14. The sample from the upper data group has essentially no clay, is cemented by quartz, and has obvious pores (Fig. 15A). The sample from the lower data group has abundant authigenic clay, which has reduced pore-aperture size and permeability (Fig. 15B). The obvious grain size difference between samples in 15A and B is coincidental. Very fine- and fine-grained sandstones occur in both groups of data.

Rocks plotting in the data group near the microporosity pole require a massive fracture treatment to make an economic well. Rocks in the upper data group do not. In most cases, logs alone do not provide definitive data to distinguish between these two distinctly different types of sandstone. A microlog would provide a measure of invasion and, therefore, matrix permeability for rocks in the upper group of data. However, these logs are not run often.

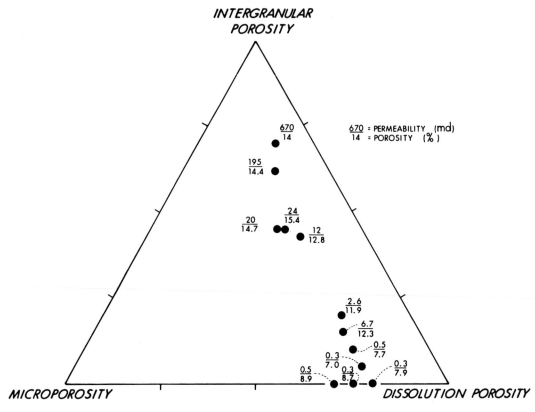

FIG. 13.—Triangular plot of porosity types for Permian sandstones, South Africa. There is a strong tendency for permeability to increase in the direction of the intergranular porosity pole.

Muddy Sand reservoirs often have small pore apertures and low permeability, but adequate porosity for storage of hydrocarbons (dashed curve, Fig. 16). This sample, which is from an oil reservoir, has 14% porosity and 0.34 md permeability. The sandstone has small pore apertures because of authigenic clay and required a massive hydraulic fracture treatment to be economically productive. About 50% of the pore apertures in this reservoir rock have a radii greater than 0.28 μm.

The solid curve in Figure 16 is an example of better reservoir rock from the Muddy Formation. Pore apertures are larger and the rock has 19.5% porosity and 119 md. permeability. Rock

of this type does not require fracture treatment to make a well.

The Muddy Formation is a good example of how pore geometry may control fluid flow and water saturation. Intergranular macropores hold mobile fluids, such as oil, gas, and some water, while micropores hold irreducible water, which is relatively immobile. Log calculations may indicate water saturations are too high for a productive interval. However, the reservoir may be capable of essentially water-free production because the water is predominantly irreducible. Artificial fractures often are needed to provide commercial productive rates because of small pore apertures and low permeability. A sample situated near the

FIG. 15.—Scanning electron micrographs showing differences between two groups of samples plotted on Fig. 13. A, This example, from the upper data group, has little if any clay, quartz cement, and much larger pore apertures. Porosity is 19.5% and permeability 119 md. B, Example representative of the data group near the microporosity pole has abundant authigenic clay, which has reduced porosity, pore apertures, and permeability. This example has 14% porosity and 0.34 md. The difference in grain size between A and B is coincidental: both data groups contain fine- and very fine-grained sandstones.

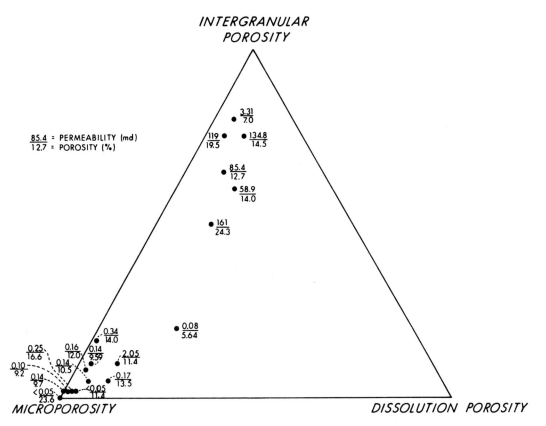

$$\frac{85.4}{12.7} = \begin{array}{l} \text{PERMEABILITY (md)} \\ \text{POROSITY (\%)} \end{array}$$

FIG. 14.—Triangular plot of porosity types for Muddy Sandstone (Cretaceous), Colorado and Wyoming. There are two groups of data: one near the microporosity pole and the other in the upper part of the triangle. Both groups have comparable porosities (up to 24%), but considerably different permeabilities. Data near the microporosity pole have permeabilities less than 1 md (except for one sample), whereas data in the upper group range from 3.31 to 161 md. Rocks near the microporosity pole require massive hydraulic fracture treatment the other rocks do not.

A   **B**

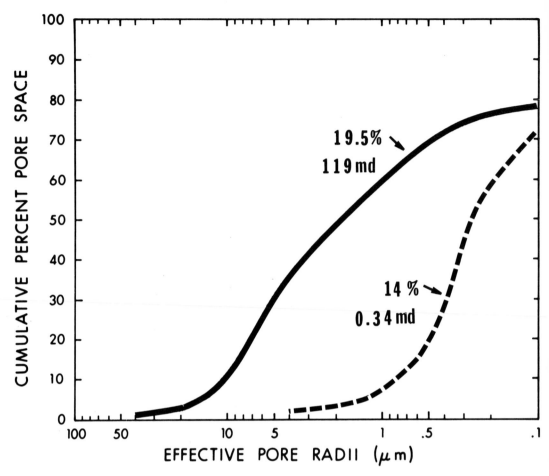

Fig. 16.—Mercury injection curves for two Muddy Sand reservoirs illustrated in Fig. 15. The solid curve is from the coarser, essentially clay-free sandstone of Fig. 15A. This sample has relatively large pore apertures, which is reflected in the good permeability (119 md). The dashed curve was derived from the finer sandstone (Fig. 15B), which has abundant authigenic clay that reduces pore apertures. The rock has 14% porosity, but only 0.34 md permeability. This sandstone required a fracture treatment to make an economic well.

microporosity-intergranular porosity base line nearer to the intergranular porosity pole (for example, 50% microporosity) could have relatively high irreducible water saturations, but with a better interconnected macropore system would not require artificial fractures for permeability.

CONCLUSIONS

1. Sandstone reservoirs often have pores of diverse origin and variable size.

2. Pore geometry influences the type, amount, and rate of production from reservoirs.

3. The best sandstone reservoirs, in terms of volume and flow rate, have intergranular porosity.

4. Potential log calculation problems for water saturation exist for rocks with abundant microporosity.

5. Fractures, either natural or induced, are required to provide economic deliverability rates for reservoirs with abundant microporosity and/or isolated dissolution porosity.

6. More cores will be needed in the future for petrographic study because available logs often cannot discriminate between important differences in pore geometry.

7. Study of porosity in rocks can help explain reservoir behavior and aid in anticipating potential reservoir problems.

ACKNOWLEDGEMENTS

I thank Amoco Production Company for permission to publish this paper, and also express gratitude to R. R. Thompson, H. D. Winland, D. J. Hartmann, J. B. Thomas, and R. A. Nelson for the helpful discussions and/or critical review of the manuscript.

REFERENCES

DEER, W. A., HOWIE, R. A., AND ZUSSMAN, J., 1962, Rock forming minerals, v. 4, framework silicates: New York, Wiley, 435 p.

HEALD, M. T., AND LARESE, R. E., 1973, The significance of solution of feldspar in porosity development: Jour. Sed. Petrology, v. 43, p. 458–460.

LARESE, R. E., 1974, Petrology and stratigraphy of the Berea Sandstone in the Cabin Creek and Gay-Fink Trends, West Virginia: PhD. Diss., Univ. West Virginia, 246 p.

LINDQUIST, SANDRA, 1976, Leached porosity in overpressured sandstones—Frio Formation (Oligocene), south Texas [abs.]: Am. Assoc. Petroleum Geologists Bull., v. 60, p. 1612–1613.

MORGAN, J. T., AND GORDON, D. T., 1970, Influence of pore geometry on water-oil relative permeability: Jour. Petroleum Technology, October 1970, p. 1199–1208.

PITTMAN, E. D., AND DUSCHATKO, R. W., 1970, Use of pore casts and scanning electron microscope to study pore geometry: Jour. Sed. Petrology, v. 40, p. 1153–1157.

ROWSELL, D. M., AND DE SWARDT, A. M. J., 1974, Secondary leaching porosity in Middle Ecca sandstones: South Africa Geol. Soc. Trans., v. 77, p. 131–140.

SCHMIDT, V., MACDONALD, D. A., AND PLATT, R. L., 1976, Pore geometry and reservoir aspects of secondary porosity in sandstones [abs.]: CIM-CSPG Joint Meeting on Enhanced Recovery, June 7–11, 1976, Program and Abs., p. 106–107.

SHENHAV, H., 1972, Lower Cretaceous sandstone reservoirs, Israel; petrography, porosity, permeability: Am. Assoc. Petroleum Geologists Bull., v. 55, p. 2194–2224.

STANTON, G. D., AND MCBRIDE, E. F., 1976, Factors influencing porosity and permeability of Lower Wilcox (Eocene) sandstone, Karnes County, Texas [abs.]: Am. Assoc. Petroleum Geologists and Soc. Econ. Paleontologists and Mineralogists Ann. Meeting Abs., v. 1, p. 119.

WINCHELL, A. N., AND WINCHELL, HORACE, 1951, Elements of optical mineralogy: New York, John Wiley and Sons, 551 p.

SEPM Special Publication No. 26, p. 175–207, March 1979

THE ROLE OF SECONDARY POROSITY IN THE COURSE
OF SANDSTONE DIAGENESIS

VOLKMAR SCHMIDT AND DAVID A. MCDONALD[1]
Petro-Canada, Calgary, Alberta, and Mobil Oil Canada Ltd., Calgary, Alberta

ABSTRACT

Secondary porosity plays an important role in the diagenesis of some sandstones. The volume of secondary porosity equals or exceeds that of primary porosity in the sandstones of many sedimentary basins worldwide, and a significant percentage of the world's reserves of natural gas and crude oil are contained in secondary sandstone porosity. Prudhoe Bay Field and the Jurassic fields of the North Sea are examples of the many giant hydrocarbon accumulations in secondary sandstone porosity.

Chemical, physical, physicochemical, biochemical and biophysical processes result in secondary sandstone porosity through leaching and shrinkage of rock constituents, or through the opening of fractures and porous burrows and borings. Secondary sandstone porosity can originate anywhere in the sedimentary crust: (1) before effective burial in the environment of deposition (eogenetic)[2]; (2) at any depth of burial above the zone of metamorphism (mesogenetic)[2]; and (3) during exposure following a period of burial (telogenetic)[2]. Secondary porosity may occur in sandstones of any mineralogical or textural composition and of any Phanerozoic age. It is most common in sandstones that have undergone relatively long lasting, deep burial and have lost their primary porosity.

Most of the secondary porosity in ancient sandstones originated as a result of mesogenetic leaching of the carbonate minerals calcite, dolomite and siderite. This decarbonatization removes depositional carbonate constituents and diagenetic carbonate such as cements or replacements. Most of the mesogenetic decarbonatization results from the decarboxylation of organic matter in strata adjacent to the sandstone during the course of organic maturation. The process of decarboxylation leads to the generation of carbon dioxide which, in the presence of water, produces carbonic acid. This acid reacts with the carbonate minerals.

In most instances it is possible to differentiate microscopically between primary and secondary sandstone porosity. Thus it is possible to trace the loss of primary porosity during burial. In the presence of water and hydrostatic pressure, primary sandstone porosity cannot exist beyond specific limits of temperature-time exposure except for a small volume of irreducible lamellar porosity between grains. The limiting temperature-time exposure increases with increasing mineralogical stability of the sandstones and, subordinately, with increasing grain size.

The mesodiagenesis of sandstones can be divided into four stages: (1) immature—mechanical compaction; (2) semi-mature—chemical compaction of primary porosity; (3) mature—only secondary porosity present; and, (4) supermature—no effective primary or secondary porosity.

Decarbonatization may create considerable quantities of secondary porosity during semi-mature mesodiagenesis. However, the average addition of carbonate to the sandstone in this diagenetic stage usually exceeds the average carbonate removal.

Decarbonatization culminates during mature mesodiagenesis at which stage it greatly outweighs carbonatization. Much secondary sandstone porosity, therefore, originates after effective primary porosity has been lost. Fractures and irreducible lamellar porosity apparently provide sufficient access for decarbonatizing fluids to start the leaching process even in sandstones of low permeability.

Enormous volumes of carbonate move upwards in solution from diagenetically mature sandstones and are, at least in part, reprecipitated in immature and semi-mature sandstones. Within a subsiding prism of clastic sediments much of the carbonate content is being recycled upwards in this fashion and sandstones at shallower depths are being enriched in carbonate.

Primary migration of hydrocarbons commonly follows closely after the secondary porosity has been formed, because in the maturation of organic matter, the main phase of hydrocarbon generation follows after the culmination of decarboxylation. This close association of source and reservoir in time and space favours the accumulation of hydrocarbons in secondary porosity.

In the presence of pore water, secondary porosity is gradually reduced during deep burial although at a much slower rate compared to primary porosity.

The main geological and economic significance of secondary sandstone porosity is that it extends the depth range for effective sandstone porosity far below the generally accepted depth limit for effective primary porosity. Generation and primary migration of hydrocarbons occurs mainly below the range of effective primary porosity.

---

[1] Present address: Petro-Canada, Calgary, Alberta.

[2] Diagenesis terminology adopted from Choquette & Pray (1970).

Copyright © 1979, The Society of Economic
Paleontologists and Mineralogists

The path of primary migration and the site of accumulation of hydrocarbons are, therefore, commonly controlled by the distribution of secondary porosity.

INTRODUCTION

The subject of secondary porosity in sandstones received little attention in the published literature prior to 1975. Most workers considered only a very small portion of sandstone porosity to be of secondary origin. Except for fractures, most accounts of secondary porosity described outcropping sandstone formations where invading meteoric water had removed soluble constituents (Sedimentation Seminar, 1969; Hraber & Potter, 1969). Krynine (1941) indicated that leaching of carbonate in the Oriskany Sandstone may possibly have occurred in the subsurface. Proshlyakov (1960) was probably the first author to convincingly report significant amounts of sandstone porosity that formed in the subsurface in the presence of saline formation-water. The first detailed discussion of the possible processes which create secondary porosity in the subsurface was published by Savkevic (1971). Rowsell and De Swardt (1973) observed secondary porosity of probable subsurface origin in the Middle Ecca sandstones of Pennsylvanian age in the northern Karoo basin of South Africa. They were the first authors outside Russia to apply the concepts developed by Russian geologists concerning mesogenetic porosity. Until 1976, these Russian and South African studies went largely unnoticed in North America. Unaware of the above studies, several groups of North American geologists have, during the last several years, recognized the common occurrence of secondary sandstone porosity that originated in the subsurface.

Recently, results of these investigations have appeared in the literature and several workers have described occurrences from the subsurface where the porosity originated after burial (Schmidt, 1976; Stanton & McBride, 1976; Alcock & Benteau, 1976; Pittmann, this volume; Hayes, this volume). Hayes and the authors of the present paper recognized the widespread occurrence of secondary sandstone porosity as early as 1970. Subsequently the authors refined the criteria for recognizing secondary porosity (Schmidt et al., 1977) and studied the phenomenon of secondary sandstone porosity in various geological settings in Canada, Alaska and Europe. A study of the Parsons Sandstone of the Mackenzie Delta (Schmidt, *ibid.*) provided several new concepts on the origin of secondary porosity in the subsurface. McBride and his students have applied these concepts and criteria very successfully when investigating secondary porosity in the subsurface of southern Texas (Stanton & McBride, 1976; Lindquist, 1976).

As the authors' studies progressed, it became apparent that much secondary porosity previously has been misidentified as primary porosity, and their views on the abundance of secondary porosity have been changing with increasing information (Fig. 1). At the present time it is certain that at least one-third of total sandstone porosity is of secondary origin. It appears possible that secondary porosity in sandstone is more abundant than primary sandstone porosity. Undoubtedly, secondary sandstone porosity is of major geological significance. Its origin, stability, and distribution form important aspects of sandstone diagenesis.

The study of secondary sandstone porosity is still very much in its infancy. However, the available information is sufficient to bring the emerging role of secondary porosity in sandstone diagenesis into perspective. This paper is intended to provide a preliminary account of the occurrence of secondary porosity in sandstones and to follow its evolution through the course of diagenesis. In this way a useful stepping stone will be established for other workers who may be interested in further investigating this very important subject.

GEOLOGICAL OCCURRENCE AND CAUSE

Textural Origin.—We recognize five principal classes of secondary sandstone porosity that can be differentiated on the basis of process of origin and fabric relationships (Fig. 2): (1) fractures, (2) shrinkage voids, (3) voids after sedimentary material, (4) voids after authigenic cement, and (5) voids after authigenic replacement minerals. The texture of secondary sandstone porosity and the criteria for its recognition are discussed in more detail in a separate paper of this publication (Schmidt and McDonald).

Secondary porosity can originate from fracturing, shrinkage, and dissolution only if the grain or crystal framework of the rock is sufficiently strong to prevent immediate collapse. There is a limit to the amount of secondary porosity that can be formed in a given sandstone under specific conditions of stress because the supportive strength of the rock framework will ultimately fail leading to reduction of porosity by collapse.

Usually textural origin and abundance of secondary porosity in sandstones with little or no primary porosity can be reliably determined using petrographic criteria. The textural relationship between secondary porosity and sandstone host provides evidence of the diagenetic changes that affected the rock prior to and following the

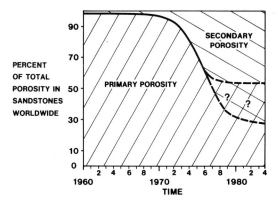

Fɪɢ. 1.—Change of interpretation of nature of sandstone porosity.

formation of the secondary porosity. For example, secondary pores which cut across welded grain fabrics indicate that welding occurred before leaching. On the other hand, secondary pores that are lined by bitumen originated prior to hydrocarbon migration. Thus diagenetic sequences can be established and fitted to the geological history of the sandstones.

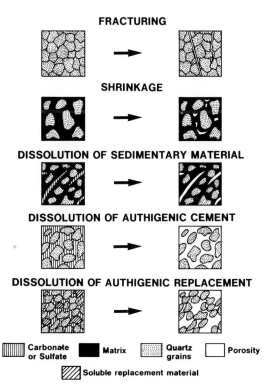

Fɪɢ. 2.—Textural origin of secondary sandstone porosity.

Regimes of diagenesis.—Secondary sandstone porosity is formed and preserved, changed and destroyed in almost any conceivable diagenetic environment. The system of diagenetic regimes that Choquette and Pray (1970) formulated for the study of porosity in carbonate rocks is equally appropriate for investigation of secondary porosity in sandstones and has been adopted in this paper. *Eodiagenesis* is defined as the regime at or near the surface of sedimentation where the chemistry of the interstitial water is mainly controlled by the surface environment prior to effective burial (effective burial is burial under strata that seal the sandstone from a predominant influence of surface agents on the chemistry of the interstitial water). *Mesodiagenesis* is the subsurface regime during effective burial. *Telodiagenesis* represents the regime at or near the surface after effective burial. The amounts of secondary porosity originating in each diagenetic regime differ greatly (Fig. 3).

A minor portion of secondary porosity evolves during eodiagenesis, mainly as a result of dissolution of sedimentary and eogenetic constituents, although fracturing and shrinkage may be subordinate contributors. In some instances eogenetic processes created considerable secondary porosity, for example, in calcareous quartz sandstones of Pleistocene and Holocene age from the Trucial Coast (unpublished petrographic study by Schmidt).

By far the largest amount of secondary porosity is produced during mesodiagenesis, and most of it can be attributed to leaching of sedimentary, eogenetic, and mesogenetic carbonate constituents (Hayes, this volume; Schmidt, 1976). Fractures form an important, although subordinate, portion of mesogenetic sandstone porosity. Mesogenetic shrinkage porosity plays a minor role and much of the shrinkage occurs during shallow burial.

Only a minor share of the total sandstone porosity originates during telodiagenesis, mainly as the result of leaching and, subordinately, due to fracturing. This we conclude from the comparison of outcrop samples and subsurface cores of numerous sandstone formations, and from the stratigraphic consideration that only a small percentage of sandstones have undergone a period of telodiagenesis.

Diagenetic processes.—The individual diagenetic processes that result in secondary porosity vary significantly in their quantitative importance (Fig. 4).

Fracturing of rocks, grains and intergranular constituents generally creates only insignificant to minor pore volume. However, rock fractures can, on occasion, form the major porosity type in some sandstone with low matrix porosity.

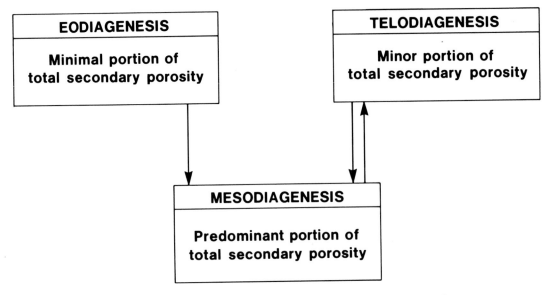

F<small>IG</small>. 3.—Diagenetic regimes of development of secondary sandstone porosity.

DIAGENETIC PROCESSES		PORTION OF SECONDARY POROSITY
	ROCK FRACTURING	* MINOR
	GRAIN FRACTURING	MINOR
	SHRINKAGE	* MINOR
DISSOLUTION OF	CALCITE	MAJOR
	DOLOMITE	MAJOR
	SIDERITE	MAJOR
	SULFATE	* MINOR
	OTHER EVAPORITES	* MINOR
	SILICATE	VERY MINOR
	OTHER NONSILICATE	VERY MINOR

* MAY BE OF MAJOR IMPORTANCE IN INDIVIDUAL STRATIGRAPHIC UNITS

F<small>IG</small>. 4.—Diagenetic processes creating secondary sandstone porosity.

Shrinkage, if present, usually supplies little porosity although exceptions do occur.

The vast majority of the total volume of secondary sandstone porosity results from the dissolution of carbonate minerals. Calcite, dolomite, and siderite each are the precursors of secondary porosity on a major scale (Figs. 5A–C, 6). The dissolved carbonate constituents mainly consist of cements, but also include substantial percentages of sedimentary and replacive carbonate.

The sulfate minerals such as anhydrite, gypsum, barite, and celestite commonly are subject to leaching (Fig. 5D). This may occur during any stage of diagenesis. The secondary porosity resulting from the removal of sulfates is minor in most sandstone formations. However, it can be of major importance in some instances, for example, in Cambrian sandstones of the Northwest Territories (McDonald, in progress).

The dissolution of nonsulfate evaporite minerals such as halite and sylvite appears to create only a small fraction of secondary sandstone porosity because of the relatively infrequent occurrence of these evaporite minerals in sandstones. Porosity of this origin, however, is easily misidentified and may be much more common than is presently realized. Hartman (1968) recognized a case of leaching of halite that created the reservoir for the Pelahatchie Field in the Gulf Coast region of the United States. Therefore, dissolution of the evaporite minerals can, in some instances, develop secondary porosity of major importance. It may occur either in the subsurface or near the surface in contact with meteoric waters.

Direct dissolution of silicate minerals such as quartz or feldspar generally creates little or no secondary porosity. Dissolution of silicate minerals as a rule occurs along grain contacts without creating porosity. However, Hayes (this volume) reports a case of significant leaching of silicate minerals in Tertiary sandstones of South Central Alaska. Heald and Larese (1973) attribute the porosity in honeycombed feldspar of Paleozoic sandstones in West Virginia and Ohio to direct dissolution. Their evidence (undissolved calcite cement), however, is not conclusive, as leaching of carbonate may be followed by precipitation of carbonate cement. Silicate minerals often are replaced by non-silicate minerals, principally carbonates. These replacive minerals, in turn, frequently are dissolved (Figs. 5E, F) and the resulting secondary porosity may be mistakenly attributed to direct leaching of the silicate minerals.

The dissolution of other non-silicate minerals including, for example, phosphate and oxide minerals contributes very little secondary porosity in sandstones.

Causes.—The conditions which bring about the generation of secondary porosity in sandstones are the result of chemical, physicochemical, physical, biochemical, and biophysical processes.

Chemical processes such as dilution of the interstitial water or changes in the ratios of ion species may cause void-creating dissolution at constant temperatures and pressures. The formation of carbonic acid in the interstitial water is a well known example. It causes lowering of the pH and dissolution of carbonate minerals. In the telogenetic regime carbonic acid forms mainly from atmospheric carbon dioxide. During mesodiagenesis most of the carbon dioxide that forms carbonic acid originates from organic matter undergoing thermomaturation (Fig. 7). Tissot et al. (1974) demonstrated that this release of mesogenetic carbon dioxide occurs over a wide range of temperature/time exposures. Savkevic (1971) suggested that both the interlayer water which is released from montmorillonite during its mesogenetic transformation to illite and CO_2 originating from the oxidation of organic matter could cause subsurface brines to become so undersaturated in respect to carbonate minerals that the latter are dissolved. Parker (1974) concluded that carbon dioxide originating from a plutonic intrusion was responsible for the mesogenetic leaching of carbonate which created the secondary sandstone porosity in the Smackover sandstones of the Thomasville Field, Mississippi. Hydrogen sulfide may also cause mesogenetic dissolution of carbonate (Parker, *ibid.*).

Physiochemical processes can cause dissolution and shrinkage because changes in temperature and pressure affect the solubility of minerals if the salinity and ionic ratio of the interstitial waters remain constant. For instance, pore waters that move from zones of hydrostatic pressure into zones of geopressures may become undersaturated with respect to carbonates on account of the pressure increase. This could lead to mesogenetic dissolution of carbonate.

Physical processes may create conditions for fracturing and shrinkage. Changes of hydraulic and mechanical stress and also thermal expansion and contraction are common causes for fracturing. The stresses that cause fracturing in sandstones may originate externally, e.g. overburden, or internally within the sandstones, e.g. thermal contraction.

Biochemical processes occasionally trigger void-creating dissolution. A host of boring organisms employ biochemical dissolution of rock material to construct their domiciles or to make space for their holdfasts or roots. Metabolic dissimilation by algae and other organisms can result in carbonic acid and leaching of carbonate. Similarly, sulfate reducing bacteria are capable of causing

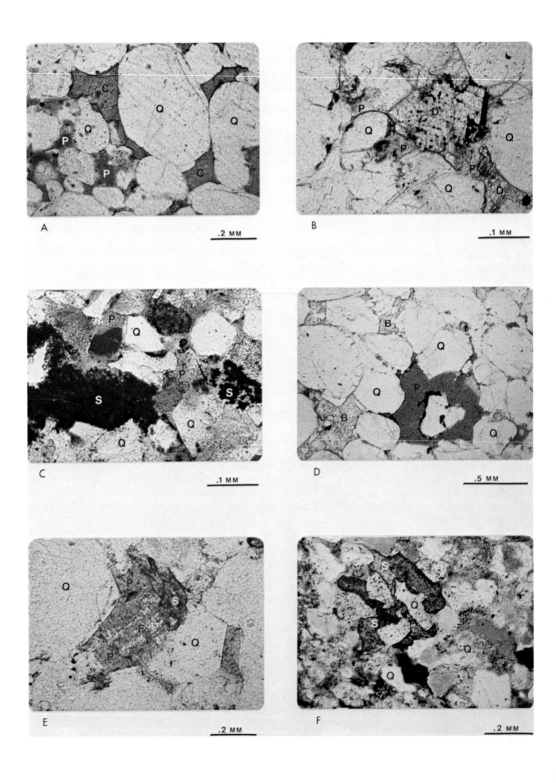

the dissolution of sulfate minerals.

Biophysical processes cause very little secondary porosity if one discounts the redistribution of primary porosity by burrowing organisms. Mechanical boring and burrowing can create open voids and the growth of roots may lead to fracturing of sandstones.

Mesogenetic decarbonatization porosity.—It is obvious from the preceding discussion that mesogenetic decarbonatization created the vast majority of secondary porosity in sandstones and is, therefore, of the greatest interest. Decarbonatization is here used as a general term for the dissolution of any textural and mineralogical type of carbonate from sandstones or other rocks. The available information suffices to outline various aspects of the occurrence of mesogenetic decarbonatization porosity.

A selection of important occurrences of mesogenetic decarbonatization porosity is listed in Table 1. In all these examples mesogenetic decarbonatization porosity occurs as the predominant or exclusive type of porosity throughout a considerable part of each basin. The incidence of hydrocarbon accumulations in these sandstones indicates that mesogenetic decarbonatization porosity is a very favorable habitat for the trapping of oil and gas. Many giant fields fall into this category including the Prudhoe Bay Field and the Jurassic fields of the North Sea. They represent a significant percentage of global reserves of natural gas and crude oil. Porosity and permeability of these reservoirs can reach very high values (Table 2). Individual samples may have more than 40 volume percent mesogenetic decarbonatization porosity, and permeability of several darcies. Average porosity for individual reservoir zones ranges from 5 to 30 volume percent.

The distribution of the many known examples of mesogenetic decarbonatization porosity can be correlated with a number of geological parameters (Fig. 8). The porosity is found in sandstones ranging in geological age from Tertiary to Cambrian and may even occur in Proterozoic sandstones. The ratio of decarbonatization porosity to primary porosity increases with increasing geological age given similar depth and temperature of burial, and similar lithology.

Sandstone lithology places no restriction on the occurrence of mesogenetic decarbonatization porosity. It may be present in sandstones of any primary textural and mineralogical composition in any state of diagenetic alteration. Neither paleogeography nor geological setting appear to have any limiting influence. Mesogenetic decarbonatization porosity occurs in every sizable sedimentary basin in which sandstones have been examined using the criteria discussed elsewhere in this volume (Schmidt and McDonald).

Mesogenetic decarbonatization porosity may originate at depths ranging from shallow to 4,000 meters. Greater depths of origin are probable but have not so far been observed. Maximum development of secondary porosity, however, usually occurs within an intermediate depth range, as will be discussed later in this paper. At present, confirmed depths of preservation of mesogenetic decarbonatization porosity range from surface to 6,000 meters. Extrapolation of available data suggests that this porosity type can exist at even greater depths. In sandstones of high mineralogical maturity decarbonatization porosity may possibly extend to a depth of 8,000 meters (Fig. 12).

TEXTURAL STAGES OF MESODIAGENESIS

The improved ability to differentiate between primary and secondary porosity permits the trac-

---

Fig. 5.—Mesogenetic dissolution porosity. *A*, Mesogenetic dissolution of poikilotopic calcite cement created secondary porosity in Cambrian quartz arenite, Northwest Territories, Canada. Polarizer only. P = secondary porosity (blue); Q = quartz grains and mesogenetic syntaxial quartz overgrowth (white); C = mesogenetic calcite cement (red). *B*, Mesogenetic dissolution of dolomite cement created secondary porosity in Lower Cretaceous quartz arenite, Scotian Shelf, Canada. Polarizer only. P = secondary porosity (blue); Q = quartz grains and mesogenetic syntaxial overgrowth; D = dolomite (high relief). *C*, Mesogenetic dissolution of siderite created secondary porosity in Jurassic quartz arenite, Statfjord Field, North Sea. Half crossed nicols. P = secondary porosity (blue); Q = quartz grains; S = siderite (brownish, very high relief). *D*, Mesogenetic dissolution of poikilotopic barite cement created secondary sandstone porosity in Cambrian quartz arenite, Northwest Territories, Canada. Polarizer only. P = secondary porosity (blue); Q = quartz grains and mesogenetic syntaxial quartz overgrowth (white); B = barite (moderately high relief). *E*, Siderite partially replaced feldspar. Subsequent mesogenetic dissolution of replacement siderite created secondary porosity in Lower Cretaceous subfeldspathic arenite, Mackenzie Delta, Canada. Polarizer only. P = secondary porosity (blue); Q = quartz grains and mesogenetic syntaxial quartz overgrowth (white); F = feldspar (honeycombed grain); S = siderite (brownish, very high relief). *F*, Siderite marginally replaced quartz. Subsequent mesogenetic dissolution of replacement siderite and siderite cement created secondary porosity in Triassic quartz arenites, Prudhoe Bay Field, North Slope, Alaska. Half Crossed nicols. P = secondary porosity (blue); Q = quartz grains; S = siderite (very high relief).

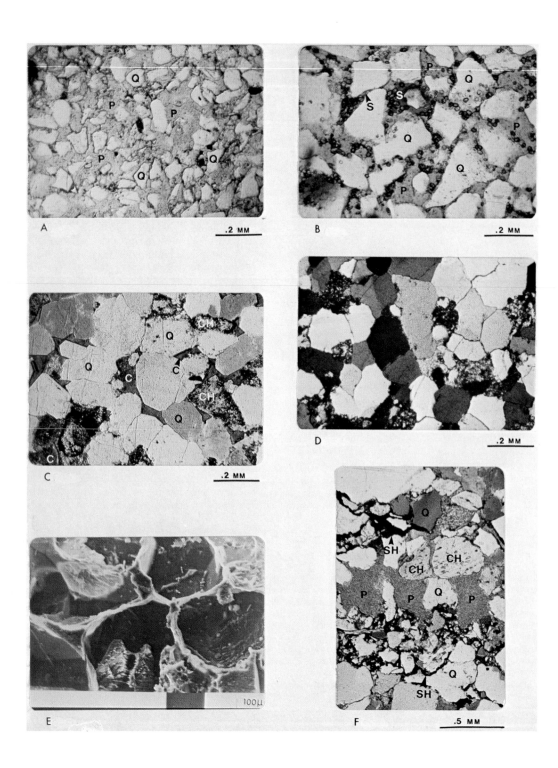

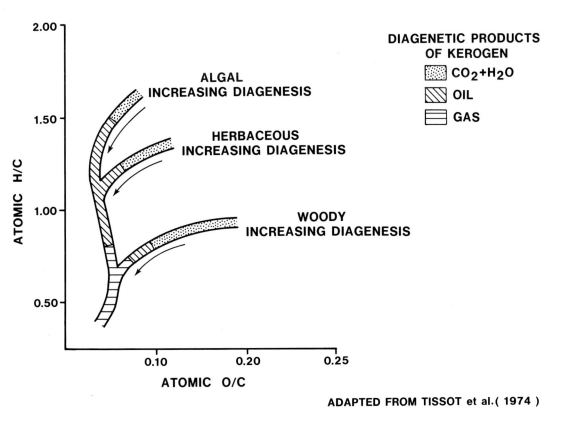

FIG. 7.—Diagenetic evolution of kerogen.

ing of the diagenetic alteration of each of the two porosity classes in response to progressive burial. This provides an excellent means of relating mesogenetic sandstone diagenesis to burial history. We propose four textural stages of sand-stone mesodiagenesis that are defined by four petrographically recognizable stages of the burial diagenesis of sandstone porosity (Fig. 9). These are in order of progressive burial: (1) immature stage; (2) semi-mature stage; (3) mature stage;

FIG. 6.—Stages of textural mesodiagenesis. *A*, Immature stage of textural mesodiagenesis, Cretaceous quartz arenite, Scotian Shelf, Canada. Polarizer only. P = primary porosity (blue); Q = quartz grains (white). *B*, Semi-mature stage of textural mesodiagenesis. Incipient chemical compaction of Cretaceous quartz arenite, Scotian Shelf, Canada. Polarizer only. P = primary porosity (blue); Q = quartz grains (white); S = eogenetic siderite cement (brownish, very high relief). *C*, Semi-mature stage of textural mesodiagenesis. Advanced cementation of primary porosity by syntaxial quartz overgrowth followed by cementation of residual primary porosity by mesogenetic poikilotopic calcite, Lower Cretaceous quartz arenite, Mackenzie Delta, Canada. Half crossed nicols. Q = quartz grains and mesogenetic quartz overgrowth; CH = chert grains; C = calcite cement (red). *D*, Mature stage of textural mesodiagenesis. Complete loss of reducible primary porosity by chemical compaction and cementation by syntaxial quartz overgrowth, Lower Cretaceous quartz arenite, Mackenzie Delta, Canada. Crossed nicols. *E*, Mature stage of textural mesodiagenesis. Epoxy cast of lamellar porosity and secondary intergranular porosity of Lower Cretaceous quartz arenite, Mackenzie Delta, Canada. Scanning-electron micrograph. *F*, Mature stage of textural mesodiagenesis. Complete loss of reducible primary porosity by chemical compaction. Subsequent dissolution of sedimentary and diagenetic carbonate created secondary porosity. Grain fracturing resulted from increased stress on grains adjacent to secondary pores. Jurassic quartz arenite, Beryl Field, North Sea. Half crossed nicols. P = secondary porosity (blue); Q = quartz grains; CH = chert grains; SH = stylolitized carbonaceous/argillaceous microlaminae (black).

TABLE 1.—SIGNIFICANT OCCURRENCES OF MESOGENETIC DECARBONATIZATION POROSITY

AREA	GEOLOGICAL AGE OF SANDSTONES	HYDROCARBON RESERVOIR	SOURCE OF INFORMATION
Mackenzie Delta, Canada	Cretaceous, Tertiary	Yes	Authors
Anderson Plain, Canada	Cambrian	Yes	Authors
Alberta, Canada	Devonian	Yes	Alcock & Benteau (1976)
Alberta, Canada	Cretaceous	Yes	Authors
British Columbia Shelf, Canada	Tertiary	No	Authors
Scotian Shelf, Canada	Jurassic, Cretaceous	Yes	Authors
Labrador Shelf, Canada	Cretaceous, Tertiary	Yes	Authors
North Slope, Alaska	Triassic, Jurassic	Yes	Authors
Cook Inlet, Alaska	Jurassic, Cretaceous, Tertiary	Yes	Hayes (this volume)
Gulf Coast, U.S.A.	Cretaceous, Tertiary	Yes	Stanton & McBride (1976)
Wyoming, U.S.A.	Pennsylvanian	Yes	Fox et al. (1975)
Venezuela	Tertiary	Yes	Authors
North Sea	Permian, Triassic, Jurassic	Yes	Authors
Northern Germany	Pennsylvanian to Jurassic	Yes	Authors
South Africa	Pennsylvanian	No	Roswell & DeSwardt (1974)
Ciscaucasus, Russia	Jurassic, Cretaceous	Yes	Proshlyakov (1960)

and, (4) supermature stage.

Description.—The *immature stage* is characterized by mechanical compaction of clean, uncemented sands with primary intergranular porosity (Fig. 6A). The compaction is accomplished by deformation of ductile grains, rotation of grains, and fracturing of grains. It reduces both primary rock volume, and primary porosity and permeability. Chemical compaction as defined below is negligible or absent. Any significant chemical compaction would tend to lithify the rock and make appreciable mechanical compaction impossible. Secondary porosity may exist. It can

TABLE 2.—VALUES OF SECONDARY POROSITY AND PERMEABILITY CREATED BY MESOGENETIC DECARBONATIZATION OF SANDSTONES (BASED ON LABORATORY ANALYSES, MICROSCOPIC ANALYSES, AND LOG ANALYSES)

INDIVIDUAL SAMPLES

Porosity:	Trace to > 40 vol. %
Permeability:	Nil to several darcies

NET PAY ZONES

Porosity:	5 vol. % to 30 vol. % (average 18 vol. %)
Permeability:	A few millidarcies to > 1 darcy

either be inherited from eodiagenesis or may originate during the immature stage.

The *semi-mature stage* is marked by the onset of pervasive chemical compaction, while, at the same time, mechanical compaction of primary porosity becomes insignificant or ceases entirely. We define chemical compaction as being essentially accomplished through dissolution of sand grains at points and interfaces of contact. In the process rock volume and the percentage of intergranular primary porosity are diminished. The dissolved material may reprecipitate within the sandstone formation as pore cement further reducing the porosity.

The coexistence of reducible primary porosity and pervasive chemical compaction define the range of the semi-mature stage (Figs. 6B, C). Secondary porosity can originate in the semi-mature stage and may coexist with inherited eogenetic and immature-stage secondary porosity. At the end of the semi-mature stage the primary porosity has reached irreducible levels. The "irreducible porosity" consists of narrow gaps between grains or diagenetic crystals a fraction of a micron to several microns wide (Fig. 6D). It is irreducible with respect to chemical compaction and cementation but not to recrystallization. The irreducible porosity in sandstones forms an interconnected system of lamellar pores with extremely low permeability analogous to the irreducible lamellar porosity in carbonate rocks described by Wardlaw (1976). The amount of irreducible porosity decreases with increasing grain size. It com-

GEOLOGICAL ATTRIBUTES	RANGE OF DECARBONATIZATION POROSITY
GEOLOGIC AGE	CAMBRIAN TO TERTIARY
LITHOLOGY	SANDSTONES OF ANY TEXTURAL AND MINERALOGICAL COMPOSITION
TYPE OF SEDIMENTARY BASIN	ANY SIZABLE SEDIMENTARY BASIN
DEPTH OF ORIGIN OF DECARBONATIZATION POROSITY	SHALLOW TO GREATER THAN 3500M(11,500 FT.)
PRESENT DEPTH	SURFACE TO GREATER THAN 6000M(20,000 FT.)

FIG. 8.—Geologic occurrence of significant mesogenetic decarbonatization porosity in sandstones.

monly ranges from about 0.5 percent to 2.5 volume percent.

The *mature stage* is characterized by the absence of primary porosity except for irreducible lamellar pores (Fig. 6E). Secondary porosity can be inherited from preceding stages or may originate during the mature stage (Fig. 6F). The secondary porosity undergoes chemical compaction

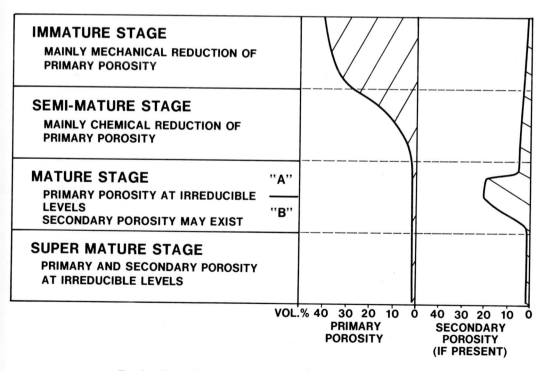

FIG. 9.—Textural stages of mesodiagenesis of sandstone porosity.

and minor mechanical compaction. The mature stage ends when chemical compaction of reducible secondary porosity has reached completion, that is, when it cannot exist any longer for a geologically significant period of time. Two sub-stages can often be identified. *Mature stage "A"* or *early mature stage* is the phase of maximum development of secondary porosity. Chemical compaction of secondary porosity is very subordinate during this interval. *Mature stage "B"* or *late mature stage* is characterized by the gradual destruction of secondary porosity mainly by chemical compaction, and little or no generation of secondary porosity.

The *supermature stage* shows both primary and secondary porosity at irreducible levels. Secondary porosity could conceivably be formed through fracturing and leaching but it would be rapidly eliminated. The advent of metamorphism marks the end of the supermature stage and the conclusion of mesodiagenesis.

In determining the textural stages of mesodiagenesis in sandstones using the above criteria the effects of the following must be discounted: (1) geo-pressures; (2) unusual local chemical conditions; (3) pore filling by hydrocarbons; (4) extrastratal cementation; and (5) unusual local conditions of temperature and pressure such as might be caused by tectonism and vulcanism. The petrographic analysis of a sandstone cannot, by itself, determine whether it presently still resides within the diagenetic zone that affected it last. This question must be answered by geological analysis of the sedimentary basin. It is possible to deduce from the present distribution of regimes of mesodiagenesis the zones of currently active burial diagenesis for specific sandstone lithologies. In similar fashion, one is able to reconstruct ancient regimes of mesodiagenesis.

Influence of sandstone mineralogy.—Figure 10 shows a schematic plot of the depth ranges of textural maturity grades of burial diagenesis versus mineralogical maturity of sandstones. The basic assumptions for the plot are: (1) the subsidence rate of the sedimentary basin is thirty meters per one million years; (2) the sedimentation rate equals the sum of subsidence and compaction; (3) the geothermal gradient is 2.7 degrees Celsius per one hundred meters; and (4) the sandstones are medium grained. Depths of individual zones of textural diagenetic maturity become shallower with decreasing mineralogical maturity, a fact which has been observed by other workers (Galloway, 1974).

Surprisingly, the transition from the semi-mature zone to the mature zone occurs at relatively shallow depths. This implies that in most sedimentary basins effective primary sandstone porosity is restricted to less than half the sedimentary column. The volume of the mature zone in the majority of sedimentary basins exceeds the combined volumes of the immature and semi-mature zones. Thus the volume of sediments which is prospective for secondary porosity is more than double the volume of sediments which is prospective for effective primary porosity.

The large vertical extent of the mature zone compared with that of the semi-mature zone is unexpected. The higher temperature of the mature zone must increase the rate of reaction of chemical compaction if other conditions remain constant. It is obvious that some of these other conditions must have changed thereby hindering chemical compaction. At the present time it is not certain which changes are responsible for the delay in the destruction of secondary porosity in the mature zone. Future investigations will have to solve this problem. It is possible that changes in the chemical environment or changes in the pore geometry and/or changes in the submicroscopic morphology of the interfaces at grain contacts may be the cause.

Influence of temperature and time.—The active stages of burial diagenesis of porosity are schematically plotted in Figure 11 in relationship to residence temperature (residence depth) and residence time. The assumed sandstone lithology is a medium-grained quartz arenite and the chosen geothermal gradient is 2.7 degrees Celsius per one hundred meters. It can be seen that the level of maturity increases with both increasing residence temperature and time. Lengthening of the residence time beyond 400 million years, however, produces very little change.

A similar relationship would be found if the diagram were plotted for other mineralogical classes of sandstone. The position of the zones of textural maturity would shift somewhat towards the upper left (lower residence temperature and shorter residence time) with decreasing mineralogical maturity. These relationships indicate that the texturally mature zone becomes volumetrically more important as the geothermal gradient and the age of the sediments increase.

Porosity range.—Figure 12 shows a schematic plot of the range of primary and secondary porosity versus depth in medium-grained quartz arenites. The assumptions made in constructing the plot are the same as for Figure 10.

Maximum primary porosities decline with increasing depth as a result of mechanical and chemical compaction. At a depth of about 3,000 meters the mature zone is reached and only one to two volume percent of irreducible primary porosity remains.

Maximum secondary porosities exceed 40 vol-

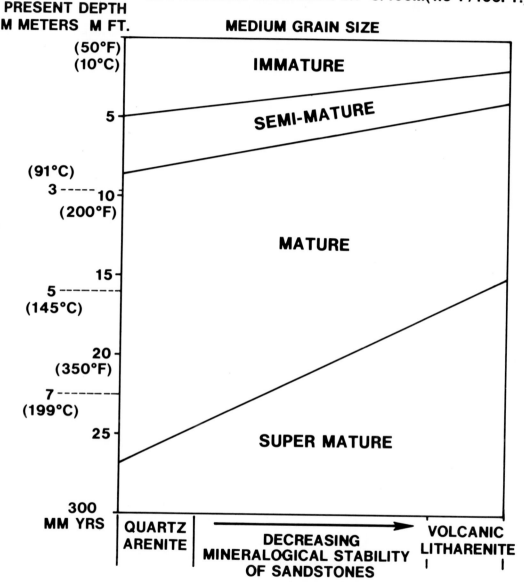

SEDIMENTATION RATE: 30.5M(100FT.)/1,000,000 YRS.
GEOTHERMAL GRADIENT: 2.7°C/100M(1.5°F/100FT.)

FIG. 10.—Influence of sandstone mineralogy on burial diagenesis of porosity.

ume percent above 4,000 meters, that is, in the immature, semi-mature and upper part of the mature zone. From there they decline steadily with increasing depth in the middle and lower part of the mature zone. At an extrapolated depth of about 8,000 meters secondary porosity should diminish to irreducible levels.

Significantly, secondary porosity can be higher than original primary porosity in the immature, semi-mature, and upper mature zones. In addition, the depth limit for porosity over 10 volume percent is more than twice as deep in the case of secondary porosity compared to that of primary porosity. The mineralogically less mature sandstones ex-

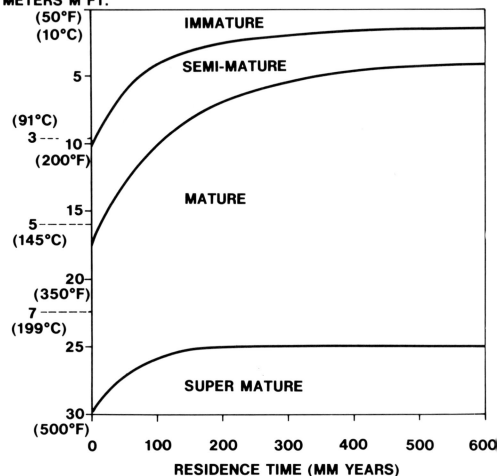

LITHOLOGY: MED. GRAINED QUARTZ ARENITE
GEOTHERMAL GRADIENT: 2.7°C/100M(1.5°F/100FT.)

Fig. 11.—Influence of temperature and time on burial diagenesis of porosity.

hibit qualitatively similar relationships between the textural stages of mesodiagenesis and porosity (Galloway, 1974; Hayes, this volume).

Diagenesis of Quartz Arenites

The sandstones of the highest mineralogical stability, the quartz arenites, have been selected to trace in detail the role of secondary porosity during the course of their diagenesis. This choice was made for two reasons: (1) the data base for this sandstone lithology is the most comprehensive; and (2) primary porosity survives much longer in quartz arenites than in sandstones of lower mineralogical maturity. Secondary porosity may be expected to play a relatively less important role in quartz arenites compared to the latter. Thus a baseline for the significance of secondary porosity can be established.

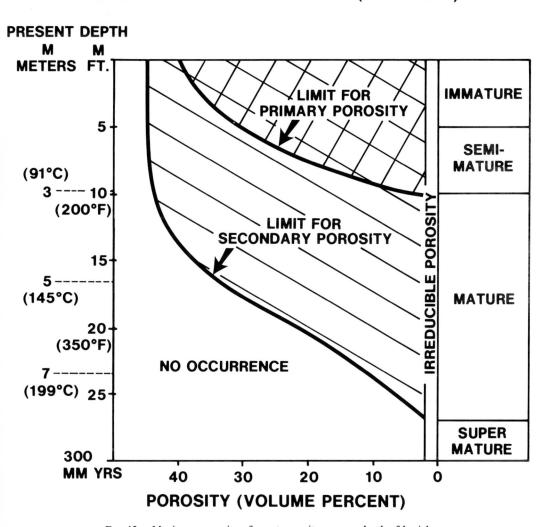

LITHOLOGY: MEDIUM GRAINED QUARTZ ARENITE
SEDIMENTATION RATE: 30.5M(100FT.)/1,000,000 YRS.
GEOTHERMAL GRADIENT: 2.7°C/100M(1.5°F/100FT.)

FIG. 12.—Maximum porosity of quartz arenites versus depth of burial.

It is necessary to follow the path of typical diagenetic histories of individual sandstones in order to better understand the vertical distribution of primary and secondary porosity. Four types of diagenetic histories will be discussed: (1) quartz arenites free of carbonate; (2) quartz arenites with sedimentary and eogenetic carbonate; (3) quartz arenites with mesogenetic carbonate; (4) quartz arenites with sedimentary, eogenetic and mesogenetic carbonate.

The diagenesis diagrams (Figs. 15–20) chart the composition of hypothetical quartz arenites from

the time of deposition to the advent of metamorphism. These diagrams have been constructed by piecing together petrographical and geological observations of numerous samples.

Quartz arenites free of carbonate.—The loss of primary porosity in quartz arenites is best examined in samples that remain free of carbonate or other readily soluble constituents throughout their diagenesis. The primary intergranular porosity and the rock volume of the quartz arenite shown in Figure 15 are reduced by mechanical compaction during the immature stage. Chemical compaction and reprecipitation of the dissolved silica as cement reduce the intergranular porosity to irreducible lamellar porosity during the semi-mature stage. A considerable reduction in rock volume accompanies this process. Thereafter the sandstone remains unchanged until some recrystallization occurs during the supermature stage (Fig. 13A).

The quartz arenite illustrated in Figure 16 received silica cement from an extrastratal source with the onset of the semi-mature stage. The silica cementation prevented chemical compaction (Fig. 13B). Many coarse grained quartz arenites show this type of diagenesis. Possible sources of the extrastratal silica cement include: (1) chemical compaction of adjacent very fine-grained quartz arenites and quartz siltstone; (2) replacement of quartz grains by carbonate; (3) degradation of feldspars; and (4) clay mineral diagenesis in adjacent shales.

The quartz arenite shown in Figure 17 experienced chemical compaction without reprecipitation of the dissolved silica as cement. Therefore, the rock volume is greatly reduced during the semi-mature stage (Fig. 13C). Of necessity, the dissolved silica migrates away from the sandstone bed. Very fine grained quartz arenites frequently follow this diagenetic path.

The three case histories outlined above demonstrate the early loss of primary porosity. Clearly, mesogenetic decarbonatization porosity cannot develop because of the absence of carbonate throughout the history of the rocks. Such carbonate-free quartz arenites are best suited for determining the first three stages of burial diagenesis.

Quartz arenites with sedimentary and/or eogenetic carbonate.—A large percentage of quartz arenites contain significant amounts of sedimentary and eogenetic carbonate (as also do other sandstone lithologies). The sources of this carbonate are: (1) erosion of carbonate rocks; (2) marine environments; (3) evaporitic environments; (4) deltaic environments; (5) lacustrine and paludal environments; (6) fluviatile environments; and, (7) subaerial environments. The dominant original carbonate minerals are siderite, dolomite, low-magnesium calcite, high magnesium calcite, and aragonite. In most instances the latter two minerals subsequently convert to low-magnesium calcite.

The diagenesis diagram of a fairly common type of quartz arenite is shown in Figure 18. The original sand contains some sedimentary carbonate. Carbonate cement fills part of the intergranular porosity in the eogenetic regime and, in doing so, moderately lithifies the sandstone. Because of this lithification, no mechanical compaction occurs during the immature stage of mesodiagenesis. Chemical compaction takes place during the semi-mature stage, considerably reducing rock volume and porosity. The dissolved silica reprecipitates as intergranular cement within the sandstone bed and further reduces the porosity. At the beginning of the mature stage "A," the sandstone contains only irreducible lamellar porosity (Fig. 13D). However, a considerable amount of porosity is subsequently created through complete decarbonatization (Figs. 13D, E). Minor mechanical and chemical compaction occurs during the remaining mature stage "A." Chemical compaction becomes more active during the mature stage "B" and the secondary porosity declines to an irreducible remnant of lamellar porosity. At this point the supermature stage is reached.

This diagenetic history demonstrates that secondary porosity survives chemical compaction longer during deep burial than primary porosity does at much shallower depth. Decarbonatization can occur at any stage of burial diagenesis and

---

FIG. 13.—Porosity diagenesis of quartz arenites. *A*, Complete loss of reducible primary porosity by quartz dissolution along grain contacts (chemical compaction) and syntaxial quartz overgrowth. Quartz arenite lacking carbonate. Mature stage. Lower Cretaceous, Mackenzie Delta, Canada. Half crossed nicols. *B*, Complete loss of reducible primary porosity due to cementation by syntaxial quartz overgrowth (chemical compaction). Quartz arenite lacking carbonate. Mature stage. Lower Cretaceous, Mackenzie Delta, Canada. Half crossed nicols. *C*, Complete loss of reducible primary porosity by quartz dissolution at grain contacts (chemical compaction). Quartz arenite, silty/argillaceous, lacking carbonate. Mature stage. Lower Cretaceous, Mackenzie Delta, Canada. Half crossed nicols. Q = quartz grains; M = silty/argillaceous matrix; PY = pyritized material. *D*, Complete loss of reducible primary porosity due to mechanical compaction and dissolution at grain contacts. Quartzose/sideritic/argillaceous/cherty/micaceous litharenite with abundant sedimentary and eogenetic siderite. Mature stage. Jurassic, Statfjord Field, North Sea. Polarizer only. Q = quartz grains (white); S = siderite (black); MI = mica SH/CH = shale fragments and chert grains (brown). *E*, Partial mesogenetic dissolution of sedimentary and eogenetic siderite created secondary porosity. Sideritic/quartzose litharenite. Mature stage. Jurassic, Statfjord Field, North Sea. Polarizer only. P = secondary porosity (blue); Q = quartz grains (white); S = siderite. *F*, Near complete mesogenetic dissolution of sedimentary and eogenetic carbonate created 40 volume percent secondary porosity (core analysis). Same original composition as Figure 13E. Mature stage. Jurassic, Statfjord Field, North Sea. Polarizer only. P = secondary porosity (blue); Q = quartz grains (white); S = siderite (black).

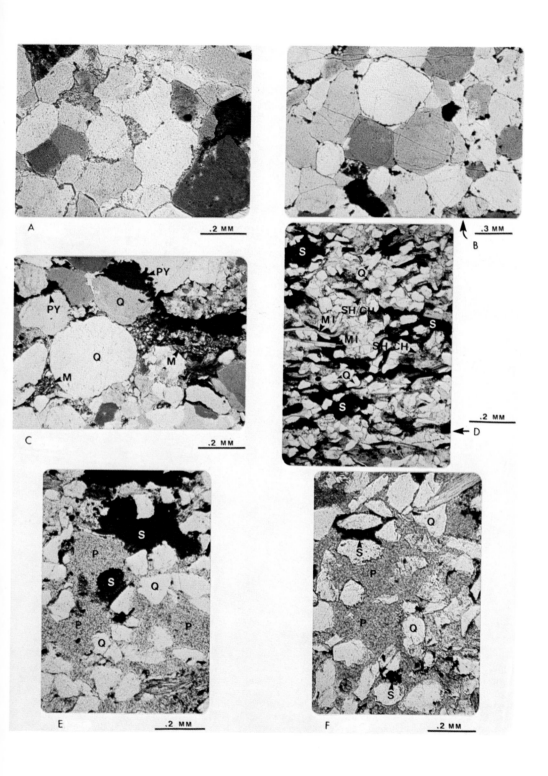

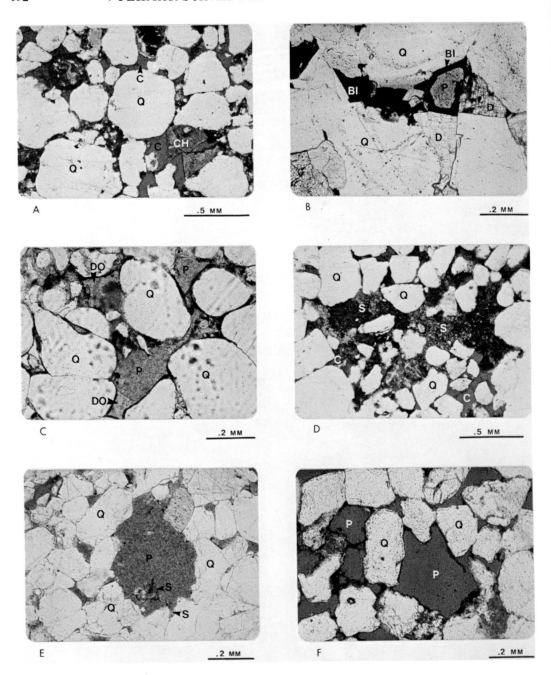

Fig. 14.—Porosity diagenesis of quartz arenites. *A*, Complete loss of reducible primary porosity due to (1) mechanical compaction (fractured chert grain); (2) incipient chemical compaction; and, (3) cementation by mesogenetic poikilotopic calcite. Quartz arenite. Mature zone. Lower Cretaceous, Mackenzie Delta, Canada. Polarizer only. Q = quartz grains (white); CH = chert grain (brown); C = calcite cement (red). *B*, Partial mesogenetic dissolution of mesogenetic dolomite created secondary porosity in Cambrian quartz arenite. Prior to dissolution, mesogenetic dolomite replaced mesogenetic syntaxial quartz overgrowths along the grain boundaries, and completely cemented reducible primary porosity. Migration of crude oil occurred after secondary porosity was formed as documented by bitumen coating secondary pores. Mature zone. Northwest Territories, Canada. Polarizer only. P = secondary porosity (blue); Q = quartz grains and syntaxial quartz overgrowth; D = cementing and replacive dolomite; BI = bitumen. *C*, Complete dissolution of mesogenetic calcite cement created secondary

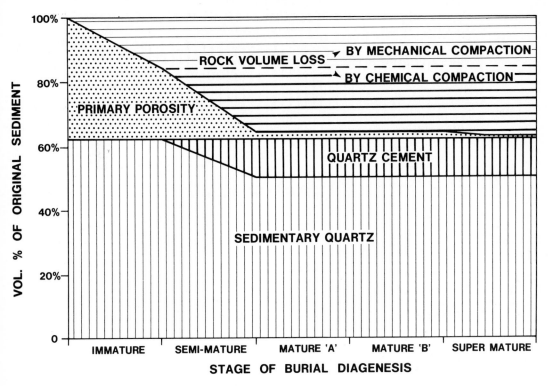

FIG. 15.—Burial diagenesis of quartz arenite with quartz dissolution equal to quartz precipitation.

individual sandstones may be subjected to one or several periods of decarbonatization. However, decarbonatization reaches a pronounced maximum at the beginning of the mature stage "A" in quartz arenites. Decarbonatization is certainly not inevitable; many quartz arenites containing carbonates are not affected by it and remain tight throughout the semi-mature and mature stages.

Quartz arenites with mesogenetic carbonate.—

Many quartz arenites that were buried containing no carbonate, later receive mesogenetic carbonate in the form of cement or replacement. The dominant mesogenetic carbonate minerals are calcite, dolomite, and siderite. Mesogenetic carbonatization is frequently succeeded by partial or complete decarbonatization.

Figure 19 illustrates a typical case history of mesogenetic carbonatization and decarbonatiza-

---

porosity in Cambrian quartz arenite (same core as Figure 5A). Cementation by precursor calcite occurred after minor chemical compaction and cementation by syntaxial quartz overgrowth (semi-mature stage). Migration of crude oil occurred after decementation and left secondary pores partially filled with dead oil. Mature zone. Northwest Territories, Canada. Polarizer only. P = secondary porosity (blue); Q = quartz (white); DO = dead oil (yellow); *D*, Complete loss of reducible primary porosity in quartz arenite containing sedimentary and eogenetic siderite and mesogenetic calcite cement. Sequence of porosity loss: (1) mechanical compaction of siderite pellets; (2) chemical compaction and minor mesogenetic cementation by syntaxial quartz overgrowth; and, (3) mesogenetic cementation by poikilotopic calcite. Mature zone. Lower Cretaceous, Mackenzie Delta, Canada. Polarizer only. Q = quartz (white), S = siderite (brown); C = calcite. *E*, Near complete dissolution of sedimentary and eogenetic siderite and mesogenetic calcite created secondary porosity in quartz arenite. Dissolution of carbonate followed after complete loss of reducible primary porosity as described for Figure 14D. Mature zone. Lower Cretaceous, Mackenzie Delta, Canada. Polarizer only. P = secondary porosity (blue); Q = quartz grains and syntaxial quartz overgrowth (white); S = siderite (very high relief). *F*, Complete dissolution of sedimentary, eogenetic and mesogenetic carbonate in quartz arenite. Precursor mesogenetic carbonate marginally replaced quartz grains and syntaxial quartz overgrowth. Dissolution of carbonate followed after complete loss of reducible primary porosity as described for Figure 14D. Mature zone. Lower Cretaceous, Scotian Shelf, Canada. Polarizer only. P = secondary porosity (blue); Q = quartz (white).

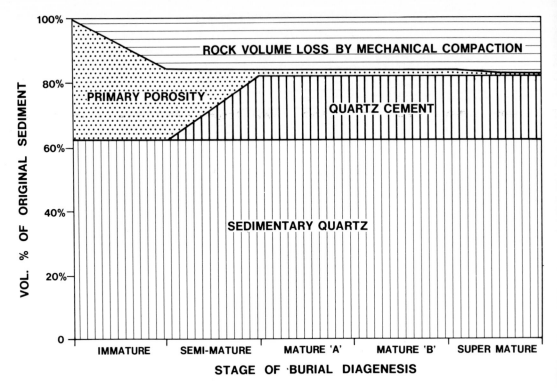

Fig. 16.—Burial diagenesis of a quartz arenite with extrastratal source of quartz cement and without quartz dissolution at grain contacts.

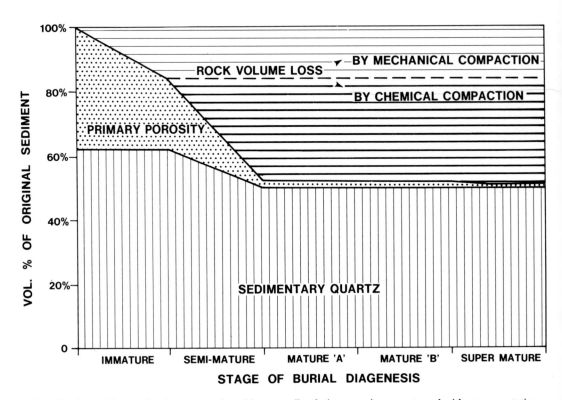

Fig. 17.—Burial diagenesis of quartz arenite with quartz dissolution at grain contacts and without cementation.

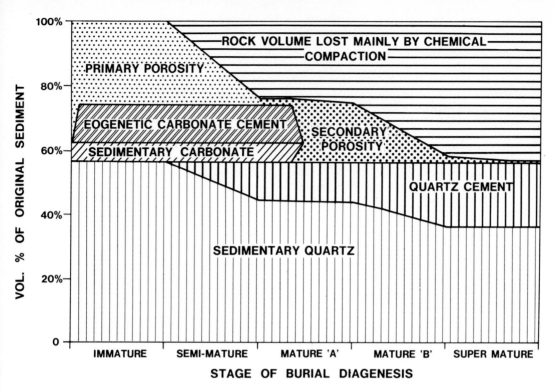

Fig. 18.—Burial diagenesis of a quartz arenite showing eogenetic carbonatization and mesogenetic decarbonatization.

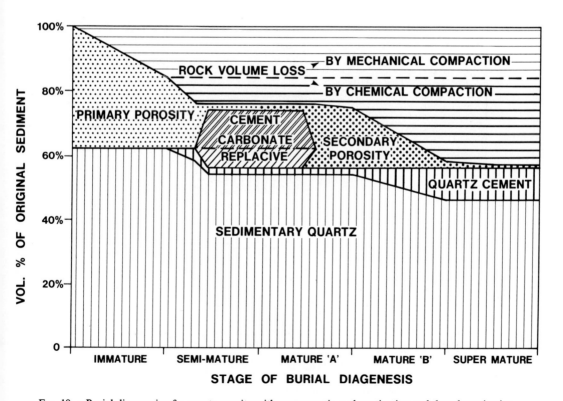

Fig. 19.—Burial diagenesis of a quartz arenite with mesogenetic carbonatization and decarbonatization.

tion. Diagenesis during the immature and early semi-mature stages follows the same path as in Figure 15. Carbonatization during the semi-mature stage reduces the remaining intergranular porosity to an irreducible volume of lamellar porosity and replaces part of the quartz cement and margins of quartz grains. (Fig. 14). The carbonatization also halts chemical compaction. No further change occurs until decarbonatization takes place during the early mature stage (Figs. 14B, C). The volume of the decarbonatization porosity is larger than the volume of primary porosity at the onset of carbonatization because carbonate cement and replacive carbonate have both been completely leached. The subsequent diagenesis follows a similar pattern to that described for Figure 18.

Carbonatization can occur at any stage of mesogenetic sandstone diagenesis. However, in quartz arenites a distinct maximum of carbonatization occurs during the last two-thirds of the semi-mature stage with carbonate cement occupying mainly primary porosity. This zone of maximum carbonatization in many sedimentary basins forms a distinct zone of carbonate enrichment which may be referred to as a "carbonate curtain."

During the process of mesogenetic carbonatiza-

tion of quartz arenites large volumes of quartz are replaced by carbonate. The silica must go into aqueous solution and is available for re-precipitation. This silica appears to be a major source of the silica overgrowth cement which reduces primary porosity during the semi-mature stage.

Quartz arenites with sedimentary, eogenetic and mesogenetic carbonate.—A fairly common, although complex, case history of diagenesis is shown in Figure 20. The original quartz sand contains a moderate amount of sedimentary carbonate. Eogenetic replacement and cementation add more carbonate and slightly consolidate the sediment. Mechanical compaction during the immature stage is only minor because of the eogenetic carbonatization. Some mesogenetic carbonatization, including both replacement and cementation, occurs after some chemical compaction during the semi-mature stage. Chemical compaction resumes its activity during the remaining part of the semi-mature stage because mesogenetic cementation is incomplete (Fig. 14D). At the same time incomplete decarbonatization takes place creating some secondary porosity. The sandstone enters the mature zone containing considerable amounts of secondary porosity and a

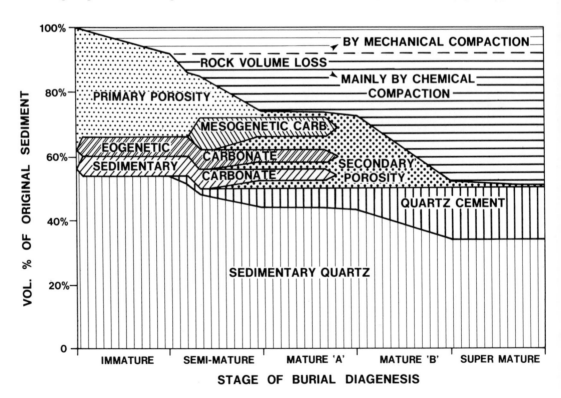

FIG. 20.—Burial diagenesis of a quartz arenite showing eogenetic carbonatization and mesogenetic carbonatization with mesogenetic decarbonatization creating an overlap.

small amount of irreducible primary porosity (Fig. 14E). During mature stage "A" all remaining carbonate constituents are dissolved, greatly increasing the amount of secondary porosity (Fig. 14F). Destruction of the secondary porosity during mature stage "B" follows a similar pattern to that described for Figure 18. The final rock volume in the supermature stage is only half that of the original quartz sand.

The above case history shows that decarbonatization can create exceedingly high porosities in quartz arenites which contain sedimentary, eogenetic, and mesogenetic carbonate including a considerable fraction of replacement carbonate. Multiple pulses of incomplete decarbonatization are very common, but are extremely difficult to recognize microscopically. Individual quartz arenites may also be subjected to several phases of mesogenetic carbonatization, some of which can be readily distinguished under the petrographic microscope. Usually, electron luminescence microscopy and microprobe analysis must be applied to solve the more complex sequences of diagenetic events.

Synthesis.—The principal observations concerning the burial diagenesis of quartz arenites are summarized in Figure 21. The sequence of diagenetic events is mainly controlled by residence temperature and residence time. Vitrinite asso-

ciated with quartz arenites records the temperature-time exposure by its change in reflectance which can be used as a scale for the thermomaturation of quartz arenites. Thus specific reflectivity values of vitrinite correspond to textural stages of mesodiagenesis.

Mechanical compaction during the immature stage mainly affects primary porosity, reducing it by about one quarter. Mesogenetic carbonatization, decarbonatization, and decarboxylation of organic matter in intercalated shales operate at extremely low levels during the immature stage.

Quartz diagenesis, that is, the chemical compaction of quartz arenites and silica cementation, operates most strongly during the semi-mature stage, mainly reducing primary porosity. Carbonatization reaches its maximum during the last two-thirds of the semi-mature stage, chiefly filling primary porosity but also a considerable volume of secondary porosity. Decarbonatization and decarboxylation are fairly active throughout the semi-mature stage. Moderate generation of liquid hydrocarbons in intercalated shales may take place during the latter part of the semi-mature stage. Loss of porosity predominates over porosity gain though a considerable amount of secondary porosity is formed. All effective primary porosity has been destroyed by the end of the semi-mature stage but an appreciable amount of

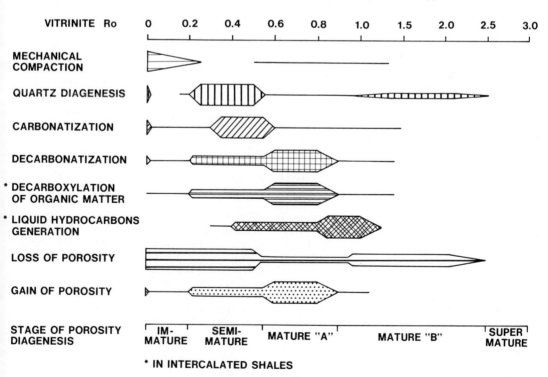

FIG. 21.—Burial diagenesis of quartz arenites.

secondary porosity does exist.

The mature stage "A" is characterized by maximum decarbonatization and decarboxylation of organic matter. Generation of liquid hydrocarbons is, for the most part, moderate but increases to maximum levels towards the end of the mature stage "A." Carbonatization, quartz diagenesis and mechanical compaction operate at low levels. Gain of secondary porosity is at its maximum and results mainly from decarbonatization. It exceeds loss of secondary porosity by a wide margin.

The initial phase of mature stage "B" shows low levels of carbonatization, decarboxylation, decarbonatization, mechanical compaction, and quartz diagenesis, whereas the generation of liquid hydrocarbons continues for a short period, at its maximum level before decreasing. Loss of secondary porosity is minor and gain of secondary porosity is very low.

Quartz diagenesis is the only significant diagenetic activity during the intermediate and final phases of the mature stage "B." It eventually eliminates any reducible secondary porosity. Organic metamorphism generates large volumes of methane during the intermediate phase of the mature stage "B."

The zone of maximum active decarbonatization underlies the zone of maximum active carbonatization. It appears that the former is the source of carbonate for the latter. This means that carbonate must be moving upward in aqueous solution to form the "carbonate curtain." The reasons for the precipitation of carbonate at the zone of carbonatization have not yet been determined satisfactorily. It appears as if the diagenesis of clay minerals in the intercalated shales may influence the chemistry of interstitial waters (change of ionic ratios, alkalinity, pH values) in such a way as to cause carbonate precipitation. Alternatively, formation waters which migrate upwards from a geopressure zone into zones of hydrostatic pressure could precipitate carbonates in the zone of pressure transition.

The occurrence of decarbonatization in most sedimentary basins corresponds very closely with the rate of production of carbon dioxide in intercalated shales or coals resulting from decarboxylation of maturing organic matter. Decarbonatization is most intense in quartz arenites which are closely associated with maturing organic-rich hydrocarbon source rocks. It appears as if generation of carbonic acid in the subsurface is the prime cause of mesogenetic decarbonatization. Other apparently common causes for mesogenetic decarbonatization include: (1) physicochemical gradients at the boundaries of geopressure zones; (2) release of water from clay minerals (Savkevic, 1971); and, (3) generation of hydrogen sulfide.

In many instances mesogenetic decarbonatization takes place in very tight quartz arenites. However, fractures and the irreducible lamellar porosity apparently provide sufficient access for the leaching brines to initiate decarbonatization. As secondary porosity is being created, it continuously improves access for the acid waters. The percentage of secondary porosity which can be generated by complete decarbonatization is limited both by the carbonate content of the sandstone and by the mechanical strength of the non-carbonate framework.

Quartz arenites containing carbonate may escape decarbonatization for one of the following reasons: (1) the subsurface environment does not generate chemical conditions for leaching, e.g. lack of organic matter; (2) the leaching capacity of the migrating formation water has been exhausted previously; and, (3) the leaching formation water has no access to the quartz arenite strata.

In the development of a sedimentary basin intensive decarbonatization will likely occur soon after the oldest quartz arenites have reached the mature zone. These quartz arenites contain mainly sedimentary and eogenetic carbonate. Reprecipitation of this dissolved carbonate in the overlying semi-mature zone may form a thin initial "carbonate curtain." Continued subsidence and sedimentation eventually moves this initial "carbonate curtain" into the mature zone where it may be subjected to strong decarbonatization which, in turn, could lead to a thicker "carbonate curtain" in the quartz arenites which have newly arrived in the semi-mature zone. In this manner both the zone of maximum decarbonatization and maximum carbonatization can move continually into younger sediments. In the process much of the carbonate may be recycled many times over and large volumes of carbonate may accumulate in the moving zones of active carbonatization, provided that sufficient organic matter is present throughout the sedimentary sequence to sustain decarbonatization.

Most liquid hydrocarbons and probably most of the natural gas is generated in the mature zone of burial diagenesis after the peak of development of secondary porosity. This places quartz arenites with secondary porosity in a very favorable situation to trap these hydrocarbons. Indeed, it is reasonable to assume that primary migration emplaced most oil and gas found in secondary sandstone porosity (Figs. 14B, C), whereas secondary migration supplied much of the hydrocarbon encountered in primary porosity.

THE POROSITY DIAGENESIS OF SANDSTONES OF INTERMEDIATE AND LOW MINERALOGICAL MATURITY

Sandstones of lesser mineralogical maturity than quartz arenites exhibit a similar relationship

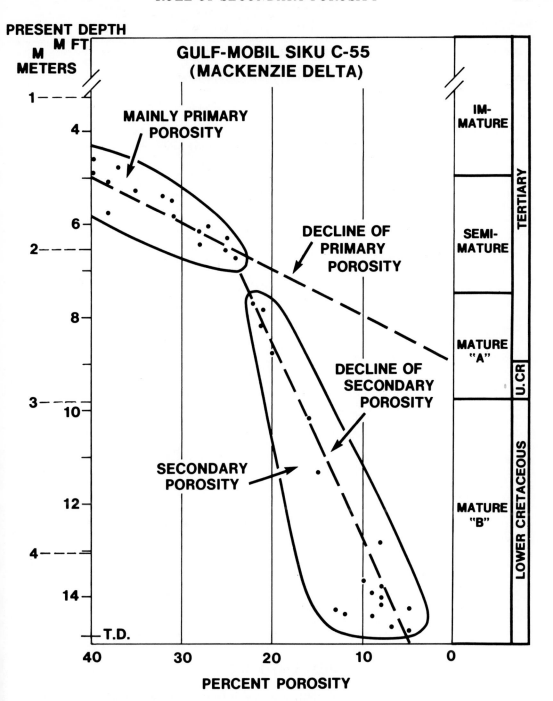

FIG. 22.—Mackenzie Delta: Depth/porosity plot showing decline of primary and secondary porosity (sonic porosities of sandstone intervals >10 ft.).

between the maturation of organic matter and the development of mesogenetic decarbonatization porosity as described above. However, both primary and secondary porosity are reduced by chemical compaction at lower temperatures and at faster rates than observed in quartz arenites. Chemical constituents derived from the dissolution of minerals such as feldspars, micas, amphiboles, and pyroxenes precipitate as mesogenetic cements mainly consisting of clay minerals

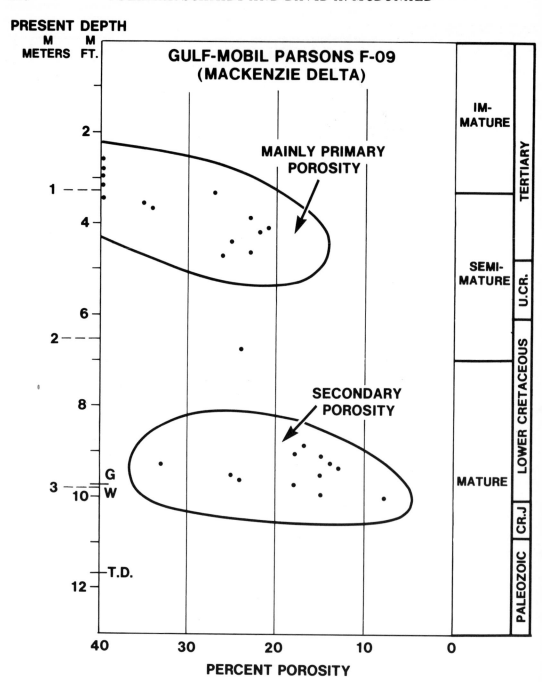

Fig. 23.—Mackenzie Delta: Depth/porosity plot showing wide range of secondary porosity (sonic porosities of sandstone intervals > 10 ft.).

Fig. 24.—Porosity variation in a sandstone zone of mature textural mesodiagenesis, Lower Cretaceous, Mackenzie Delta. A, Secondary porosity created by mesogenetic leaching of mainly sedimentary and eogenetic carbonates. Mature stage. Lower Cretaceous quartz arenite, Mackenzie Delta, Canada. Polarizer only. P = secondary porosity (blue); Q = quartz (white). B, Secondary porosity created by mesogenetic leaching of sedimentary porosity, eogenetic carbonate and mesogenetic intergranular carbonate cement. Mature stage. Lower Cretaceous quartz

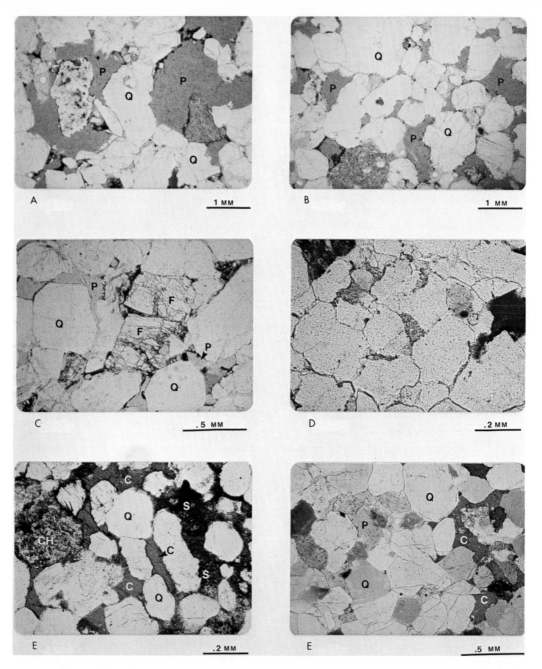

arenite, Mackenzie Delta, Canada. Polarizer only. P = secondary porosity (blue); Q = quartz (white). C, Secondary porosity created by mesogenetic leaching of mainly mesogenetic intergranular carbonate cement. Feldspar grains were fractured after leaching of mesogenetic carbonate that partially replaced the feldspar. Mature stage. Lower Cretaceous subfeldspathic arenite. Mackenzie Delta, Canada. Polarizer only. P = secondary porosity (blue); Q = quartz (white); F = feldspar (fractured grains). D, Lack of effective porosity due to absence of carbonate when sandstones entered the mature stage. Lower Cretaceous quartz arenite. Mackenzie Delta, Canada. Polarizer only. E, Lack of effective porosity due to absence of mesogenetic leaching of sedimentary eogenetic and mesogenetic carbonate. Mature stage. Lower Cretaceous sublithic arenite. Mackenzie Delta, Canada. Polarizer only. Q = quartz grains and mesogenetic syntaxial quartz overgrowth; S = sedimentary siderite pseudomatrix and eogenetic siderite replacing silicate grains along the boundaries and cementing pores (very high relief); CH = chert grain; C = mesogenetic poikilotopic calcite cementing pores and replacing quartz grains and quartz cement (red). F, Low effective porosity due to incomplete mesogenetic leaching of mesogenetic calcite. Mature stage. Lower Cretaceous quartz arenite. Mackenzie Delta, Canada. Half crossed nicols. P = secondary porosity (blue); Q = quartz grains and mesogenetic syntaxial quartz overgrowth; C = mesogenetic poikilotopic calcite cement.

and zeolites (Hayes, this volume). Chemical compaction and associated intrastratal precipitation of cements may collectively be termed framework diagenesis, analogous to quartz diagenesis. Mesogenetic carbonatization in these sandstones involves more replacement and less cementation when compared with quartz arenites. Carbonatization tends to culminate during the early phase of mature stage "A" at about the same level of thermomaturation as in quartz arenites.

In general, the development and disappearance of mesogenetic secondary porosity follows a similar pattern in sandstones of intermediate and low mineralogical maturity to that observed in quartz arenites. The detail of the diagenetic histories of sandstones of lesser mineralogical stability is often very complex and much more work remains to be done to establish the basic relationships as clearly as is now possible with quartz arenites. The Cretaceous sandstones of the Labrador Shelf, the Tertiary sandstones of the Mackenzie Delta, and the Mesozoic and Tertiary sandstones of the Cook Inlet are prime candidates for such work. These sandstones of intermediate to low mineralogical maturity contain large hydrocarbon accumulations in reservoirs of secondary sandstone porosity.

EXAMPLES OF POROSITY DISTRIBUTION

Plots of sandstone porosity versus depth are easily constructed using core analyses and/or log interpretations from wells. Petrographic analysis of the sandstones and application of the criteria and concepts developed in this paper allow a much more complete interpretation of such porosity/depth plots than has hitherto been possible.

Mackenzie Delta example.—Figure 22 represents a porosity/depth plot illustrating the rate of decline of primary and secondary sandstone porosity of a well in the Mackenzie Delta which penetrated Tertiary sandstones of intermediate mineralogical maturity and Lower Cretaceous quartz arenites. The Tertiary sandstones above a depth of 2,100 meters have porosity which is predominantly primary and which declines rapidly with depth. Primary porosity has been reduced by both framework diagenesis and by carbonate

cementation. Both processes are apparently active at the present time. Below 2100 meters the sandstone porosity is essentially secondary and declines with depth at a much slower rate compared with that of primary porosity. Active maximum decarbonatization occurs between 2,400 and 2,500 meters. The relatively high porosities below 4,000 meters do not necessarily indicate decarbonatization at that depth; rather they represent a zone of exceedingly high decarbonatization with porosities probably exceeding 30 volume percent which subsequently has been reduced to the present levels by quartz diagenesis.

Another well in the Mackenzie Delta with similar stratigraphy to the above well shows a wide range of secondary porosity within the narrow depth interval 2,650 to 3,050 meters (Fig. 23). This zone is in the mature stage "A" of burial diagenesis and the sandstones from 2,650 to 2,900 meters are gas bearing. The secondary porosity is the result of decarbonatization involving the leaching of sedimentary, eogenetic, and mesogenetic carbonate (Figs. 24A–C). High original carbonate content and nearly complete decarbonatization are the attributes of the sandstone intervals with high secondary porosity. Low secondary porosities are shown by sandstone intervals which either originally contained only moderate amounts of carbonate or experienced incomplete decarbonatization (Figs. 24D–F). Accumulation of the gas occurred after decarbonatization during the mature stage "A" of burial diagenesis. The presence of hydrocarbons had little or no effect on the preservation of porosity. However, if the gas bearing sandstones were to be buried deeply enough to enter mature stage "B" of burial diagenesis, then the presence of hydrocarbons would prevent quartz diagenesis and preserve porosity.

Scotian Shelf example.—Porosities of Cretaceous and Upper Jurassic sandstones of a well on the Scotian Shelf are plotted versus depth in Figure 26. The sandstones are principally composed of quartz arenites, feldspathic quartz arenites, and glauconitic quartz arenites, and originally contained considerable amounts of sedimentary and eogenetic carbonate. Intercalated shales vary greatly in their mineralogy and contain very low

FIG. 25.—Sequence of stages of textural mesodiagenesis with depth in Cretaceous sandstones of the Scotian Shelf. *A*, Immature stage. High primary porosity in Cretaceous quartz arenite. Mobil Citnalta I-59, Scotian Shelf, Canada. Polarizer only. P = primary porosity (blue); Q = quartz grains (white). *B*, Semi-mature stage. Primary and secondary porosity in glauconitic quartz arenite. Incomplete mesogenetic cementation by poikilotopic calcite was followed by partial mesogenetic leaching of calcite. Cretaceous. Mobil Citnalta I-59, Scotian Shelf, Canada. Polarizer only. P = primary and secondary porosity (blue); Q = quartz grains and mesogenetic syntaxial quartz overgrowth; C = calcite (red); G = sedimentary and eogenetic glauconite (greenish). *C*, semi-mature stage. Cementation of secondary and primary porosity by mesogenetic syntaxial quartz overgrowth. Cretaceous

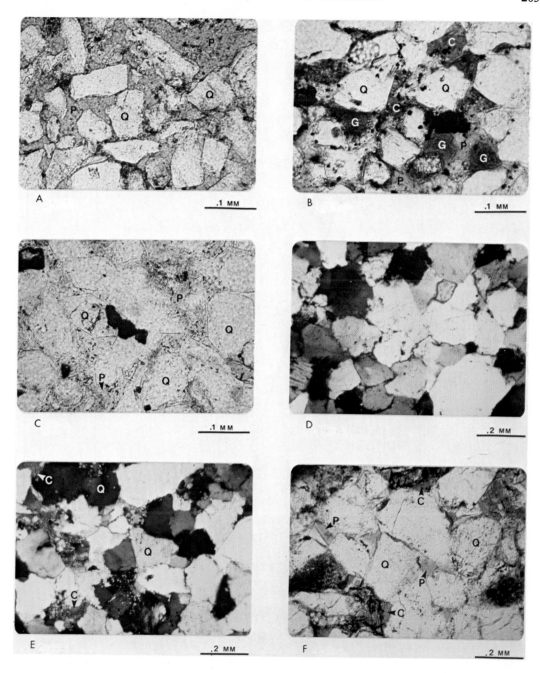

quartz arenite. Mobil Citnalta I-59, Scotian Shelf, Canada. Polarizer only. P = primary and secondary porosity (blue); Q = quartz (white). *D*, Mature stage. Lack of effective porosity due to absence of carbonate when sandstone entered the mature stage. Cretaceous quartz arenite. Mobil Citnalta I-59, Scotian Shelf, Canada. Crossed nicols. *E*, Mature stage. Lack of effective porosity due to absence of mesogenetic leaching of mesogenetic calcite cement. Cretaceous quartz arenite, Mobil Citnalta I-59, Scotian Shelf, Canada. Crossed nicols. Q = quartz grains and mesogenetic syntaxial quartz overgrowth cement; C = mesogenetic poikilotopic calcite cement. *F*, Mature stage. Presence of secondary porosity due to mesogenetic leaching of mesogenetic poikilotopic calcite. Cretaceous subfeldspathic arenite. Mobil Citnalta I-59, Scotian Shelf, Canada. Polarizer only. P = secondary porosity (blue); Q = quartz grains and mesogenetic syntaxial quartz overgrowth cement. C = mesogenetic calcite cement and calcite replacing detrital grains and quartz cement along the boundaries.

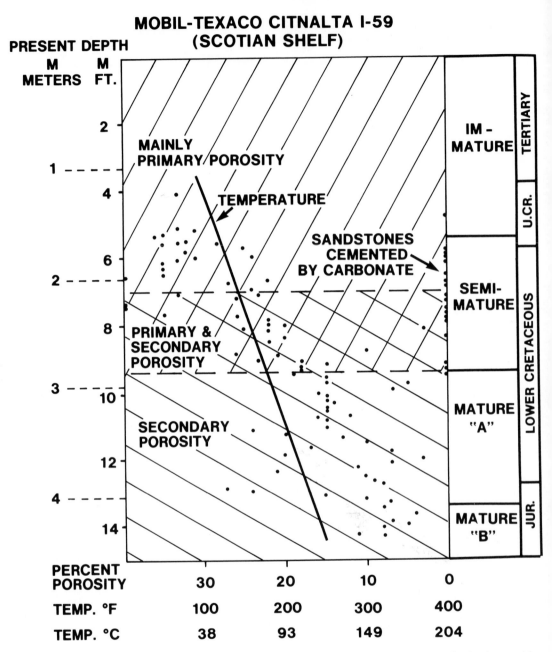

FIG. 26.—Scotian Shelf: Depth/porosity plot showing overlap of primary and secondary porosity (sonic porosities of sandstone intervals >10 ft.).

to moderately high amounts of organic matter of widely varying composition.

Primary and secondary porosity overlap throughout the semi-mature stage of burial diagenesis to form a gradation from very high primary porosities at the top to high secondary porosities at the bottom. Tight sandstones containing abun-dant mesogenetic carbonate cement are interca-lated with the porous sandstones which experi-enced considerable decarbonatization (Figs. 25A–C). Thus multiple zones of carbonatization alter-nate with multiple zones of decarbonatization possibly because of the variable content and type of organic matter and lithology of the intercalated

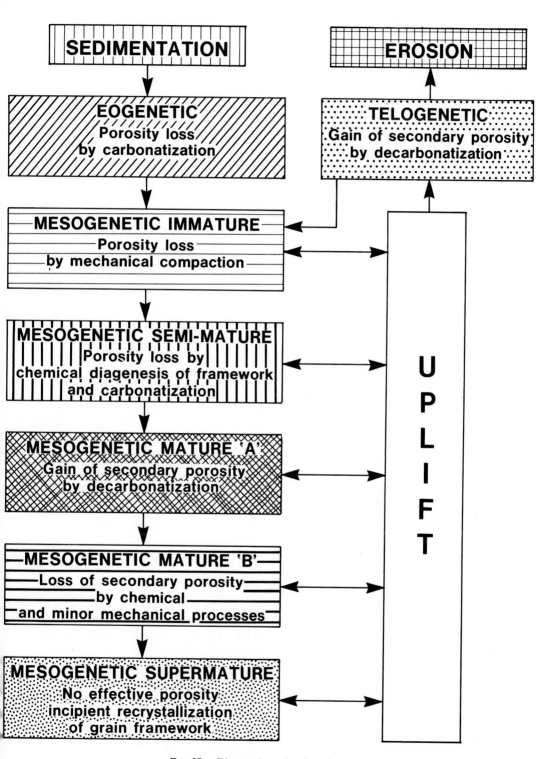

Fig. 27.—Diagenesis cycle of sandstones.

shales. It is likely that a number of horizons of carbonatization and decarbonatization are presently active.

In mature stage "A" of burial diagenesis all sandstones containing carbonate experienced renewed decarbonatization to some degree, whereas carbonatization was negligible (Figs. 25D–F). The sandstones with high secondary porosities are often closely associated with hydrocarbon source rocks, and contain condensate and natural gas. Quartz diagenesis and framework diagenesis of other grains is responsible for the decline of secondary porosity in the mature stage "B" of burial diagenesis.

CONCLUSIONS

The following conclusions concerning the role of secondary porosity in the course of sandstone diagenesis can be drawn from the above discussion.

1. Secondary porosity plays a pre-eminent role in the subsurface mesodiagenesis of sandstones. In addition, a significant amount of secondary porosity may occasionally develop during early diagenesis (eodiagenesis), and frequently develops during erosional diagenesis (telodiagenesis). The origin and destruction of secondary porosity and associated diagenetic processes are key elements in the diagenesis cycle of sandstone (Fig. 27).

2. A large number of textural and genetic types of secondary sandstone porosity exist. Several processes are capable of creating significant volumes of secondary sandstone porosity and these include dissolution of a number of minerals, shrinkage of certain minerals, and fracturing. Dissolution of carbonate minerals creates by far the largest volume of secondary sandstone porosity in all three diagenetic regimes.

3. Decarbonatization during eodiagenesis and telodiagenesis is caused mainly by carbonic acid which is derived from meteoric and biogenic carbon dioxide. Mesogenetic decarbonatization appears to result mainly from leaching by carbonic acid which is derived from the decarboxylation of maturing organic matter in intercalated shales. This decarboxylation occurs over a wide range of temperature-time exposures but most of the decarboxylation occurs after the sandstones have lost their primary porosity.

4. Decarbonatization is the source of dissolved chemical constituents which, for the most part, migrate upwards into overlying sandstones and are precipitated there as mesogenetic cement and replacement. In a subsiding prism of accumulating sediments repeated recycling of carbonate may occur leading to very high concentrations of carbonate in the zone of carbonatization and very high secondary porosities in the underlying zone of decarbonatization.

5. Mesogenetic sandstone decarbonatization is generally controlled by the amount and type of organic matter in intercalated shales and their temperature-time exposure. The texture and composition of the non-carbonate fraction of the sandstones appears to have little influence on decarbonatization. Significantly, decarbonatization can create porosity in tight sandstones because of the presence of irreducible lamellar porosity.

6. Secondary porosity in any sandstone lithology resists reduction by chemical compaction much more than does primary sandstone porosity. However, the rates of reduction of both primary and secondary porosity by chemical compaction are influenced by temperature and mineralogical maturity of the sandstones. Therefore, mapping of the diagenetic maturity of sandstones is only of value if there is reasonable uniformity of mineralogical maturity.

7. The maximum depth of effective secondary porosity created by mesogenetic decarbonatization is more than double that of effective primary porosity in sandstones of high mineralogical stability. It is more than three times the maximum depth of effective primary porosity in sandstones of low mineralogical stability.

8. The maturation of the hydrocarbon source rocks appears to be directly responsible for the generation of most secondary sandstone porosity. The majority of conventional crude oil and natural gas in clastic sequences has been generated in the source rocks after the intercalated sandstones had lost their primary porosity and after they had gained their secondary porosity. For this reason secondary sandstone porosity is a favorable habitat for crude oil and natural gas in clastic sequences.

ACKNOWLEDGEMENTS

Research for this paper was conducted at the geological laboratory of Mobil Oil Canada, Ltd. and since 1976 also at the geological research laboratory of Petro-Canada. The authors would like to thank both companies for their generous support in every phase of the preparation of this paper and for permission to publish. Special thanks are due to Petro-Canada for providing funds for printing of the colored microphotographs. Thanks are also extended to the drafting department of Mobil Oil Canada Ltd. for preparing the excellent illustrations. The authors thankfully appreciate the advice and assistance of the many people that made this paper possible, including: Brian Miller—illustrations and microphotography; David Blair—thin sections; Susan Peters and Sylvia Bates—typing; Jack Thomas, Monte Lerand and Norman Wardlaw—critical reading; John Halsey, Marvin Meloche, Bill Monroe, Hans

Nelson, Henry Nelson, Ron Platt and James Scott—discussion of petrological and geological aspects; Ellis Bray and Trevor Powell—discussion of geochemical aspects, and, last but not least, Nadine McDonald and Sylvia Schmidt are thanked for patience and support as much of this paper was written at the homes of the authors.

REFERENCES

ALCOCK, F. G., AND BENTEAU, 1976, Nipisi Field—A Middle Devonian clastic reservoir, *in* M. M. Lerand (ed.), The sedimentology of selected clastic oil and gas reservoirs in Alberta: Canadian Soc. Petroleum Geology, Spec. Pub., 125 p.

CHOQUETTE, P. W., AND PRAY, L. C., 1970, Geologic nomenclature and classification of porosity in sedimentary carbonates: Am. Assoc. Petroleum Geologists Bull., v. 54, p. 207–250.

FOX, J. E., LAMBERT, P. W., MAST, R. F., NUSS, N. W., AND REIN, R. D., 1975, Porosity variation in the Tensleep and its equivalent, the Weber Sandstone, western Wyoming; a log and petrographic analysis, *in* D. W. Bolyard (ed.), Deep drilling frontiers of the central Rocky Mountains: Denver, Colorado, Rocky Mountain Assoc. Geologists, p. 185–216.

GALLOWAY, W. E., 1974, Deposition and diagenetic alteration of sandstone in northeast Pacific arc-related basins: Implications of greywacke genesis: Geol. Soc. America Bull., v. 85, p. 379–390.

HARTMAN, J. A., 1968, The Norphlet Sandstone, Pelhatchie Field, Rankin County, Mississippi: Gulf Coast Assoc. Geol. Socs. Trans., v. 18, p. 2–11.

HEALD, M. T., AND LARESE, R. E., 1973, The significance of solution of feldspar in porosity development: Jour. Sed. Petrology, v. 43, p. 458–460.

HRABER, S. V., AND POTTER, P. E., 1969, Lower West Baden (Late Mississippian) sandstone body of Owen and Green Counties, Indiana: Am. Assoc. Petroleum Geologists Bull., v. 53, p. 2150–2160.

KRYNINE, P. D., 1941, Petrographic studies of variation in cementing material in the Oriskany sand: Pennsylvania State College Bull. 33, p. 108–116.

LINDQUIST, S., 1976, Leached porosity in overpressured sandstones—Frio Formation (Oligocene), south Texas [abs.]: Am. Assoc. Petroleum Geologists Bull., v. 60, p. 1612.

PARKER, C. A., 1974, Geopressures and secondary porosity in the deep Jurassic of Mississippi: Gulf Coast Assoc. Geol. Socs. Trans., v. 24, p. 69–80.

PROSHLYAKOV, B. K., 1960, Reservoir rocks as a function of their depth and lithology [in Russian]: Geol. Nefti i Gaza, v. 4, no. 12, p. 24–29.

ROWSELL, D. M., AND DE SWARDT, A.M.J., 1974, Secondary leaching porosity in Middle Ecca Sandstones: Geol. Soc. South Africa Trans. and Proc., v. 77, p. 131–140.

SAVKEVIC, S. S., 1971, The possible connection between the leaching-induced porosity of rocks and the primary stage of petroleum generation (migration) [in Russian]: Akad. Nauk SSSR Izv. Ser. Geol., v. 6, p. 70–77.

SCHMIDT, V., 1976, Secondary porosity in the Parsons Lake Sandstone [abs.]: Geol. Assoc. Canada and Mineralog. Assoc. Canada Ann. Meeting Abs., v. 1, p. 50.

———, McDONALD, D. A., AND PLATT, R. L., 1977, Pore geometry and reservoir aspects of secondary porosity in sandstones [abs.]: Geol. Assoc. Canada and Mineralog. Assoc. Canada Ann. Meeting Abs., v. 2, p. 106.

SEDIMENTATION SEMINAR, 1969, Bethel Sandstone (Mississippian) of western Kentucky and south-central Indiana, a submarine-channel fill: Kentucky Geol. Survey Rept. Inv. 11, ser. X, 24 p.

STANTON, G. D., AND McBRIDE, E. F., 1976, Factors influencing porosity and permeability of Lower Wilcox (Eocene) Sandstone, Karnes County, Texas [abs.]: Am. Assoc. Petroleum Geologists and Soc. Econ. Paleontologists and Mineralogists Ann. Meeting Abs., v. 1, p. 119.

TISSOT, B., DURAND, B., ESPITALIE, J., AND COMBAY, A., 1974, Influence of nature and diagenesis of organic matter in formation of petroleum: Am. Assoc. Petroleum Geologists Bull., v. 58, p. 499–506.

WARDLAW, N. C., 1976, Pore geometry of carbonate rocks as revealed by pore casts and capillary pressure: Am. Assoc. Petroleum Geologists Bull., v. 60, p. 245–257.

SEPM Special Publication No. 26, p. 209–225, March 1979

TEXTURE AND RECOGNITION OF SECONDARY POROSITY IN SANDSTONES

VOLKMAR SCHMIDT AND DAVID A. MCDONALD[1]
Petro-Canada, Calgary, Alberta, and Mobil Oil Canada Ltd., Calgary, Alberta

ABSTRACT

Secondary porosity in sandstones can be classified according to origin and pore texture. Five significant genetic classes of secondary porosity are defined by the following processes of origin: (1) fracturing; (2) shrinkage; (3) dissolution of sedimentary grains and matrix; (4) dissolution of authigenic pore-filling cement; and, (5) dissolution of authigenic replacive minerals. Hybrid pores are characterized either by the coexistence of several genetic classes of secondary porosity or by the coexistence of primary and secondary porosity.

Secondary porosity appears in five major groups of pore textures: (1) intergranular pores; (2) oversized pores; (3) moldic pores; (4) intra-constituent pores; and, (5) open fractures. Some secondary porosity mimics the entire range of pore sizes and pore textures of primary sandstone porosity. Other secondary porosity bears a general resemblance to the textures of primary porosity but differs in detail. Secondary porosity may also appear in textures that are entirely different from those of primary porosity.

In most instances it is possible to identify the occurrence of secondary porosity in thin section using a set of simple petrographic criteria that include: (1) partial dissolution; (2) molds; (3) inhomogeneity of packing; (4) oversized pores; (5) elongate pores; (6) corroded grains; (7) intra-constituent pores; and, (8) fractured grains. In medium- and coarse-grained sandstones secondary porosity can, in some instances, be observed by the naked eye.

The detailed analysis of the petrological attributes of secondary porosity may require the use of advanced analytical techniques, such as cathode luminescence petrography, scanning electron microscopy, pore-cast examination, microprobe analysis and stable-isotope analysis. In most sandstones, however, a surprising amount of important information can be obtained simply by the careful and methodical use of conventional petrographic microscopy.

INTRODUCTION

The importance of secondary porosity in sandstones and its role in the course of sandstone diagenesis have been explained in detail in Schmidt and McDonald (this volume). Secondary porosity constitutes the predominant or exclusive form of effective porosity in the reservoir sandstones of many oil and gas fields. The exploration and exploitation of such sandstone reservoirs will clearly benefit from an accurate identification of the secondary nature of the porosity and of its textural relationship with the host rock (Hayes, this volume; Pittman, this volume).

Frequently secondary sandstone porosity, with the exception of fractures, is still largely mistaken for primary porosity and commonly goes unnoticed. This is due to the wide variety of textures of secondary porosity which often mimic those of primary porosity, and to the fact that most investigators are unfamiliar with the diagnostic criteria for recognizing secondary porosity in sandstones.

The intention in this paper is to outline the textural spectrum of secondary sandstone porosity and to provide criteria which facilitate its recognition. It is an extension of a previously published account of textural and diagnostic aspects of secondary sandstone porosity (Schmidt et al., 1977). We hope that this paper will be useful to those who pursue the fascinating subject of sandstone diagenesis so that secondary porosity in sandstones can be more consistently and accurately reported in future.

GENETIC-TEXTURAL CLASSES OF POROSITY

Secondary porosity in sandstones is mainly the result of dissolution of non-silicate constituents, predominantly carbonate minerals. The soluble precursors of this dissolution porosity occur in three textural forms: sedimentary material, authigenic cement, and authigenic replacement. Fracturing and shrinkage of rock constituents may also create significant secondary porosity in sandstones, though usually in subordinate amounts.

It is useful, for geological interpretations, to base the definition of the principal classes of secondary porosity on textural origin. In addition, the textures in which secondary porosity occurs must be classified in such a manner as to make their description easy and objective.

Principal genetic classes.—We recognize five principal classes of secondary porosity that can be differentiated on the basis of process of origin and textural relationships (Fig. 1): (1) porosity created by fracturing; (2) porosity created by

[1]Present address: Petro-Canada, Calgary, Alberta.

Copyright © 1979, The Society of Economic Paleontologists and Mineralogists

shrinkage; (3) porosity created by dissolution of sedimentary constituents; (4) porosity created by dissolution of authigenic cementing minerals; (5) porosity created by dissolution of authigenic replacive minerals.

Porosity created by fracturing encompasses any newly formed fractures (Fig. 3A) including those formed due to stresses resulting from shrinkage of rock constituents or whole rocks. If fractures become filled by cement or sediment then these fillers or their replacive successors may be dissolved selectively giving rise to second cycle fracture porosity. Such reopened fractures would be included in the appropriate class of dissolution porosity.

Shrinkage porosity, excluding shrinkage fractures, forms through dehydration and/or recrystallization of a number of minerals such as glauconite (Fig. 3B) and hematite, or aggregates such as mud. Shrinkable constituents may occur as grains, parts of grains, matrix, authigenic cement and authigenic replacement. Accordingly, shrinkage porosity consists of a large variety of porosity textures. Shrinkage pores generally vary

in size from submicroscopic dimensions to the dimensions of adjacent sand grains. However, larger shrinkage pores may occur.

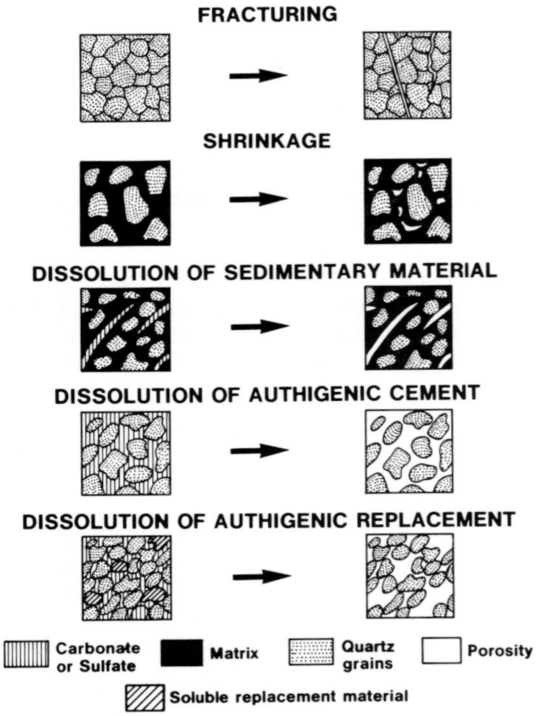

Porosity created by dissolution of sedimentary material is very common and important. It results from the selective dissolution of soluble grains and soluble matrix. These are in most cases composed of carbonate minerals (Fig. 3C). A large number of porosity textures arise from the dissolution of sedimentary constituents. Pore size varies from submicroscopic voids a fraction of a micron in diameter to vugs several centimeters across. Voids frequently exceed the size of adjacent grains.

Porosity originating from dissolution of authigenic cement is probably the most common porosity class. The majority of dissolved cements consist of the carbonate minerals calcite, dolomite and siderite (Fig. 3D). The precursor cements may have occupied any type of primary or secondary porosity. Dissolution of cement may, therefore, reopen any conceivable type of primary and secondary porosity textures.

Porosity resulting from dissolution of authigenic replacive minerals commonly forms a significant percentage of secondary sandstone porosity. It is formed by the selective dissolution of soluble minerals, dominantly calcite, dolomite and siderite, that previously replaced sedimentary constituents and/or authigenic cements (Fig. 3E). The precursor replacement itself may have been either "selective" or "non-selective" as defined by Choquette & Pray (1970). Dissolution of replacive minerals, as with the dissolution of cements, may create any imaginable type of porosity texture.

Pores of hybrid origin.—Individual pores may be of complex origin, either being composed of several genetic classes of secondary porosity or being part primary and part secondary in origin. Such pores of hybrid origin can be termed "hybrid pores" (Fig. 2). For example, replacement of the margins of sand grains frequently occurred simultaneously with the cementation of the adjacent intergranular spaces by the same mineral (Fig. 3F). Complete dissolution of the authigenic mineral will create hybrid pores because both pore cement and grain replacement are removed.

A large percentage of secondary porosity is found in hybrid pores and they may appear in the form of all the pore textures shown by secondary porosity. Generally, individual pores of each porosity texture can form through numerous combinations of genetic classes.

FRACTURING

SHRINKAGE

DISSOLUTION OF SEDIMENTARY MATERIAL

DISSOLUTION OF AUTHIGENIC CEMENT

DISSOLUTION OF AUTHIGENIC REPLACEMENT

Carbonate or Sulfate   Matrix   Quartz grains   Porosity

Soluble replacement material

FIGURE 1.—Genetic classes of secondary sandstone porosity.

TEXTURAL SPECTRUM OF SECONDARY POROSITY

The textures in which secondary sandstone porosity occurs must be classified in such a manner as to make their description objective,

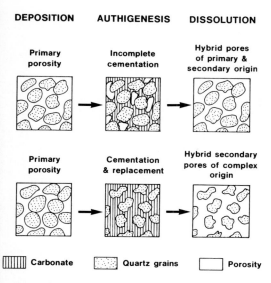

DEPOSITION   AUTHIGENESIS   DISSOLUTION

Primary porosity → Incomplete cementation → Hybrid pores of primary & secondary origin

Primary porosity → Cementation & replacement → Hybrid secondary pores of complex origin

▓ Carbonate   ▒ Quartz grains   □ Porosity

FIGURE 2.—Textural development of hybrid pores.

informative and manageable. Several descriptive groups of pore textures can be differentiated in sandstones using, in part, the nomenclature for pore textures that Choquette & Pray (1970) proposed for carbonate rocks. These groups include the following: (1) intergranular pore textures; (2) oversized pore texture; (3) moldic pore textures; (4) intra-constituent pore textures; (5) fracture pore textures.

Each group of pore textures consists of two or more distinct types of pore textures. The textural spectrum of secondary sandstone porosity is represented by these types of pore textures as they occur in various genetic classes of secondary porosity (Table 1).

Intergranular pore textures.—Pores between grains form the textural group of intergranular pores (Fig. 5). The intergranular pores may be lined by fringing cement or syntaxial cement. Three types of secondary intergranular pore textures can be distinguished: (1) regular intergranular; (2) reduced intergranular; and (3) enlarged intergranular.

TABLE 1.—TEXTURAL SPECTRUM OF SECONDARY SANDSTONE POROSITY

Porosity Textures	Genetic Classes of Secondary Porosity				
	Result of Fracturing	Result of Shrinkage	Result of Dissolution of Sediment	Result of Dissolution of Cement	Result of Dissolution of Replacement
INTERGRANULAR TEXTURES:					
Regular intergranular		X P	X P&C	X P&C	X P&C
Reduced intergranular		X P	X P&C	X P&C	X P&C
Enlarged intergranular		X P	X P&C	X P&C	X P&C
OVERSIZED TEXTURES:					
Oversized fabric selective		X	X	X	X
Oversized crosscutting				X	X
MOLDIC TEXTURES:					
Grain mold		X P	X P&C	X P&C	X P&C
Cement mold		X P		X P&C	X P&C
Replacement mold		X P		X P&C	X P&C
INTRA-CONSTITUENT TEXT.:					
Intragranular		X	X	X	X
Intra-matrix		X	X	X	X
Intra-cement		X		X	X
Intra-replacement		X	X	X	X
FRACTURE TEXTURES:					
Rock fractures	X		X P&C	X P&C	X P&C
Grain fractures	X			X P&C	X P&C
Intergranular fractures	X			X P&C	X P&C

P&C indicates open void may extend over part of the textural precursor or over the complete textural precursor.
P   indicates open void may extend only over part of textural precursor.

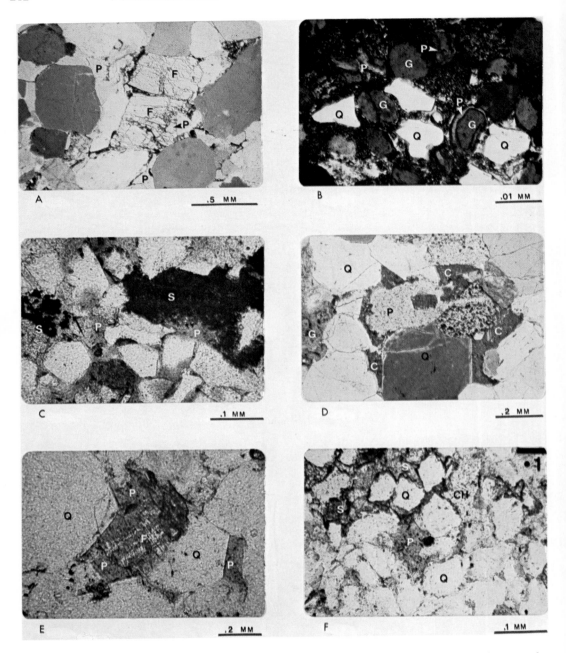

FIG. 3.—*Examples of genetic classes of secondary sandstone porosity. A*, Example of fracture porosity: secondary pores resulting from fracturing of feldspar grains. Half crossed nicols. Lower Cretaceous, Mackenzie Delta, Canada. P = porosity (blue); F = fractured feldspar. *B*, Example of shrinkage porosity: secondary pores resulting from shrinkage of glauconite grains. Polarizer only. Cretaceous, Scotian Shelf, Canada. P = porosity (blue); G = glauconite (olive); Q = quartz (white). *C*, Example of porosity after dissolved sedimentary material: secondary pores resulting from dissolution of sedimentary siderite matrix and siderite grains. Polarizer only. Jurassic, Statfjord field, North Sea. P = porosity (blue); S = microcrystalline siderite (very dark brown). *D*, Example of porosity after dissolved cement: secondary pore resulting from dissolution of intergranular calcite cement. Half crossed nicols. Lower Cretaceous, Mackenzie Delta, Canada. P = porosity (blue); C = calcite (red); Q = quartz grains; G = glauconite grain (green). *E*, Example of porosity after dissolved replacement: secondary

Regular intergranular pore texture essentially reflects depositional intergranular spaces in size and shape (Figs. 4A, B), and is identical with primary intergranular pore texture. The secondary pores may occupy intergranular spaces entirely or they may share individual intergranular spaces with matrix, cement, replacement or primary porosity thus forming "complete" or "partial" secondary pores of this texture.

Secondary pores of regular intergranular texture form a significant percentage of secondary sandstone porosity. They result from the following: (1) shrinkage of intergranular sedimentary matrix (e.g. shrinkage of glauconite matrix); (2) dissolution of intergranular sedimentary matrix (e.g. dissolution of carbonate matrix); (3) dissolution of intergranular cement (e.g. dissolution of intergranular carbonate and sulfate cement); (4) dissolution of intergranular replacement (e.g. dissolution of carbonate that replaced glauconite matrix); and (5) any combination of these genetic-textural processes of origin (e.g. dissolution of both carbonate cement and carbonate matrix within the same intergranular space).

Reduced intergranular pore texture develops where depositional intergranular spaces are reduced by any of the following: (1) grain deformation; (2) chemical compaction through dissolution at grain contacts; (3) syntaxial cementation; and, (4) fringing cementation. This pore texture mimics that of reduced primary intergranular porosity (Fig. 4C).

Secondary pores of reduced intergranular texture represent a considerable portion of secondary sandstone porosity. They occur both in the partial and in the complete form. The genetic porosity classes and hybrid genetic pore types encountered are the same as those listed for regular intergranular pore texture. The secondary porosity appearing in the reduced intergranular texture commonly experienced little or no modification after it originated (Fig. 6). However, regular intergranular pores of secondary origin and enlarged intergranular pores can be altered to reduced intergranular pores during further diagenesis.

Enlarged intergranular pore texture forms either by enlargement of depositional intergranular space or by enlargement of previously reduced intergranular space (Fig. 4D). The enlargement of the intergranular space can take place in three ways: (1) shrinkage of the grain framework (e.g. shrinkage of glauconite grains); (2) dissolution of grain margins, syntaxial cement or fringing cement (e.g. dissolution of the margins of siderite grains); and, (3) replacement of grain margins, syntaxial cement or fringing cement followed by selective dissolution of the replaced mineral (e.g. marginal replacement of quartz grains by siderite followed by dissolution of the siderite). In most instances, secondary enlarged intergranular pores differ in shape from regular or reduced primary intergranular pores. Pore boundaries are predominantly concave and the adjacent grains are often corroded.

Pores of enlarged intergranular texture constitute a major portion of secondary sandstone porosity. They may occur either in the partial or in the complete mode. A single textural-genetic process may open both the precursor intergranular space and its enlargement (e.g. dissolution of sedimentary intergranular matrix associated with marginal dissolution of adjacent grains). Most commonly, however, enlarged intergranular pores are of hybrid origin (e.g. dissolution of intergranular cement associated with dissolution of replacive minerals at the margins of adjacent grains). Genetic porosity classes and hybrid pore types are the same as those previously indicated for regular intergranular pore texture.

Oversized pore textures.—Pores that exceed the diameter of adjacent grains by a factor of at least 1.2 are, with the exception of fractures, included in the textural group of oversized pores. Two types of secondary oversized pore textures can be differentiated: (1) oversized fabric-selective; and, (2) oversized cross-cutting.

Oversized fabric-selective pore texture describes pores whose shape generally follows fabric elements of the host rock (Figs. 4 E, F). The same texture is described as "fenestrate" by Choquette & Pray (1970). It developed selectively at the expense of certain textural elements of the sandstone. Similar pore textures of primary origin are rare but do occur (e.g. keystone vugs formed in muds by escaping air).

Secondary pores of oversized fabric-selective texture are fairly important and fall into four genetic classes: (1) shrinkage (e.g. shrinkage of

pores resulting from dissolution of replacive siderite that partially replaced feldspar grain. Polarizer only. Lower Cretaceous, Mackenzie Delta, Canada. P = porosity (blue); F = feldspar (honeycombed grain); Q = quartz (white). *F*, Example of hybrid porosity: hybrid secondary pores resulting from the dissolution of intergranular siderite cement and siderite that replaced the margins of quartz and chert grains. Polarizer only. Triassic, Prudhoe Bay Field, North Slope, Alaska. P = porosity (blue); S = siderite (brownish, high relief); Q = quartz grains (white); CH = chert grains (light tan, low relief).

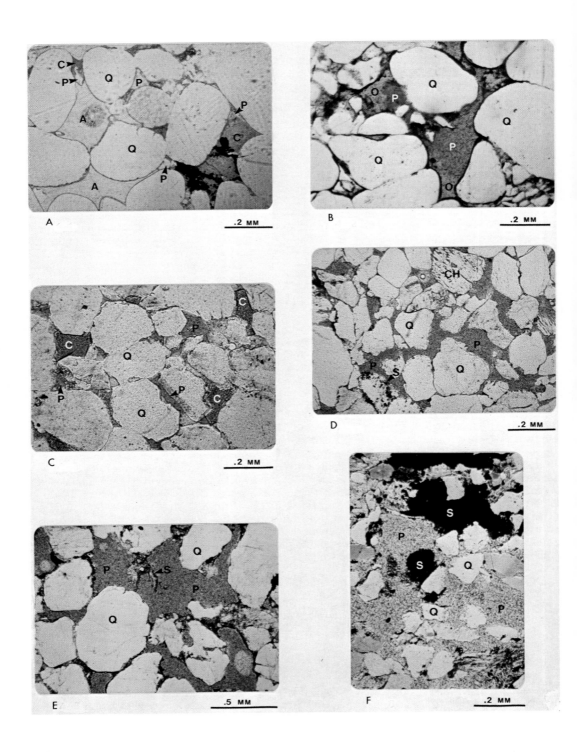

Regular inter-granular pore texture

Reduced inter-granular pore texture

Enlarged inter-granular pore texture
(Alteration of regular intergranular space)

Enlarged inter-granular pore texture
(Alteration of reduced intergranular space)

Quartz grains   porosity

FIG. 5.—Intergranular textures of secondary porosity.

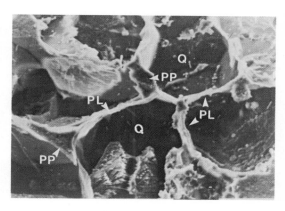

FIG. 6.—Two forms of reduced intergranular porosity: (1) reduced intergranular porosity of lamellar shape that is part primary and part secondary in origin; (2) reduced intergranular pores of polygonal shape are of secondary origin resulting from the dissolution of carbonate cement after the intergranular spaces had been reduced by diagenesis. Scanning electron photomicrograph of epoxy replica of porosity. Lower Cretaceous, Mackenzie Delta, Canada. PL = lamellar pores; PP = polygonal pores; Q = quartz grains removed by treatment with hydrofluoric acid.

oversized patches of highly shrinkable matrix); (2) dissolution of sedimentary material (e.g. dissolution of intergranular matrix and adjacent grains); (3) dissolution of cement (e.g. dissolution of cement filling oversized pores); and, (4) dissolution of replacement (e.g. dissolution of carbonate that replaced matrix and adjacent grains). Hybrid pores are common and may represent any combination of these classes (e.g. dissolution of intergranular cement and adjacent grains). Oversized fabric-selective pore texture also is frequently of hybrid primary-secondary origin (e.g.

primary intergranular pores combine with secondary porosity created by dissolution of soluble grains).

Oversized crosscutting pore texture is characterized by pore boundaries that cut across the fabric elements of the host rock. Such a texture cannot be of primary origin.

Pores of oversized crosscutting texture are extremely rare but can be valuable as a criterion to establish diagenetic sequences. They result mainly from the dissolution of minerals that indiscriminately replaced patches of the sandstone and,

←

FIG. 4.—*Example of secondary pore textures in sandstones. A*, Regular intergranular pores of primary origin filled by calcite and anhydrite cement. Incipient dissolution of cement created partial secondary pores of regular intergranular texture. Polarizer only. Cambrian, Northwest Territories, Canada. Union I.O.E. Stopover L-34, 2794 ft (852 m). P = porosity; Q = quartz grains; C = calcite cement; A = anhydrite cement. *B*, Regular intergranular pores of secondary origin resulting from dissolution of intergranular carbonate and sulfate cement. Polarizer only. Same location as for Fig. 4–1. Depth 2786 ft. (849 m). P = porosity (blue); Q = quartz grains (white); O = residual oil (yellow). *C*, Secondary pores of reduced intergranular texture resulting from dissolution of intergranular calcite cement. Polarizer only. Cambrian, Northwest Territories, Canada. P = porosity (blue); Q = quartz (white); C = calcite (red). *D*, Secondary pores of enlarged intergranular texture resulting from dissolution of siderite cement and replacive siderite. In places the enlarged intergranular pores are connected and form channels. Half crossed nicols. Jurassic, Beryl Field, North Sea. P = porosity (blue); Q = quartz grains; CH = chert grain; S = siderite remnant. *E*, Secondary pore of oversized fabric-selective texture resulting from the dissolution of replacive siderite and intergranular siderite cement. Polarizer only. Jurassic, Beryl Field, North Sea. P = porosity (blue); Q = quartz grains (white); S = siderite remnant (high relief). *F*, Secondary pores of oversized fabric-selective texture resulting from dissolution of sedimentary siderite grains and siderite matrix. Polarizer only. Jurassic, Statfjord Field, North Sea. P = porosity (blue); S = microcrystalline siderite (very dark).

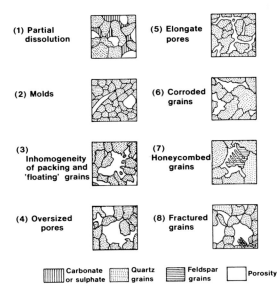

Fig. 7.—Petrographic criteria for recognition of secondary sandstone porosity.

subordinately, from the dissolution of cement following the cementation of such pores.

Moldic pore textures.—Pores that show characteristic outlines of the texture of their precursors comprise, with the exception of fractures and intergranular pores, the textural group of moldic pores. Three types of moldic pore textures can be found: (1) grain molds; (2) cement molds; and, (3) replacement molds. Molds formed by dissolution can be either partial or complete. Shrinkage can only create partial molds. Moldic pore textures are always of secondary origin.

Grain-mold pore texture forms where secondary porosity is created selectively at the expense of grains which are encased by other grains, matrix, and/or cement or, by minerals replacing the above (Figures 10B, 10E).

Pores of grain-mold texture are very common and form a considerable percentage of secondary sandstone porosity. Four genetic classes can be recognized: (1) shrinkage (e.g. partial molds created by shrinkage of glauconite grains); (2) dissolution of sedimentary grains; (3) dissolution of cement that filled a first-cycle grain mold thus creating a second-cycle grain mold; (4) dissolution of replacive minerals (e.g. dissolution of anhydrite that selectively replaced carbonate grains). Molds of mixed primary-secondary origin may occur (e.g. dissolution of a grain with primary intragranular porosity).

Cement mold pore texture is the result of at least three successive diagenetic changes: (1) the precursor cement filled part of a pore developing

euhedral crystal faces or an otherwise characteristic morphology; (2) the remaining pore was later filled by another material overlying the precursor cement; and (3) the porosity creating process selectively affected the precursor cement.

Pores of cement-mold texture are rare but provide a good criterion for establishing diagenetic sequences. Three genetic classes can be differentiated: (1) shrinkage creating partial molds; (2) dissolution of cement; and, (3) dissolution of minerals that selectively replaced the characteristic cement textures.

Replacement-mold pore textures originate if replacive minerals develop euhedral crystal faces or an otherwise characteristic morphology and if, subsequently, a porosity creating process selectively affects the replacement.

Pores of replacement-mold texture are rare but are useful for establishing diagenetic sequences. Three genetic classes can be observed: (1) shrink-

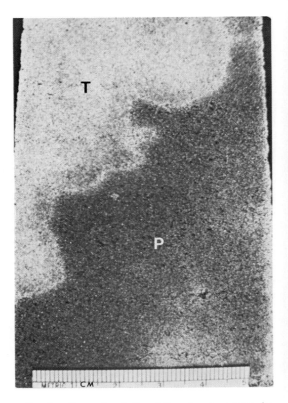

Fig. 8.—Example of dissolution front: contact between sandstone with high secondary porosity resulting from dissolution of calcite cement (dark) and non-porous sandstone containing a high amount of calcite cement that filled primary porosity (light). Core photograph. Lower Cretaceous, Mackenzie Delta, Canada. P = sandstone porosity app. 25%; T = tight sandstone with 25% calcite cement.

Fig. 9.—Example of macroscopic vuggy porosity: conglomeratic sandstone contains high vuggy porosity resulting largely from the dissolution of siderite clasts. Core photograph. Lower Cretaceous, Mackenzie Delta, Canada.

age creating partial molds; (2) dissolution of cement filling a first cycle replacement mold; and, (3) dissolution of replacive minerals (e.g. dissolution of euhedral anhydrite crystals replacing carbonate matrix and grains).

Intra-constituent pore textures.—The intra-constituent pore textures include all pores within individual textural constituents. Intra-constituent pores range in size from a fraction of a micron to nearly the diameter of the host constituent. Four types of secondary intra-constituent pore textures can be recognized: (1) intragranular; (2) intra-matrix; (3) intra-cement; and, (4) intra-replacement.

Intragranular pore textures result from processes creating porosity within grains rather than only at the grain margins. Grains with a high percentage of intragranular porosity can be termed "honeycombed grains" (Fig. 11B, C). Such grains have been described by Rowsell and De Swardt (1974) as "skeleton grains" and by Fox et al. (1975) as "leached grains." They are clearly of secondary origin. In grains containing only a

relatively small amount of intragranular porosity the nature of the porosity is more difficult to ascertain because many grain types may have some primary intragranular porosity. Both submicroscopic pore diameters (less than 4 microns) and microscopic pore diameters are common in this type of secondary pore texture.

Secondary pores of intragranular texture are fairly abundant. They result from the following processes: (1) internal shrinkage of grains (e.g. shrinkage of a glauconite grain); (2) internal dissolution of grains (e.g. dissolution of siderite in a sideritic chert grain); (3) internal selective dissolution of cement that may have occupied either primary or secondary intragranular voids (e.g. dissolution of carbonate cement filling primary pores in a chert grain); and, (4) internal selective dissolution of minerals that replaced part of a grain (e.g. dissolution of carbonate that incompletely replaced a feldspar grain). Some grains may contain both primary and secondary intragranular porosity.

Intra-matrix pore textures develop within matrix in a similar fashion to that described for intragranular pore textures (Fig. 11E). Much of the intra-matrix porosity is submicroscopic (less than 4 microns in diameter). In many instances it is difficult or even impossible to differentiate between primary and secondary intra-matrix porosity.

Secondary pores of intra-matrix texture are fairly common. The same genetic classes are encountered as listed for intragranular pores. Coexistence of primary and secondary porosity is common.

Intra-cement pore textures originate through processes affecting the interior of cements (Fig. 11D). Intra-cement pores larger than 20 microns in diameter are in most cases of secondary origin as primary intra-cement pores of that size are rare. However, smaller intra-cement pores of primary origin are common, as for example in authigenic clay cements. These are often difficult to differentiate from secondary pores of similar size.

Secondary pores of intra-cement texture rarely contribute a significant amount of sandstone porosity. However, they do provide a good criterion for establishing the sequence of diagenetic events. Intra-cement pores develop through the following processes: (1) internal shrinkage of cement (e.g. shrinkage of glauconite cement); (2) internal incomplete dissolution of cement; (3) internal selective dissolution of minerals that replaced part of the cement (e.g. selective dissolution of calcite that replaced the interior of chert cement).

Secondary and small primary intra-cement pores commonly coexist.

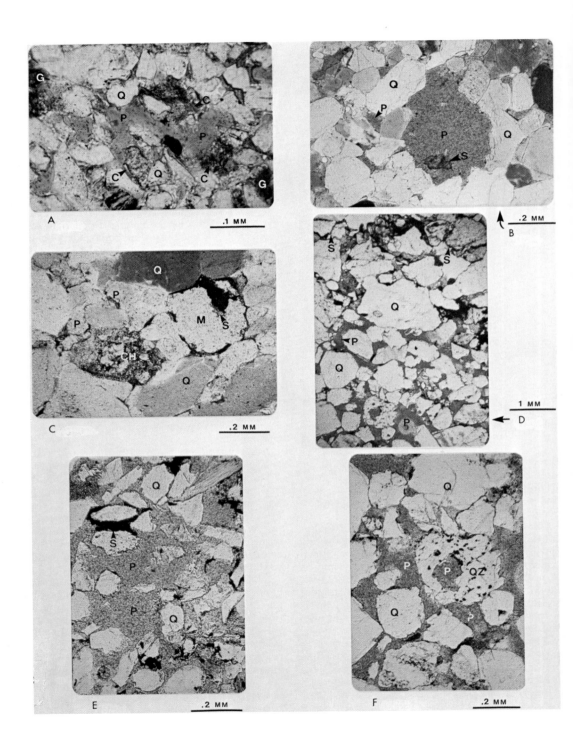

Intra-replacement pore textures originate in the interior of replacive rock constituents in a similar style to that described for intra-cement pore textures. However, pores inside replacive constituents can also be inherited from the precursors (e.g. replacement of a grain with intragranular porosity) or they may be created during the replacement (e.g. replacement of a feldspar grain by porous kaolinite). The pore size ranges from fractions of a micron to dimensions close to the diameter of the replacement textures.

Secondary pores of intra-replacement texture usually form only very small volumes of porosity in sandstones. They develop through the following processes: (1) internal shrinkage of replacive minerals (e.g. shrinkage of replacive glauconite); (2) internal selective dissolution of sedimentary material during replacement process (e.g. dissolution of feldspar during replacement by kaolinite); (3) internal selective dissolution of cement within replacive textures; and, (4) internal dissolution of the replacive minerals.

Fracture pore textures.—Parting and separation of rocks or rock constituents along certain planes creates fractures. Dissolution of material that subsequently filled fractures gives rise to "reopened" fractures. Original and reopened fractures are included in the group of fracture pore textures. Three types of fracture pore textures can be distinguished in sandstones: (1) open rock fractures; (2) open grain fractures; and, (3) open intergranular fractures.

Open rock fractures have a plane of parting that extends over more than a single grain or a single intergranular space. Rock fractures often follow grain boundaries, but in well indurated sandstones they may cut through individual sand grains. They may also cut through matrix, cement, replacement, and other diagenetic fabrics. For this reason they are excellent tools for the investigation of diagenetic sequences (e.g. a stylolite cut by an open fracture predates fracturing). Shape, orientation and size of rock fractures may provide clues to their origin. Open rock fractures in sandstones range in size from microscopic hair fractures less than a millimeter long to fissures of considerable length and width.

Open rock fractures are a very common textural type of porosity but their main importance is the permeability they impart to many sandstone formations. Four genetic classes of open rock fractures can be identified: (1) original fractures; (2) reopened fractures resulting from dissolution of sedimentary material (e.g. filling of a fissure during exposure followed by dissolution); (3) reopened fractures resulting from dissolution of cement; and, (4) reopened fractures resulting from dissolution of replacive minerals. Filled fractures may be partially or completely reopened by dissolution.

Open grain fractures are characterized by planes of parting that are confined to individual grains (Fig. 11F). Fractures cutting completely through grains are clearly of secondary origin whereas fractures traversing only part of a grain may be either primary or secondary in origin.

The incidence of open grain fractures varies considerably depending on the diagenetic history of the sandstones. They contribute only an insignificant amount of porosity but are of diagnostic value for developing an understanding of diagenesis and porosity history. Three genetic classes of open grain fractures occur: (1) original fractures; (2) reopened fractures resulting from dis-

---

Fig. 10.—*Examples of criteria for recognition of secondary sandstone porosity. A*, Example of partial dissolution: high secondary porosity created by partial dissolution of calcite cement and calcite replacing glauconite. Secondary porosity consists of intergranular pores and oversized fabric selective vugs. Polarizer only. Cretaceous, Scotian Shelf, Canada. P = porosity (blue); C = calcite (red); Q = quartz grains (white); G = glauconite (brownish-greenish). *B*, Example of grain mold: mold of large siderite grain resulting from nearly complete dissolution of siderite. Mold surrounded by welded quartz grains. Half crossed nicols. Lower Cretaceous, Mackenzie Delta, Canada. P = porosity (blue); S = siderite remnant (high relief); Q = quartz grains (white). *C,*Example of grain mold: grain mold resulting from dissolution. The original grain was coated by clay cement. The remaining rim of clay cement has become the shell for the grain mold. Half crossed nicols. Lower Cretaceous, Mackenzie Delta, Canada. P = porosity (blue); Q = quartz grains; CH = chert grain with intergranular porosity; M = grain mold; S = siderite remnant. *D*, Example of inhomogeneity of packing: sandstone, in part, contains high effective porosity (approx. 25 vol. %) and relatively loose packing. Porosity was created by dissolution of siderite cement and siderite marginally replacing quartz grains. Elsewhere the sandstone has lost all primary porosity through grain interpenetration and stylolitization and contains no effective porosity. Polarizer only. Jurassic, Beryl Field, North Sea. P = porosity (blue); Q = quartz and quartzite grains (white); S = stylolite. *E*, Example of oversized pores and "floating" grains: exceedingly high secondary porosity (approx. 40 vol %) resulted from the dissolution of siderite matrix, siderite grains and siderite that replaced the margins of sand grains. Polarizer only. Jurasssic, Statfjord Field, North Sea. P = porosity (blue); Q = quartz grains (white); S = siderite (very dark). *F*, Example of corroded grains: detail of Fig. 10D. Dissolution of replacive siderite gave rise to corroded margins of grains and intragranular pore in quartzite grain. Polarizer only. P = porosity (blue); Q = quartz grains, in part, fractured (white); QZ = quartzite grain (white).

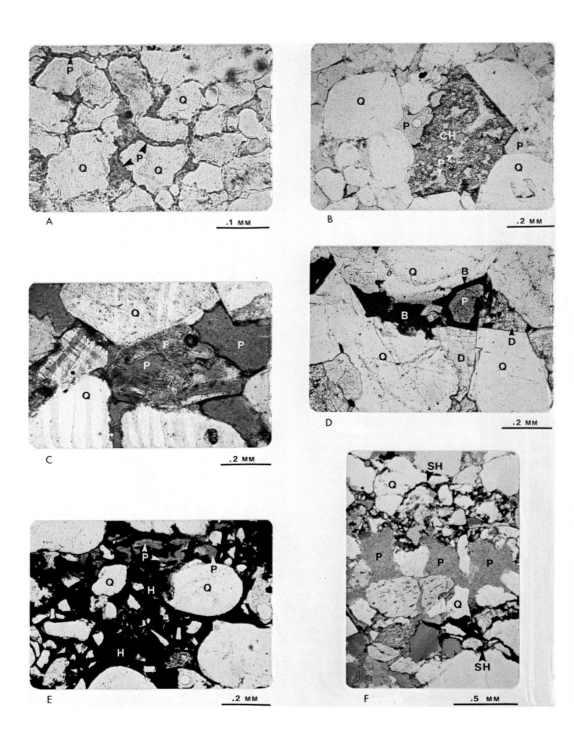

solution of cement; and, (3) reopened fractures resulting from dissolution of minerals that replaced fracture cement.

Open intergranular fractures are confined to constituents in single intergranular spaces. They occur in intergranular matrix, in intergranular cement, and in intergranular replacive minerals. They are always of secondary origin. The fractures may dissect the entire intergranular space or traverse only part of it.

Open intergranular fractures are rare but provide excellent evidence for establishing sequences of diagenetic events including both mechanical and chemical compaction of the grain framework. The same genetic classes of open intergranular fractures exist as are listed for grain fractures.

Synopsis of porosity texture.—It is evident from the preceding discussion that any textural type of secondary porosity can belong to at least three genetic porosity classes including, in every case, voids after authigenic replacement and voids after authigenic cement. In addition, each textural type of secondary porosity includes hybrid pores containing two or more genetic classes. Most pore types can also be of mixed primary and secondary origin.

The majority of secondary sandstone porosity is found in textures that are either identical to, or resemble to some degree, the textures of primary sandstone porosity. However, a considerable portion of secondary sandstone porosity is found in textures that are distinctly different. As will be discussed later, these textures provide evidence for the identification of secondary porosity.

Pittmann (this volume) defines three geometric-textural classes of sandstone porosity: (1) intergranular porosity; (2) dissolution porosity; and, (3) microporosity. Secondary sandstone porosity is not restricted to the above class of dissolution porosity but is also common in the classes of intergranular porosity and microporosity.

It is readily apparent that effective secondary porosity (porosity that gives rise to appreciable permeability) is found in sandstones of any primary texture including unwinnowed sandstones that never possessed any effective primary porosity. Although effective secondary porosity may simply add to existing effective primary porosity it is commonly found in sandstones that have lost their effective primary porosity.

Porosity of a sandstone can only be increased by fracturing, shrinkage or dissolution if the grain or crystal framework of the sandstones is sufficiently strong to prevent immediate collapse. For this reason there is a limit to the amount of secondary porosity that can develop in a given sandstone lithology under specific conditions of stress because the supportive strength decreases with increasing porosity and the framework will ultimately fail.

Secondary sandstone porosity may be reduced and texturally modified by the same processes that reduce primary porosity: (1) authigenic cementation; (2) dissolution at grain contacts; and, (3) mechanical compaction. These textural processes not only reduce the size of pores and change their shape but frequently obscure the evidence for their secondary origin.

RECOGNITION

It is important to realize that most secondary sandstone porosity closely resembles or exactly mimics primary porosity. This is the reason why secondary sandstone porosity has largely remained unnoticed until recently. It follows that,

Fig. 11—*Examples of criteria for recognition of secondary sandstone porosity. A*, Example of elongate pores: the elongate pores resulted from marginal replacement of quartz grains by carbonate minerals along irreducible lamellar pores followed by dissolution of carbonate. Polarizer only. Cambrian, Northwest Territories, Canada. P = porosity (blue); Q = quartz grain (white). *B*, Example of honeycombed grain: dissolution of primary carbonate siderite inclusion in chert created high intragranular porosity in chert grain. Polarizer only. Lower Cretaceous, Mackenzie Delta, Canada. P = secondary intragranular and intergranular porosity (blue); Q = quartz grains (white); CH = chert grain. *C*, Example of honeycombed grain: intragranular porosity in feldspar grain resulted from dissolution of replacive carbonate. Half crossed nicols. Cretaceous, Scotian Shelf, Canada. P = intergranular and intragranular porosity (blue); Q = quartz grains; F = feldspar (honeycombed). *D*, Example of intra-cement pores: partial dissolution of dolomite cement created intra-cement pores which were later filled by bitumen. Cambrian, Northwest Territories, Canada. P = porosity (blue); D = dolomite cement and replacive dolomite (light tan to golden); B = bitumen (black); Q = quartz grains (white). *E*, Example of intra-matrix pores: shrinkage of glauconite and/or hematite created intra-matrix pores. Polarizer only. Cambrian, Northwest Territories, Canada. P = porosity (blue); H = hematite matrix which probably replaced glauconite matrix; Q = quartz grains (white). *F*, Example of open grain fracture: reducible primary intergranular porosity was completely lost as result of stylolitization, chemical grain interpenetration and syntaxial quartz overgrowth. Subsequent dissolution of sedimentary and diagenetic carbonate created secondary porosity. Grain fracturing resulted from increased stress in a pillar of grains supporting the roof of large adjacent secondary pores. Jurassic, Beryl Field, North Sea. Half crossed nicols. P = secondary porosity (blue); Q = quartz grains and metaquartzite grains; SH = stylolitized argillaceous/carbonaceous microlaminae (black).

in the study of secondary sandstone porosity, it is necessary to develop readily observable diagnostic criteria for recognizing or suspecting its presence. Additionally, a suitable analytical approach must be chosen for verifying suspected cases and for recognizing the quantity, texture, origin, and textural modification of secondary porosity.

Petrographic criteria.—In many instances, the secondary nature of sandstone porosity can be identified by using petrographic criteria that are easily observable in thin sections under the petrographic microscope. Some of these can also be observed, on occasion, in hand specimens. The following eight petrographic criteria appear to be the most useful (Fig. 7): (1) partial dissolution; (2) molds; (3) inhomogeneity of packing; (4) oversized pores; (5) elongate pores; (6) corroded grain margins; (7) intra-constituent pores; and, (8) fractured grains.

Partial dissolution of soluble constituents is by far the most conclusive criterion and it is also very common. Dissolution of soluble sedimentary and authigenic constituents is, in many instances, incomplete and patches of remnant material occur adjacent to pores (Fig. 10A). Frequently the remnants have a corroded appearance. Care must be taken to determine the partial dissolution of cements because incomplete cementation of porosity may produce very similar textures. Indicators for the partial dissolution of authigenic cements are: (1) corroded surfaces; (2) uniform extinction of isolated remnants of poikilotopic cement crystals; (3) intra-cement pores; and, (4) disrupted growth zonations in the cement. In some instances, partial dissolution produces large diagenetic structures that can be observed in hand specimens without the aid of a microscope (Fig. 8).

Molds of sedimentary particles, cement and replacive minerals (Fig. 10B, C) are excellent diagnostic features if the outlines of the moldic pores clearly portray the characteristic shapes of their precursors. Grain molds are especially useful because of their frequent and widespread occurrence. Commonly, molds can be identified directly in drill cuttings and hand specimens using only a wellsite binocular microscope or a handlens. Molds of large debris (Fig. 9) and large authigenic textures are visible to the naked eye.

Inhomogeneity of packing is a very useful and common criterion. Sandstones displaying marked inhomogeneity with areas of loosely-packed grains and high intergranular porosity adjacent to areas of tightly-packed grains and little or no porosity (Fig. 10D) reflect an original inhomogeneity in the distribution of soluble matrix or cement. The tight packing is the result of mechanical compaction and chemical grain interpenetration in areas lacking intergranular matrix or cement. In adjacent areas the presence of intergranular constituents prevented compaction and grain interpenetration. Later dissolution of soluble cement or matrix created the secondary porosity between the loosely-packed grains. Individual grains may straddle the boundary between open and tight packing thereby forming very diagnostic fabrics. For example, one part of a mica fragment may be strongly deformed between compacting grains, while the other part of the mica retained its original shape and forms the boundary of a pore in an area of open packing.

Inhomogeneity of packing can be seen best in thin sections oriented normal to bedding. However, it can often be recognized in drill cuttings, cores or outcrop samples by means of a stereo microscope, handlens and, on occasion, the naked eye.

Oversized pores that have a significantly larger diameter than that of adjacent grains are common and provide good evidence for secondary porosity (Fig. 10E). Most oversized pores are fabric selective and result mainly from the selective dissolution of soluble sedimentary clasts and lenses of matrix or of their replacive successors.

Oversized pores frequently occur together with inhomogeneity of packing and may also form channels, in which cases they clearly indicate the presence of secondary porosity. However, as mentioned earlier, oversized pores can also be created by sedimentary processes. Oversized pores can often be recognized without the aid of thin sections.

Elongate pores, if numerous, indicate the presence of secondary porosity. Replacement processes often operate at the margins of tightly-packed grains. If these replacive minerals are dissolved, the sandstone will exhibit a high incidence of elongate intergranular pores (Fig. 11A). This criterion has to be used with caution because primary elongate pores are common in sandstones with abundant platy grains and in well packed and very fine-grained sandstones with grains of high angularity. Elongate pores are best observed in thin section.

Corroded grains adjacent to pores very frequently are a useful criterion for secondary porosity. They generally are associated with enlarged intergranular pores (Fig. 10E) and result mainly from dissolution of soluble minerals that unevenly replaced the margins of sand grains. Quartz grains with corroded syntaxial overgrowths of authigenic quartz are reliable indicators of secondary porosity. However, mildly corroded grains may be of sedimentary origin. Additionally, unrounded, fine sand grains may easily be mistaken for corroded grains. The criterion of corroded grain margins, therefore, must be applied with care. The reliability generally increases with increasing severity of the corrosion, because severely corroded grain margins are not likely to survive sedimentary transport.

The observation of diagenetic corrosion of grains is best accomplished in thin section. However, corroded grains can be recognized in drill samples of medium and coarse-grained sandstones with the well site binocular microscope. In the absence of cores, loose corroded grains may be the only direct evidence of the nature of porosity, if sandstones with high secondary porosity are encountered in wells.

Intra-constituent pores are fair to excellent indicators of secondary porosity. Among constituents with intra-granular pores, honeycombed grains provide conclusive evidence for postdepositional leaching, because they would quickly disintegrate during sedimentary transport. They are mainly the result of leaching of carbonates which partially replaced sand grains—typically feldspars, clay pellets and chert fragments (Figs. 11B, C). Honeycombed grains are easy to recognize in thin section and have been mentioned as evidence for secondary porosity by several authors, including Rowsell and De Swardt (1974), Stanton and McBride (1976), Hayes (this volume), and Pittmann (this volume). Other types of intra-constituent pores that occasionally provide evidence for secondary porosity include: (1) isolated intragranular pores; (2) intra-cement pores (Fig. 11D); (3) intra-matrix pores (Fig. 11E); and, (4) intra-replacement pores. These intra-constituent pores generally must be examined in thin section in order to establish their secondary nature.

Open grain fractures are a very useful criterion in sandstones that experienced grain welding and syntaxial overgrowth of grains. They generally represent framework failure caused by the generation of a high percentage of secondary porosity during burial (Fig. 11F). Clearly open grain fractures formed after grain welding and syntaxial overgrowth had taken place since pre-existing grain fractures would have been healed during the development of syntaxial overgrowths. Grain fractures are best examined in thin section.

Method of analysis.—For a thorough analysis of secondary sandstone porosity the following sequence of steps should be taken: (1) recognize the presence of secondary porosity; (2) identify the textural types of secondary porosity present; (3) determine the textural-genetic origin of the secondary porosity and any subsequent textural modification; (4) ascertain the abundance of secondary porosity and the abundance and texture of any coexisting primary porosity; and, (5) determine the sequential order of diagenetic changes that affected the sandstone, including the alteration of primary porosity and the generation and alteration of secondary porosity.

The stratigraphic distribution of porosity may, in some instances, suggest secondary origin. For example, a plot of porosity versus depth may show a sudden increase in porosity at great depth beneath a long interval of gradually declining porosities (Proshlyakov, 1960). Certain physical reservoir characteristics may also provide individual evidence for secondary porosity (Schmidt et al., 1976).

Direct evidence for secondary porosity can, on occasion, be observed macroscopically, or else with the aid of a hand lens or a stereo microscope. In most instances, however, direct evidence can only be obtained by other methods of observation. The occurrence of secondary porosity can usually be detected by examining a few dozen thin sections with a good petrographic microscope and applying the criteria mentioned earlier. The pore system of the sandstones should be thoroughly impregnated with colored epoxy resin before thin sectioning in order to emphasize pores and to prevent damage to pore boundaries during grinding. A combination of as many criteria as can be observed should be taken into account because it may not be possible to arrive at a conclusion by using only one or two criteria. Thin section analysis of drill cuttings can produce excellent results since a single thin section may show up to fifty cuttings portraying the entire lithologic spectrum of a sandstone interval.

Conventional petrographic microscopy may not suffice to positively identify the secondary porosity of some sandstones. In such cases cathode luminescence microscopy, exography, scanning-electron microscopy and microprobe analysis will probably permit detection of the secondary porosity.

The accurate identification of the various textural types of secondary porosity in a sandstone unit requires nothing less than a thorough petrographic examination of thin sections representing the entire spectrum of lithologies present. In addition, a study of pore casts is always advisable.

If a significant amount of pores and other textural features measure less than 10 microns then it is necessary to employ scanning-electron microscopy of rock samples and pore casts.

The detection of the textural-genetic origin of secondary porosity requires the petrographic comparison of samples showing fully developed secondary porosity with those showing only incipient development of secondary porosity and those without any secondary porosity. In addition to petrographic microscopy and scanning-electron microscopy of samples and pore casts it is often useful to apply cathode luminescence microscopy and microprobe analysis. In the case of dissolution porosity, comparison of casts of artifical pores with casts of natural pores provides a powerful analytical tool. The casts of artificial pores are obtained by acid treatment of samples containing soluble constituents but devoid of secondary porosity.

Absence of significant amounts of primary porosity can usually be recognized in sandstones with secondary porosity. However, in sandstones with significant amounts of both primary and secondary porosity it is often difficult to assess the relative abundance of each form of porosity. This is especially true if primary and secondary porosity coexist in a large percentage of the pores. In such cases it is advisable to study, for comparison, the texture of primary porosity in sandstones of the same original lithology and the same state of compaction but without the development of secondary porosity. In some instances only part of the porosity can be recognized positively as primary or secondary while the origin of the remaining part of the porosity remains undetermined.

The final step in the petrographic analysis of secondary porosity is to establish the sequence of diagenetic events. The generation of secondary porosity may have occurred only one time or several times during the diagenetic history. Much of the evidence for the sequence of diagenetic events in a sandstone unit is established by the careful analysis of the types of textures of the secondary porosity and its genetic origin. For example, the fabric relationships between fractures and diagenetic textures and structures often provides an excellent means of establishing sequences of diagenetic events in sandstone. More evidence may be obtained by comparison with a sandstone unit of similar original composition that experienced less diagenetic alteration.

In addition to the analytical techniques discussed above, the following analytical methods may, on occasion, be useful in retracing the diagenetic history: (1) X-ray diffraction analysis; (2) stable isotope analysis; (3) analysis of fluid inclusion; and, (4) analysis of the thermal alteration of organic matter. In working with all these data it is necessary to apply the principle of multiple working hypotheses strictly.

The petrologic record of many sandstone units is insufficient to conclusively establish their diagenetic history. In these cases, the integration of the petrological data with other geological information such as burial history, compaction history, and the history of fluid migration often results in the correct interpretation of the diagenesis.

CONCLUSIONS

Secondary pores in sandstones can be objectively described on the basis of their textural and genetic aspects, and a very large number of porosity types can be defined. Many of the textures of secondary porosity strongly resemble or mimic those of primary porosity, whereas other textures of secondary porosity differ greatly. In most instances simple petrographic criteria permit the recognition of secondary porosity in thin section. However, the investigation of texture, origin, and alteration of secondary porosity sometimes requires more advanced analytical methods. The quantitative differentiation between coexisting primary and secondary porosity and the establishment of the sequential order of diagenetic events are the most difficult steps in the analysis of secondary sandstone porosity.

ACKNOWLEDGEMENTS

Research for this paper was conducted at the geological laboratory of Mobil Oil Canada Ltd. and since 1976 also at the geological research laboratory of Petro-Canada. The authors would like to thank both companies for their generous support in every phase of the preparation of this paper and for permission to publish. Special thanks are due to the drafting department of Mobil Oil Canada for supplying the excellent illustrations, and to Petro-Canada for providing funds for printing of the colored illustrations. The authors greatly appreciate the expert assistance of: Brian Miller—microphotography and assembly of the manuscript; David Blair—thin sections; and Susan Peters—typing.

REFERENCES

CHOQUETTE, P. W., AND PRAY, L. C., 1970, Geologic nomenclature and classification of porosity in sedimentary carbonates: Am. Assoc. Petroleum Geologists Bull., v. 54, p. 207–250.

FOX, J. E., LAMBERT, P. W., MAST, R. F., NUSS, N. W., AND REIN, R. D., 1975, Porosity variation in the Tensleep and its equivalent, the Weber Sandstone, western Wyoming; a log and petrographic analysis *in* D. W. Bolyard (ed.), Deep drilling frontiers of the central Rocky Mountains: Denver, Colorado, Rocky Mountain Assoc. Geologists, p. 185–216.

PROSHLYAKOV, B. K., 1960, Reservoir rocks as a function of their depth and lithology [in Russian]: Geo. Nefti i Gaza, v. 4, no. 12, p. 24–29.

ROWSELL, D. M., AND DE SWARDT, A. M. J., 1974, Secondary leaching porosity in Middle Ecca Sandstones: Geol. Soc. South Africa Trans. and Proc., v. 77, p. 131–140.

SCHMIDT, V., MCDONALD, D. A., AND PLATT, R. L., Pore geometry and reservoir aspects of secondary porosity in sandstones: Canadian Soc. Petroleum Geologists Bull., v. 25, p. 271–290.

STANTON, G. D., AND MCBRIDE, E. F., 1976, Factors influencing porosity and permeability of Lower Wilcox (Eocene) Sandstone, Karnes County, Texas [abs.]: Am. Assoc. Petroleum Geologists and Soc. Econ. Paleontologists and Mineralogists Ann. Meeting Abs., v. 1, p. 119.

SEPM Special Publication No. 26, p. 227–242, March 1979

DIAGENESIS OF VOLCANIC SANDSTONES

RONALD C. SURDAM AND JAMES R. BOLES
The University of Wyoming, Laramie, 82071, and The University of California,
Santa Barbara, 93106

ABSTRACT

It is increasingly apparent that temperature effects have been overemphasized in evaluating many diagenetic reactions associated with burial. The classic concept of burial metamorphism is far too simplistic to explain the wide variation in reactions and reaction sequences observed in many diagenetic terranes. This is particularly true when considering the complex problem of diagenetic alteration of volcanogenic sandstones. For example, changing the geothermal regime from area to area cannot explain the common observation that individual mineral ranges broadly overlap and are not related to stratigraphic position.

The diagenetic reactions of interest in volcanogenic sandstones such as: glass→clay, glass→zeolite, zeolite→ zeolite, plagioclase→clay, or zeolite, among others, involve a fluid phase and commonly ionic species in the fluid phase. Consider for example the typical diagenetic reaction of heulandite→laumontite ($Ca^{++} + Ca_3 K_2 Al_8 Si_{28} O_{72} \cdot 24H_2O \rightarrow Ca_4 Al_8 Si_{16} O_{48} \cdot 16H_2O + 2K^+ + 12SiO_2 + 8H_2O$). Obviously the problem is not one of just thermal stability, but is one of chemical or ionic stability as well. Such factors as fluid flow and composition are as significant as depth of burial in controlling the distribution of diagenetic mineral phases in volcanogenic sandstones. Variations in fluid flow, and more importantly fluid composition, can explain many of the perplexing questions that previously were inadequately explained by thermal variations alone. Fluid effects are most pronounced in the early stages of diagenesis when the fluid/solid ratio is high, and in the later stages during fracturing and/or dewatering.

INTRODUCTION

Since the classic work of Coombs (1954) there has been an increasing interest in the diagenesis of volcanogenic sedimentary rocks. The study of diagenetic processes, particularly with respect to volcanogenic sediments, is significant for it relates directly to the problem of clastic reservoir characteristics. Volcanogenic sediments are generally characterized by highly reactive materials such as glass, plagioclase and volcanic lithic fragments. This clastic material is particularly susceptible to hydration, and in contact with water it will react to form diagenetic phases. Commonly these reactions involve the alteration of a relatively dense phase to form a less dense hydrous diagenetic phase; hence these reactions significantly affect and reduce the porosity and permeability of the sediment. There is a direct relationship between diagenesis and porosity and permeability in volcanogenic sediments. This is especially true with regard to the Mesozoic and Tertiary basins of the Pacific margin. Thus the determination of the diagenetic history of a prism of sediments in one of these basins is essential to evaluating them as potential petroleum habitat.

The early work of Coombs (1954, 1960, 1961), and Coombs, Ellis, Fyfe and Taylor (1959) has dominated much of our thinking concerning the diagenesis of volcanogenic rocks. This early work placed a great deal of emphasis on the apparent correlation between diagenetic mineralogy and stratigraphic position. As a consequence, many of the published studies on the diagenesis of volcanogenic rocks in the 1960's and 1970's interpreted the diagenesis of these rocks in terms of "burial metamorphism." The model that evolved from this work is essentially that of a prism of chemically unstable clastic debris that adjusts to a thermal gradient through diagenetic reactions after burial. This widely accepted model has resulted in an emphasis on "burial metamorphism" and temperature effects. It is the thesis of this paper that the classic concept of "burial metamorphism" is far too simplistic to explain the wide variation in reactions and reaction sequences observed in many diagenetic terranes (see also Surdam, 1973; Boles and Coombs, 1977). This is particularly true when considering the complex problem of diagenetic alteration of volcanogenic sandstones.

Consider the wide variation in stratigraphic distribution of key minerals such as heulandite, laumontite and prehnite in "low grade metamorphic" or diagenetic terranes from around the world (see Fig. 4, Zen, 1974, p. 453). To explain these variations by thermal effects alone, assuming steady state conditions, requires radical variations in geothermal regimes from area to area. Even more detrimental to proponents of thermal controls in terms of diagenesis of volcanogenic sediments is the type of mineral variations observed in contiguous areas (Fig. 1). The kind of diagenetic mineral variations in immediately adjacent areas, such as the Taringatura and Hokonui

Copyright © 1979, The Society of Economic Paleontologists and Mineralogists

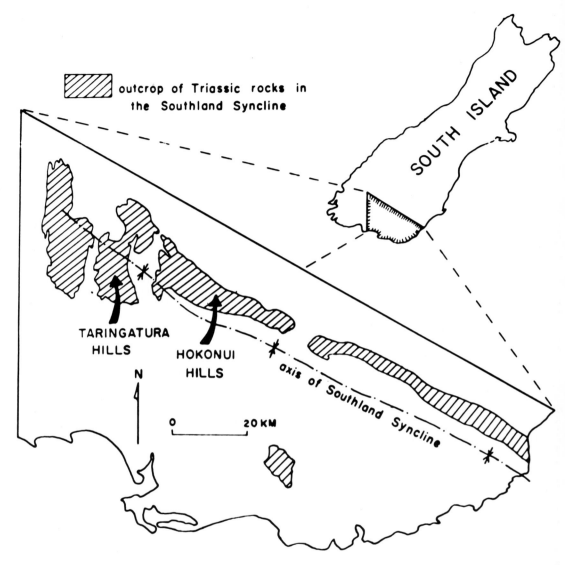

Fig. 1.—Map showing location of Hokonui Hills, Taringatura Hills, and outcrop of Triassic rocks in the Southlank Syncline, South Island, New Zealand.

Hills in New Zealand, that have identical geological histories cannot be explained by radical variations in geothermal gradients (Fig. 2). Thermal controls also cannot explain the 10 km stratigraphic overlap of heulandite, laumontite and prehnite in the Hokonui Hills (Fig. 2, and Boles and Coombs, 1977). It is becoming increasingly clear that this type of wide overlap of key minerals, suppposedly in reaction relationship, is common in volcanogenic sedimentary terranes (Surdam, 1973, Boles and Coombs, 1975, 1977).

In contrast to these large scale variations there also are mineralogical variations in volcanogenic sediments on a much smaller scale that are incompatible with a thermal control interpretation. For example, the alteration of the Gavenwood Tuffs in the Hokonuis described by Boles and Coombs (1975) demonstrated that the reaction boundary between heulandite and laumontite clearly cuts stratigraphic boundaries. Or consider the recent findings of Read and Eisbacher (1974) that heulandite and laumontite-quartz assemblages are interbedded in the Sustut Group of British Columbia. Further they suggest that the composition

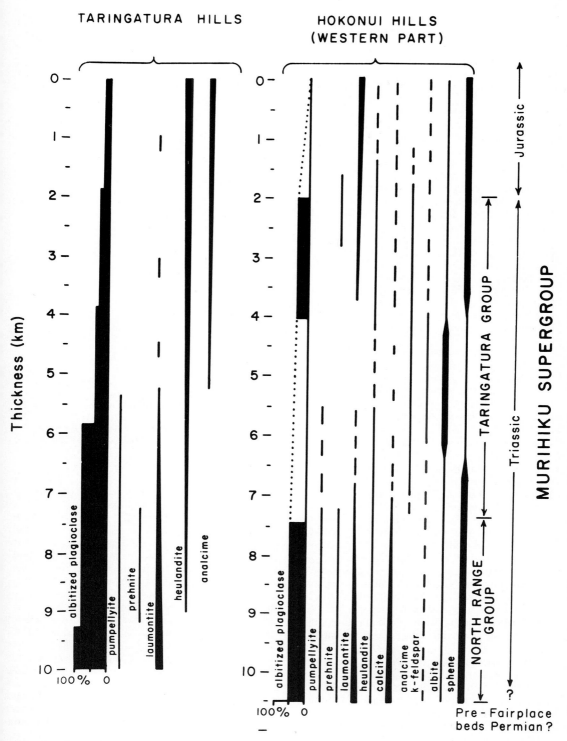

Fig. 2.—Comparison of mineral distributions in Taringatura Hills (Coombs, 1954) and Hokonui Hills (Boles and Coombs, 1977).

and amount of volcanic detritus determine the type of alteration. Thermal effects alone are inadequate when trying to understand the diagenesis of volcanogenic sandstones. Other parameters are as important, if not more important, than temperature in the process we call diagenesis.

ESSENTIAL PROBLEM

The essential problem is to understand in some detail the processes involved in the diagenesis, and hence the parameters that control it, and ultimately to construct a deterministic model of the diagenesis. A most significant result of this model will be predictive ability relative to porosity and permeability of volcanogenic sandstones. The first step in reaching this goal and the goal of this paper is to discuss in qualitative terms the mechanisms and processes characterizing the diagenesis of volcanogenic sandstones. From this discussion will come a descriptive framework for the diagenesis. Elsewhere in this volume Wood and Surdam will use this descriptive framework to discuss the quantitative aspects of diagenesis and hence develop the theoretical base on which to construct the deterministic model.

P-T CONDITIONS

Before proceeding with a discussion of reactions characterizing the diagenesis of volcanogenic sandstones, it is important to discuss the broad P-T space in which the reactions occur. Because wairakite and lawsonite generally are absent in the volcanogenic sandstones of interest, the reactions laumontite→lawsonite and laumontite→wairakite can be used to determine the upper P-T limits. Assuming $P_T = P_{H_2O}$, the upper limits for the P-T space are easily delineated from these reactions (see Fig. 3). Those limits are approximately 3 kb pressure and 300° C temperature. However, if $P_T > P_{H_2O}$, the maximum temperature for the laumontite→wairakite reaction could be drastically reduced. In a typical volcanogenic terrane the fluid pressure may be less than load pressure, particularly in the upper portions of the section or in the vicinity of joints or fractures deeper in the section. The absence of the laumontite→lawsonite reaction suggests that load pressures did not exceed 3 kb or that the maximum depth of burial did not exceed approximately 11 km (Liou, 1971).

The lower limits of the P-T space are much more difficult to determine. Laumontite seems to be universally found in the volcanogenic sandstones; therefore the lower stability of this phase can be of use in this determination. Seki and others (1969) report the occurrence and apparent formation of laumontite at $75 \pm 5°$ C in the Katayama geothermal field, Japan. Castaño and Sparks (1974) describe laumontite at a depth of

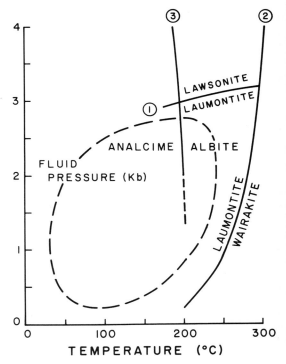

FIG. 3.—P_{fluid}-T diagram for the equilibrium reactions: (1) laumontite = lawsonite + 2 quartz + fluid (Liou, 1971), (2) laumontite = wairakite + fluid (Liou, 1971), and analcime + quartz = albite + fluid (Liou, 1971). Dashed line is approximate boundary of diagenesis of volcanogenic sandstones. Modified after Boles and Coombs (1975).

3.1 km. and 104° C in Miocene to Eocene sediments in California, whereas Merino (1975a, 1975b) reports its formation in the Kettleman North Dome, California at a depth of 4 km and a temperature of 100° C. Read and Eisbacher (1974) have shown that laumontite has formed in the sandstones of the Brothers Peak Formations of British Columbia at temperatures less than 60° C. Boles and Coombs (1975) report laumontite in the youngest rocks in the sequence in the Hokonuis that are estimated to have been buried less than 1.5 km and at temperatures of 50° C or lower.

It is important to note that at least in the Hokonuis some of the laumontite had a heulandite precursor (Boles and Coombs, 1975, 1977). Therefore the diagenesis began at even lower temperatures. In fact, even the heulandite may have had a diagenetic precursor such as phillipsite. Judging from modern deep-sea sediments, the phillipsite could have formed at or near the sediment-water interface.

Other diagenetic phases commonly observed in volcanogenic sediments are carbonates and clays. Anderson and others (1976) using isotope data from calcite and clays have shown that these diagenetic phases are produced in deep-sea sediments over the temperature range 10–60° C.

Therefore, it is concluded that the reactions of interest in the study of the diagenesis of volcanogenic sediments take place over a broad range of temperatures (10–200+° C) and pressures up to 3 kb. Although much of this P-T space has traditionally been assigned to the realm of "burial metamorphism" we hasten to point out that the rocks we are discussing are not schistose, but instead retain the textures and fabrics of sandstones and commonly contain less than 25% diagenetic minerals.

DIAGENETIC REACTIONS

There is an abundance of evidence suggesting that the diagenetic phases found in volcanogenic sandstones are the result of the alteration of plagioclase, and/or volcanic glass or lithic fragments (Surdam, 1973; Boles and Coombs, 1975, 1977; Read and Eisbacher, 1974 among others). The evidence includes plagioclase partially or completely altered to zeolites (Fig. 4), albitization of plagioclase (Fig. 5), glass shards replaced by zeolites (Fig. 6), volcanic lithic fragments replaced by zeolites and phyllosilicates (Fig. 7), and plagioclase grains with clay rims. The most prevalent alteration products include zeolite, calcite, clays, albite and K-feldspar (Boles and Coombs, 1977). Basically the reactions forming these diagenetic minerals are of three types: (1) hydration, (2) carbonatization, (formation of carbonates), and (3) dehydration. As has been shown by Galloway (1974) these three types of reactions commonly can be placed in a temporal sequence. Early diagenesis commonly is characterized by hydration and carbonatization reactions, whereas later diagenesis is characterized by dehydration reactions.

HYDRATION REACTIONS

The very earliest diagenetic reactions in volcanogenic sandstones are hydration. Figure 8 shows a Jurassic volcanogenic sandstone (OU27562) from the Kelvin Peak Formation of New Zealand, that has calcite filling the pores; however, note the hydration on the plagioclase grains. Petrographically the calcite cement looks to be very early, i.e., a typical stage 1 calcite pore filling of Galloway (1974, p. 383, Fig. 5A). However the earliest diagenetic feature in the rock is the hydration rims on the plagioclase. It is

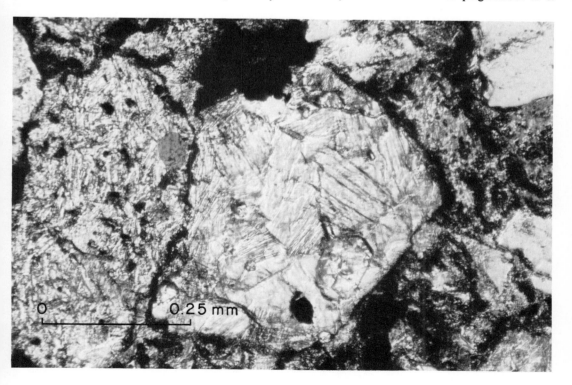

Fig. 4.—Plagioclase grain replaced by laumontite.

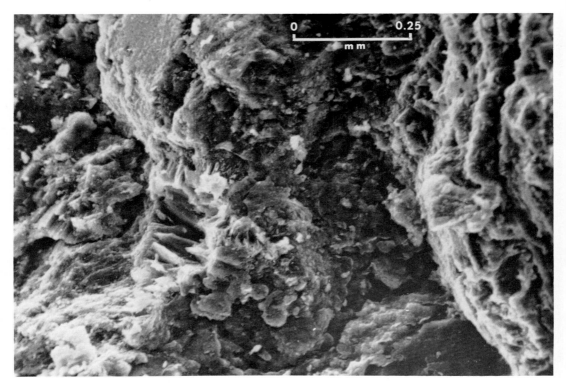

FIG. 5.—Detrital plagioclase grain completely replaced by laumontite and albite.

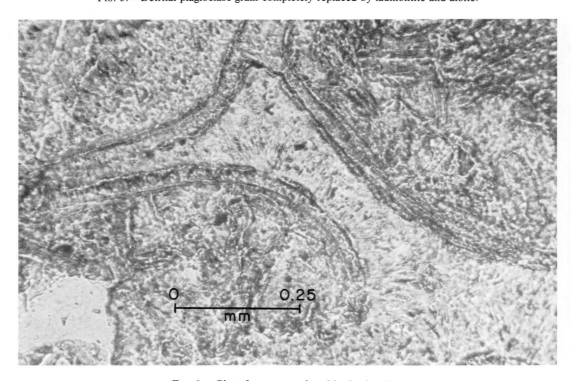

FIG. 6.—Glass fragment replaced by heulandite.

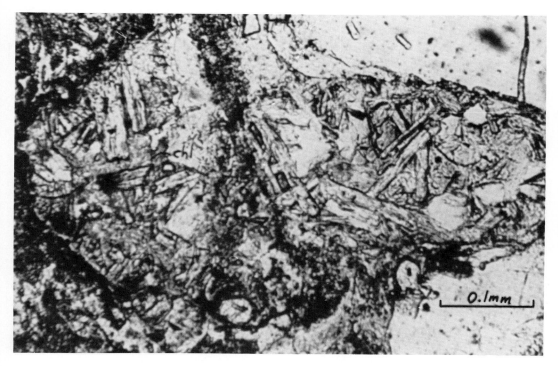

FIG. 7.—Volcanic lithic fragment replaced by laths of heulandite and chlorite (chl).

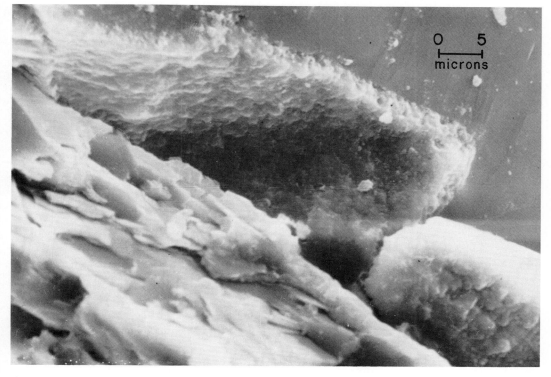

FIG. 8.—SEM photomicrograph of "hydrated" rim on plagioclase grain. Rim is 5–10 microns wide. Note calcite cement in foreground.

fortunate that the early calcite cement sealed this rock, thereby preventing further hydration reactions, or otherwise all evidence of the early hydration reactions would have been destroyed. Commonly if the rock is not sealed early, the hydration reactions precede and ultimately alter the plagioclase or glass fragments completely, resulting in the obliteration of all traces of earlier reactions. These and other hydration reactions are ubiquitous in volcanogenic terranes (Surdam, 1973; Boles and Coombs, 1974, 1977; Read and Eisbacher, 1974; among others), for in every case where detailed petrographic work has been done the reaction: glass + $H_2O\rightarrow$ zeolite or plagioclase + $H_2O\rightarrow$ zeolite has been documented. The textural evidence supporting this documentation includes heulandite pseudomorphous after glass shards, laumontite pseudomorphous after plagioclase, and partially hydrated "glass" and plagioclase grains. What has not been emphasized in previous studies is the importance of these early hydration reactions.

These hydration reactions are particularly important in discussing the diagenesis of volcanic sandstones for they increase the pH of the solution and they release cations into solution, i.e. (Ca-silicate + $H_2O\rightarrow$ H-silicate + Ca^{++} + $2OH^-$). This increase in pH and salinity has a direct bearing on all subsequent diagenetic reactions. The elevated pH stabilizes the alkaline-earth carbonates and the increased salinity affects the kinetics of zeolite forming reactions. Hay (1965) has documented that the rates of the reactions plagioclase $\rightarrow$ zeolite and glass $\rightarrow$ zeolite are demonstrably increased with increasing salinity and pH.

It is important to note that plagioclase $\rightarrow$ zeolite or andesitic glass $\rightarrow$ zeolite reactions do not necessarily require large amounts of mass transfer. Table 1 compares andesitic glass with heulandite and andesine plagioclase with laumontite based on a Barth standard cell of 160 oxygens. Basically, assuming the conservation of aluminum, the andesitic glass $\rightarrow$ heulandite and the andesine plagioclase $\rightarrow$ laumontite only requires the addition of H_2O and variations in cations.

Porosity.—The hydration reactions have significant effects on the porosity and permeability of sandstones. There is a rather significant decrease in porosity associated with the hydration of an andesitic glass-andesine plagioclase mixture. It can be shown that a volcanogenic sandstone with a 20% porosity could be sealed off without the addition or subtraction of material, with the exception of the addition of water.

More specifically, Boles and Coombs (1977) discuss the volume relations associated with plagioclase alteration in sandstones of the Hokonuis. They point out that in rocks where clasts of originally calcic plagioclase are partially albitized and partially replaced by laumontite, the probable hydration reaction has the form: $NaAlSi_3O_8 \cdot CaAl_2Si_2O_8 + 2SiO_2 + 4H_2O\rightarrow NaAlSi_3O_8 + CaAl_2Si_4O_{12} \cdot 4H_2O$. By this reaction a volume (V) of plagioclase yields an equal volume of 1:1 albite-laumontite intergrowth plus 0.53 V additional laumontite that is available to replace SiO_2 consumed in the reaction (0.22 V if derived from quartz) together with pore space.

For those individual grains of plagioclase and larger volumes of rock in which complete albitization occurs, Na^+ ions must be received from solution and excess Ca^{2+} ions are released into

TABLE 1.—COMPARISON OF ANDESITIC GLASS WITH HEULANDITE, AND ANDESINE PLAGIOCLASE WITH LAUMONTITE, ON THE BASIS OF 160 OXYGENS.

Element	Andesite	Heulandite	Element	Andesine	Laumontite
Al	19.18	19.18	Al	26.65	26.65
Si	54.90	56.96	Si	53.30	52.07
Fe	4.05	0.01	Fe	0.11	0.49
Mg	4.82	0.56	Mg	0.05	0.62
Ca	6.14	6.26	Ca	6.69	11.78
Na	7.34	1.69	Na	12.41	2.10
K	1.53	2.82	K	0.32	0.49

solution: $NaAlSi_3O_8 \cdot CaAl_2Si_2O_8 + 3SiO_2 + 2H_2O + Na^+ \rightarrow 2NaAlSi_3O_8 + 0.5CaAl_2Si_4O_{12} \cdot 4H_2O + 0.5Ca^{++}$.

In this case if the SiO_2 is provided by local replacement of quartz, pore space amounting to 12 percent of the volume of original plagioclase may be filled by laumontite, or much more if the SiO_2 is introduced in solution (Fig. 9). Such reactions can readily account for ratios of laumontite cement to albitized andesine approaching 1:2 in some Hokonui rocks. Production of laumontite may be expected to drastically reduce porosity and permeability in a rock, and hence to impede any subsequent reactions requiring transport of ions in solution.

Hydration of either glass, volcanic lithic fragments or plagioclase grains will have a pronounced effect on the porosity and permeability of volcanogenic sandstones. Large decreases in porosity can be accomplished by little more than the addition of water and minor variations in cations and/or SiO_2. In other words, these reactions are not dependent on the transfer of large amounts of material. However, if the porosity is to be conserved during the reactions, then large amounts of material must be removed and the system open with a substantial amount of fluid flowing through the sandstone in order to remove material.

Judging from petrographic examination, the alteration of glass to zeolites occurs relatively early in the diagenetic history whereas the albitization of plagioclase and resultant laumontite cement is probably a later reaction (Boles and Coombs, 1977). The porosity reduction will be directly proportional to the percentage of reactive material (glass, volcanic lithic fragments, plagio-

clase grains, etc.) and the plagioclase/glass ratio in the sandstone, original porosity, permeability (fluid flux) and fluid composition, among other factors. It is most important to note that porosity can be reduced or eliminated early in the diagenetic history and at relatively shallow burial depths.

Thermal effects.—The most spectacular aspect of the hydration reactions is in the realm of thermal effects. The thermal effect is spectacular because the hydration reactions under discussion are strongly exothermic. For purposes of illustration, consider the hydration of plagioclase in a volcanogenic sandstone. Typically these sandstones will consist of 40% plagioclase of approximately andesine composition (Galloway, 1974, p. 382 and appendix tables 1, 2, 3). Therefore, the plagioclase in these sandstones contains up to 20% of the anorthite molecule that could be available for hydration. In order to evaluate the thermal effects of the hydration of plagioclase, assume that the sandstone has the same density/porosity vs. depth of burial and thermal gradient characteristics as the sandstones shown in Figure 10 of Galloway (1974, p. 386, Shell Anglo E-66 and B-10). At a depth of 1.5 km the sandstone would have a density of 2.3, 20% porosity, and be at a temperature of about 60° C. We will approximate the plagioclase hydration as follows: $CaAl_2Si_2O_8 + 2SiO_2 + 4H_2O \rightarrow CaAl_2Si_4O_{12} \cdot 4H_2O$. From this reaction we can approximate the amount of heat released from the plagioclase hydration reactions in a typical volcanogenic sandstone. We will assume that all the anorthite in the sandstone is hydrated, i.e., the reaction runs to completion. The heat of reaction can be calculated from the thermochemical data of Robie and Waldbaum (1968) and Zen (1972). The ΔH_r at 60° C is approximately -15 k cal/mole anorthite.[1] The heat of reaction for the rock is calculated as follows: 1 cc of rock contains 0.2 cc of anorthite (An); 0.2 cc of An of density 2.76 g/cc and mol. wt. of 278 g/mole is equivalent to 0.0020 moles of An; therefore $0.0020 \times 15,000 = 30$ cal/cc rock. One cm^3 of the sandstone weighs 2.3 g, and it is 20% H_2O and 80% solids; therefore one cc of rock consists of 0.2 g H_2O and 2.1 g of solids. The heat capacity of the rock (Cp_t) can be calculated as follows:

$$Cp_{(H_2O)}f_{H_2O} + Cp_{ss}f_{ss} = Cp_t \quad \text{and}$$

$$Cp_{(H_2O)}\left(\frac{0.2}{2.3}\right) + Cp_{(ss)}\left(\frac{2.1}{2.3}\right) = Cp_t$$

EFFECT OF ALBITIZATION ON POROSITY

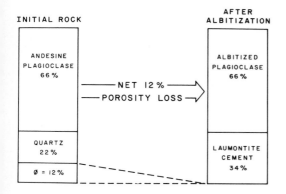

INITIAL ROCK

AFTER ALBITIZATION

ANDESINE PLAGIOCLASE 66 %

ALBITIZED PLAGIOCLASE 66 %

— NET 12 % →
— POROSITY LOSS ⌐

QUARTZ 22 %

LAUMONTITE CEMENT 34 %

∅ = 12 %

Fig. 9.—Schematic diagram showing the effect on porosity resulting from the albitization of calcic plagioclase grains in a volcanogenic sandstone.

[1] Due to the uncertainties of the ΔH values, the ΔH of this reaction could range from 8 to 22 kcal/mole.

Using the heat capacity values from Goranson (1942) this expression can be evaluated:

$$1\left(\frac{.2}{2.3}\right) + 0.22\left(\frac{2.1}{2.3}\right) = Cp_t \therefore Cp_t$$

$$= 0.66 \text{ cal/cc}°$$

Therefore if all the heat generated by the hydration of anorthite in a typical volcanogenic sandstone were conserved, the temperature of the rock would rise by about 45° C (30 cal/cc rock/0.66 cal/cc°). Although speculative this calculation suggests that the thermal effects of the hydration reactions could be significant. The above example completely ignored the hydration of glass and volcanic lithic fragments, so the thermal effect could be even larger.

Hydration reactions have the potential to cause significant perturbations in thermal gradients in sedimentary basins containing a high percentage of volcanogenic sediments. At the very least, the heat evolved through the exothermic hydration reactions will enhance kinetically other organic and inorganic reactions.

The glass hydration reactions occur at shallower depths than the plagioclase hydration reactions, and therefore the latter reaction will have a more significant effect on the geothermal gradient of the sequence. By assuming a reaction rate it is possible to speculate on the geothermal effect of the plagioclase hydration in a sequence of volcanogenic sediments. Assuming that hydration of the andesine plagioclase (40%) in a 10 km thick stratigraphic section takes 10 million years, the geothermal gradient could be increased by 5–10%. If the hydration was completed in 1 million years the geothermal gradient could be increased up to 30%.

CARBONATIZATION REACTIONS

Carbonatization reactions resulting in calcite cement or pore fillings are another type of reaction of early diagenesis (Galloway, 1974). Although early calcite cement[2] is common in volcanogenic sandstones that have undergone diagenesis, it is by no means ubiquitous. Many of the early hydration reactions that were discussed previously are ready sources of Ca^{++}. In addition, the connate waters (marine water in most cases) associated with the sandstones also contain considerable amounts of Ca^{++} (0.010 molality) and are convenient sources of Ca^{++}. In contrast, HCO_3^- in normal marine waters is an order of magnitude

[2]The kind of calcite cement under discussion is pore filling (Galloway, 1974, p. 383, fig. 5A) in contrast to late diagenetic calcite that obliterates detrital grains (Galloway, 1974, p. 383, fig. 6D).

less abundant (0.0024 molality). The limiting constraint on carbonatization reactions in volcanogenic terranes appears to be the source of HCO_3^- ions. There are three apparent sources of HCO_3^- or CO_2 to the sediments: (1) the atmosphere, (2) biological decomposition of organic matter and (3) dissolution of fossil material. As Berner (1971) points out, the biological reactions of greatest importance are: (1) oxidation of organic material by aerobic organisms, (2) fermentation by bacteria and (3) reduction of SO_4^- by bacteria. Recent isotopic studies of authigenic calcites in deep sea sediments suggest an organic matter source for the carbon (Anderson and others, 1976). Thus, it appears that the amount and distribution of organic matter in the sediments will be the limiting factor relative to carbonatization reactions. This probably explains why early calcite cement is common, but not ubiquitous in volcanogenic sandstones. Calcite producing reactions can be self limiting in terranes containing volcanogenic sandstones, for very early they can completely eliminate porosity, sealing off the sand; thus preventing any further diagenetic reaction.

DEHYDRATION REACTIONS

Dehydration reactions are common in the diagenetic history of many volcanogenic sandstones. These reactions are usually late in the diagenetic sequence and are commonly associated with fractures, joints or faults. Significant mass transfer of material can be associated with these late dehydration reactions. Both Na and Ca metasomatism may occur during the late diagenesis of volcanogenic sandstones. Dehydration reactions that have been documented to be commonly associated with the diagenesis of volcanogenic sediments include among others the following (Surdam, 1973, Boles and Coombs, 1975, 1977); H = heulandite, L = laumontite, Pr = prehnite, An = analcime, Ab = albite, Pu = pumpellyite).

$$\text{1.} \quad \overset{H}{Ca_3K_2Al_8Si_{28}O_{72}\cdot23H_2O} \rightarrow \overset{L}{3CaAl_2Si_4O_{12}\cdot4H_2O}$$
$$+ 10SiO_2 + 2KAlSi_3O_8 + 11H_2O$$

$$\text{2.} \quad 3Ca^{++} + \overset{H}{Ca_3K_2Al_8Si_{28}O_{72}\cdot23H_2O}$$
$$\overset{Pr}{\rightarrow 3Ca_2Al_2Si_3O_{10}(OH)_2} + 2KAlSi_3O_8$$
$$+ 13SiO_2 + 17H_2O + 6H^+$$

$$\text{3.} \quad 8Na^+ + \overset{H}{Ca_3K_2Al_8Si_{28}O_{72}\cdot23H_2O}$$
$$\overset{An}{\rightarrow 8NaAlSi_2O_6\cdot H_2O} + 12SiO_2 + 2K^+ + 3Ca^{++}$$
$$+ 15H_2O$$

4. $8Na^+ + Ca_3K_2Al_8Si_{28}O_{72} \cdot 23H_2O \rightarrow \overset{Ab}{8NaAlSi_3O_8}$

$+ 4SiO_2 + 23H_2O + 2K^+ + 3Ca^{++}$

5. $\overset{An}{NaAl_2Si_2O_6 \cdot H_2O} + SiO_2 \rightarrow \overset{Ab}{NaAlSi_3O_8} + H_2O$

6. $\overset{L}{CaAl_2Si_4O_{12} \cdot 4H_2O} + Ca^{++}$

$\rightarrow \overset{Pr}{Ca_2Al_2Si_3O_{10}(OH)_2} + SiO_2 + 2H_2O + 2H^+$

7. $\overset{L}{2CaAl_2Si_4O_{12} \cdot 4H_2O} + 2Ca^{++} + (Fe, Mg)^{++}$

$+ Fe^{+++} \rightarrow \overset{Pu}{Ca_4(Fe, Mg)^{2+}Fe^{3+}Al_4Si_6O_{21}(OH)_7}$

$+ 2SiO_2 + 9H^+$

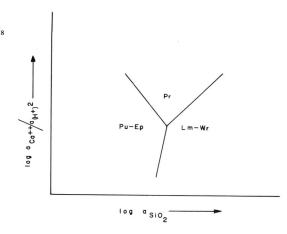

Fig. 10.—Activity diagram depicting phase relations of hydrous calcium aluminosilicates minerals. Diagram constructed at an unspecified temperature and pressure in the presence of water. Pu = pumpellyite, Ep = epidote, Pr = prehnite, Lm = laumontite; Wr = wairakite. After Surdam (1973).

REACTION CONTROLS

As already discussed the reactions involving the hydrous calcium aluminosilicates seem to be relatively unaffected by stratigraphic position in volcanogenic sandstones (Fig. 2). For example, the distribution patterns of heulandite, laumontite, prehnite and pumpellyite widely overlap in most volcanogenic sandstones. The geometry of the mineral patterns strongly suggests that factors other than temperature are important in determining the diagenetic mineral "stability" fields.

The observed distribution patterns of the hydrous calcium aluminosilicate minerals, and analcime and albite can be explained readily in terms of fluid composition. It has been shown that within an appropriate range of temperature and total pressure (see Fig. 10) and in the presence of H_2O, any of the hydrous calcium aluminosilicates being discussed could be stable, depending on the activities of Ca^{++}, SiO_2, and H^+ (Surdam, 1973). Thus the gross overlap of diagenetic mineral zones in volcanogenic sandstones can be explained in terms of the activities of ionic species in the aqueous phase. In fact, variations in fluid flow, and more importantly in fluid composition, explain many of the perplexing questions that previously were inadequately explained by thermal variations alone.

Compositional effects.—To further illustrate the importance of fluid composition on dehydration reactions, consider the following example discussed by Boles and Coombs (1977). A laumontite-cemented sandstone high in the Taringatura Group contains scattered patches of heulandite and a few calcite concretions. A silty lens within the unit is cemented partly by heulandite and partly by laumontite and contains minor prehnite which is several times more abundant in the heulandite-cemented area than in the laumontite-cemented area. Underlying the sandstone

is a 1 m thick, dark gray tuffaceous siltstone with numerous plant fragments, some of which are partially pyritized. The siltstone bed contains numerous tiny heulandite-filled vugs, some of which are partially or completely replaced by prehnite ± K-feldspar and quartz.

It is suggested that differences in pore fluid composition played an important role in the distribution of phases at such outcrops. Relative stability fields for prehnite, laumontite, and heulandite are shown in Fig. 11 based on the following equations:[3]

$CaAl_2Si_7O_{18} \cdot 6H_2O = CaAl_2Si_4O_{12} \cdot 4H_2O$
heulandite   laumontite

$+ 3SiO_2 + 2H_2O$

$CaAl_2Si_7O_{18} \cdot 6H_2O + Ca^{2+} = Ca_2Al_2Si_3O_{10}(OH)_2$
heulandite   prehnite

$+ 4SiO_2 + 4H_2O + 2H^+$

$CaAl_2Si_4O_{12} \cdot 4H_2O + Ca^{2+} = Ca_2Al_2Si_3O_{10}(OH)_2$
laumontite   prehnite

$+ SiO_2 + 2H_2O + 2H^+$

From the common association of laumontite with authigenic quartz the line of quartz saturation in Fig. 11 is presumed to pass through the laumontite field rather than that of heulandite.

Heulandite, initially formed from glass in a local

[3] Any SiO_2 dissolved in the fluid phase would occur as one or more of the hydrated silica species.

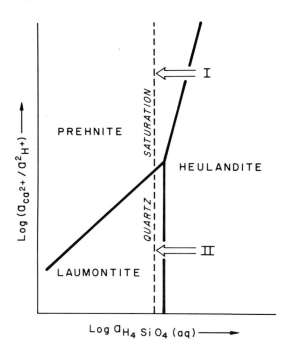

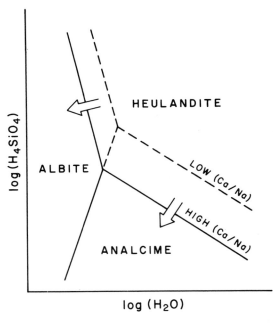

FIG. 11.—Activity diagram showing phase relations for laumontite, $CaAl_2Si_4O_{12} \cdot 4H_2O$; heulandite, $CaAl_2Si_7O_{18} \cdot 6H_2O$, and prehnite, $Ca_2Al_2Si_3O_{10}$ $(OH)_2$. Arrows show direction of the most common reactions between the phases in Triassic-Jurassic rocks of the Southland Syncline, New Zealand. After Boles and Coombs (1978).

FIG. 12.—Activity diagram showing the phase relations between heulandite-analcime and albite. Note that reactions in this system are affected by not only the activities of H_2O and H_2SiO_4, but also the Ca/Na ratios.

environment of high $a\mathrm{SiO_2}$, will, with falling $a\mathrm{SiO_2}$, tend to convert to prehnite rather than laumontite if the activity ratio $a_{\mathrm{Ca^{2+}}}/a^2_{\mathrm{H^+}}$ is high.

In many of the pore fluids the ratio $a_{\mathrm{Ca^{2+}}}/a^2_{\mathrm{H^+}}$ probably is buffered by calcite. At fixed T, P this ratio in a fluid in equilibrium with calcite is inversely related to $\mathrm{P_{CO_2}}$. Preservation of organic material and formation of pyrite suggests that pore fluids in the siltstone were relatively reducing compared to those in the sandstone, and thus $\mathrm{P_{CO_2}}$ may have been relatively low. Assuming that $a_{\mathrm{Ca^{2+}}}/a^2_{\mathrm{H^+}}$ was close to equilibration with calcite, then this ratio would have been higher in the siltstone than in the sandstone. Heulandite altered to prehnite (path "I," Fig. 11) in siltstone, whereas it altered to laumontite (path "II") in the sandstone. Relatively low permeabilities in the siltstone apparently prevented $\mathrm{P_{CO_2}}$ from becoming homogenized with fluid in the overlying sandstone.

The heulandite→analcime and the heulandite→ albite reactions also are strongly controlled by fluid composition. From Figure 12 it can be seen that heulandite can be caused to react to analcime

or albite by simply lowering the Ca/Na ratio of the fluid phase. Whether heulandite reacts to form analcime or albite will largely be a function of the activity of $\mathrm{SiO_2}$ in the fluid; if $a_{\mathrm{SiO_2}}$ is high, heulandite will react to form albite and if the $a_{\mathrm{SiO_2}}$ is low, it will react to form analcime. It is important to note that Figure 12 is constructed at a specific temperature and in the presence of H_2O.

Another compositional effect that should be noted in discussing the diagenesis of volcanogenic sandstones is the close relationship between the composition of the detrital clasts and the distribution of authigenic minerals. For example, in the Hokonuis, new-formed laumontite and heulandite, chlorite, and sphene are most abundant in sandstones rich in andesitic or basaltic clasts (Boles, 1974). Laumontite and heulandite are similarly abundant in Jurassic andesitic sandstones of the Catlins district in New Zealand (Speden, 1971). In contrast, sandstones rich in rhyolitic to dacitic clasts are characterized by abundant new-formed albite, K-feldspar, quartz, and minor chlorite and sphene. Similarly, Stewart (1974, p. 1141) states that the presence of laumontite is closely controlled by the "presence of abundant intermediate and basic volcanic debris"

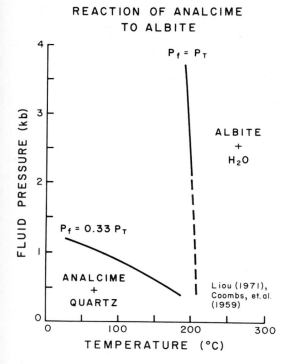

FIG. 13.—Diagram showing the effect of varying the P_f/P_T ratio on the analcime + SiO_2 → albite + SiO_2 reaction.

in sandstones of the western Olympic Peninsula, Washington.

Pressure effects.—Pressure, particularly the relationship between fluid pressure (P_f) and total or lithostatic pressure (P_T), can have profound effects on dehydration reactions (Fig. 13; Greenwood, 1961). Figure 13 demonstrates that analcime in a volcanogenic sandstone could become unstable if the system went from $P_f = P_T$ to $P_f < P_T$ conditions. This type of fluid pressure drop could easily take place in a terrain undergoing fracturing and faulting. This relationship is true for the hydrous calcium aluminosilicates as well. In most volcanogenic sandstones undergoing diagenesis, the P_f probably ranges from P_f = lithostatic pressure to P_f = hydrostatic pressure.

It is not surprising that many dehydration reactions in volcanogenic sandstones are associated with fractures, joints and faults (Figs. 14, 15). Table 2 shows some of the dehydration reactions in volcanogenic sandstones that can be documented to be associated with, and controlled by fracturing in the Hokonui area.

It is well known that the relationship between P_f and P_T varies widely in sedimentary basins. For example in the Gulf Coast Geosyncline fluid pressures vary significantly. Hydrostatic conditions (P_f = 0.5) P_T are found as deep as 5 km, but in some areas conditions where $P_f = 0.9\ P_T$ are found as shallow as 3 km (Dickinson, 1953; Jones, 1969). Furthermore pressure gradients may increase gradually over a considerable depth interval, or they may increase rapidly from hydrostatic to lithostatic over a depth of not more than a few kilometers. Generally $P_f = P_T$ consistently

TABLE 2.—DEHYDRATION REACTIONS COMMONLY ASSOCIATED WITH FRACTURING IN VOLCANOGENIC SANDSTONES.

1) $Ca_3K_2Al_8Si_{28}O_{72} \cdot 23H_2O \longrightarrow 3CaAl_2Si_4O_{12} \cdot 4H_2O + 10SiO_2 + 2KAlSi_3O_8 + 11H_2O$
    HEULANDITE   *LAUMONTITE*

2) $8Na^+ + Ca_3K_2Al_8Si_{28}O_{72} \cdot 23H_2O \longrightarrow 8NaAlSi_3O_8 + 4SiO_2 + 23H_2O + 2K^+ + 3Ca^{++}$
    HEULANDITE   *ALBITE*

3) $2CaAl_2Si_4O_{12} \cdot 4H_2O + 2Ca^{++} + (Fe, Mg)^{++} + Fe^{+++} \longrightarrow$
    LAUMONTITE $Ca_4(Fe, Mg)^{2+} Fe^{3+} Al_4 Si_6 O_{21} (OH)_7 + 2SiO_2 + 9H^+$
                                    PUMPELLYITE

4) $NaAlSi_2O_6 \cdot H_2O + SiO_2 \longrightarrow NaAlSi_3O_8 + H_2O$
    ANALCIME   *ALBITE*

FIG. 14.—Albite veinlet in an analcime-rich siltstone.

only in the deepest parts of sedimentary basins, and perhaps in less deeply buried beds of very low permeability.

The significance of this discussion to diagenetic reactions is well illustrated by considering a hypothetical low temperature reaction $X = Y + H_2O$ for which equilibrium curves corresponding to P_f/P_t ratios of 0.5, 0.75, 0.87, and 1.0 respectively

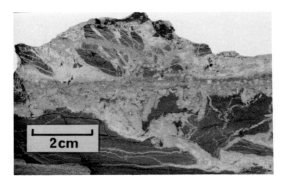

FIG. 15.—Laumontite veins in a heulandite-rich silt-stone.

are as shown in Figure 16 (see Boles and Coombs, 1977). Assume a thermal gradient of 25° C/km and that the fluid pressure gradient increases rapidly from a hydrostatic to a lithostatic gradient over a 2 km interval (path A). The change in equilibrium position as a result of changing P_f/P_t ratios could result in the following sequence: at depths less than 3.5 km, phase X; 3.5 to 5.6 km, phase $Y + H_2O$; 5.6 km to 7 km, phase X; and below 7 km, phase $Y + H_2O$. Phase X and Y could coexist stably at three temperatures corresponding to depths of 3.5 km, 5.6 km, and 7 km.

It is concluded that during progressive burial of a sedimentary pile, gross overlap in mineral distributions may occur where dehydration reactions such as quartz + analcime to albite, and heulandite to laumontite, feldspar, and quartz, are sensitive to variations in P_f/P_t ratios, and where the fluid pressure gradient increases rapidly over a small depth interval. In cases where the fluid pressure gradient increases gradually with depth (curve B, Fig. 16) overlapping equilibrium mineral distributions will not occur if the position of the equilibrium curve changes at a faster rate than the fluid pressure gradient. For curve B,

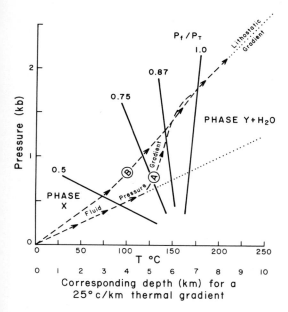

FIG. 16.—Equilibrium curves for hypothetical reaction x = y + H$_2$O at various P$_f$/P$_T$ ratios. Also shown is a lithostatic gradient of 250 bar/km, a near-hydrostatic gradient of 125 bar/km, and two fluid-pressure gradients (dashed curves A and B) after Boles and Coombs (1977).

phase Y + H$_2$O will become stable only at P$_f$/P$_t$ ratio of 1.0. If fluid pressure gradients vary from place to place, and from permeable to impermeable beds within a sedimentary basin, the resulting mineral distributions may be very complex, and furthermore fracturing, resulting in a lowered fluid pressure, may increase the complexity by promoting dehydration reactions (Boles and Coombs, 1977).

DESCRIPTIVE FRAMEWORK FOR DIAGENESIS OF VOLCANOGENIC SANDSTONES

The framework that evolves from this discussion of the diagenesis of volcanogenic sandstones is shown in Figure 17. Generally this diagenesis can be divided temporally into early diagenesis and later diagenesis. However, there can be considerable overlap in the hydration and dehydration reactions. The early diagenesis is characterized

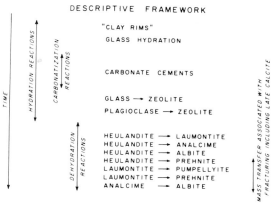

FIG. 17.—Descriptive framework for the diagenesis of volcanogenic sandstones.

by hydration and carbonatization reactions. If the sandstone contains a high percentage of reactive material (glass, plagioclase and volcanic lithic fragments) the original porosity of the rock will be greatly reduced or eliminated during this stage of diagenesis. The most significant hydration reactions are glass→zeolite and plagioclase→zeolite. During the later stages of diagenesis, dehydration reactions become dominant. Commonly the dehydration reactions are associated with fracturing. Mass transfer may be associated with these late dehydration reactions. It is speculated that secondary porosity could develop in conjunction with the mass transfer of material.

Thus fluid effects are most pronounced in the early stages of diagenesis when the fluid/solid ratio is high, and in the later stages during fracturing and/or dewatering. It is concluded that fluid flow and composition are at least as significant, if not more significant, than depth of burial in controlling the distribution of diagenetic mineral phases in volcanogenic sandstones.

ACKNOWLEDGEMENTS

The authors gratefully acknowledge support from the Marathon Oil Company, the American Chemical Society, and the National Science Foundation for supporting various aspects of this work.

REFERENCES

ANDERSON, T. F., DONNELLY, T. W., DREVER, J. I., ESLINGER, E., GIESKES, J. M., KASTNER, M., LAWRENCE, J. R., AND PERRY, E. A., 1976, Geochemistry and diagenesis of deep-sea sediments from leg 35 of the Deep Sea Drilling Project: Nature, v. 261, No. 5560, p. 473–476.

BOLES, J. R., 1974, Structure, stratigraphy, and petrology of mainly Triassic rocks, Hokonui Hills, Southland, New Zealand: New Zealand Jour. Geology and Geophysics, v. 17, p. 337–374.

—— AND COOMBS, D. S., 1975, Mineral reactions in zeolitic Triassic tuff, Hokonui Hills, New Zealand: Geol. Soc. America Bull., v. 86, p. 163–173.

—— AND ——, 1977, Zeolite facies alteration of sandstones in the Southland Syncline, New Zealand: Am. Jour. Sci., v. 277, p. 982–1012.

CANTAÑO, J. R., AND SPARKS, D. M., 1974, Interpretation of vitrinite reflectance measurements in sedimentary rocks and determination of burial history using vitrinite reflectance and authigenic minerals: Geol. Soc. America Spec. Paper 153, p. 31–52.

COOMBS, D. S., 1954, The nature and alteration of some Triassic sediments from Southland, New Zealand: Royal Soc. New Zealand Trans., v. 82, p. 65–109.

——, 1960, Lower grade mineral facies in New Zealand: 21st Internat. Geol. Congress, Copenhagen 1960, Rept., pt. 13, p. 339–351.

——, 1961, Some recent work on the lower grades of metamorphism: Australian Jour. Sci., v. 24, p. 203–215.

——, ELLIS, A. J., FYFE, W. S., AND TAYLOR, A. M., 1959, The zeolite facies with comments on the interpretation of hydrothermal syntheses: Geochim. et Cosmochim. Acta, v. 17, p. 53–107.

DICKINSON, G., 1953, Geological aspects of abnormal reservoir pressures in Gulf Coast Louisiana: Am. Assoc. Petroleum Geologists Bull., v. 37, p. 410–432.

GALLOWAY, W. E., 1974, Deposition and diagenetic alteration of sandstone in northwest Pacific arc-related basins: Implications for greywacke genesis: Geol. Soc. America Bull., v. 85, p. 379–390.

GREENWOOD, H. J., 1961, The system $NaAlSi_2O_6-H_2O$-argon: Total pressure and water pressure in metamorphism: Jour. Geophys. Research, v. 66, p. 3923–3946.

HAY, R. L., 1965, Zeolites and zeolitic reactions in sedimentary rocks: Geol. Soc. America Spec. Paper 85, 130 p.

JONES, P. H., 1969, Hydrodynamics of geopressure in the northern Gulf of Mexico: Jour. Petroleum Technology, v. 21, p. 803–810.

LIOU, J. G., 1971, P-T stabilities of laumontite, wairakite, lausonite, and related minerals in the system $CaAl_2Si_2O_8-SiO_2-H_2O$: Jour. Petrology, v. 12, p. 379–411.

MERINO, E., 1975a, Diagenesis in Tertiary sandstones from Kettleman North Dome, California—I. Diagenetic mineralogy: Jour. Sed. Petrology, v. 45, p. 320–336.

——, 1975b, Diagenesis in Tertiary sandstones from Kettleman North Dome, California—II. Interstitial solutions: Distribution of aqueous species at 100 C and chemical relation to the diagenetic mineralogy: Geochim. et Cosmochim. Acta, v. 39, p. 1629–1645.

READ, P. B., AND EISBACHER, G. H., 1974, Regional zeolite alteration of the Sustut Group, north-central British Columbia: Canadian Mineralogists, v. 12, p. 527–541.

ROBIE, R. A., AND WALDBAUM, 1968, Thermodynamic properties of minerals and related substances at 298.15° K (25.0° C) and one atmosphere (1.013 bars) pressure and at higher temperatures: U.S. Geol. Survey Bull. 1259, 256 p.

SEKI, Y., ONUKI, H., OKUMURA, K., AND TAKASHIMA, I., 1969, Zeolite distribution in the Katayama geothermal area, Onikobe, Japan: Japanese Jour. Geology and Geography, v. 40, p. 63–79.

SPEDEN, I. G., 1971, Geology of Papatowi subdivision south-east Otago: New Zealand Geol. Survey Bull., m. s. 81, 166 p.

STEWART, R. J., 1974, Zeolite facies metamorphism of sandstones in the western Olympic Peninsula, Washington: Geol. Soc. America Bull., v. 85, p. 1139–1142.

SURDAM, R. C., 1973, Low-grade metamorphism of tuffaceous rocks in the Karmutsen Group, Vancouver Island, British Columbia: Geol. Soc. America Bull., v. 84, p. 1911–1922.

ZEN, E-AN, 1972, Gibbs free energy, enthalpy, and entropy of ten rockforming minerals: Calculations, discrepancies, implications: Am. Mineralogist, v. 57, p. 524–553.

——, 1974, Burial metamorphism: Canadian mineralogist, v. 12, p. 445–455.

SEPM Special Publication No. 26, p. 243–250, March 1979

APPLICATION OF CONVECTIVE-DIFFUSION MODELS TO DIAGENETIC PROCESSES

JAMES R. WOOD AND RONALD C. SURDAM
The University of Wyoming, Laramie, 82701

ABSTRACT

Diagenesis of volcanogenic sandstones is characterized by the alteration of glass and feldspar (plagioclase) to carbonates, clays and zeolites. These alteration products are commonly distributed throughout the body in well defined zones, but the chemical and physical controls on the spatial location of these zones is poorly understood. A quantitative model describing these processes has been constructed by combining the equations describing chemical reaction with those governing mass transfer. This approach leads to a set of differential equations with associated boundary conditions constrained by a set of mass action equations. In this framework the identity and spatial distribution of the reaction products can be shown to originate as a consequence of counter-current mass flows in which different aqueous species diffuse in opposite directions due to imposed boundary conditions. In the case of opposing diffusion currents containing components which are capable of reacting to form a solid precipitate, a well-defined precipitation zone will form. The positions of these zones are a function of the boundary conditions and the strength of the sources and sinks.

The calculation emphasizes the importance of knowing whether or not the system was open or closed with respect to fluid flow and/or gas exchange and shows that the Peclet number is a key parameter as it not only affects the spatial distribution of the alteration products but also effects the magnitude of the precipitation flow.

INTRODUCTION

The alteration of rocks *in situ* through the action of aqueous fluids has attracted considerable attention over the years from a number of investigators and has resulted in nearly as many contrasting points of view. The diagenetic alteration of sandstones, particularly volcanogenic sandstones, has attracted a proportionate share of interest, and there has been fairly sharp debate in the literature over questions regarding process and controlling parameters. In particular case of zeolization, for example, the role of thermal control (Coombs, 1960) versus a "solution" control (Surdam and Boles, this volume) has been at issue. In general, however, one can make the point that no alteration process has been characterized sufficiently to permit resolution of questions such as this. One approach, which does not appear to have been tried to date, and which might go a long way toward resolving questions of this nature is a purely formal mathematical approach in which the processes are modelled in terms of differential equations and solutions are sought in terms of analytical functions or computer simulations. One advantage of such an approach is that the relationships between the various parameters, temperature and solution composition for example, are clearly displayed and the relative importance of each can be evaluated, often quantitatively. Other advantages are that variables which previously may not have been thought to be important may come to the fore, and quite often a fully developed model possesses a predictive capability beyond its explanatory function. The disadvantages of a quantitative approach are primarily in developing solutions to the differential equations. The equations describing a geological process can usually be set up readily enough, but they often are so numerous, contain so many terms, and are so strongly coupled that explicit analytical solutions are not possible to obtain. In the case of rock alteration another problem arises, namely how to characterize the spatial and temporal distribution of the reaction products. Solution chemistry has proven capable of dealing with the dissolved constituents of the fluid phase in a satisfactory manner, but not with the solid phases which precipitate out of the fluid phase.

It has only been since 1972 that a satisfactory method for handling precipitation flows has been developed (Helfferich and Katchalsky, 1970), but the method is extremely straightforward and lends itself readily to the analysis of mineral precipitation in geologic systems. The main thrust of this paper is to exploit the breakthrough that Helfferich and Katchalsky have provided and to adapt their treatment to a geological environment. A logical starting point is with a qualitative discussion of the model, followed by the mathematical description, and then some typical solutions.

Copyright © 1979, The Society of Economic Paleontologists and Mineralogists

THE PHYSICAL MODEL

In spite of statements to the contrary it is fair to say that all diagenetic processes involve mass transfer on some scale in addition to chemical reaction. The transfer involved may be extremely local and the system can be considered as "closed", or quantities of material can be transported over large distances in which case the system is usually more profitably treated as an "open" system. We will not dwell on the finer points involved in the concepts of open versus closed systems except to note that in a mathematical treatment this generally means that closed systems are treated in terms of internal sources and/or sinks and that sources and sinks in open systems are treated in terms of boundary conditions. The distinction between an open and a closed system is important but perhaps not so critical as might be inferred from the literature devoted to the matter. For diagenetic processes we generally only have to make the distinction between the flow of large quantities of aqueous fluids through porous media and the release and almost immediate precipitation of constitutents from the solid phases. In other words we can have simultaneously an open system characterized by the flow of fluid through a sandstone and a closed system in which a component such as aluminum is conserved at a particular location ($\bar{x}$) for all time. A general physical model for diagenetic processes should provide for both bulk fluid flow and very local precipitation of minerals.

Bulk fluid flow can be treated quantitatively in terms of the Navier-Stokes equations, which are usually reduced to a Darcy's Law form for processes involving flow in porous media. The precipitation of solids however is more difficult to treat since what is desired is a description of both the total and instantaneous amounts of materials precipitated from the fluid as a function of time and space as the fluid executes some motion of its own. In this paper we will employ the terminology of Helfferich and Katchalsky (*ibid*) and use j_i ($\bar{x}$, t) to designate the flow of solid phase i (dim j = moles/cm^2 −sec). This is of course the instantaneous precipitation flow but the total flow can be obtained from the j_i by integrating over time.

The principal aim of this paper is to develop an analytical expression for $j(\bar{x}, t)$ that can be adapted to a variety of geological conditions including the case where the fluid velocity, U, is non-zero. Helfferich and Katchalsky (*ibid*) have provided a general framework for purely diffusive processes and our strategy will be to expand their treatment to include the effects of a moving fluid.

If partial equilibrium (Thompson, 1959; Helgeson, 1968) is assumed between the fluid and all

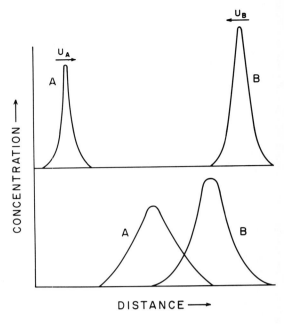

FIG. 1.—Generalized schematic diagram for countercurrent flow. Two concentration waves, A. and B, move toward one another with relative velocity $(U_A − U_B)$ (top). At some time the waves collide (bottom) and the potential for the precipitation of a solid phase exists where the two waves overlap.

reaction products (precipitates) the only feasible mechanism for the precipitation of material from the fluid under isothermal, isobaric conditions is the collision of two (or more) counter-current mass flows. Counter-current flow can be defined as movement of two or more waves of different composition toward one another. The movement can be due to either diffusion or fluid flow (infiltration) or some combination of both (Fig. 1). For the case involving two waves, if one wave contains a dissolved substance A and the second a dissolved substance B which are capable of reacting to form a solid, say $AB_{(s)}$, then that solid may precipitate from the fluid phase when the wave fronts collide (Fig. 1b). The only condition is that the solubility product for the solid phase be exceeded at some point during the crossing of the two waves. This is the simplest possible configuration and more complex situations involving more dissolved components and/or solid precipitates can easily be construed, but the main features of the counter-current model are displayed in the two wave model.

THE MATHEMATICAL MODEL

The mathematical description of a counter-current flow system is also relatively simple; it is based on the simultaneous solution of a set of differential equations known as the convective-diffusion equations (eqn. 1). These equations are modified slightly to include source and sink terms and solutions are sought which satisfy the chosen initial and boundary conditions. This is one of basically two approaches which have been taken to describe non-equilibrium processes in natural systems, the other is a PATHCALC-type of analysis in which attention is focused on the chemical reactions taking place in the system (Helgeson, 1968) but does not explicitly involve the transport equations for either diffusion and infiltration. This approach has been described in some detail; however, it is not well suited to processes involving fluid movement, and since fluid velocities are most likely non-zero in general when dealing with alteration in sandstones, we will proceed along the lines involved in the second approach, starting with the transport equations and then considering the consequences of chemical reactions occuring as the fluid moves through a given section of rock.

In this case the convective-diffusion equation (Daily and Harleman, 1966, p. 427) provides a convenient starting point,

$$Dc_i/Dt = D_i^2 \, c_i \nabla^2 \, c_i \qquad (1)$$

where Dc_i/Dt is the total or Eulerian derivitive and may be expanded to

$$Dc_i/Dt = \partial c_i/\partial t + u \partial c_i/\partial x$$
$$+ v \partial c_i/\partial y + w \partial c_i/\partial z. \qquad (2)$$

u, v, and w are the x, y, and z components of the fluid velocity $\bar{q}$, t is time, c_i is the (molar) concentration of i in the fluid, and D_i is the diffusion coefficient for i. One such equation is written for each aqueous species which is capable of moving independently in the fluid and a mass action equation of the form

$$\pi a_i = K_r \text{ (i.e. } a_{Ca^{++}} \cdot a_{CO_3^=} = K) \qquad (3)$$

is written for any reactions which may occur in the system. K_r is the equilibrium constant for the r-th reaction and a_i is the activity of the i-th species. There is one (convective-diffusion) equation for each aqueous species and one (mass action) equation for each solid phase which may precipitate out of the fluid. If the concentrations, $c(\bar{x}, t)$, and the precipitation flows, $j(\bar{x}, t)$, both functions of time and space, are regarded as the unknowns, solutions which specify these quantities may be obtained from the set of diffusion and mass action equations. Precipitation flows $j(\bar{x}, t)$ and internal sources, $s(x, t)$ may be included in the model simply by adding them to (1),

$$Dc_i/Dt = D_i \nabla^2 c_i + s(\bar{x}, t)$$
$$- j(\bar{x}, t). \qquad (4)$$

In this paper we shall regard a source $s(\bar{x}, t)$ as a process which adds material to the solution while a sink $j(\bar{x}, t)$ is a process which removes material from the solution. Sources can be either (a) dissolving solid phases or, (b) reservoirs such as the oceans and atmosphere which maintain relatively fixed concentrations and are linked to the system. As far as the mathematical model is concerned the difference between (a) and (b) is that (a) represents a distributed source in the system while (b) represents a source at the boundary of the system and is treated as a boundary condition. The model developed here requires that an analytic function be specified for the sources initially but the spatial distribution and strength of the sinks can be computed (provided that the sinks involved are precipitated solid phases). The principal difference between the treatment adopted here and other treatments of non-equilibrium flows is that this approach permits the calculation of the spatial distribution of the precipitation flux $j(\bar{x}, t)$, from the transport equations. The mass action equations are also necessary, but as we will see they function as constraints on the transport equations. In the following paragraphs we will develop several models involving precipitation in porous media and try to draw some general conclusions that can be expected to apply to a wide variety of diagenetic environments.

SOME SIMPLIFYING ASSUMPTIONS

However, before proceeding it is convenient to make some simplifying assumptions of this point. As it stands, the convective-diffusion equation (1) is difficult to solve for even one component, but since the treatment of the most rudimentary geologic system requires consideration of at least two species, it is advantageous to simplify as much as possible before attempting particular solutions. An assumption which simplifies the problem considerably is to assume that the geologic processes relating to diagenesis reflect steady-state conditions; that is the record preserved in the rocks reflects conditions which were maintained virtually unchanged for long periods of time. In a strict sense these probably should be termed "quasi-static processes" since there was a temporal variation involved both in achieving a steady-state and then decaying to the present state, but it seems reasonable to assume that the alteration which occurred under unsteady conditions is negligible compared to that which occurred during the steady state. This assumption can be tested mathematically by showing that the steady-state persisted for a time Δt which was large compared to (1) the time $\Delta t'$ required to reach that state and (2) the time $\Delta t''$ required to decay from the steady-state to non-reactive conditions. For a steady-state, eqn. (1) becomes

$$\bar{q} \cdot \nabla c_i = D_i \nabla^2 c_i + s(\bar{x}) - j(\bar{x}) \qquad (5)$$

where $\bar{q}$ is the velocity vector for the fluid.

A second useful approximation is to assume that the pertinent features of the model can be extracted from the one-dimensional form of (5),

$$U dc_i / dx = D_i d^2 c_i / dx^2 + s(x) - j(x) \qquad (6)$$

where U is the magnitude of fluid velocity (in the +x direction).

And finally, although this is not really an assumption, it is useful to use non-dimensional quantities. We shall non-dimensionalize the following quantities according to

$$c^* = c / c^\circ \qquad (7)$$

$$x^* = x / l$$

where c°, and l, are characteristic concentrations and distances respectively. Making these substitutions in (6) and dividing by the diffusion coefficient D yields

$$(Ul/D) dc^* / dx^* = d^2 c^* / dx^{*2} + s(x) - j(x) \qquad (8)$$

The dimensionless quantity in parenthesis (Ul/D) is referred to as the Peclet number, Pe, and is a measure of the effectiveness of mass transfer by fluid motion relative to diffusive transport. For large Pe, transport of a component by bulk fluid flow will dominate over diffusion, while the opposite is true for small Pe.

GENERAL SOLUTIONS

Solutions to (1) are difficult to obtain, even for simple boundary conditions and it is easier to generate solutions to (8). There is the added advantage that such solutions tend to provide deeper insights into the nature of the convective-diffusion equations. In this section solutions to the steady-state equation (8) will be sought in terms of the Peclet number and the emphasis will be on analysing the effect of a moving fluid on the diffusion and precipitation profiles.

PURELY DIFFUSIVE SYSTEMS $(Pe = 0)$

For small Pe numbers diffusion dominates the mass transfer and for Pe strictly equal to zero and for no internal sources $(s(x^*)=0)$ we have

$$D \frac{d^2 c^*}{dx^2} = j(x^*) \qquad (9)$$

Note that eqn. (9) provides an analytical expression for the precipitation flow, $j(x^*)$, if the diffusion profile for one species is known. An expression of the form (9) is written for each diffusing species and $j(x^*)$ is eliminated algebraically. Since the total number of equations (convective-diffusion + mass action) is equal to the number of unknowns (diffusion profiles and precipitation flows) there is a unique solution, and, due to the structure of the problem, the precipitation flows can always be eliminated algebraically.

This may be demonstrated through a simple example. Consider a system consisting of two diffusing species, A and B, in H_2O. For A and B we write

$$D_A d^2 c_A^* / dx^{*2} - j_{AB} = 0 \qquad (10a)$$

and

$$D_B d^2 c_B / dx^{*2} - J_{AB} = 0 \qquad (10b)$$

where the subscript AB on j_{AB} refers to the precipitation reaction

$$AB_{(s)} = A_{(aq)} + B_{(aq)}. \qquad (11)$$

The mass action equation for (11) is

$$C_A C_B = K$$

or dividing through by C°,

$$C_A^* C_B^* = K /_{(C^\circ)} 2 = K^*$$

Subtracting 10b from 10a to eliminate j_{AB}, the general solution to the system may be shown to be

$$D_A c_A^* - D_B c_B^* = Ax^* + B \qquad (12)$$

Where A and B in (12) are parameters to be determined from the boundary conditions. For the set of boundary conditions (BC)

BC.1 $c_A^* = c_A^\circ$, $c_B^* = 0$ $(x = 0)$ (13a)

BC.2 $c_A^* = 0$, $c_B^* = c_B^\circ$ $(x = 1)$ (13b)

A and B will be the constants

$$A = -(D_A C^\circ_A + D_B C^\circ_B) \qquad (14a)$$

$$B = D_A C^\circ_A \qquad (14b)$$

It is important to keep in mind that (12) is valid for all x^* whether or not precipitation occurs in the system. Eqn. (12) is not however very useful as it stands since it involves both c^*_A and c^*_B. The principal contribution of Helfferich and Katchalsky (ibid) was to recognize that the mass action equation for (11) could be used to eliminate either c^*_A or c^*_B from (12). Eliminating c^*_B yields a quadratic in c^*_A only

$$(c^*_A)^2 (Ax + B) c^*_A - K^* = 0 \qquad (16)$$

which may be solved for c^*_A

$$c^*_A = (P + Q)/2 \qquad (17)$$

where

$$Q = Ax + B \qquad (18a)$$

and

$$P = (Q^2 + 4K^*)^{1/2} \qquad (18b)$$

It may not seem necessary to write the solution in terms of P and Q at this point. However the notation becomes treacherous further on and the notation adopted here seems preferable to that of Helfferich and Katchalsky (ibid).

Eqn. (17) gives the concentrations of c^*_A across the precipitation zone. To compute the width of the precipitation zone it is necessary to match the first derivatives for the c^*_A on both sides of the boundaries.[1] Eqn. (16) may be differentiated to obtain these matching conditions as well as the precipitation flows.

The first derivitive is

$$c^{*'}_A = (Q' + P')/2 \qquad (19)$$

while the second derivitive is

[1]This condition results from the argument that if the first derivatives are not the same a discontinuity in the c* functions results and an infinite precipitation flux must obtain at the boundary. This argument may be clarified by noting that, according to (10 a, b), the precipitation flow, j_{AB}, is directly proportional to the second space derivitive of both c^*_A and c^*_B. Consequently a discontinuity in the first (space) derivative implies an infinite second derivative and an infinite precipitation flow, which is not physically realistic. We will therefore impose the condition that the first space derivatives must match at the boundaries of the precipitation zones.

$$c^{*''}_A = (Q'' + P'')/2 \qquad (20)$$

but from (18b) $P^2 = Q^2 + 4K^*$, so

$$P' = QQ'/P \qquad (21)$$

and

$$P'' = QQ''/P + 4K^* (Q')^2/P^3. \qquad (22)$$

Eqns. (19) and (20) become

$$c^{*''}_A = (P + Q) Q'/2P \qquad (23)$$

and

$$c^*_A = 1/2 ((P + Q) Q''/P + 4K^* (Q')^2/P^3) \qquad (24)$$

For pure diffusion the precipitation flow is given by either (10a) or (10b) and may be written

$$j^* = D_A c_A^{*''} = -2K^* D_A (Q')^2/P^3 \qquad (25)$$

The first term in (24) drops out since $Q(x^*)$ is given by (18a) and the second derivative is zero. The fact that this second derivative of $Q(x^*)$ goes to zero for diffusive processes suggests that the term $(P + Q) Q''/P$ in (24) is a convective term and that the total precipitation for a process involving fluid transport will be the purely diffusive flow plus a term proportional to Q''.

SYSTEMS INVOLVING BOTH DIFFUSION AND INFILTRATION
$$(Pe > 0)$$

For systems involving bulk fluid flow the Pe number is non-zero and the solution to (8) can still be expressed in terms of (16) and (17) but for

$$Q(x^*) = (e^{Pe x^*} - 1)/_{Pe} + B.[1] \qquad (26)$$

The total precipitation flow (j_T) can be deduced from (8) to be of the form

$$j^*_T = Pe . c^{*'}_A - c''_A \qquad (27)$$

or

$$j^*_T = -(2K^* A^2 . e^{2Pe x^*})/P^3 = j^*_D . e^{2Pe x^*} \qquad (28)$$

where the subscript T indicates the total precipitation flow and subscript D refers to the pure diffusion flow. Since the quantity Pe.x* will always be positive (U is defined to positive in

[1]Note that the constants A and B in (12) must be redefined using (18a) and (26).

the +x direction) eqn. (28) shows that the precipitation flow will always be greater for a convective-diffusion process than for a purely diffusive process. This may be demonstrated more clearly by consideration of a few explicit calculations.

RESULTS

While (28) predicts that the precipitation flow will increase with increasing Pe, it is not clear if there will be any other effects, nor is it obvious what effect changes in K^* will produce. Calculations have been carried out on a number of systems and the results of these calculations are summarized in Figures 2 to 6. Figure 2 shows the general features of the model. Note the symmetrical shape of the concentration and precipitation curves and that the maximum in the precipitation flow occurs where the two concentration curves cross (x = 0.5). This is typical of diffusion dominated systems, and it appears that the Pe number here (0.01) is too low for any infiltration effects to show; however increasing the Pe number results in a substantial shift in the precipitation flow (Fig. 3), as well as the development of a distinct asymmetry, with a sharp boundary on the upstream side and a gradual tapering off on the downstream side (the fluid flow is always in the +x direction). In addition the width of the precipi-

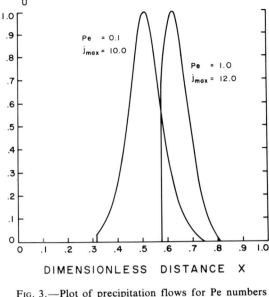

FIG. 3.—Plot of precipitation flows for Pe numbers equal to 0.1 and 1.0, all other parameters remaining the same as for fig. 2. Note the shift in the precipitation flow in the direction of the fluid flow and the distinct asymmetry in the precipitation curves as the Pe number increases.

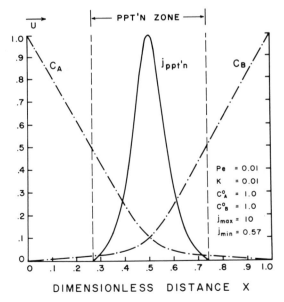

FIG. 2.—Plot of precipitation flow, J, versus dimensionless distance. Concentration profiles are shown in dash-dot lines while the precipitation zone is bounded by dashed lines. (Note that j is scaled to lie between 0 and 1 by the relation $j = (j - j_{min})/(j_{max} - j_{min})$.) The vector U refers to the fluid velocity.

tation zone has decreased, but the maximum in the precipitation flow, j_{max}, has increased by nearly 20%.

The effect of changing the equilibrium constant, K^*, is illustrated in Figure 4. Here the equilibrium constant has been decreased by 3 orders of magnitude from that in the preceding figures (2–3), and it is apparent that the major effect has been to localize the bulk of the flow in a narrow spike, although the width of the total precipitation zone is approximately the same as before. However, j_{max} has increased dramatically from 1 (Fig. 2) to 270 (in relative flow units). Thus the general conclusion is that the more insoluble the precipitate the more localized and intense the precipitation flow. And as before increasing the Pe number shifts the flow downstream and increases j_{max}, in this case by about 10%.

From these calculations it is apparent that the Pe number has a strong influence on the locus of the precipitation flow, but in general not much effect on the shape of the precipitation curve. The same effect, a shift in the precipitation curve, can also be achieved by introducing an asymmetry in the solution concentrations at the boundaries. As shown in Figures 5 and 6, by reducing c_A^o from 1.0 to 0.1 the precipitation zone is shifted

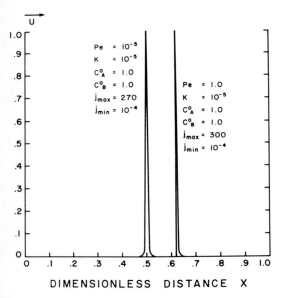

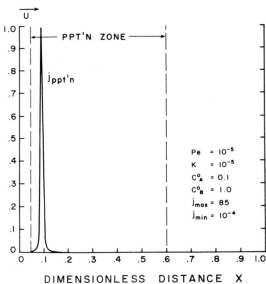

FIG. 4.—Plot of precipitation flows for a phase with an equilibrium constant 3 orders of magnitude less than in figs. 2 and 3. The effect of the increasing Pe number is to shift the precipitation spike downstream but does not change the shape of the curve appreciably. The smaller K value produces a sharp maximum in the precipitation flow compared to the larger value.

FIG. 6.—Effect of changing boundary conditions on position and shape of precipitation curve for parameters set as in fig. 4 except $c_A^o = 0.1$ instead of 1.0.

upstream (closer to C_A^o) and j_{max} increases by about 40%.

CONCLUSIONS

Although only relatively simple systems have been considered so far it is clear that there are substantial differences between purely diffusive (static) systems and those characterized by a non-zero fluid velocity (dynamic systems). One important difference from a geologic point of view is the shift in the location of the precipitation flow downstream with increasing Pe number. It is also significant that dynamic systems will precipitate larger amounts of material per unit time than static systems, suggesting that a dynamic system will be more effective in cementing a porous body or reducing porosity than a static system. This observation is somewhat at odds with the intuitive feeling that a system with a large fluid flux should increase porosity as a result of dissolution of material, and it should be emphasized that this contrary result depends on the existence of several limiting conditions. One of course is that the system can develop current flow in the first place, and that a phase will precipitate when these currents collide, that is that partial equilibrium can be assumed. This in turn depends on the appropriate conditions prevailing at the system boundaries and on the absence of any internal sources.

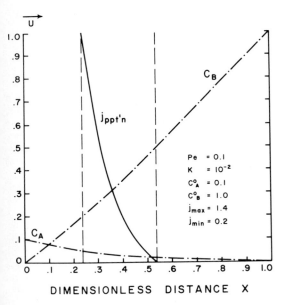

FIG. 5.—Effect of changing boundary conditions on position and shape of precipitation curve. All parameters same as for fig. 2 except $c_A^o = 0.1$ instead of 1.0.

It will be interesting in future studies to examine the consequences of having either discrete or continuous sources of material in the system. It will also be of interest to investigate the properties of composite flows (i.e. precipitation flows of two or more phases) as well as the effects of having precipitates with more complex stoichiometries than simply AB, such as zeolites and feldspars. While it will not be difficult to treat these variations theoretically in terms of setting up the differential equations and obtaining solutions for the concentration profiles, it may prove quite difficult to determine the locations of the precipitation zones since this involves solving an auxiliary set of equations requiring the matching of derivatives of the concentration profiles. This is not an insurmountable problem, but at the present it is not clear that a general analytic solution can be obtained. Rather it appears that computer simulation of somewhat specific systems will be required.

However it does appear that the Helfferich-Katchalsky treatment of precipitation flows is not only applicable to geologic processes, but that even greater insights into cementation and precipitation phenomena can be obtained by modifying their treatment to provide for fluid flow. This seems to provide a very general framework upon which to build even more elaborate models, perhaps eventually providing for the effects of changing the tortuosity as the body proceeds to seal itself. The expectation is that cementation processes in general may eventually prove to involve feedback loops in the sense that the final state of the system depends on the nature of the preceeding state. For example, precipitation of the first phase may alter the flow characteristics of the system to the extent that the later dissolution and precipitation of phases could obliterate all traces of the initial precipitate. In any event one thing does seem assured and that is that rock alteration should not be considered simply in terms of uncoupled chemical reactions and transport processes. Rather both reaction and mass transfer should be treated simultaneously, with a particularly careful appraisal of the mode of mass transfer.

ACKNOWLEDGEMENTS

This work was supported by a grant from the Marathon Oil Company and by NSF Grants DES75-01293 and EAR75-01293. Acknowledgement is made to the Donors of the Petroleum Research Fund for partial support of this research (PRF Grant No. 9602-G2).

REFERENCES

COOMBS, D. S., 1960, Lower grade mineral facies in New Zealand: 21st Internat. Geol. Congr., Copenhagen 1960, Rept., pt. 13, p. 339–351.

DAILY, JAMES W., AND HARLEMAN, DONALD R. F., 1966, Fluid dynamics: Reading, Massachusetts, Addison-Wesley Publishing Co., Inc., 454 p.

HELGESON, H. C., 1968, Evaluation of irreversible reactions in geochemical processes involving minerals and aqueous solutions: 1. Thermodynamic relations: Geochim. et Cosmochim. Acta, v. 32, p. 853–877.

HELFFERICH, F., AND KATCHALSKY, A., 1970, A simple model of interdiffusion with precipitation: Jour. Phys. Chemistry, v. 74, p. 308–314.

THOMPSON, J. B., 1959, Local equilibrium in metasomatic processes, *in* P. Abelson (ed.), Researches in geochemistry: New York, John Wiley and Sons, p. 427–457.

SEPM SPECIAL PUBLICATION No. 26, P. 251–262, MARCH 1979

DIAGENETIC CONTROL OF RESERVOIR QUALITY IN ARC-DERIVED SANDSTONES: IMPLICATIONS FOR PETROLEUM EXPLORATION[1]

WILLIAM E. GALLOWAY

Bureau of Economic Geology, The University of Texas at Austin, 78712

ABSTRACT

The potential of a sandstone to serve as a reservoir for producible hydrocarbons is closely related to its diagenetic history, which, in turn, is dependent upon its composition. Convergent plate-margin basins, which formed on the flanks of contemporaneous or precursor andesitic volcanic arcs, received large volumes of detritus reworked from either the arc of its tectonically uplifted plutonic roots. Arc-derived sands of the Bristol, Gulf of Alaska, Queen Charlotte, and Grays Harbor-Chehalis basins (northeast Pacific) are mineralogically similar suites dominated by plagioclase, and by volcanic rock fragments. Diagenesis of these mineralogically immature sands at shallow to moderately deep burial (15,000 feet or 5,000 m) produced a systematic sequence of authigenic cements that include (1) localized, early calcite pore fill; (2) clay rims; (3) laumontite or phyllosilicate pore fill; and (4) late calcite pore fill/replacement and siliceous overgrowths. Each diagenetic stage reduced reservoir porosity and permeability and, correspondingly, increased bulk density and interval velocity of sand sections. Well-developed clay rims in fine-grained sand reduced maximum permeability to a few tens of millidarcys; samples containing stage 3 laumontite or phyllosilicate typically have less than 10 millidarcys permeability.

Authigenesis of stage 2 and 3 cements is, in part, temperature controlled. Reservoir properties thus degenerate systematically with increasing depth of burial and increasing degree of heating, and they may produce a diagenetically controlled economic basement well within the range of normal drilling. Generation of oil is also temperature controlled, and the optimum thermal window lies mainly within sediments characterized by stage 3 diagenesis and consequent poor reservoir quality. Prediction of a diagenetic economic basement is necessary for realistic early assessment and systematic exploration of convergent arc-related plate-margin basins.

INTRODUCTION: DIAGENESIS AND RESERVOIRS

Sandstones consist of assemblages of finely-divided, discrete grains of a variety of different chemical compounds and mixtures. Like all chemical compounds, the grains are stable in some chemical and physical environments, and unstable in others. If subjected to a changing environment and consequent disequilibrium conditions, sand grains tend to react by producing new products which are stable in the ambient environment. Sand grains also have specific mechanical properties, and changes in the physical environment induce changes in the mechanical properties of the grains. The physical and chemical changes in sand after its deposition constitute diagenetic alterations, and resulting diagenetic features include (1) mechanical deformation of grains; (2) solution of grain material; (3) alteration of grains; and (4) precipitation of pore-filling cements.

Diagenesis begins immediately after deposition; it continues during burial and uplift of the sandstone until outcrop weathering reduces it again to sediment. The succession of physical and chemical environments experienced by a sandstone produces an end product characterized by a specific suite of diagenetic features. The nature of this end product depends to a large degree on the initial mineralogical composition of the sands, and on the composition of the enclosing basin-fill sediments. The principal factors determining the diagenetic history for a particular compositional suite include time-dependent exposures to varying temperatures, pressures, and pore fluid chemistry. All these factors are, in themselves, historical aspects of the reservoir. One parameter may clearly dominate for certain mineralogical suites or in certain geological settings.

Of primary importance to the petroleum geologist is the obvious fact that each of the diagenetic features produced during burial and uplift of an originally porous, permeable sandstone affects its reservoir quality. The ability of a reservoir to produce hydrocarbons is thus intimately related to its diagenetic history. Mineralogic suites which are unstable in subsurface environments must be regarded with special caution as potential reservoirs.

The objectives of this paper are (1) to review a systematic diagenetic sequence typical of arc-derived sandstones, (2) to indicate relations between diagenesis and petrophysical properties of

[1]Published by permission of the Director, Bureau of Economic Geology, The University of Texas at Austin. The author acknowledges permission of the Continental Oil Company for release of data contained in this report. Drafting was supervised by W. Rigsby (Conoco) and J. W. Macon (Bur. Econ. Geol.). R. G. Loucks read the final manuscript and supplied helpful critique.

Copyright © 1979, The Society of Economic Paleontologists and Mineralogists

such sandstones, and (3) to indicate the potential significance of diagenesis as a factor in the analysis of the resource potential of arc-related sedimentary basins.

ARC-DERIVED SANDSTONES: SETTING AND COMPOSITION

Convergent continental margins, such as the northeast Pacific coast of North America, are characterized by active volcanic/plutonic arcs and older, unroofed plutonic cores. Numerous small to large sedimentary basins form marginal to these volcanic/plutonic arcs in both fore-arc and back-arc positions (Dickinson, 1974). Much of the terrigenous sediment infilling these basins is derived from the tectonically active arc; the sediment is rich in eroded plutonic and volcanic rock fragments and constituent minerals. Sands are compositionally heterogeneous and contain a mineralogically unstable suite of minerals.

Sample suites representative of arc-derived sandstones from four northeast Pacific margin basins, including the Bristol basin, Gulf of Alaska sedimentary basin, Queen Charlotte basin, and

Grays Harbor-Chehalis basins (Fig. 1), were assembled. Although geographically separated, each of these basins has several common geologic features. (1) All are Tertiary basins formed along an active plate margin. (2) Each is associated with Mesozoic and Tertiary intrusive and extrusive complexes. Evidence for some volcanism contemporaneous with deposition is present in each. (3) All are associated with older, complexly-deformed Mesozoic strata. (4) Structural styles indicate a history of compression. The geologic and stratigraphic settings of three sample suites were given in Galloway (1974); Stonley (1967) described the Gulf of Alaska sedimentary basin.

Depositional environments of sample sandstone units ranged from continental-fluvial to glacial-influenced marine shelf and upper slope. No deep water basinal fan or turbidite sequences have been documented in parts of these basins sampled.

Examination of the sample suites allowed comparison of diagenetic features produced in arc-derived sandstones over a wide range of geologic variables, including:

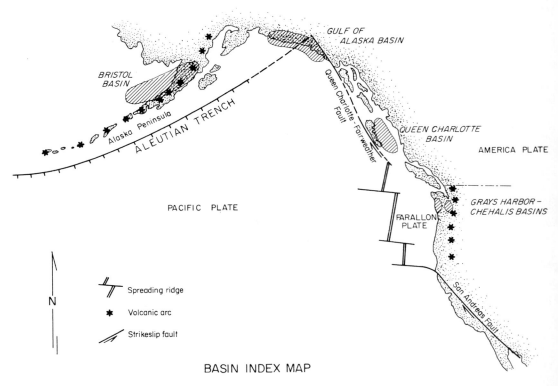

BASIN INDEX MAP

FIG. 1.—Index map of northeast Pacific margin showing location of basins sampled and principal structural features.

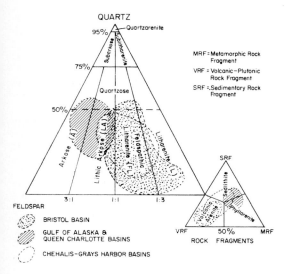

MRF = Metamorphic Rock Fragment
VRF = Volcanic–Plutonic Rock Fragment
SRF = Sedimentary Rock Fragment

FELDSPAR

BRISTOL BASIN

GULF OF ALASKA & QUEEN CHARLOTTE BASINS

CHEHALIS–GRAYS HARBOR BASINS

FIG. 2.—Sandstone composition triangle and composition fields of sandstone suites. Classification modified from Folk (1974).

Age:	Eocene to Pliocene
Depth of Burial:	0 to 15,000 feet (0 to 4,500 m)
Ambient Thermal Gradient:	1.0 to 3.0° F / 100 feet (1.84 to 5.5° C / 100 m)
Pressure Gradient:	Normal hydrostatic = 0.465 psi/foot, (0.10 Kg/cm²)
Depositional Environment:	Continental fan to marine shelf and slope

Within this framework, relations were analyzed between diagenetic, thermal, chemical, and burial histories.

Composition.—Compositional data for the sandstone suites are summarized in Figure 2. Detailed petrographic data are tabulated in Galloway (1974). Point counts of more than 200 thin sections show that the arc-derived sandstones in both fore-arc and back-arc basins are quartz-poor, plagioclase arkoses and litharenites. Plagioclase is the dominant feldspar, constituting as much as 75 percent of total detrital grains. Volcanic rock fragments are the second most abundant grain type, comprising up to 91 percent of some samples. Samples rich in vitric material, including ash and pumice, are not common and are excluded from the study. Quartz content rarely exceeds 50 percent and averages 25 percent. Mafic minerals are common to abundant. Such a mineralogically unstable, heterogeneous composition is

typical of many graywackes found in much older plate-margin settings.

DIAGENESIS OF ARC-DERIVED SANDSTONES

Before outlining the observed diagenetic history of the arc-derived sandstone suite, the descriptive terminology should be reviewed. Diagenetic features observed are schematically illustrated in Figure 3. *Clay rims* and *clay coats* form rinds around detrital sand grains. Clay rims consist of clay flakes generally oriented perpendicular to the surface of the detrital grain; they form primarily by authigenesis of the clay mineral. Clay coats, in contrast, show preferred clay orientation parallel to the grain surface; they are typically formed by illuviation of colloidal material onto the grains. *Pore-filling cement,* as the name implies, occupies pore space between the detrital grains. Mineralogy of the pore-filling cement usually differs from that of the framework grains. *Overgrowths,* on the other hand, develop in crystallographic continuity with grains of the same mineralogy. Mechanically unstable grains are compressed and crushed between more rigid framework grains. Along with detrital mud matrix, which recrystallizes to form clay-chert intergrowths, such mechanically unstable grains fill

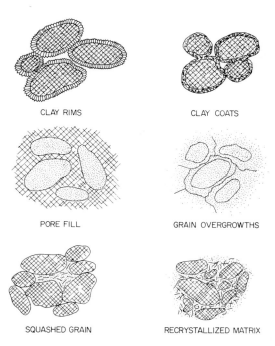

CLAY RIMS

CLAY COATS

PORE FILL

GRAIN OVERGROWTHS

SQUASHED GRAIN

RECRYSTALLIZED MATRIX

FIG. 3.—Diagenetic features observed in sample suites. For description see text.

areas between larger grains. Each of the above features results in increased consolidation of the sandstone, and consequent loss of porosity and permeability.

Diagenetic Sequence.—Arc-derived sandstones display features indicative of both mechanical and chemical diagenesis. However, if only well-winnowed, texturally mature, initially porous, fine- to medium-grained sandstones are considered, chemical diagenesis is primarily responsible for the consolidation of the sandstones, and four sequential diagenetic stages are recognized in each sample suite (Fig. 4). These stages have been described in detail in previous paper (Galloway, 1974), and only major attributes will be reviewed here.

Stage 1: Calcite pore-filling cement formed very early in the diagenetic history of the sandstones. Sparry and, rarely, micritic calcite pore fill was observed. Early formation of the calcite is indicated by the loose grain packing of calcite-cemented sandstones, the random distribution of such sandstones throughout the stratigraphic sections studied, and the insulation of calcite-cemented sandstones from further diagenetic modification. Distribution of calcite-cemented sandstone is partly related to depositional environment, and consequently it probably is facies-controlled.

Stage 2: Authigenic clay rims, usually consisting of chlorite or montmorillonite, surround detrital grains. The clay rims formed at shallow to intermediate depths of burial (1,000 to 4,000 feet; 300 to 1,300 m), and they were widespread in all four sample suites. Clay rims that formed near grain-to-grain contacts were deformed and extruded as increasing depth of burial caused further mechanical compaction of the sandstone.

Stage 3: Increasing diagenetic intensity typical of intermediate depths of burial (3,000 to 10,000 feet; 1,000 to 3,000 meters in the sample suites examined) produced a pore-filling cementation stage. Remaining open pore spaces were infilled by authigenic laumontite (a hydrous calcium aluminum silicate), or by well-crystallized phyllosilicate, usually chlorite or montmorillonite, although kaolinite occurs in a few samples. Stage 2 clay rims were preserved and form halos around the detrital grains, separating them from the pore-filling cement. Although the relative timing of phyllosilicate versus laumontite authigenesis may have varied, both seem to have formed at about the same point in the consolidation history of the sandstones. However, it is rare to find both in the same sample. Formation of a specific mineral phase during stage 3 diagenesis is probably dependent on regional or local variations in pore fluid chemistry, as suggested by Surdam and Boles (this vol.).

Stage 4: At greater depths of burial, a variety of alteration and replacement reactions complicates both the fabric and the mineralogy of the sandstones. Spotty calcite replacement of feldspar grains, volcanic rock fragments, and matrix occurred, along with chlorite replacement of rock fragments, heavy minerals, and matrix. Development of quartz and feldspar overgrowths locally produced welded fabrics. Recognition of original clay coats is difficult.

As indicated on Figure 4, mechanical crushing and compacting of sandstones begins soon after burial, as overburden stress increases. Initially, soft rock fragments and micas were deformed and crushed. Such crushing proceeded until cementation in stage 3 produced a rigid, self-supporting grain framework. High pressures resulting from very deep burial or tectonic stress further deformed soft grains, and may have fractured competent minerals such as feldspar.

EFFECT ON RESERVOIR QUALITY

The progressive diagenetic alteration of arc-derived sandstones produces a predictable series of changes in average porosity and permeability of potential reservoir sand bodies.

A composite curve summarizing a semiquantitative relationship between porosity and diagenetic stage (Fig. 4) was prepared by averaging laboratory-measured porosities for groups of samples representing each diagenetic stage from all four basins. All sands were texturally mature and initially deposited with porosities ranging up to 40 percent. Development of early calcite pore fill (diagenetic stage 1) reduced measured porosities to about 10 percent (ranging from 5 to 15 percent), but only affected a small volume of the total section. Most sands were unaffected by stage 1 calcite cementation. Sandstones exhibiting stage 2 clay rims retain relatively high porosities, ranging from 15 to 31 percent, depending on the degree of mechanical compaction. Authigenic clays fill only about 2 percent of the intergranular pore space (based on optical point counts), and actual porosity reduction is even less because considerable microporosity remains within the clay rim itself. Stage 3 formation of laumontite or phyllosilicate pore-filling cement markedly reduced porosity to an average of only 10 percent. The maximum porosity measured in any sample exhibiting stage 3 diagenesis was 17 percent. Onset of stage 4 further reduced the already-low porosity.

Porosity loss can be viewed as a fairly continuous process as depth of burial and consequent diagenetic stage increase; permeability loss, on the other hand, occurs almost entirely during formation of clay rims in stage 2. Although the

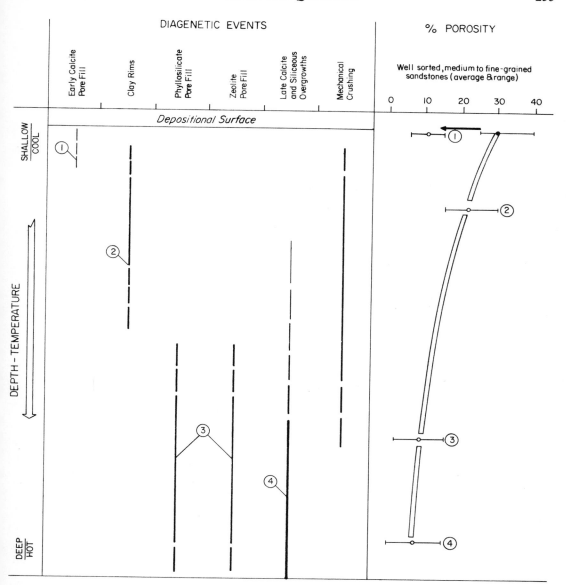

Fɪɢ. 4.—Sequential development of diagenetic features in arc-derived sandstones based on paragenetic sequence and/or first occurrence in wells. The vertical bars denote interpreted relative depth range of major diagenetic events (specific events defining stages are numbered). Right hand curve shows successive porosity decrease for sandstones in successive diagenetic stages. Circles indicate average porosity for all measured samples within each stage; bars show the range of all measurements. Porosity curve is calibrated for fine- to medium-grained sandstones.

addition of solid material within pore spaces between detrital grains is minimal during clay authigenesis, the platy clay flakes act like baffles extending into the pore throats, where they retard fluid flow out of all proportion to their size.

A simple geometric exercise illustrates the ef-

fect of clay coats on packed spherical grains. The addition of a clay rim around a typical detrital grain produces a 1 to 6 percent increase in the radius of the grain. However, this minor increase in grain cross-sectional area (and proportional decrease in total intergranular pore space) reduces the diameter of pore throats by a much larger factor than 1 to 6 percent. For example, a 4 percent increase in grain diameter results in a 26 percent reduction in pore-throat diameter. In the simple case of packed spheres, permeability is proportional to the square of pore-throat diameter, thus further magnifying permeability reduction.

Although not treated as a separate variable in this study, grain size is also an important control on permeability reduction. Coarse sandstones usually experience less serious permeability loss due to the development of clay rims than do fine-grained sandstones, since the initial pore-throat diameters were larger in the coarse grains. In addition, coarser grains present less surface area per unit volume of grain and pore, making clay rims volumetrically less significant in coarse- than in fine-grained sandstones. Conversely, permeability of very fine-grained sandstones and siltstones is severely affected by the formation of clay rims. The authigenic clay also tends to result in high irreducible water saturation and increased surface reactivity (Pittman, this vol.).

Quantitative evaluation of permeability is difficult, for several reasons. Relatively undisturbed samples can be obtained only from continuous diamond cores. Side-wall core plugs usually show evidence of fracturing, or of disrupted grain fabric; outcrop samples contain iron oxides and other dispersed products of surficial weathering. The best measurements indicated that clay authigenesis during stage 2 reduced permeability of texturally mature, fine- to medium-grained sandstones to a few tens of millidarcys. Sandstones affected by stage 3 diagenesis have, at most, a few millidarcys permeability.

EFFECT ON PETROPHYSICAL PROPERTIES

The filling of original porosity with various types of cements obviously affects both bulk density and sonic wave velocity within the sandstone. Because unstable sandstones react to form cements at shallow to intermediate depths of burial, the gradient of density increase with depth is high, and deep samples approach zero porosity—that is, bulk density equals grain density of the sandstone. A comparison of sandstone density profiles derived from conventional subsurface density logs, one from a representative well penetrating interbedded Plio-Miocene arc-derived sandstone and mudstone in the Queen Charlotte basin, and the other from a well penetrating a mineralogically mature Pliocene section in the Gulf Coast basin (Fig. 5A), shows that consolidation rates are much greater in the former. Significantly, arc-derived sands compact along nearly the same trend as associated mudstones. Mudstones in the Gulf Coast well, on the other hand, are appreciably more dense than equivalent sandstones at depths below 4,000 feet (1,300 m). In summary, the consolidation rate of unstable arc-derived sandstone is much faster than for otherwise similar, mineralogically stable sandstone, and arc-derived sandstones and mudstones display similar compaction curves.

A similar comparison of sandstone and mudstone interval velocity versus depth (Fig. 5B) for stable and unstable lithologic sequences, using sonic logs from the same wells, shows that arc-derived sands and muds exhibit faster interval velocities at equivalent depths of burial. Again, curves for sandstone and mudstone velocity in the Queen Charlotte basin are similar, with the sandstones tending to have slightly faster velocities than the equivalent mudstones (Fig. 5B). The reverse is true for Gulf Coast well.

Approximate velocity and density gradients can be derived remotely from reflection seismic and gravity data, respectively. Relatively dense, high velocity, Tertiary terrigenous clastic sections can reasonably be inferred to contain unstable, diagenetically altered sandstones, particularly in basins that lie along convergent plate margins.

FACTORS CONTROLLING DIAGENETIC STAGE

Geologic relationships in the basins examined indicate that maximum degree of heating is the primary control on the diagenetic stage reached by sandstones of the unstable arc-derived suite. Data supporting this conclusion have been reviewed by Galloway (1974, p. 385–386). Because maximum degree of heating depends upon thermal gradient (which commonly ranges from 1 to 3° F/100 feet; 1.84 to 5.5° C/100 m), as well as upon depth of burial, a wide depth range for first appearance of stage 2 and 3 diagenetic features is readily explained.

Log and core data from the Queen Charlotte basin (Fig. 6) provide the best example of the direct relationship between thermal gradient and diagenetic destruction of reservoir quality. Plots of logged sandstone interval velocity versus depth for five wells fall into two groups, one from an area of relatively cool thermal gradients (approximately 1.4° F/100 feet; 2.5° C/100 m), the second from a relatively warm area (1.7 to 1.9° F/100 feet; 3.1 to 3.4° C/100 m). Velocity increases more rapidly with depth in the wells with high ambient thermal gradients, indicating greater consolidation of the sandstones. Compilation of reservoir data from logs and side-wall core analyses confirms the prediction that sandstone porosity and permeability both are lower at equivalent maximum depths of burial in the warmer wells (Fig. 6). Furthermore, as anticipated, maximum permeabilities below 10 millidarcys occur at

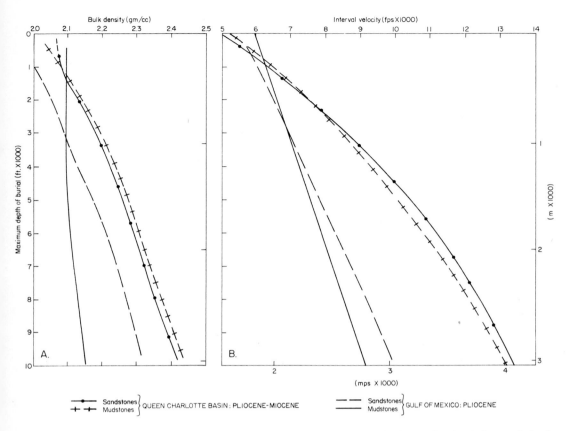

Fig. 5.—Comparison of log density (A) and interval velocity (B) gradients with increasing depth for arc-derived, mineralogically unstable sandstones and mineralogically stable sandstones and their interbedded mudstones. Consolidation gradients are much higher for unstable lithologic suites. Sandstone porosity was calculated assuming a grain density of 2.7 and salt water saturation.

depths of less than 10,000 feet (3,050 m).

These data are evidence of a direct effect of temperature upon the degree of diagenetic alteration, and, in turn, upon the consequent reservoir quality of the sandstones. In addition, duration of heating at the maximum exposure temperature, detailed composition of the sand (plagioclase- or volcanic rock fragment-dominated), variations in original grain size or sorting, geochemical history of contained pore fluids, and pore pressure must all affect the stage of diagenesis attained. They will also assuredly preclude an ideal correlation between thermal history and degree of consolidation, such as demanded by Stephenson (1977). However, these factors do appear to be secondary in overall importance to the effect of temperature.

Objections to the importance of temperature as a determinant of diagenetic stage attained have been noted by several authors, including Surdam and Boles, Davies and Almon, and Burns and

Ethridge (this vol.), as well as by Stephenson (1977). However, many of the proposed deviations from the diagenetic sequence described in this paper are easily reconciled. Lack of well-developed clay rims or pore fill in impermeable or detrital matrix-rich sands substantiates the hypothesis that fluid movement is necessary for formation of such cements (Stewart and McCulloh, Burns and Ethridge, this vol.), but these sands obviously have no initial or subsequent reservoir potential, and their diagenetic history is primarily one of mechanical compaction. The sequence of chemical diagenetic events outlined above applies only to well-winnowed, texturally mature, initially porous, fine- to medium-grained sandstones. Diagenesis of volcaniclastic sequences by authigenesis of smectite and hydrous zeolites in shallow coastal plain aquifers or soil horizons (Davies and Almon, this vol.) is not temperature related. Local tuffaceous horizons, paleosoils, and shallow flu-

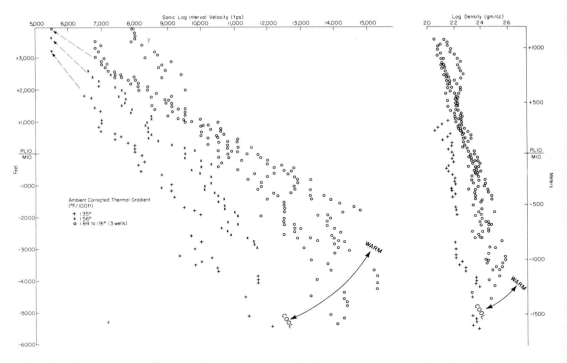

FIG. 6.—Sandstone consolidation gradients, as expressed by log interval velocity and log density measurements for two sets of wells from the Queen Charlotte basin. Wells from the area of relatively high thermal gradient display greater increase with depth of both consolidation indices. Other geologic variables are relatively unchanged, suggesting the importance of temperature in determining diagenetic stage. The top of the Miocene was used as a common datum to remove effects of young structural growth.

vial sequences were also noted in sample suites from the Grays Harbor-Chehalis and Bristol basins. However, such sequences constitute volumetrically insignificant components of these tectonically active, marine-dominated depositional basins. These shallow diagenetic features might best be considered variations in the stage 1 cementation phase—geographically restricted and usually facies related.

Surdam and Boles (this vol.) correctly point out the significant effect variable pore fluid composition will have on diagenetic processes. The diagenetic sequence and its inferred temperature dependence are based on examination of four basins, which not only contain compositionally similar suites of sediments, but which also have similar histories of deposition and subsequent compactional dewatering of thick sections of marine sediments. As a result, they have probably experienced generally parallel histories of pore-fluid movement and chemical evolution. Since vitric pyroclastics are not major components of the basin fills sampled and were not included in the analysis, there is little reason to suspect

unusual or locally aberrant solution chemistry. The limited variety of authigenic and replacement minerals in the samples supports this inference. At the same time, temperature dependence of clay dewatering (Burst, 1969; Perry and Hower, 1972), and organic maturation and resulting decarbonatization (Schmidt and McDonald, this vol.), both provide pervasive thermally controlled milestones in basin pore fluid migration and chemical evolution.

Establishing a thermal calibration for the diagenetic stages is not possible with the data at hand. However, the formation of laumontite during stage 3 does provide a crude yardstick. Laumontite occurs at ambient temperatures of 150° to 200° F (65° to 95° C) in both the Queen Charlotte and Grays Harbor sample suites. This range is somewhat lower than reported by other studies (Stewart and Hay, this vol.), and it probably represents a minimum formation temperature. Genesis of clay rims, with resulting permeability reduction, occurs at even cooler temperatures, however, and is far advanced by the time burial temperatures approach 200° F (95° C). Temperature relationships could be documented better by combining paleothermometry, using microscopic or chemical analysis of kerogen.

Results of this study have twofold application in the evaluation of exploration potential of arc-related sedimentary basins. First, rapid loss of reservoir potential with increasing depth of burial defines a relatively shallow economic basement and, thus, limits the volume of sediment to be tested by drilling. Second, the overlap between the hydrocarbon generation window and the zone of acceptable reservoir quality may be narrow.

Diagenetic control of economic basement.—The dramatic decrease in both porosity and permeability with increasing diagenetic stage displayed by mineralogically unstable arc-derived sandstones suggests that exploration potential of fore-arc and back-arc sedimentary basins will be limited by a diagenetically controlled economic basement. Commercial production of hydrocarbons from reservoirs with the very low permeabilities typical of late stage 2, stage 3, or stage 4 will be difficult, especially in remote areas where costs are high. In any economic and geologic framework, there are minimum reservoir characteristics necessary

to support commercial production. For remote areas, an average minimum value for porosity is 20 percent and for permeability is 10 millidarcys.

The sequential consolidation of arc-derived sandstones with increasing depth of burial (Fig. 7) defines a porosity basement at the beginning of stage 3 pore-filling cementation and probably will produce a permeability basement at even shallower depths within the zone of stage 2 clay authigenesis.

Because diagenetic destruction of reservoir quality is a progressive phenomenon, the potential is low for reservoir improvement below the economic basement defined by the consolidation gradient. Production would depend on enhancement of the reservoir by natural fracturing or secondary leaching of grains or cements. Development of leached porosity, such as that described by Schmidt and McDonald (this vol.) might enhance porosity and permeability of stage 3 or 4 samples, but numerous measurements did not reveal any samples with reservoir qualities adequate for frontier levels of oil production.

Petroleum generation and migration.—The thermal maturation of hydrocarbons (documented by Connan, 1974) is best illustrated by the concept of a liquid window (Pusey, 1973) or thermal-

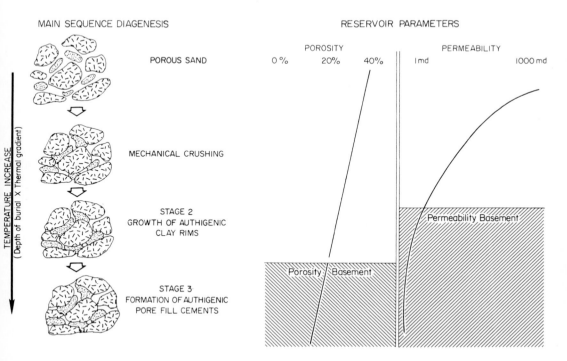

Fig. 7.—Sequential diagenetic stages in arc-derived sandstones and relative positions of porosity and permeability basement, assuming economic reservoirs require 20 percent porosity and at least 10 md permeability.

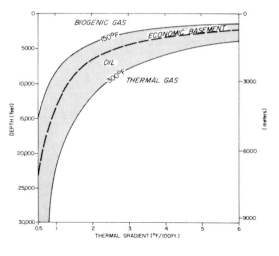

FIG. 8.—Depth and thickness of the liquid window within which oil is generated (after Pusey, 1973) and approximate position of a temperature-dependent economic basement placed at the transition from stage 2 to stage 3 diagenesis. Much of the zone of oil generation lies below the depth of preservation of adequate reservoir quality (assuming a minimum acceptable permeability of 10 md).

both above and below the diagenetic economic basement (Fig. 9). In both instances traps must have formed before or contemporaneous with generation and migration, postmigration structures and structurally influenced stratigraphic trap configurations will be barren. Oil generated and trapped above the economic basement may remain within the shallow section that contains sandstones of adequate reservoir quality, or it may be buried by subsequent subsidence and deposition below the level of the regional economic basement (Fig. 9). This latter possibility is potentially of interest. Because oil is a nonpolar fluid, it does not provide a reactive medium capable of solution and precipitation of mineral substances. Once a reservoir sandstone is saturated with oil, it is protected from further flushing by reactive pore waters, chemical diagenesis is effectively arrested, and porosity and permeability will be preserved to greater depths than predicted by regional consolidation gradients. Such preservation of "fossil" porosity and arrested diagenesis has been noted by several authors, including Yurkova (1970), Zaripov (1971), and Prozorovich (1975). Mechanical compaction will continue, however, and some loss of reservoir quality will occur with increasing depth of burial. However, economically producible oil may be found below the regional economic basement if the timing of generation, migration, trapping, and burial was optimum.

Oil generated below the economic basement must migrate vertically into shallower, more permeable and porous reservoirs to form commercial accumulations. Thus, the presence of vertical conduits, such as faults, for petroleum migration provides positive exploration criteria in arc-related basins dominated by unstable sandstones. Although oil that remains below the economic basement during migration may be trapped, reservoir properties of the sandstones mitigate against commercial production. Later tectonic uplift of the reservoir will not necessarily improve reservoir quality, although the shallower depths might improve production economics and permit exploitation.

The awareness of and accurate prediction of the timing of diagenesis of both organic and inorganic components and fluid migration pathways in arc-related basins are paramount in assessing regional resources and developing exploration strategy. The results of work on arc-derived sandstones show that combination of conventional petrographic approaches with determination of regional geological parameters controlling diagenetic history can yield predictive models that may significantly improve basin evaluation. Petrographic observations can be extrapolated beyond available sample control by relating dia-

gradient-defined depth range within which liquid hydrocarbons are generated and preserved. Because most oil is generated at temperatures above 150° F (65° C) and converts to gas at temperatures exceeding 300° F (150° C), the vertical range of the window decreases systematically with increasing thermal gradient (Fig. 8). Most large, geologically young (Mesozoic and Tertiary) oil fields lie within depth ranges corresponding to the liquid window.

Because a diagenetically controlled economic basement in arc-derived sands is also temperature dependent, it too rises in the section as thermal gradient increases. Stage 2 clay authigenesis is well underway by the time temperatures are sufficiently high for initiation of oil generation, and stage 3 pore-filling cementation probably begins well above the 300° F base of the liquid window (Fig. 8). Thus, the interval of petroleum generation and initial migration lies partly or mostly within that part of the section characterized by marginal to poor reservoirs. In contrast, reservoir preservation in more stable Tertiary sands typically extends below the liquid window and has not been a limiting factor in determining the exploration potential of passive plate-margin basins such as the Gulf Coast.

Various sequences of events may occur in basins where liquid hydrocarbons are generated

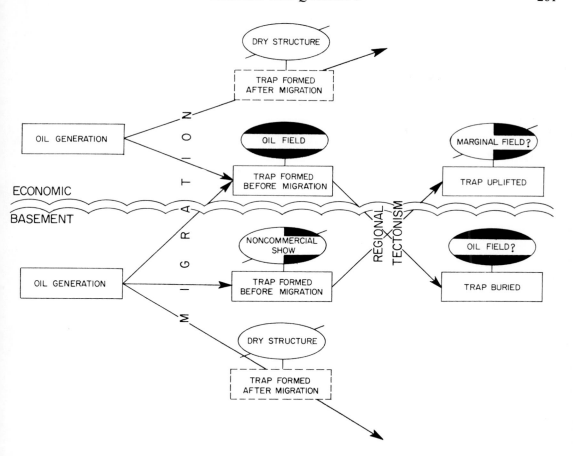

Fig. 9.—Possible oil generation and migration pathways in a sedimentary sequence containing a shallow, diagenetically defined economic basement. Shallow oil generated above economic basement may be trapped in sandstones with adequate reservoir quality. Such reservoirs may later be buried, producing a "fossil" reservoir below regional economic basement. Oil generated below economic basement must migrate vertically into shallow traps to produce a commercial deposit.

genetic features to petrophysical properties of the total section, such as density and interval velocity gradients. Indirect measurements of these petro-physical properties by seismic, gravity, or limited well-log analysis provide a regional framework for application of such consolidation models.

REFERENCES

Burst, J. F., 1969, Diagenesis of Gulf Coast clayey sediments and its possible relation to petroleum migration: Am. Assoc. Petroleum Geologists Bull., v. 53, p. 73–93.

Connan, Jacques, 1974, Time-temperature relation in oil genesis: Am. Assoc. Petroleum Geologists Bull., v. 58, p. 2516–2521.

Dickinson, W. R., 1974, Sedimentation within and beside ancient and modern magmatic arcs, *in* R. H. Dott, Jr., and R. H. Shaver (eds.), Modern and ancient geosynclinal sedimentation: Soc. Econ. Paleontologists and Mineralogists Spec. Pub. 19, p. 230–239.

Folk, R. L., 1974, Petrology of sedimentary rocks: Austin, Texas, Hemphills, 170 p.

Galloway, W. E., 1974, Deposition and diagenetic alteration of sandstone in northeast Pacific arc-related basins: Implications for graywacke genesis: Geol. Soc. America Bull., v. 85, p. 379–390.

Perry, E. A., Jr., and Hower, John, 1972, Late-stage dehydration in deeply buried pelitic sediments: Am. Assoc. Petroleum Geologists Bull., v. 56, p. 2013–2021.

PROZOROVICH, G. E., 1970, Determination of the time of oil and gas accumulation by epigenesis studies: Sedimentology, v. 15, p. 41–52.

PUSEY, W. C., 1973, Paleotemperatures in the Gulf Coast using ESR-kerogen method: Gulf Coast Assoc. Geol. Socs. Trans., v. 23, p. 195–202.

STEPHENSON, L. P., 1977, Porosity dependence on temperature: Limits on maximum possible effect: Am. Assoc. Petroleum Geologists Bull., v. 61, p. 407–415.

STONLEY, R., 1967, The structural development of the Gulf of Alaska sedimentary province in southern Alaska: Geol. Soc. London Quart. Jour., v. 123, p. 25–27.

YURKOVA, R. M., 1970, Comparison of post-sedimentary alterations of oil- and gas- and water-bearing rocks: Sedimentology, v. 15, p. 53–68.

ZARIPOV, O. G., 1971, Ovliyanii neftyanykh uglevodorodov na raspredeleniye vtorichnogo v terrigennykh kollktorakh nefti (na primere mestorozhdniy zapadnoy Sibiri i Bashkirii) [Effect of petroleum hydrocarbons on the distribution of secondary quartz in terrigenous oil reservoirs in oil fields of western Siberia and Bashkiria]: Akad. Nauk SSSR Doklady, v. 197, p. 443–445.

SEPM Special Publication No. 26, p. 263–279, March 1979

PETROLOGY AND DIAGENESIS OF DEEP-WATER SANDSTONES, OUACHITA MOUNTAINS, ARKANSAS AND OKLAHOMA

ROBERT C. MORRIS, KENNETH E. PROCTOR,[1] AND MICHAEL R. KOCH
Northern Illinois University, DeKalb, 60115

ABSTRACT

The Stanley and Jackfork Groups of the Ouachita Mountains consist of 18,000 feet of interbedded sandstones and shales deposited during the Late Mississippian and Early Pennsylvanian. Interest in their hydrocarbon potential has led to study of textures, compositions, and diagenetic alterations of these sandstones. The data and conclusions presented in this study are based on petrographic examination and porosity and permeability measurements of 187 samples collected from outcrop.

The Stanley sandstones are generally poorly sorted, very fine-grained feldspathic- and quartz wackes. They average 8% feldspar, 14% matrix, and 5% silica cement. Porosities range from 0.5–26% and permeabilities from 0.05–23 md.

Jackfork sandstones are predominantly moderately to poorly sorted, fine- to very fine-grained quartz arenites. They contain an average of 2% feldspar, 5% matrix, and 9% quartz cement. Porosities range from 0.5–14% and permeabilities from 0.05–9 md.

Pressure solution, silica cementation, and replacement of plagioclase by calcite have acted to reduce reservoir potential in both units, whereas corrosion and dissolution of framework grains have added secondary porosity. The presence of halloysite and kaolinite characterizes sandstones affected by surface leaching. Well sorted quartz arenites have poor reservoir quality as a result of extensive silica cementation. Characteristics associated with the retention or secondary development of reservoir potential include poor sorting, small mean grain sizes, and high matrix content.

INTRODUCTION

The Ouachita Mountains of Oklahoma and Arkansas (Fig. 1) are formed by a thick succession of folded and faulted strata that constitutes one of the thicker Paleozoic depocenters of North America. The rocks of this sinuous 200 mile-long complex are collectively termed the Ouachita Facies (Cline, 1970; Morris, 1974a). These rocks contain all the essentials of an ancient slope/ rise/deep-sea fan/abyssal plain system. Studies of approximately 30 partial or complete stratigraphic sections by the senior author have led him to the conclusion that a south-facing muddy slope and rise system dominated by soft-sediment sliding and slumping apparently interfingered with one or more westward-building deep-sea fans. The resulting sedimentary succession of thick shales which can act as both source rocks and reservoir seals, and interbedded sandstones to serve as reservoirs, offers the basic elements for hydrocarbon generation and entrapment.

This study focuses on the textural and compositional character of surface samples of the Carboniferous Stanley-Jackfork sandstones. Our purpose is to describe and compare the pertinent textures, compositions, porosities, permeabilities,

and facies of these sandstones, to highlight the principal diagenetic alterations, and to speculate on the controls of diagenesis. Although dry gas has been produced from some Carboniferous reservoirs in the study area, most of the two dozen exploration wells have encountered Stanley-Jackfork sandstones which are too impermeable or "tight" to produce economically. We feel that the degree of diagenetic alteration controls the distribution of the favorable reservoir sandstones. The intensity of diagenesis in turn is controlled by degree of tectonism, original texture and composition, and chemistry of pore waters.

STRATIGRAPHY

The Paleozoic strata in the Ouachita Mountains form a thick, deep-water succession of sedimentary rocks (Briggs, 1973; Cline, 1970; Morris, 1974a, 1974b; Seely, 1963). The Carboniferous portion of the flysch sequence is made up of interbedded sandstones and shales of the Stanley and Jackfork Groups.

The Stanley Group comprises most of the Mississippian section of the Ouachitas (Morris, 1974b). It attains a thickness in excess of 11,000 feet (Cline, 1960). By using a number of telescoping stratigraphic sections taken from outcrops, we have constructed a simplified isopach map (Fig. 2) of the entire Stanley. The most obvious trend is that the unit thins across the overthrust

[1]Present address: Texaco Inc., P.O. Box 2420, Tulsa, Oklahoma.

Copyright © 1979, The Society of Economic Paleontologists and Mineralogists

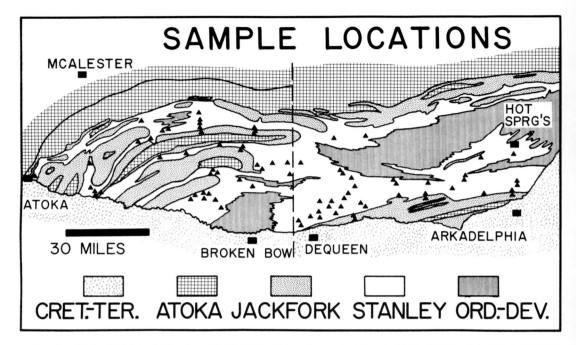

FIG. 1.—Generalized geologic map of Ouachita Mountains and Arkoma basin. Faults and minor outcrops are omitted. Sample locations are indicated by triangles.

belt of Oklahoma and Arkansas. The Stanley can be subdivided into the Tenmile Creek (base), Moyers, and Chickasaw Creek Formations (top) (Cline, 1960). We will ignore the Chickasaw Creek Formation in this report because of its lack of significant sands. The Tenmile Creek Formation has a maximum development of 9,500 feet in the central Ouachitas of Oklahoma and thins markedly to the north and west. A thin but distinctive siliceous shale and chert (Battiest Chert) subdivides the unit into two subequal members (Shelburne, 1960). A number of exploration wells located over the Jumbo and Clayton anticlines have penetrated the Lower Tenmile Creek Member. The Upper Tenmile Creek Member consists of more shale and less sandstone than the Lower Tenmile Creek. However, this member does contain some beds of pebble-conglomerate sandstone as well as fine-grained, massive-bedded sandstones. Some of these sandstones are tightly cemented, others are more poorly cemented.

The Moyers Formation occurs between the Tenmile Creek and Chickasaw Creek Formations. Where recognizable, the unit varies between 900–1600 feet thick. Most sandstones in the Moyers are fine-grained feldspathic wackes. Sole markings and cut-and-fill scour features are common. Petrographically, they resemble Tenmile Creek

sandstones, both in composition and in texture.

The Jackfork Group conformably overlies the Stanley Group and is considered to be Lower Pennsylvanian. Although the Jackfork has additional subdivisions (Cline, 1960; Morris, 1971a), they will not be considered in this paper. We have constructed an isopach map (Fig. 3) that utilizes published thicknesses (Cline, 1960; Morris, 1971a) as well as some unpublished work

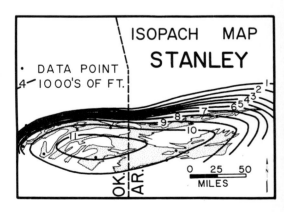

FIG. 2.—Simplified isopach map of Stanley Group. Contours in thousands of feet.

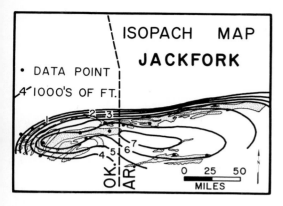

FIG. 3.—Simplified isopach map of Jackfork Group. Contours in thousands of feet.

of the senior author. The basic pattern for the Jackfork is that it becomes thinner to the north and west. Where thicker, the unit has a higher proportion of sandstone. Sandstones less than 3 feet thick commonly are interbedded with dark shales. Various kinds of sole markings occur on the sharp bases of these sandstones and, along with graded bedding and other sedimentary structures, furnish evidence of rapid deposition of sands by turbidity currents upon soft muds or watery sands (Cline, 1970; Lowe and LoPiccolo, 1974). Tops of the sandstones may be distinctly rippled or else gradational with overlying mudrocks. Trace fossils along the bedding planes suggest a deep-water environment for the Jackfork (Chamberlain, 1971).

SEDIMENTARY FACIES

Morris (1974a) proposed a formal classification of Ouachita Carboniferous flysch facies in which four major facies are represented. Sediment is thought to have entered the basin in four major ways: (1) by settling out from suspension; (2) by slumping or sliding, (3) as turbidity currents, and (4) as debris flows. When the study samples were collected in the field, each sampled interval was assigned one of the facies designations of Morris (1974a) through the study of sedimentary structures and bedding characteristics. Our petrographic work did not confirm textural differences for each of these sandstone facies. However, it is possible to distinguish textural differences in two distinct types of sandstones: (1) debris-flow and/or proximal turbidite sandstones and (2) distal turbidite sandstones. The porosity and permeability averages are higher in the first group and also there is more textural variation than in the distal turbidite facies whose

permeability and porosity averages and range are less. We have concluded that the different textures are partially due to their initial depositional processes and partially due to different diagenetic histories.

Debris-flow sandstones commonly are thick-bedded, structureless and weakly cemented. Angular shale clasts are interspersed throughout the middle and upper parts of many beds. The sandstones have sharp bases but almost no hieroglyphs on the soles of the beds as is common on turbidite sandstones. Most are fine- to medium-grained. Rare medium-grained sandstones may contain quartz pebbles, sandstone clots, and even crinoid columnals. We agree with Graham and others (1976) and Niem (1976) that Carboniferous sandstones in the Ouachita trough were deposited on a deep-sea fan. Accordingly, we have looked through our field data concerning Stanley-Jackfork sandstones in the hope of finding bedding characteristics similar to those noted by Mutti (1977) for deep-sea fan deposits in Spain. If this model can be applied to the rocks in our study, the debris-flow sandstones most likely are infillings of broad, shallow distributary channels.

Thick-bedded sandstones with deep, irregular scours on their tops form a distinctive, ridge-forming series of sandstones with little or no interbedded shales. The scour fillings consist of sandstones with similar colors, textures, and compositions, so that individual beds are difficult to distinguish. These scoured sandstones are fine- to medium-grained, well sorted and characteristically ridge-forming. Morris (1974a, 1977b) referred to these sandstones as proximal turbidites. The extremely high current velocities necessary to create such severe scour must have been confined. Logical environments for such high-velocity flows are lower fan channels and perhaps channel-mouth bars such as described by Mutti (1977).

Distal turbidites (Morris, 1974a) consist of even-bedded sandstones rhythmically interbedded with subequal amounts of gray shale or mudstone. Such rocks were considered to be the most common type of flysch by Cline (1970). Toolmark casts, flute casts, and load structures occur on the bases of many sandstones. Internally, the beds may be massive or graded. Size-grading of framework grains is less common than content-grading in which matrix material increases upward. Internal stratification includes parallel-, convolute-, and cross-laminations. Some dish structures and other dewatering features are common within Jackfork sandstones (Lowe and LoPiccolo, 1974). Tops of sandstones may be featureless. Distal turbidite sandstones comprise the major part of Stanley-Jackfork sandstones. From their distribu-

TABLE 1.—AVERAGES OF TEXTURAL PARAMETERS

Unit and State	Number of Samples	Median Mdφ	Mean Mφ	Sorting σφ	Skewness αφ	Effective Porosity φ%	Permeability (Md)
Jackfork Group							
Pj (Okla)	35	2.91	3.14	1.15	0.19	7.3	0.90
Pj (Ark)	12	2.80	2.94	0.96	0.15	5.2	0.11
Pj (TTL)	47	2.88	3.09	1.10	0.18	6.76	0.70
Stanley Group							
All Ms (Okla)	91	3.31	3.62	1.34	0.21	7.31	0.33
All Ms (Ark)	49	3.18	3.35	1.13	0.14	4.58	0.24
All Ms (TTL)	140	3.27	3.53	1.27	0.19	6.40	0.31
Msm (Okla)	32	3.20	3.57	1.39	0.26	6.3	0.42
Msm (Ark)	3	2.68	3.05	1.16	0.32	8.2	1.11
Msm (TTL)	35	3.15	3.53	1.37	0.27	6.46	0.50
Mstu (Okla)	33	3.37	3.62	1.34	0.18	8.2	0.16
Mstu (Ark)	14	3.26	3.44	1.16	0.14	3.6	0.06
Mstu (TTL)	47	3.34	3.57	1.28	0.17	6.98	0.13
Mstl (Okla)	20	3.43	3.72	1.29	0.22	8.0	0.46
Mstl (Ark)	18	3.22	3.36	1.10	0.13	5.2	0.29
Mstl (TTL)	38	3.33	3.55	1.20	0.18	6.67	0.39
Mst (Okla)	6	3.24	3.52	1.30	0.12	4.4	0.15
Mst (Ark)	14	3.15	3.31	1.12	0.13	4.0	0.22
Mst (TTL)	20	3.18	3.37	1.17	0.13	4.12	0.20

tion and bedding features, we have concluded that most of this facies was developed as widespread progradational lobes in front of distributary channels of a marine fan (Mutti, 1977). Some of these thin-bedded turbidites may have been deposited as overbank clastics of an inner fan.

TEXTURE

Textural analyses were made from thin sections by measuring the greatest diameter of the grain under the cross hairs at each of 200 points. The median ($Md\phi$), mean ($M\phi$), standard deviation or sorting ($\sigma\phi$), and skewness ($\alpha\phi$) were calculated from cumulative curves of this data using the methods of Inman (1952). The averages of these parameters are summarized according to unit and state in Table 1.[2]

The analyses indicate that the sandstones in Oklahoma have slightly finer average grain sizes and poorer sorting than those in Arkansas for both Stanley and Jackfork Groups. In the same manner, the sandstones in the Stanley Group tend

[2]Data sheets listing the textural parameters, mineral percentages, porosities, permeabilities, facies, and outcrop locations for the individual samples are available upon request from the authors.

to have finer average grain size and be more poorly sorted than those in the Jackfork Group.

No quantitative measurements were made of grain morphologies, but certain empirical observations became readily apparent. Framework grains in both the Stanley and Jackfork Groups are somewhat elongated, although this phenomenon is slightly more pronounced in the Jackfork samples. Surface features of the framework grains thought due to corrosion, alteration, and replacement were observed in thin section as well as with the scanning electron microscope (SEM).

MINERALOGY

Mineral percentages were determined from thin sections by counting the type of material under the cross hairs at each of 200 points. The summary of average mineral percentages according to unit and state is shown in Table 2. Figures 4 and 5 show the composition of framework grains in Stanley and Jackfork sandstones using the upper half of the standard sandstone classification chart by Gilbert (*in* Williams and others, 1954). The most significant contrast between the two units is that the Stanley sandstones contain less quartz and cement, and more feldspar, lithic fragments, and matrix than do the Jackfork sandstones. This same general distinction was reported by Morris

TABLE 2.—SUMMARY OF AVERAGE MINERAL PERCENTAGES ACCORDING TO UNIT AND STATE

Unit and State	N	Q1	Q2	Q3	F_{ut}	F_t	RF_s	RF_m	RF_i	Mat	SiO_2 Cem	$CO_3^=$ Cem	HM	Other
Jackfork Gp.														
Pj (Okla)	35	21.6	47.8	7.5	1.8	1.6	0.4	2.8	tr	6.4	9.1	tr	0.4	tr
Pj (Ark)	12	21.5	47.0	9.5	0.9	0.4	1.1	3.9	tr	4.9	8.8	tr	0.5	1.4
Pj (TTL)	47	21.6	47.6	8.1	1.6	1.3	0.6	3.1	tr	6.0	9.0	tr	0.4	0.5
Stanley Gp.														
All Ms (Okla)	91	14.5	45.0	6.4	4.7	3.2	0.8	3.5	tr	16.0	3.6	1.4	0.4	tr
All Ms (Ark)	49	17.9	45.8	6.3	4.7	3.2	0.8	3.3	0.5	9.0	7.4	tr	0.7	tr
All Ms (TTL)	140	15.7	45.2	6.4	4.7	3.2	0.8	3.5	tr	13.6	5.0	1.0	0.5	tr
Msm (Okla)	32	11.6	46.9	7.8	3.9	2.7	0.9	4.2	tr	15.8	3.1	2.5	0.4	tr
Msm (Ark)	3	17.8	47.3	9.0	1.5	0.7	0.8	9.0	—	10.2	2.5	—	0.5	0.7
Msm (TTL)	35	12.1	46.9	7.9	3.7	2.5	0.9	4.6	tr	15.4	3.0	2.3	0.4	tr
Mstu (Okla)	33	16.2	45.2	4.6	5.4	3.6	0.5	2.7	tr	16.9	3.6	0.8	0.4	tr
Mstu (Ark)	14	17.8	47.8	5.3	3.9	3.9	0.4	2.0	tr	9.3	7.5	—	0.8	tr
Mstu (TTL)	47	16.7	45.9	4.8	5.3	3.7	0.5	2.5	tr	14.6	4.8	.05	0.5	tr
Mstl (Okla)	20	15.9	42.7	6.7	4.6	3.1	1.1	3.9	tr	15.9	4.3	1.0	0.6	tr
Mstl (Ark)	18	15.3	44.9	7.6	4.4	3.1	1.5	4.2	0.6	8.9	8.3	0.6	0.6	tr
Mstl (TTL)	38	15.6	43.7	7.1	4.5	3.1	1.3	4.1	tr	12.6	6.2	0.8	0.6	tr
Mst (Okla)	6	16.6	40.8	7.5	5.3	3.7	0.9	3.2	0.7	12.3	4.6	—	0.3	4.2
Mst (Ark)	14	21.2	44.7	5.2	5.0	3.3	0.4	2.2	0.8	8.7	7.2	tr	0.6	tr
Mst (TTL)	20	19.8	43.6	5.9	5.1	3.5	0.5	2.5	0.8	9.8	6.4	tr	0.5	1.2

Q1—Percentage of unstrained, single grains of quartz. Q2—Percentage of strained, single grains of quartz displaying undulatory extinction. Q3—Percentage of composite or polycrystalline grains of quartz; includes detrital chert. F_{ut}—Percentage of untwinned feldspar. F_t—Percentage of twinned feldspar. RF_s—Percentage of sedimentary rock fragments. RF_m—Percentage of metamorphic rock fragments. RF_i—Percentage of igneous rock fragments. Mat—Percentage of matrix. SiO_2/Cem—Percentage of silica cement; includes quartz overgrowths and chalcedony. $CO_3^=$/Cem—Percentage of carbonate cement; includes carbonates replacing grains and matrix. HM—Percentage of heavy minerals. Other—Percentage of other constituents not covered by the categories listed above; includes organic material.

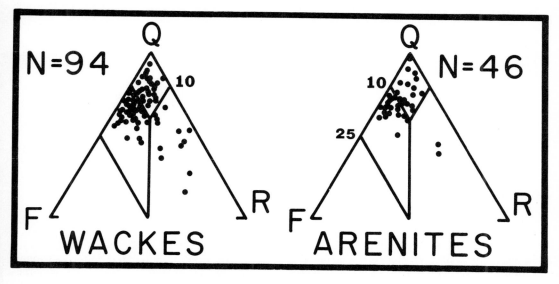

FIG. 4.—Triangular composition diagrams for Stanley Group sandstones used in this study. Note: the upper 50% of the total field of Williams and others (1954) is used.

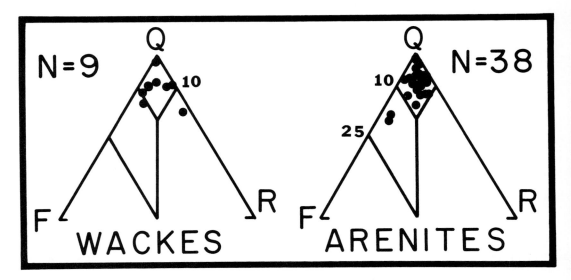

F<small>IG</small>. 5.—Triangular composition diagrams for Jackfork Group sandstones used in this study. Note: the upper 50% of the total field of Williams and others (1954) is used.

(1974a, 1977a) using data from several earlier studies.

Quartz.—Of the total mineralogy, detrital quartz forms an average of 67.3% in the Stanley sandstones and 77.3% in the Jackfork. The types of quartz noted were: (1) unstrained single grains, (2) strained single grains displaying undulatory extinction, and (3) composite or polycrystalline grains. Strained single grains of quartz make up nearly two-thirds of the total quartz in both groups. Polycrystalline quartz is the least abundant variety, and includes grains derived from metamorphic and igneous rocks, as well as chert.

Feldspar.—Feldspar averages 7.9% of the mineral grains for the Stanley sandstones, and 2.9% for Jackfork sandstones. Some types of feldspar are shown in Figure 6A-D. Untwinned feldspar, mostly orthoclase, is the most common variety observed in both Groups, followed in abundance by twinned plagioclase and rare grains of microcline. Extinction angles of combined Carlsbad-Albite twins indicate that the majority of the plagioclase is either andesine or oligoclase. Most of the plagioclase grains, and some of the orthoclase grains, exhibit signs of weathering and/or chemical alteration. The effects most commonly observed were alteration to clay, dissolution, and replacement by calcite or siderite.

Rock fragments.—Lithic grains make up 4.3% of the grains in the Stanley sandstones, and 3.7% in the Jackfork sandstones. Clasts of sedimentary, metamorphic, and igneous rocks are all present in the Stanley and Jackfork Groups.

Metamorphic rock fragments (Fig. 6E, F) are prevalent, and include biotite-, chlorite-, and quartz-mica schists, phyllite, and slate. These clasts frequently are contorted as a result of sedimentary loading or tectonism. An unknown amount may have been deformed to produce pseudo-matrix in a manner noted by Dickinson (1970).

The most common sedimentary rock fragments include shale, silty shale, and mudstone. Rip-up clasts of dark shale are exceedingly common in debris-flow sandstones. Less common are fragments of indurated siltstone or sandstone. Siliceous shale and impure chert fragments are abundant in certain thin sections. Triangular plots of polycrystalline quartz, metamorphic rock fragments, and sedimentary rock fragments for Tenmile Creek (Lower Stanley) and Jackfork sandstones are presented in Figures 7 and 8. The similar fields probably reflect a similar provenance for the two units.

Only traces of igneous rock fragments are present in Jackfork sandstones. In the Stanley, most igneous clasts are tuff fragments characterized by disoriented laths of plagioclase, orthoclase, quartz, and micas in a matrix of vesicular or divitrified glass. An excellent description of these tuffs is provided by Niem (1977).

Matrix.—All rocks studied have a high matrix content as determined by thin section examination, averaging 13.6% of the total rock in Stanley sandstones and 6.0% in Jackfork sandstones. Matrix, as discussed here, refers to all materials which are too fine to be identified with the petrographic microscope. It thus includes clay

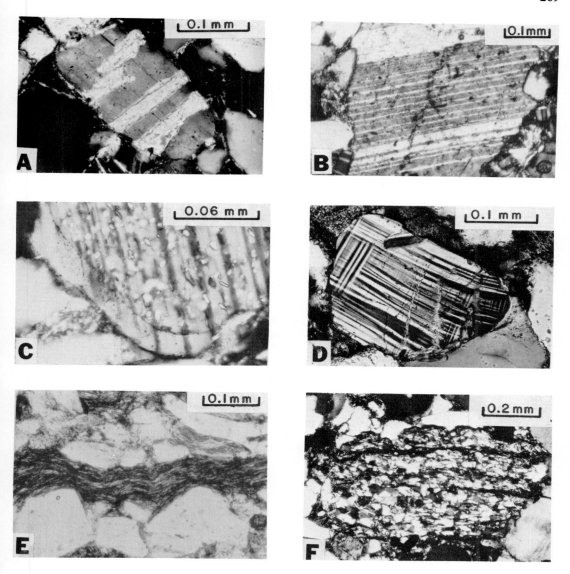

FIG. 6.—Selected photomicrographs from thin sections of Stanley and Jackfork sandstones. *A*, sample 63, Lower Tenmile Creek Formation (crossed nicols), potassium-feldspar grain partially replaced by calcite. Calcite also has etched an adjacent quartz grain and replaced some of the matrix. *B*, sample 53, Upper Tenmile Creek Formation (crossed nicols), slightly altered plagioclase grain embayed by smaller grains of quartz and feldspar. *C*, sample 174. Upper Tenmile Creek Formation (crossed nicols), overgrowth rim developed on plagioclase grain. *D*, sample 174, Upper Tenmile Creek Formation (crossed nicols), rounded microcline grain with almost no reaction rim and no feldspar overgrowth. *E*, sample 16, Jackfork Sandstone (plain light), phyllite clast deformed by compaction. *F*, sample 160, Lower Tenmile Creek Formation (crossed nicols), metamorphic rock fragment derived from quartz-mica schist.

minerals which may be detrital or diagenetic in origin, fine and medium silt-sized mica, quartz, and feldspar, and the products created by the breakdown of fine-grained lithic fragments or feldspar. The matrix most commonly observed

in the Stanley and Jackfork sandstones is an indistinct mix of iron oxides and clay minerals. Cryptocrystalline silica frequently is found engulfing or actually replacing the matrix.

Mineral percentages of whole rock samples

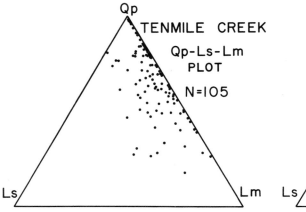

FIG. 7.—Triangular diagram comparing the detrital modes of polycrystalline quartz (Qp), sedimentary rock fragments (Ls), and metamorphic rock fragments (Lm) in Tenmile Creek sandstones, Stanley Group.

FIG. 8.—Triangular diagram comparing the detrital modes of polycrystalline quartz (Qp), sedimentary rock fragments (Ls), and metamorphic rock fragments (Lm) in various Jackfork Group sandstones.

were determined by X-ray diffraction. Due to the general scarcity of fine-grained lithic clasts, we feel that the clay mineral fraction of these analyses is representative of the clay minerals comprising the matrix. For all of the samples examined, illite averages 3.7% (0–18% range), chlorite averages 3.0% (9–12% range); trace amounts of mixed layer chlorite/montmorillonite are present also. Some sandstones contain a few percent of diagenetic kaolinite/halloysite.

Heavy minerals.—Detrital zircon is the most abundant heavy mineral in both Stanley and Jackfork sandstones. The zircon grains are moderately rounded and siltsized. Garnets are the second most abundant heavy mineral in the Stanley sandstones, but are uncommon in the Jackfork Group. Considerable solution of the exteriors of garnets has occurred. Tourmaline and rutile are present in subequal amounts in both stratigraphic units, but are subordinate to opaques which include leucoxene and traces of pyrite, magnetite and/or ilmenite. Grains of anatase, apatite, epidote, and sphene are exceedingly rare.

DIAGENESIS

A brief examination of almost any thin section of Stanley or Jackfork sandstone can leave little doubt that the present state of the rock is drastically different from that at the time of deposition. The grains have been pitted, corroded, embayed, altered, replaced, and deformed; the matrix has been replaced, engulfed, compacted and recrystallized since deposition. These changes have an impact on the classification and reservoir potential of the rocks.

Silica dissolution and cementation.—Figures

9A–F are photomicrographs of thin sections containing aspects of grain interpenetration, solution, and silica cementation so common in Stanley and Jackfork rocks. Much of this silica has been derived from solution at points of stress (pressure solution) as well as total grain surfaces (corrosion). However, as Sibley and Blatt (1976) have pointed out, insufficient silica is provided by solution to account for the entire volume of silica cement in orthoquartzites. Additional silica may have been derived from surface ground waters.

Various forms of silica are the most commonly observed variety of cement in the Stanley and Jackfork sandstones, and average 9.0% (0–17% range) in the Jackfork and 5.0% (0–18% range) in the Stanley. The forms identified are (1) microcrystalline (chalcedonic) cement around grains or as patches engulfing or replacing matrix, (2) syntaxial quartz overgrowths, and (3) quartz cement, either engulfing or replacing matrix. While only one (2.1%) of the Jackfork samples contained no silica cement, 30 (21.4%) of the Stanley samples contained none. Quartz overgrowths are more prevalent in the Jackfork sandstones than in the Stanley.

Pressure solution is one of the most important processes in diagenesis and plays a significant role in the alteration of the Stanley and Jackfork sands. This process involves the interpenetration of adjacent grains in contact under the influence of pressure and in the presence of pore waters. The dissolution of silica at the point of contact between grains under pressure is favored when the pH exceeds 9.5, and in the presence of clay (Dapples, 1967; Heald, 1956; Thomson, 1959; Weyl, 1959).

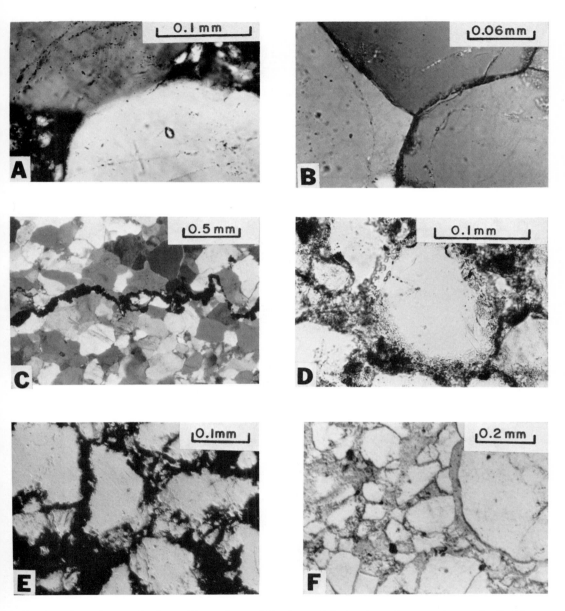

Fɪɢ. 9.—Photomicrographs from thin sections of Stanley and Jackfork sandstones. *A*, sample 61, Moyers Formation (crossed nicols), showing incipient fusion of two quartz grains due to pressure solution. The quartz grains have undergone corrosion where they are in contact with the dark, ferruginous matrix. *B*, sample 181, Lower Tenmile Creek Formation (crossed nicols), quartz overgrowths extending from three grains, greatly reducing pore space. *C*, sample 192, Jackfork Sandstone (crossed nicols), microstylolite in quartz arenite characterized by concavo-convex and sutured contacts. *D*, sample 160, Lower Tenmile Creek Formation (plain light), severely corroded quartz grain in contact with dark, ferruginous (?) matrix. *E*, sample 168, Tenmile Creek Formation (plain light), asphaltic compound from surface oil seep surrounding corroded quartz and chert grains. The corrosion and etching apparently preceded the invasion of the asphaltite. *F*, sample 110, Upper Tenmile Creek Formation (plain light), pore spaces (dark) are excessively large, suggesting surface solution.

R. C. MORRIS, K. E. PROCTOR AND M. R. KOCH

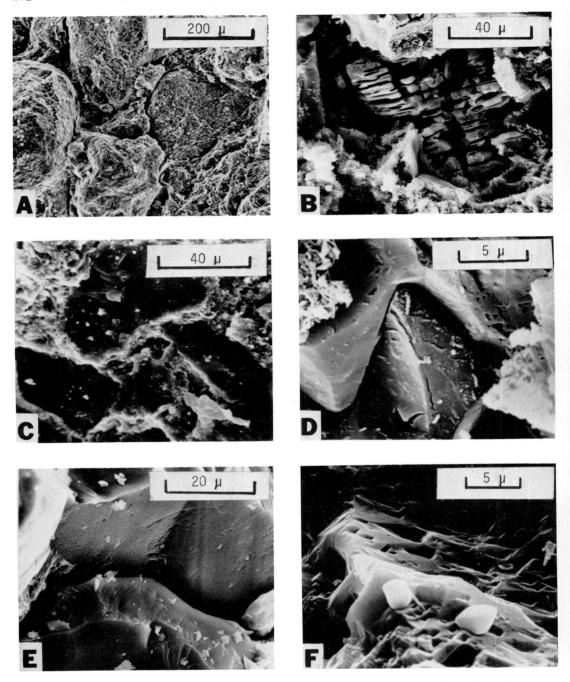

Fig. 10.—Scanning electron micrographs showing diagenetic features in Stanley and Jackfork sandstones. *A*, sample 162, Jackfork Sandstone, pores are infilled with illitic matrix. In spite of high matrix content 11%, rock has permeability of 0.36 md. *B*, sample 106, Jackfork Sandstone, partially leached feldspar grain rimmed by authigenic clay fibers. *C*, sample 105, Jackfork Sandstone, tightly packed quartz grains cemented by patches of silica, possibly intermixed with a small amount of illitic matrix. Most pores in this sample are cemented by quartz overgrowths (see 10E). *D*, sample 109, Lower Tenmile Creek Formation, interlocking quartz (sutured grain contact?) with small, triangular etch pits, and interlocking crystals of illite. *E*, sample 105, Jackfork Sandstone, quartz arenite with interlocking quartz overgrowths that totally fill pore spaces. *F*, sample 144, Upper Tenmile Creek Formation, surface of etched quartz grain.

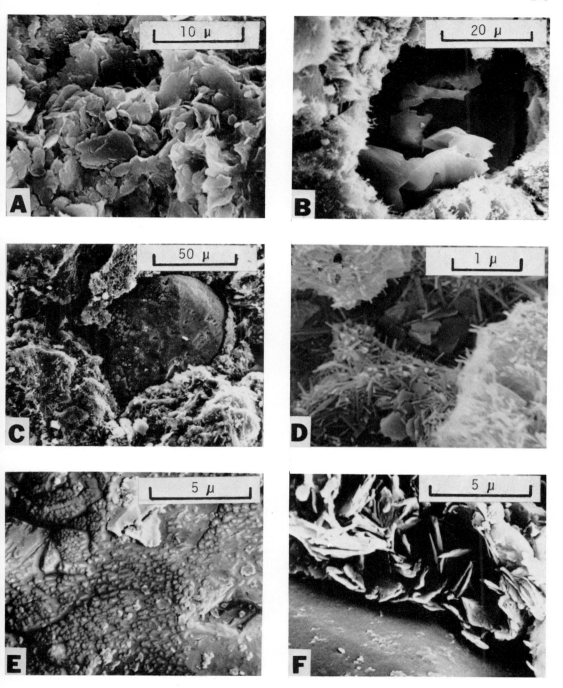

FIG. 11.—SEM micrographs of Stanley and Jackfork sandstones. *A*, sample 106, Jackfork Sandstone, subhedral, authigenic clay minerals (illite?) formed in pore of permeable sandstone. *B*, sample 179, Lower Tenmile Creek Formation, authigenic growth of fibrous halloysite lining pore walls with subhedral crystals of illite growing in center of pore enlarged by surface weathering. *C*, sample 109, Lower Tenmile Creek Formation, illitic matrix choking pore spaces and causing etching of quartz grains. *D*, sample 179, close-up of pore wall in 11B showing the fibrous halloysite and platy illite. *E*, sample 109, close-up of surface etch figures. *F*, sample 111, Lower Tenmile Creek, felted network of chlorite in pore next to quartz grain.

An obvious effect of pressure solution is the alteration of original grain shapes. By simultaneous cementation and pressure solution, original grain shapes become obscured and the resulting grains may have concavo-convex, or even sutured boundaries. Complex microstylolites are common in such rocks (Fig. 9C). Corrosion and dissolution of silica is independent of pressure solution. In thin section, quartz grains commonly have a corroded aspect over their surface (Fig. 9D–F). This phenomenon is more closely associated with clay-rich rocks. Our biggest problem has been the distinction between solution of quartz at depth from near-surface solution effects. We have made some progress through the use of X-ray data and the SEM, but many problems remain.

Use of the SEM has allowed us to see the diagenetic reactions more clearly. A sandstone with considerable matrix has little or no quartz overgrowth (Fig. 10A). Framework grains subject to weathering may undergo partial solution, alteration, or both (Fig. 10B). Quartz grains have a variety of corrosion features associated with their surfaces (Fig. 10C–F).

Partial replacement of feldspars by irregular masses of clays or micas is common in virtually every feldspar-bearing sample. Clay minerals belonging to the kaolinite group are the most common alteration products of weathered feldspars (Deer and others, 1966; Grim, 1953; Loughnam, 1969; Parham, 1969). In our study, these minerals were identified by X-ray diffraction. Subsequent SEM studies have revealed small books of kaolinite and fibers of halloysite in addition to detrital illite and chlorite. Figure 11 contains SEM micrographs of Stanley and Jackfork sandstones showing clay minerals, pore spaces and etched surfaces of quartz grains that have reacted to the matrix material. The matrix, predominantly illite and chlorite, is partially recrystallized as shown by the SEM. In general, matrix fills the pores and reduces the permeability or effective porosity. Dapples (1967) suggested that kaolinite and halloysite form in low pH, slightly positive Eh environments. Halloysite will dewater quickly with heat so its presence is strictly a surface phenomenon. Porosity and permeability values

for surface samples of sandstones containing halloysite and kaolinite probably are not reliable because they give little indication of the texture of these rocks at depth.

Stanley sandstones contain limited amounts of carbonate cements; Jackfork sandstones contain even less. Calcite accounts for over 95% of the carbonate cement. Distribution of the calcite cement is highly sporadic. From thin-section data, only five (10.6%) of the 47 Jackfork samples contain any carbonate (range zero to 3%). Twenty (14.3%) of the 140 Stanley sandstones contained carbonate cement (range zero to 32.5%). In small amounts, calcite appears as a partial or complete replacement of feldspar grains. Where more abundant, it commonly engulfs matrix, fills in pores, and etches the surrounding quartz grains. Siderite and dolomite are very scarce. Where present, they replace calcite or feldspar grains.

POROSITY AND PERMEABILITY

Plugs from outcrop samples were analyzed for effective porosity and permeability using helium as the saturating fluid. One plug was taken parallel to the bedding, the other perpendicular to the bedding so that two permeability values were obtained for each sample. When compiling the average permeabilities shown on Table 1, the largest value was used. Although not shown on Table 1, a considerable range in values was obtained for both porosity and permeability.

In order to visualize trends, we arbitrarily chose the following porosity-permeability limits for grouping these surface sandstones into three broad reservoir types. Sandstones we consider to have *favorable* gas-reservoir potentials are those containing greater than 8% effective porosity and 0.07 millidarcies (md) permeability. We consider sandstones to be *marginally favorable* as potential gas reservoirs if they have effective porosities between 5–8% and at least 0.07 md permeability. Sandstones we consider to have *unfavorable* gas-reservoir potential are those with less than 5% porosity or less than 0.07 md permeability. The distribution of the rocks in these classifications is shown on Table 3. It is immediately obvious that the majority (>60%) of sandstones in both

TABLE 3.—CLASSIFICATION OF SAMPLES BY GAS-RESERVOIR POTENTIAL

Unit	Favorable	Marginally Favorable	Unfavorable	Number of Samples
Jackfork	15(31.9)*	7(14.9)	25(53.2)	47
Moyers	9(25.7)	5(14.3)	21(60.0)	35
Tenmile Creek	25(24.1)	10(9.6)	69(66.3)	104
All Stanley	34(24.5)	15(10.8)	90(64.7)	139
Total	49(26.4)	22(11.8)	115(61.8)	186

*Number samples (percent)

the Stanley and Jackfork have "unfavorable" values of porosity and permeability. Approximately one-third of all rocks fall into "marginally favorable" or "favorable" limits. Without a doubt, the sandstones having better reservoir qualities occur in Oklahoma. Table 1 shows that in both Stanley and Jackfork sandstones, effective porosity and permeability averages are higher in Oklahoma than in Arkansas.

RESERVOIR POTENTIAL FROM PETROGRAPHY

A number of petrographic characteristics were compared in order to see if they had any relationship to the reservoir potential. The petrographic variables selected include mean grain size, sorting, percentage of matrix, and percentage of silica cement. The data were entered into a prepackaged program for regression analysis using a Wang 700B Advanced Programming Calculator. As a measure of reservoir quality, both effective porosity and maximum permeability can be compared to any petrographic variable. In this study, we made petrographic comparisons with effective porosity only. This is because a large number of samples have permeability values too low to be determined, whereas very few of these samples have comparably low porosities (i.e., effective porosity less than 0.5%). Below are a few general conclusions we made from these kinds of comparisons.

Average grain size.—An inverse relationship seems to exist between mean grain size and porosity, especially in the Jackfork and Moyers sandstones. As the mean grain size decreases, effective porosity tends to improve.

Sorting.—Most sandstones tend to have higher effective porosities as the sorting decreases. This relationship is best seen in Tenmile Creek sandstones, which have higher matrix values than Jackfork sandstones.

Matrix.—One of the most surprising trends was the relationship of the matrix content to porosity. In Tenmile Creek sandstones, porosity values show a clear increase with increasing matrix content (Fig. 12). To a lesser extent, the same trend is present in Jackfork and Moyers sandstones.

Cement.—Stanley sandstones show a strong inverse relationship between silica cement and both porosity and matrix content. As the amount of silica cement increases, the mean effective porosity decreases. For example, all samples containing more than 12% silica cement have less than 5% effective porosity and less than 10% matrix would be considered "unfavorable" gas reservoirs in this report. The relationship between the matrix content, which is proportional to porosity, and the percentage of cement is shown clearly for the Tenmile Creek sandstones (Fig. 13). Most likely, the well-sorted, matrix-poor sandstones

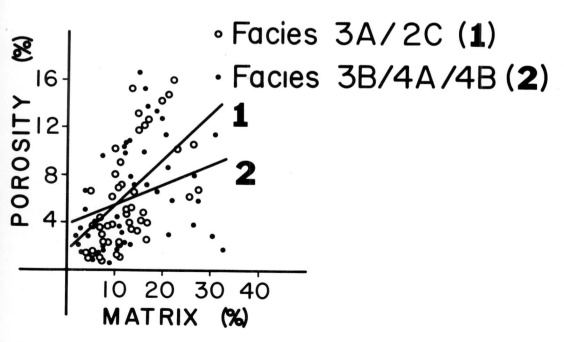

Fig. 12.—Chart showing plot of percent porosity to percent matrix, Tenmile Creek Formation. Facies 3A/2C are proximal turbidites and debris flows, respectively. Facies 3B, 4A, and 4B are various facies of distal turbidites.

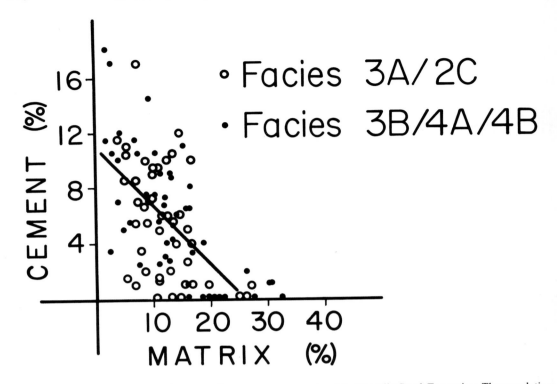

Fig. 13.—Chart showing plot of percent silica cement to percent matrix, Tenmile Creek Formation. The correlation coefficient is −0.58. See Figure 12 for facies explanation.

were ideal sites for the precipitation of silica out of the freely-migrating, siliceous fluids.

RESERVOIR POTENTIAL FROM SANDSTONE TYPE

To see if the textural parameters might be related to sandstone composition, Proctor (1974) assigned arbitrary verbal reservoir potentials to the various sandstone classes. From the summary at the bottom of Table 4, one can see the correlation between "favorable" reservoir potential and higher matrix content. Only 29.8% of the arenites have "favorable" or "marginally favorable" gas-reservoir potentials but 45.1% of the wackes fall within this desirable range.

RESERVOIR POTENTIAL AND FACIES

Comparison of the facies and reservoir potential is the third method used in the attempt to find a useful correlation. The fact that the exploration geologist can determine lithologic facies in the field without the benefit of special equipment gives this method an advantage over the others discussed earlier. The result of these correlations is that they are as good or better than those found using any other methods. Table 5 summarizes the relationships between facies and reservoir potential. From this table it is apparent that the proximal turbidite subfacies 3A is the most desirable with 47.4% of these samples having "favorable" or "marginally favorable" reservoir potentials. Disregarding the 16 samples for which the facies could not be determined, the proximal turbidites and disturbed beds (facies 2C) make up the best reservoir sands. On the other hand, distal turbidites (facies 3B, 4A, 4B) do not show any promise as reservoirs. Almost three-fourths of these sandstones have "unfavorable" reservoir potentials. Figure 14 shows tight, well-cemented turbidite sandstones overlain by friable, sandy proximal turbidites. The thin-bedded turbidite sandstones have an effective porosity of 5.8% and 0.05 md permeability. The overlying proximal turbidite sandstones have an effective porosity of 13.6% and 7.28 md permeability, a significant change in texture.

SUMMARY AND CONCLUSIONS

Though sandstones from the Jackfork and Stanley Groups have many similarities, they can be characterized petrographically. The most statistically significant differences occur in the percentage of feldspar and matrix, as well as the

TABLE 4.—RELATIONSHIP OF GAS-RESERVOIR POTENTIAL AND COMPOSITION

Sandstone Class	Gas-Reservoir Potential			Number of Samples
	Favorable	Marginally Favorable	Unfavorable	
Quartz Arenite	15(27.3)*	9(16.4)	31(56.3)	55 (29.6)
Feldspathic Arenite	1(3.7)	—	26(96.3)	27 (14.5)
Subfeldspathic Lithic Arenite	—	—	2(100.0)	2 (1.1)
Quartz Wacke	12(27.3)	7(15.9)	25(56.8)	44 (23.6)
Feldspathic Wacke	17(37.8)	6(13.3)	22(48.9)	45 (24.2)
Subfeldspathic Lithic Wacke	4(40.0)	—	6(60.0)	10 (5.4)
Lithic Wacke	—	—	3(100.0)	3 (1.6)
All Arenites	16(19.1)	9(10.7)	59(70.2)	84 (45.2)
All Wackes	33(32.4)	13(12.7)	56(54.9)	102 (54.8)

*Number samples (percent)

TABLE 5.—COMPARISON OF FACIES TYPES TO RESERVOIR POTENTIALS

Facies Type	Gas-Reservoir Potential			Number of Samples
	Favorable	Marginally Favorable	Unfavorable	
2C	3(23.1)*	3(23.1)	7(53.8)	13 (7.0)
3A	27(34.6)	10(12.8)	41(52.6)	78 (41.9)
3B	9(20.0)	7(15.6)	29(64.4)	45 (24.2)
4A	3(11.5)	1(3.9)	22(84.6)	26 (14.0)
4B	1(12.5)	—	7(87.5)	8 (4.3)
UNK	6(37.5)	1(6.2)	9(56.3)	16 (8.6)

*Number samples (percent)

values obtained for sorting and mean grain size.

The present textures and fabric of the Stanley and Jackfork sandstones are primarily the product of diagenesis. Pressure solution, corrosion, and cementation have altered many of the Jackfork arenites in such a way as to produce rocks resembling quartzites. The fine grained "matrix" in many Stanley sandstones may be higher now

Fig. 14.—Dark, distal turbidite sandstones (base) are silica-cemented, nonpermeable, very hard, with interlocking or sutured grain contacts. The scoured proximal turbidites (top) are friable, permeable, massive, and potentially excellent reservoir rocks, Jackfork Sandstone, U.S. Highway 259, 33-2N-25E, Oklahoma.

of primary porosity. This matrix also increases pH where in contact with quartz grains to promote the dissolution and removal of silica. Unfavorable reservoir potentials occur in nearly 55% of the wackes contrast with over 70% of the arenites. More than one half of the feldspathic wackes have "favorable" and "marginally favorable" reservoir potentials, probably attributable to the dissolution of feldspar.

The greatest percentage of "favorable" and "marginally favorable" reservoir potentials is found in proximal turbidites. Debris-flow sandstones, or disturbed beds (facies 2C), also have favorable reservoir potential because of their textural characteristics. Areas known to contain numerous and/or thick strata belonging to these facies deserve close scrutiny in any future drilling program.

than at the time of deposition, due to the chemical alteration of feldspars, the mechanical breakdown of argillaceous rock fragments, and precipitation from pore fluids. In general, pressure solution and silica cements are associated with low values of porosity and permeability. A certain amount of matrix seems to be beneficial to the retention

ACKNOWLEDGEMENTS

This study was supported by the Midwest Oil Company, Denver, Colorado. Laboratory analyses of porosity and permeability were supplied by Amoco Production Company, Tulsa, Oklahoma. Appreciation is expressed to both companies for their assistance. The body of this paper is a condensation of an M.S. thesis by K. E. Proctor (1974).

REFERENCES

BRIGGS, GARRETT, 1973, Geology of the eastern part of the Lynn Mountain Syncline, LeFlore County, Oklahoma: Oklahoma Geol. Survey Circ. 75, 34 p.
CHAMBERLAIN, C. K., 1971, Bathymetry and paleoecology of Ouachita geosyncline of southeastern Oklahoma as determined from trace fossils: Am. Assoc. Petroleum Geologists Bull., v. 55, p. 34–50.
CLINE, L. M., 1960, Stratigraphy of the late Paleozoic rocks of the Ouachita Mountains, Oklahoma: Oklahoma Geol. Survey Bull. 85, 113 p.
——, 1970, Sedimentary features of late Paleozoic flysch, Ouachita Mountains, Oklahoma, in J. Lajoie (ed.), Flysch sedimentology of North America: Geol. Assoc. Canada Spec. Paper 7, p. 85–101.
DAPPLES, E. C., 1967, Diagenesis of sandstones, in Gunnar Larson and G. V. Chilingar (eds.), Diagenesis of sediments: Amsterdam, Elsevier, p. 91–125.
DEER, W. A., HOWIE, R. A., AND ZUSSMAN, J., 1966, An introduction to the rock-forming minerals: New York, John Wiley and Sons, 528 p.
DICKINSON, W. R., 1970, Interpreting detrital modes of graywacke and arkose: Jour. Sed. Petrology, v. 40, p. 695–707.
GRAHAM, S. A., INGERSOLL, R. V., AND DICKINSON, W. R., 1976, Common provenance for lithic grains in Carboniferous sandstones from Ouachita Mountains and Black Warrior Basin: Jour. Sed. Petrology, v. 46, p. 620–632.
GRIM, R. E., 1953, Clay mineralogy: New York, McGraw-Hill, 384 p.
HEALD, M. T., 1956, Cementation of Simpson and St. Peter Sandstones in parts of Oklahoma, Arkansas, and Missouri: Jour. Geology, v. 64, p. 16–30.
INMAN, D. L., 1952, Measures for describing size distribution of sediments: Jour. Sed. Petrology, v. 22, p. 125–145.
LOUGHNAN, F. C., 1969, Chemical weathering of the silicate minerals: New York, Elsevier, 154 p.
LOWE, D. R., AND LOPICCOLO, R. D., 1974, The characteristics and origins of dish and pillar structures: Jour. Sed. Petrology, v. 44, p. 484–501.
MORRIS, R. C., 1971a, Stratigraphy and sedimentology of the Jackfork Group, Arkansas: Am. Assoc. Petroleum Geologists Bull., v. 55, p. 387–402.
——, 1971b, Classification and interpretation of disturbed bedding types in Jackfork flysch rocks (Upper Mississippian), Ouachita Mountains, Arkansas: Jour. Sed. Petrology, v. 41, p. 410–424.
——, 1974a, Carboniferous rocks of the Ouachita Mountains, Arkansas—A study of facies patterns along the unstable slope and axis of a flysch trough, in Garrett Briggs (ed.), Symposium on the Carboniferous rocks of the southeastern United States: Geol. Soc. America Spec. Paper 148, p. 241–279.

——, 1974b, Sedimentary and tectonic history of the Ouachita Mountains, *in* W. R. Dickinson (ed.), Tectonics and sedimentation: Soc. Econ. Paleontologists and Mineralogists Spec. Pub. 22, p. 120–142.

——, 1977a, Petrography of Stanley-Jackfork sandstones, Ouachita Mountains, Arkansas, *in* Ouachita Symposium Volume: Little Rock, Arkansas Geol. Commission, p. 146–157.

——, 1977b, Flysch facies of the Ouachita Trough—With examples from the spillway at DeGray Dam, Arkansas, *in* Ouachita Symposium Volume: Little Rock, Arkansas Geol. Commission, p. 158–168.

MUTTI, EMILIANO, 1977, Distinctive thin-bedded turbidite facies and related depositional environments in the Eocene Hecho Groups (south-central Pyrenees, Spain): Sedimentology, v. 24, p. 107–131.

NIEM, A. R., 1976, Patterns of flysch deposition and deep-sea fans in the lower Stanley Group (Mississippian), Ouachita Mountains, Oklahoma and Arkansas: Jour. Sed. Petrology, v. 46, p. 633–646.

——, 1977, Mississippian pyroclastic flow and ash-fall deposits in deep-marine Ouachita flysch trough, Oklahoma and Arkansas: Geol. Soc. America Bull., v. 88, p. 49–61.

PARHAM, W. E., 1969, Formation of halloysite from feldspar: Low temperature artificial weathering versus natural weathering: Clays and Clay Minerals, v. 17, p. 13–22.

PROCTOR, K. E., 1974, The petrography and gas-reservoir potential of Stanley-Jackfork sandstones, Ouachita Mountains, Arkansas and Oklahoma: M.S. Thesis, Northern Illinois Univ., 151 p.

SEELY, D. R., 1963, Structure and stratigraphy of the Rich Mountain area, Oklahoma and Arkansas: Oklahoma Geol. Survey Bull. 101, 173 p.

SHELBURNE, O. B., 1960, Geology of the Boktukola Syncline, southeastern Oklahoma: Oklahoma Geol. Survey Bull. 88, 84 p.

SIBLEY, D. F., AND BLATT, HARVEY, 1976, Intergranular pressure solution and cementation of the Tuscarora Orthoquartzite: Jour. Sed. Petrology, v. 46, p. 881–896.

THOMSON, ALAN, 1959, Pressure solution and porosity, *in* H. A. Ireland (ed.), Silica in sediments: Soc. Econ. Paleontologists and Mineralogists Spec. Pub. 7, p. 92–110.

WEYL, P. K., 1959, Pressure solution and the force of crystallization—A phenomenological theory: Jour. Geophys. Research, v. 64, p. 2001–2025.

WILLIAMS, HOWEL, TURNER, F. J., AND GILBERT, C. M., 1954, Petrography: San Francisco, Freeman, 406 p.

SEPM SPECIAL PUBLICATION No. 26, p. 281–306, MARCH 1979

DEPOSITION AND DIAGENESIS OF TERTIARY-HOLOCENE VOLCANICLASTICS, GUATEMALA

DAVID K. DAVIES, WILLIAM R. ALMON, SAMUEL B. BONIS, AND BRUCE E. HUNTER
Texas Tech University, Lubbock, 29409; Cities Service Oil Company, Tulsa, Oklahoma 74150;
Institute Geográfico Nacional, Divisón Geológica, Guatemala City, Guatemala; Texas Tech University,
Lubbock, 29409.

ABSTRACT

Tertiary-Holocene continental volcanic sediments in southern Guatemala were deposited in three basins each approximately 150 km long and 50 to 100 km wide. Boundaries between these basins mark the positions of transverse breaks in the underlying lithospheric slab. The rates of sediment accumulation and subsidence, and the composition, texture, and thickness of sediments can be expected to vary greatly from basin to basin. Exploration for hydrocarbon reservoirs in similar fore-arc areas should take into account that large scale correlations along depositional strike may be virtually impossible over distances greater than 50 or 100 km.

The nature, degree, and timing of the diagenesis of Guatemalan volcaniclastics poses problems as to the hydrocarbon production potential of similar areas in other parts of the world. Guatemalan continental volcaniclastics are feldspathic litharenites. Three successive episodes of diagenesis have resulted in the precipitation of the following sequence of minerals in rock pores:—hematite-goethite;—montmorillonite plus hematite;—montmorillonite plus heulandite. These minerals occur as secondary pore-linings and pore-fills. Diagenesis has resulted in significant reduction of original permeability within 2000 years of deposition. Data indicate that the diagenesis of these rocks may not be dependent on depth of burial or temperature. The major diagenetic control was the chemistry of the groundwater. Introduction of groundwater resulted in the solution of unstable components (glass, pyroxene) and penecontemporaneous precipitation from pore-fluids of dissolved ionic species. Specific cements formed in the sands at any time are considered to be a function of the chemistry of the pore-fluids. Boundaries between different diagenetic assemblages in these rocks are probably determined more by ground water chemistry than by temperature or pressure.

INTRODUCTION

Recent frontier drilling activity has spurred interest in volcanic sediments as potential reservoir rocks. With the ever widening search for hydrocarbons, "dirty" volcanic sandstones are being explored in the hope that retained porosity and permeability will be sufficient for substantial hydrocarbon accumulation. The presence of relatively large percentages of unstable components (feldspars, amphiboles, pyroxenes, glass) in many volcaniclastic deposits is of concern to the explorationist because of the susceptibility of these unstables to post-depositional alteration. Such alteration commonly results in the occlusion of primary porosity and reduction of permeability.

The reservoir potential of sedimentary deposits is in part a function of the timing, nature, and degree of diagenesis. This is particularly true for volcaniclastic rocks, where little is known about the interrelationship between diagenetic susceptibility and the timing, nature, and degree of diagenesis.

Timing of diagenesis is important because early stage diagenetic occlusion of pore-throats may prevent substantial hydrocarbon accumulation or migration. This is particularly significant in volcaniclastic sediments because timing may be intimately related to depth of burial. Does significant occlusion of pore space in volcaniclastic sediments require substantial depth of burial? If so, then hydrocarbon accumulation may be favored in these sediments.

The nature of diagenesis may be important because certain diagenetic reactions may require elevated temperatures, pressures, and brine concentrations. In young basins, the production of hydrocarbons may be speeded up by rapid burial and concomitant temperature increase. On the other hand, too high a temperature may cause destruction of hydrocarbons, particularly oil. But what temperatures and pressures are required to produce the diagenetic assemblages in volcanic basins? The nature of diagenesis is also important from an engineering viewpoint. The chemistry of the pore fluids and resultant diagenetic pore fills will directly affect engineering aspects of drilling, drilling fluids, and stimulation designs. Owing to the composition of volcanic sediments and the tectonic setting of volcanic areas, the physicochemical controls (temperature, pressure, concentration) may be distinctly different than for more mature, non-volcanogenic sediments.

Exploration in volcanic sediments must not consider diagenesis alone. Also important are the

Copyright © 1979, The Society of Economic
Paleontologists and Mineralogists

size and tectonic setting of basins in which volcaniclastic sediments are deposited. Attempts at
regional correlation must be carried out within
the tectonic framework of the basin of deposition.
Key factors to successful exploration will thus
depend on correct recognition and prediction of
diagenetic changes as well as the "correlatability"
of individual units within the area of interest.

This paper deals with both the deposition and
diagenesis of continental volcanic sediments in
a fore-arc basin. Although this area is presently
non-productive, we feel that the style of deposition and diagenesis may be typical of fore-arc
basins in general. This paper focusses specifically
on regional aspects of sediment deposition, as
well as the timing, nature, and degree of diagenesis
in rocks ranging from 3 years to 35 million years
old.

LOCATION AND TECTONIC SETTING

Southern Guatemala is a classic area of fore-arc
sedimentation. It is located at a convergent lithospheric plate junction, being flanked to the south
by the topographic expression of a subduction
zone, the Middle American Trench, and to the
north by an imposing range of andesitic stratovolcanoes (Figs. 1, 2). Tectonic development of this
area has been dominated by interaction of the
underthrusting Cocos plate and overriding Carib-
bean plate (Figs. 1, 2).

Seismologic, structural, and volcanologic data
"suggest a segmented underthrusting process in
which both the underthrust slab and the overriding
wedge of lithosphere are broken" (Carr, 1976,
p. 828). Separate segments of the underthrust slab
are considered to descend into the mantle with
different strikes and dips (Stoiber and Carr, 1973;

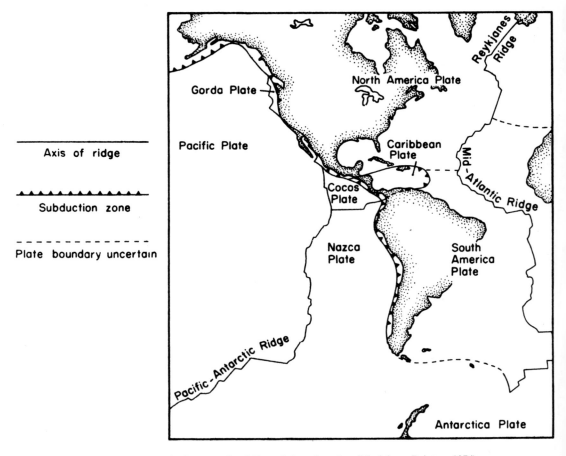

FIG. 1.—Tectonic framework of Central Americas (modified from Painter, 1974).

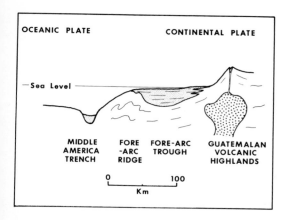

FIG. 2.—Sedimentary basins associated with the convergent lithospheric plate junction in Central America. Section is drawn from the Volcano Fuego to the Middle America Trench. The thickness of the fore-arc trough is assumed.

Carr and Stoiber, 1977). Thus the convergent plate margin in Central America is broken by transverse structures into eight segments, each extending from the trench to the volcanic arc (Fig. 3). The lithosphere in Guatemala may be divided into three segments each approximately 150 km long and ranging in width from 60 km to 100 km.

SEDIMENT DEPOSITION

The surficial geology of the volcanic province and Pacific coastal plain of Guatemala indicates

a complex Holocene history (Figs. 4, 5) which we consider related to the segmentation of the lithospheric plates. In western and eastern segments of Guatemala (Fig. 5) the coastal plain is generally less then 20 km wide (from volcanic province to the ocean). Holocene sedimentation rates are relatively low, streams are often incised, and Pleistocene and Tertiary sediments cover large areas of these segments. In the central segment of Guatemala, the coastal plain is 40 km wide. Sedimentation rates are very high, and active floodplains cover most of the coastal plain. Thus the surficial geology of the coastal plain allows for ready subdivision into three distinct segments, based on width of the coastal plain, rates of sedimentation, and ages of sediments exposed (Fig. 5). These divisions, based on surface geology, agree well with the segmentation of the lithospheric plates as proposed by Carr and Stoiber (1977) and Stoiber and Carr (1973) (Fig. 3).

The apparent coincidence of surficial coastal plain geology and segmentation of the lithospheric plates (Figs. 3, 5) may have considerable significance in terms of exploration efforts in Recent or ancient fore-arc basins. A single, relatively small geomorphic unit, such as the Guatemalan coastal plain, may be composed of several segments, each of which may have been subjected to distinct tectono-sedimentary influences. It is important to note that both composition and texture of sediments can change from one segment to the next as the composition of the source volcanoes changes from segment to segment

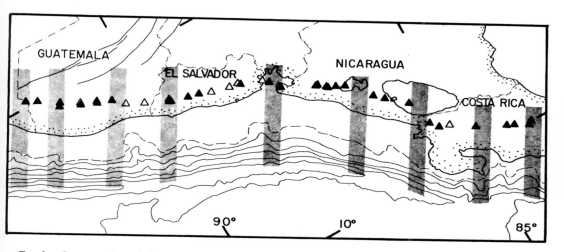

FIG. 3.—Segmentation of the Central American arc. Stippled bars mark positions of transverse structures. Solid triangles mark the location of volcanoes with historic eruptions; open triangles indicate volcanoes with solfataric activity. Solid lines in Guatemala are surface faults. (From Carr and Stoiber, 1977, fig. 1, p. 151).

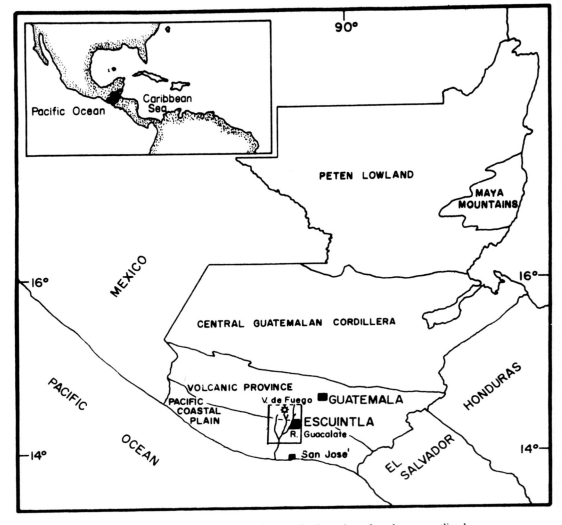

FIG. 4.—Geologic provinces of Guatemala. Location of study area outlined.

(Stoiber and Carr, 1973). The amount of sediment being deposited at any one time will also vary from segment to segment, as the rate of subsidence and rate of tephra production vary. For example, the subsiding central Guatemala segment is the most volcanologically active in Central America (Stoiber and Carr, 1973). Large volumes of sediment are being produced regularly by glowing avalanches and airfall (Davies et al., 1978). These tephra are generally redeposited by lahars and streamfloods in the same segment, resulting in a rapid build-up of sedimentary deposits. The volcanic quiescence of flanking eastern and western Guatemalan segments, combined with their lack of relative subsidence, suggests that correlative sediments in these segments may be very thin or absent.

Segmentation of subducting plates has been postulated not only for Central America, but also the Andes (Stillitoe, 1974) and the Japanese arcs (Carr et al., 1973). Thus the segmented nature of lithospheric slabs should have considerable impact on the practice of stratigraphy in fore-arc regions. If individual segments operate as quasi-independent basins of deposition, then correlations of sedimentary units along depositional strike in fore-arc basins should be attempted only with considerable caution. These basins are small,

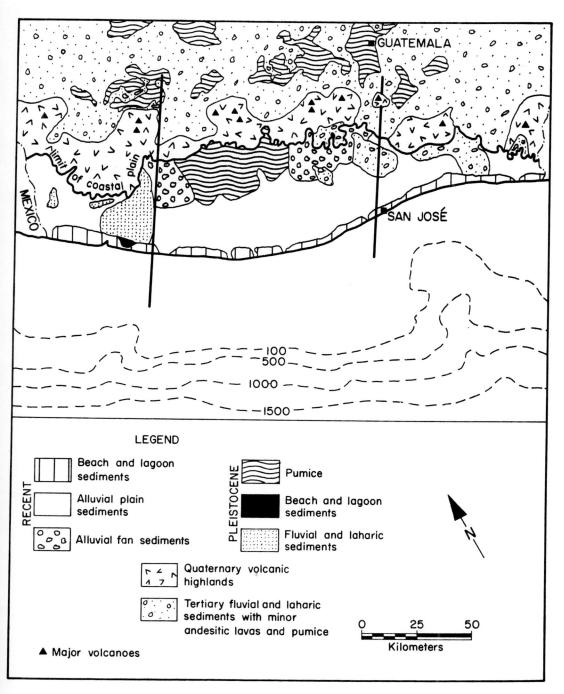

FIG. 5.—Geologic map of Pacific coastal plain, Guatemala. Vertical lines represent boundaries between the western, central, and eastern Guatemalan segments, based on surficial geology and the work of Stoiber and Carr (1973). Surficial geology was mapped using Skylab photographs, aerial photographs (1:60,000), field checking of all lithologic units, and field mapping in selected areas on a scale of 1:50,000. Isobaths in meters.

150 km long and 50 to 100 km wide. Sediments in adjacent segments can be expected to vary in composition, texture, and thickness. Rapid changes will occur at the margins of the small basins across narrow boundaries which are reflections of transverse fractures in the underlying lithosphere. Exploration efforts should take into account the variability in thickness and lithology which may be encountered between adjacent basins.

SAMPLES

Samples for diagenetic analysis were collected from exposures of continental sediments in the central Guatemalan segment (Figs. 5, 6). The geology of this area is comparatively well known, much of it having been field-mapped on a scale of 1:50,000 (Hebberger, 1977; Hunter, 1976; Tharpe, 1976; Quearry, 1975). Samples range from medium-grained sandstones to conglomerates, and are poorly to well sorted. A variety of ages and continental sedimentary processes are represented by the suite of samples selected for study (Table 1). Absolute dating of a number of the specimens is possible.

Samples with the prefix L were collected from laharic sediments deposited on the 25th of June, 1973. Virtually all of these sediments were derived from fresh volcanic ash and glowing avalanches erupted during the February 1973 eruption of the volcano Fuego.

Sample RIP was collected from a 7 meter deep foundation trench in fluvial sediments of the Rio Guacalate floodplain. Pottery fragments and field relationships indicate that these sediments are very recent, probably on the order of several hundreds of years old. Certainly they are less than 2000 years old.

Samples prefixed by ADL were collected from laharic deposits which outcrop over a large area of the Rio Guacalate floodplain (Hunter, 1976; Quearry, 1975). Pottery fragments are abundant in these samples, and have been dated as originating between 100 B.C. and 100 A.D. by archaeologist Edwin Shook (Personal Communication).

Field relationships indicate that these dated lahars are older than sample RIP, thus allowing age bracketting of sample RIP (Table 1).

Sample P was collected from a large, well exposed, generally indurated rock sequence. This rock sequence includes, at its base, layers of airfall tephra (Fig. 7). One layer is friable and composed almost entirely of hornblende crystals 1 cm in diameter. A number of these crystals were collected and K/Ar age dating was performed. This revealed the airfall tephra to be 35 m.y. (± 7 m.y.) old. (The large error factor is a result of the small sample size available for analysis. This date is surprisingly old. Tertiary continental sediments of the Pacific coastal plain have been considered to be younger than this. Thus we use this date with some trepidation, and only as an indicator of age). Samples with the prefix AP, EC, and T were collected from Tertiary rock sequences (Fig. 6).

Tertiary deposits are all continental in origin. Large vertical exposures reveal that the sediments are generally conglomeratic. Many individual beds are very thick (10 m or more) and laterally discontinuous. Channel-like erosion surfaces are common in many outcrops (Figs. 7,8,9 and 10). On the basis of comparison with recent sediments in this area, grain-supported Tertiary conglomerates and sandstones are considered fluvial in

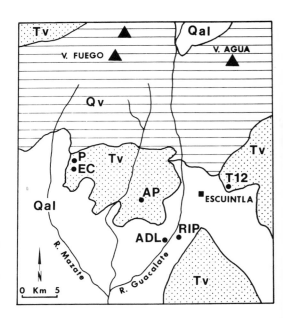

FIG. 6.—Sample localities and geologic map of study area. Localities designated by circles, volcanoes by triangles. T_v = Tertiary volcaniclastic rocks; Q_v = Quaternary volcanic rocks; Q_{al} = Quaternary alluvium.

TABLE 1.—AGE OF SAMPLES ANALYSED, AND INFERRED PROCESS OF SEDIMENT DEPOSITION

Sample Prefix	Age	Sedimentary Process
L	1973 A.D.	LAHAR
RIP	<<2000 B.P.	FLUVIAL
ADL	2000 B.P.	LAHAR
AP	Tertiary	FLUVIAL
EC	Tertiary	FLUVIAL
T-12	Tertiary	LAHAR
P	35±7 m.y.	FLUVIAL

origin, while matrix-supported deposits are probably laharic in origin.

COMPOSITION

Tertiary-Recent sediments analyzed were derived from andesitic stratovolcanoes of the nearby magmatic arc. Porphyritic volcanic rock fragments are the dominant constituent, and contain feldspar and pyroxene crystals set in a glassy ground mass (Fig. 11, Table 2). Free crystals of plagioclase feldspar and pyroxene are subordinate (Table 2). All specimens are feldspathic litharenites (classification of Folk, 1968), dominated by feldspar-rich volcanic rock fragments. Quartz is virtually absent. Semi-quantitative X-ray diffraction analyses of bulk sandstone samples further indicate the importance of both orthoclase and plagioclase feldspars in these rocks (Table 3). Most glass occurs as a groundmass in rock fragments, rather than as discrete shards.

DIAGENETIC FEATURES

Analysis of samples from continental deposits of the Guatemalan fore-arc basin enables comparison of diagenetic features developed in immature, unstable volcanic sandstones. The complete diagenetic sequence consists of the precipitation of cements in three episodes: I—Hematite-Goethite, II—Montmorillonite plus Hematite, III—Montmorillonite plus Heulandite.

The sequential development of each of these episodes of cementation can be observed both in thin section (Fig. 12) and in scanning electron micrographs (Fig. 13 through 18). Diagenetic pore-coatings and pore-fills compose more than 20 percent of individual samples (Table 2), and have resulted in a major reduction of primary porosity and permeability. Hematite-goethite, and montmorillonite form successive halos separating detrital grains from the later pore-filling heulandite cement.

Hematite-goethite.—Hematite-goethite is a common diagenetic phase and occurs in all samples studied, both in association with altering ferro-magnesian minerals and as a pore-lining. In thin section the pore-lining hematite-goethite may be seen to form a thin halo around detrital grains. In several instances, it is so well developed that the pore-system is completely filled. The pore coatings around any single grain may consist of either hematite or goethite, or the coating may be a mixture of both minerals. SEM observations indicate that pore-linings possess a "ropy" texture which preserves an extensive microporosity with-

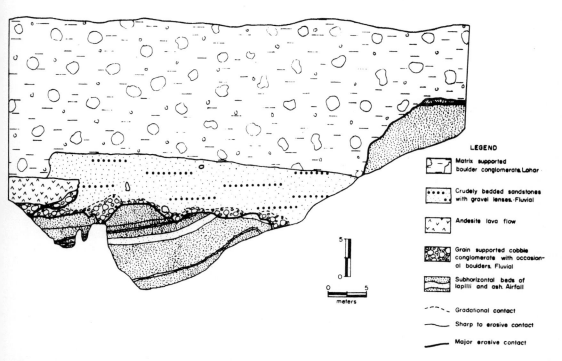

LEGEND

Matrix supported boulder conglomerate. Lahar

Crudely bedded sandstones with gravel lenses. Fluvial

Andesite lava flow

Grain supported cobble conglomerate with occasional boulders. Fluvial

Subhorizontal beds of lapilli and ash. Airfall

Gradational contact

Sharp to erosive contact

Major erosive contact

FIG. 7.—Lithologies exposed in Tertiary continental volcaniclastics at locality P. Interpretations of depositional processes for individual units illustrated in Figures 7 through 10, are given in legends. For location of individual outcrops see Figure 6.

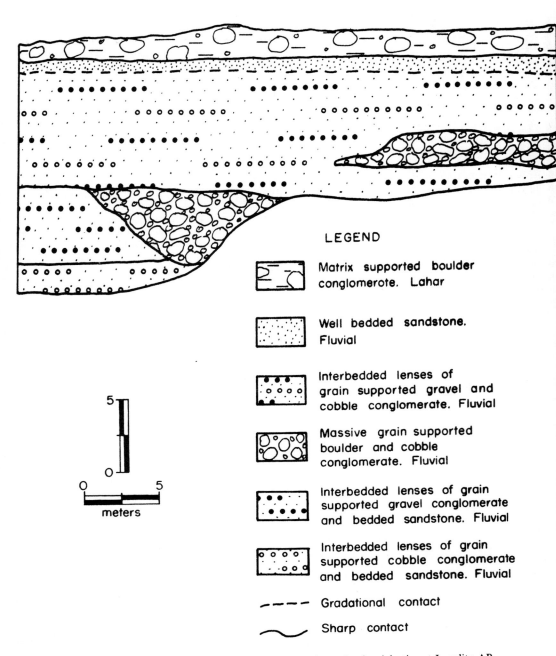

LEGEND

Matrix supported boulder conglomerote. Lahar

Well bedded sandstone. Fluvial

Interbedded lenses of grain supported gravel and cobble conglomerate. Fluvial

Massive grain supported boulder and cobble conglomerate. Fluvial

Interbedded lenses of grain supported gravel conglomerate and bedded sandstone. Fluvial

Interbedded lenses of grain supported cobble conglomerate and bedded sandstone. Fluvial

- - - - Gradational contact

〜〜 Sharp contact

meters

FIG. 8.—Lithologies exposed in Tertiary continental volcaniclastics at Locality AP.

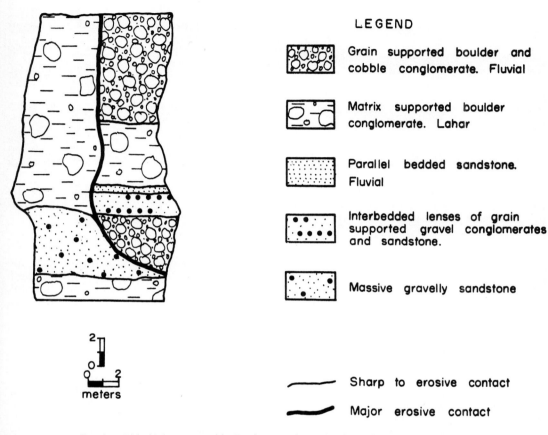

LEGEND

Grain supported boulder and cobble conglomerate. Fluvial

Matrix supported boulder conglomerate. Lahar

Parallel bedded sandstone. Fluvial

Interbedded lenses of grain supported gravel conglomerates and sandstone.

Massive gravelly sandstone

Sharp to erosive contact

Major erosive contact

FIG. 9.—Lithologies exposed in Tertiary continental volcaniclastics at Locality EC.

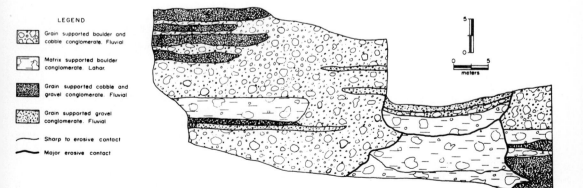

LEGEND

Grain supported boulder and cobble conglomerate. Fluvial

Matrix supported boulder conglomerate. Lahar.

Grain supported cobble and gravel conglomerate. Fluvial

Grain supported gravel conglomerate. Fluvial

Sharp to erosive contact

Major erosive contact

FIG. 10.—Lithologies exposed in Tertiary continental volcaniclastics at Locality T-12.

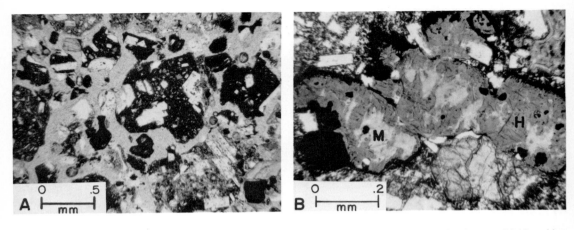

FIG. 11.—Photomicrographs of Guatemalan volcaniclastics. *A*, Field view illustrating the dominance of feldspathic volcanic rock fragments in Guatemalan volcaniclastics. Groundmass (dark) is volcanic glass. (Plain polarized light). *B*, Pyroxene crystal altered to hematite (H) and montmorillonite (M).

in the pore-lining. Numerous dehydration cracks occur in this pore-lining (Fig. 17). Microprobe analysis of hematite pore-linings indicate significant proportions of manganese (5.3% MnO_2) and titanium (1.1% TiO_2).

SEM observations confirm the fibrous nature of the goethite and also show cracks, which may represent partial dehydration. The goethite pore-lining does not show the high microporosity characteristic of the hematite. Microprobe analysis of goethite pore-linings indicate essentially pure iron, containing no manganese or titanium.

Montmorillonite plus hematite.—The first multimineral diagenetic assemblage to occur in Guatemalan volcaniclastics is montmorillonite plus hematite. This assemblage occurs as a halo around detrital grains, succeeding the previously deposited halo of hematite and goethite. It also occurs in bubbles and tubes in volcanic glass. In thin section, and with the SEM, this montmorillonite grain coating can be seen to be a fibrous to platelet-like pore-lining. Individual platelets are oriented perpendicular to the grain on which they are attached (Figs. 14–17) and may coalesce to form a continuous coat. These coats have an average thickness of 10 μ, and a maximum thickness of 30 μ. This coating often completely occludes original pore-space. Montmorillonite grain coatings occur equally on all varieties of detrital grains. Hematite may occur within the montmorillonite as a distinct layer, apparently separating the montmorillonite grain-coating into two successive layers (Fig. 12). It is possible that this hematite layer may reflect a temporary return to the pore-fluid chemistry of the earlier episode.

X-ray diffraction patterns of oriented aggregates of the less than 5 μ size fraction indicate that calcium is the major exchange ion. Chemical analyses of isolated montmorillonite pore-fill support this contention, and also demonstrate that the montmorillonite is dioctahedral (Table 4).

Montmorillonite plus heulandite.—The final diagenetic assemblage is montmorillonite plus heulandite, and represents the most intense episode of diagenesis recognized in Guatemalan volcaniclastics. The montmorillonite is fibrous to platelet-like. Heulandite occurs as elongate crystals up to 0.2 mm in length, which may form as pore-linings or as pore-fill cement (Figs. 12, 15, 16). Heulandite always occurs within pores which are lined with the montmorillonite-hematite lining of episode II (Fig. 18).

The heulandite may be identified by petrographic characteristics and X-ray diffraction patterns. Table 5 lists diffraction data for heulandite separated from the pores of the Guatemalan volcaniclastics, together with data from a reference heulandite from Prospect Park, New Jersey (Deer, Howie, and Zussman, 1966, p. 412). Chemical analyses of isolated heulandite crystals, as well as microprobe analyses of "*in situ*" crystals indicate that calcium is the dominant cation. Sodium and potassium are quantitatively less important, and occur in approximately equal amounts. The ratio Si/(Si + Al) is some 0.77 (Table 4).

Both montmorillonite and heulandite are much better developed in coarser-grained sandstone horizons than in finer-grained horizons of the same zone. This is true even if the finer-grained sediments have been more deeply buried than the coarser-grained sediments.

TABLE 2.—AVERAGE COMPOSITION OF VOLCANICLASTIC SEDIMENTS, GUATEMALA

Sample Prefix	Free Crystals			Porphyritic V.R.F's			Diagenetic Minerals			
	Feldspar	Pyroxene	Others	Feldspathic	Pyroxene	Feldspar/Pyroxene	Clay	Fe$_2$O$_2$	Heulandite	Pores
L (1973 A.D.) RIP	8	7	0	41	5	17	13	5	—	4
ADL (<2000 B.P.)	2	2	2	51	29	—	2	—	—	12
ADL (2000 B.P.)	13	12	—	25	1	4	41	2	—	2
Tertiary (35±7 m.y.)	3	4	2	34	4	28	15	4	4	1

(Data derived from point-count analysis of thin sections: 500 points per section. Data are percentages).

TABLE 3.—SEMIQUANTITATIVE X-RAY DIFFRACTION ANALYSES OF BULK SAMPLES OF GUATEMALAN VOLCANICLASTIC SANDSTONES

Sample	Orthoclase	Plagioclase	Montmorillonite	Glass	Hypersthene	Augite	Pigeonite	Hematite	Goethite	Heulandite
RIP:1	39	32	7	5	1	4	2	7	3	—
ADL:1	37	30	8	10	1	5	2	3	2	2
ADL:3	35	31	7	12	2	6	3	2	1	1
AP:2	39	34	7	5	2	4	2	3	2	3
AP:6	36	29	10	9	1	6	2	2	1	4
EC:2	33	24	11	9	1	3	3	11	2	2
T-12-27B	36	30	12	5	—	4	1	5	2	7
T-12-27E	35	30	9	6	1	4	1	4	3	7
P:6	36	26	8	7	2	5	3	3	2	8

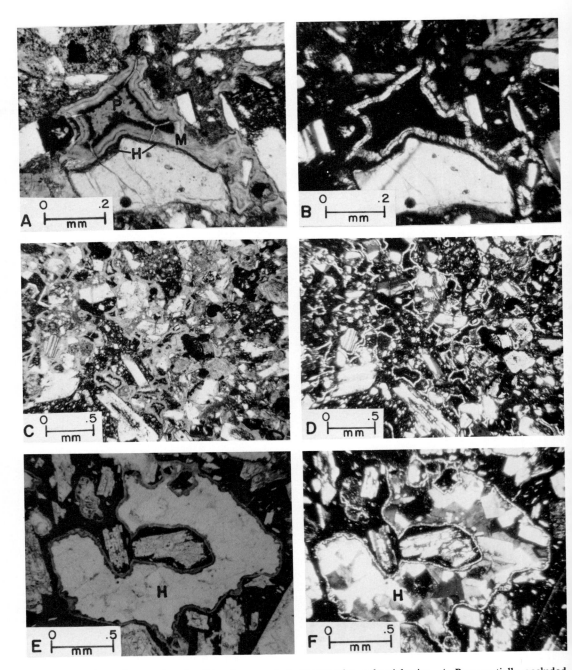

Fig. 12.—Photomicrographs of authigenic cements in Guatemalan volcaniclastics. *A*, Pore partially occluded by secondary minerals. H = Hematite-goethite halo around detrital grain. M = Montmorillonite pore-lining with central and inner layers of hematite. P = Open pore. (Plain polarized light). *B*, Crossed-nicols photograph of 12A illustrating the fibrous nature of the montmorillonite pore-lining. *C*, Field view of volcaniclastic rock with pores occluded with secondary montmorillonite plus hematite. (Plain polarized light). *D*, Crossed-nicols photograph of 12C. Note the fibrous nature of montmorillonite pore-lining (diagenetic phase II). *E*, Heulandite crystals (H) filling pore lined with hematite and montmorillonite (Plain polarized light). *F*, Crossed-nicols photograph of 12E.

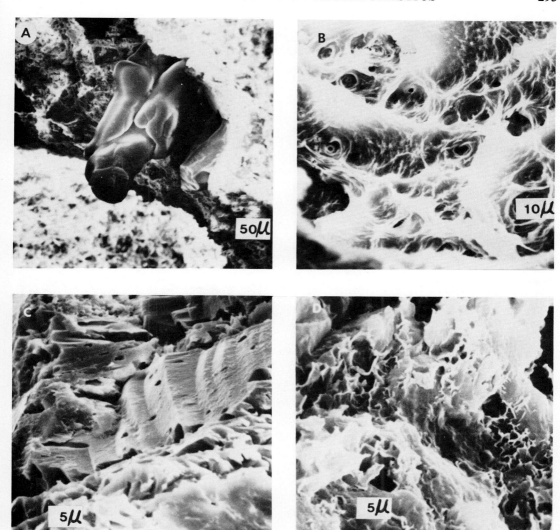

Fig. 13.—SEM's of 1973 laharic deposits. *A*, Glass shard showing evidence of airborne cooling (spindle-shape). *B*, Close up of glass-shard surface showing effects of hydration. *C*, Shards contain many bubble and gas tubes, giving the fragments a large surface area. *D*, Diagenetic montmorillonite forming in this recent lahar.

ORIGIN OF DIAGENETIC MINERALS

The post-depositional, diagenetic origin for hematite, goethite, montmorillonite, and heulandite in Guatemalan volcaniclastics is based on the following criteria:

(1) The delicate fibrous to platelet-like nature of the hematite, goethite, and montmorillonite, and their tendency to be aligned perpendicular to grain boundaries.

(2) The crystal habit of some of the heulandite.

(3) The different minerals occur sequentially within a pore as successive, concentric, grain coatings or pore-linings.

The delicate habit and orientation of the various components indicate that these minerals were not introduced into the pores in a solid state. Rather, we consider that these so-called diagenetic minerals are authigenic in origin, having been precipitated in original pore-space by moving fluids.

TIMING AND DEGREE OF DIAGENESIS

The range of samples studied enables us to suggest a time scale for the development of the full diagenetic sequence. The youngest samples analyzed (L, 3 years old, Table 1) contain volcanic glass which is slightly weathered (Fig. 13). Hema-

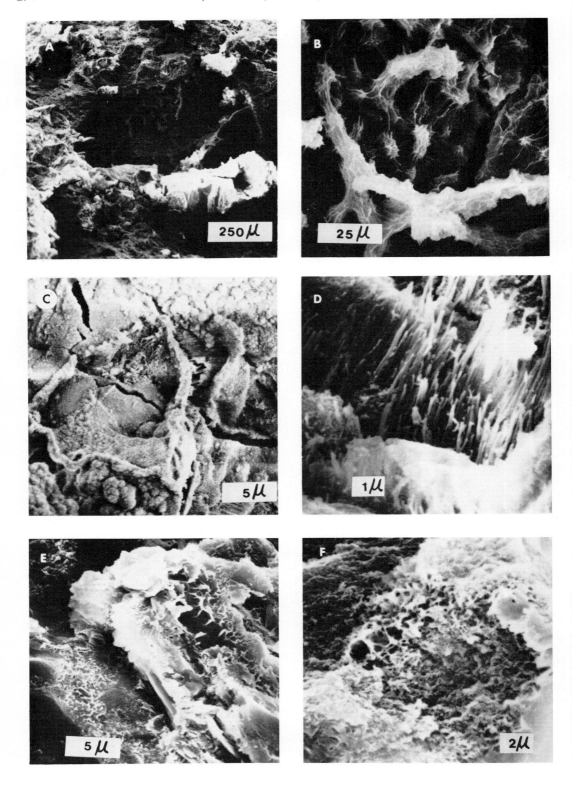

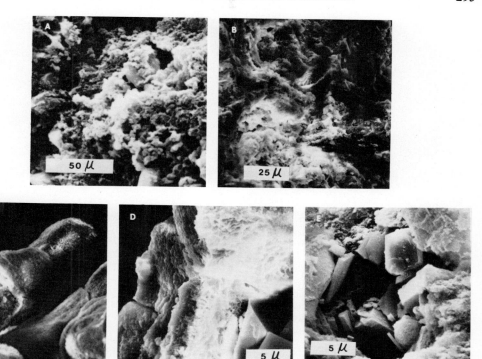

Fig. 15.—SEM's of lahar samples (ADL), 2000 years old. *A*, Diagenetic montmorillonite on pore surface. *B*, Pore-throat occluded by diagenetic montmorillonite. *C*, Hematite developed as thick pore-coating. *D*, In this micrograph, the entire sequence of cements may be seen as successive layers: hematite, montmorillonite, and heulandite. *E*, Diagenetic heulandite extensively developed as well formed crystals within the pore system.

tite-goethite halos occur in isolated areas of these samples, as does montmorillonite. Much of these cements appears (in thin section) to represent the alteration of ferro-magnesian minerals and glass. No heulandite occurs in these samples. These very young samples have an average porosity of 20% and average permeability of 1578 md (Fig. 19).

Sample RIP (<< 2000 years old) contains pore-linings of hematite, goethite, and montmorillonite. Heulandite is absent (Tables 2, 3). Average porosity is 18%, and average permeability is 731 md (Fig. 19).

Sample ADL (2000 years old) contains all three diagenetic phases from goethite pore-linings to heulandite/montmorillonite pore-fill (Tables 2, 3). The heulandite was not recognized in thin section,

probably because of its small size. However, it may be seen in SEM photographs (Fig. 15), and was revealed by X-ray analysis (Table 3). Average porosity is 14%, and average permeability is 104 md (Fig. 19). There is no evidence of substantial burial of the unit from which samples labelled "ADL" were taken. This unit is currently buried to a depth of 2 meters, in the floodplain of the Rio Guacalate. This flood plain is aggrading, and thus the 2 m burial probably represents a maximum depth of burial for this unit.

Tertiary volcaniclastics contain highest percentages of the heulandite cement. Porosity is 16% and permeability is 73 md (Fig. 19). The similarity in diagenetic assemblages between Holocene and Tertiary rocks in this area indicate that physico-chemical conditions (temperature,

Fig. 14.—SEM's of fluvial sands, <<2000 years old, sample prefix RIP. *A*, General view showing beginning of alteration in a pore. *B*, Close-up of 14A shows that glass fragments have begun to hydrate. *C*, Goethite developed from hydration of ferromagnesian minerals. *D*, Close-up of goethite mass illustrating fibrous nature. *E*, Diagenetic montmorillonite developed on a pore surface. *F*, Delicate diagenetic montmorillonite developed on top of pre-existing goethite.

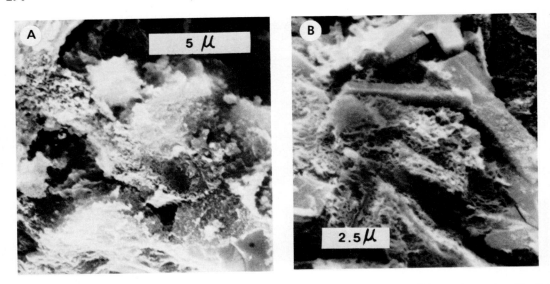

FIG. 16.—SEM's of diagenetic montmorillonite in 2000 year old lahar (ADL). A, Diagenetic montmorillonite developed as crenulated, fibrous plates. B, Montmorillonite development has continued after heulandite crystallization as evidenced by montmorillonite covering heulandite laths.

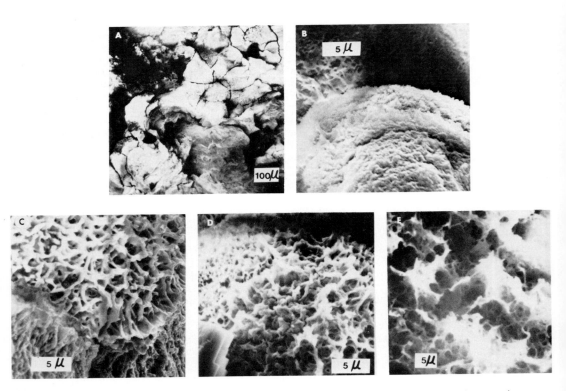

FIG. 17.—SEM's of Tertiary volcaniclastics (Sample prefix P). A, Pore lined with hematite contains many cracks indicating dehydration, perhaps from goethite. B, Hematite pore-lining with layered aspect. C, Hematite pore-lining has "ropy" texture and high degree of microporosity. D, Montmorillonite developed on top of previously developed hematite pore-lining. E, Diagenetic montmorillonite is very delicate. Note crenulations and numerous fibrous projections.

TABLE 4.—ANALYSES OF GLASS, MONTMORILLONITE AND HEULANDITE

	Glass	Glass	Mont.	Mont.	Heul.	Heul.
SiO_2	67.21	64.83	52.25	53.11	56.28	55.93
TiO_2	0.13	0.19	0.41	0.38	0.07	0.04
Al_2O_3	13.43	15.81	17.64	17.85	16.73	16.87
Fe_2O_3	1.17	1.63	4.10	3.74	1.13	1.19
FeO	0.49	0.61	0.19	0.21	0.17	0.24
MgO	1.17	1.07	3.53	3.47	0.40	0.36
CaO	1.82	1.82	1.51	1.59	6.36	6.43
Na_2O	3.52	3.40	0.27	0.23	1.74	1.68
K_2O	2.17	2.23	0.23	0.31	1.73	1.71
H_2O^+	8.71	8.50	8.51	8.25	11.54	12.03
H_2O^-	8.71	8.50	11.86	10.98	3.89	3.51
	108.53	100.09	100.50	100.12	100.04	99.99

pressure, gross chemistry) have remained essentially the same for approximately 35 million years.

PHASE RULE CONSIDERATIONS

The diagenetic minerals present in these rocks can be considered in the context of an eight component system:

$$CaO \cdot Fe_2O_3 \cdot MgO \cdot Al_2O_3 \cdot SiO_2 \cdot Na_2O$$
$$\cdot K_2O \cdot H_2O$$

For the purpose of graphical representation this system may be simplified if two assumptions are made. First, it may be assumed that H_2O is a mobile component (as defined by Thompson, 1955), and that its activity is fixed but independent of the bulk composition of the system. (The activity of H_2O in these Guatemalan volcaniclastics is fixed by the local groundwater). Second,

the activity of aqueous SiO_2 may be fixed by its equilibrium with amorphous silica (the silicic glass present in the sandstones). These two assumptions reduce the system to six components:

$$CaO \cdot Fe_2O_3 \cdot MgO \cdot Al_2O_3 \cdot Na_2O \cdot K_2O$$

This six component system can be described with the combined use of ACF and AKF diagrams (Figs. 20, 21). Arbitrary values for temperature (25° C) and pressure (1 atm) further define the system. In interpreting these diagrams it should be stressed that the diagenetic episode II, montmorillonite plus hematite, is doubtless influenced by the volcanic glass present in the rocks, and more properly might be considered montmorillonite plus hematite plus glass. Similarly, episode III, montmorillonite plus heulandite, may be considered montmorillonite plus heulandite plus glass. Figures 20 through 26 indicate that montmorillon-

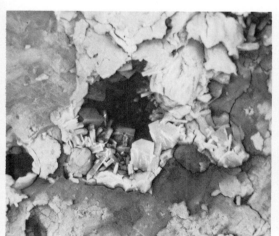

200μ

FIG. 18.—SEM stereo-pair revealing the ultimate stage in diagenesis of Tertiary volcaniclastics. Heulandite crystals have developed as a pore-fill, succeeding earlier hematite, montmorillonite pore-linings.

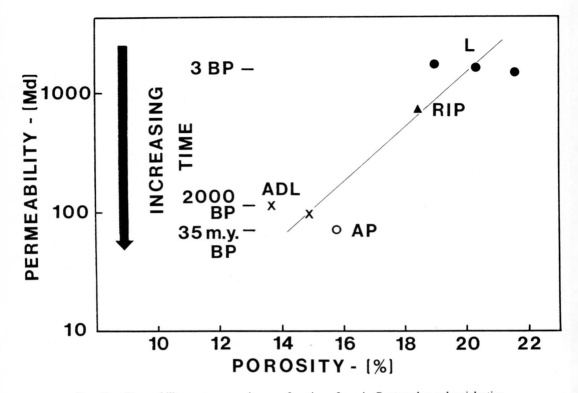

FIG. 19.—Permeability versus porosity as a function of age in Guatemalan volcaniclastics.

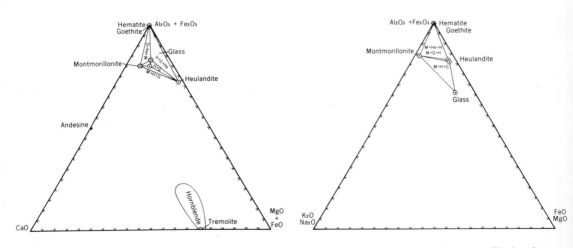

FIG. 20.—ACF Ternary diagram of montmorillonite, hematite/goethite, heulandite, and glass. This diagram reveals 3 distinct solutions to the Gibbs Phase Rule. (1) Montmorillonite plus hematite/goethite plus glass. (2) Montmorillonite plus heulandite plus glass. (3) Heulandite plus hematite/goethite plus glass.

FIG. 21.—AKF diagram of montmorillonite, hematite/goethite, heulandite and glass. This diagram reveals 2 distinct solutions to the Gibbs Phase Rule: (1) Montmorillonite plus heulandite plus glass. (2) Montmorillonite plus hematite/goethite plus heulandite.

TALBE 5.—X-RAY DIFFRACTION DATA FOR HEULANDITE ISOLATED FROM SAMPLE AP6, GUATEMALA

Sample Guatemala		Prospect Park, New Jersey*	
dobs	I/Io	dobs	I/Io
8.91	100	8.90	10
7.98	27	7.94	2
6.84	13	6.80	1
		6.63	1
5.95	10	5.92	1
		5.58	1
		5.24	1
		5.09	1
		4.89	1
4.69	17	4.69	2
4.45	20	4.45	2
4.37	8	4.36	1
3.98	22	3.97	2
3.89	33	3.89	3
3.85	12	3.83	1
		3.71	1
3.56	10	3.56	1
3.47	11	3.47	1
3.40	19	3.40	2
		3.12	1
3.09	13	3.07	1
		3.03	1
2.97	45	2.97	4
2.83	9	2.80	1

*From Deer et al., 1966, p. 412.

ite plus hematite plus glass and montmorillonite plus heulandite plus glass are topologically distinct solutions to the Gibbs phase rule.

THERMODYNAMIC CONSIDERATIONS

Equilibrium thermodynamics make possible the calculation of possible pore-water chemistry which prevailed during various stages of cementation in Guatemalan volcaniclastic deposits. Stability relationships for the various minerals may be calculated in terms of the components of the system at a fixed temperature and pressure, with mobile H_2O and a fixed activity of SiO_2 (aqueous). We realize that equilibrium reactions only pertain in a closed system in which all reactions have proceded to completion. These conditions are not met by the open system diagenesis proposed for

these rocks. However, the technique is a valid method for approximating the relationships between phases. (For a more extended discussion of the limits and application of thermodynamics to natural water systems see Morgan, 1967). The stability fields of the various silicate minerals are shown in Figures 22 through 26, and sets of possible ion activities are shown in Table 6. The set of data for pH = 6 is probably the most likely set of conditions. This would represent a dilute ground water altered by dissolution of unstable minerals in the volcaniclastic deposits.

DIAGENETIC PROCESSES

Consideration of petrographic, field, and chemical data suggests that the diagenesis of Guatemalan volcaniclastic sandstones has occurred in a near-surface, open leaching system, through the action of percolating ground waters operating at normal temperatures and pressures. (For description of a similar system see Hay, 1963). The chemical changes which occurred during diagenesis of these sandstones may be elucidated through comparison of chemical analyses of various whole rock samples containing the various diagenetic minerals (Table 7) with chemical analyses of the different diagenetic minerals (Table 4).

The starting material for diagenetic reactions is taken to be a volcanic glass of andesitic composition (Table 4), together with ferromagnesian minerals. Chemical analysis of the glassy ground mass of the porphyritic rock fragments indicates that this glass contains between 8 and 9 percent water. This high state of hydration indicates that the glass is somewhat altered, and is consistent with observational evidence (Fig. 13B). Both microprobe and whole-rock analyses show that the andesitic glass has an excess of sodium over potassium, and major amounts of calcium and magnesium (Table 4). Molar ratios of $Si/(Si + Al)$ range between 0.81 and 0.83.

Dissolution of glass and other unstable components in the sandstones by moving pore fluids results in a gradual change in bulk rock and pore fluid composition. As diagenesis progresses, the minerals precipitated contain more aluminum, iron, and calcium than the original glass, and are poorer in sodium and potassium.

TABLE 6.—POSSIBLE SETS OF CONCENTRATIONS AT THE HEULANDITE-MONTMORILLONITE BOUNDARY

	pH 7	pH 6	pH 5	pH 4	pH 3
log a (Al)	−16 to −14	−13 to −11	−10 to −8	−7 to −5	−4 to −1
log a (Ca^{++})	−7 to −6	−5 to −4	−3 to −2	−1 to 0	+1 to +2
log a (Mg^{++})	−5	−3	−1	+1	+3
log a (Na^+)	−3 to −7	−2 to −6	−1 to −5	0 to −4	+1 to −3
log a (K^+)	−4 to −7	−3 to −6	−2 to −5	−1 to −4	0 to −3
log a (H_4SiO_4)	−3.0	−3.0	−3.0	−3.0	−3.0

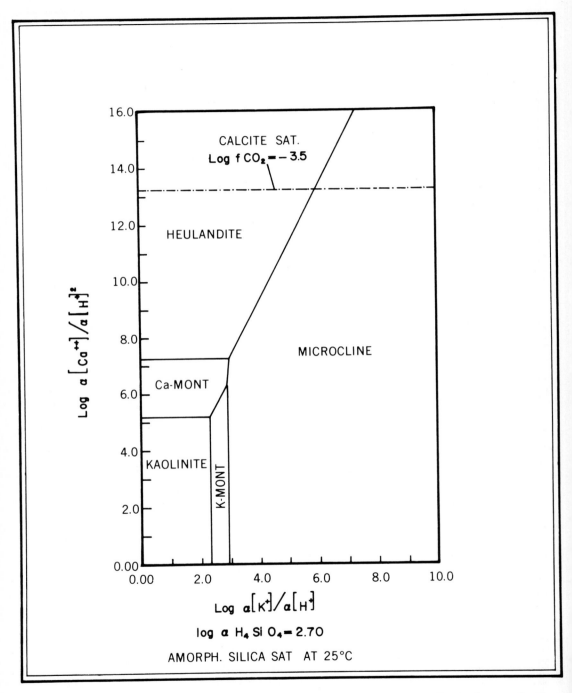

Fig. 22.—Possible phase relations in the Tertiary-Holocene volcaniclastic system, Guatemala, as a function of Calcium/Hydrogen and Potassium/Hydrogen ionic ratios in solution.

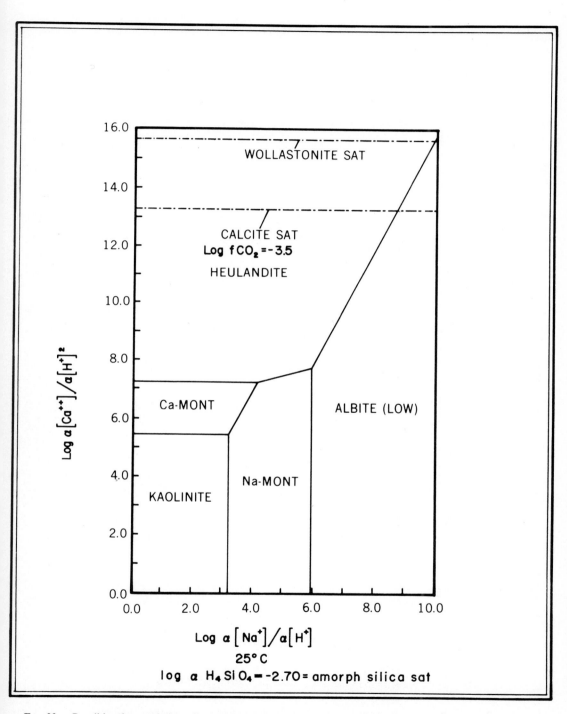

Fig. 23.—Possible phase relations in the Tertiary-Holocene volcaniclastic system, Guatemala, as a function of Calcium/Hydrogen and Sodium/Hydrogen.

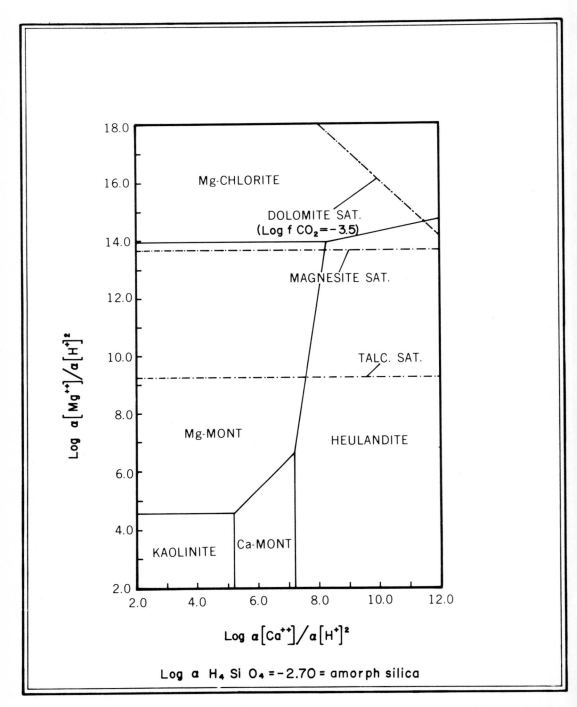

Fig. 24.—Possible phase relations in the Tertiary-Holocene volcaniclastic system, Guatemala, as a function of Calcium/Hydrogen and Magnesium/Hydrogen.

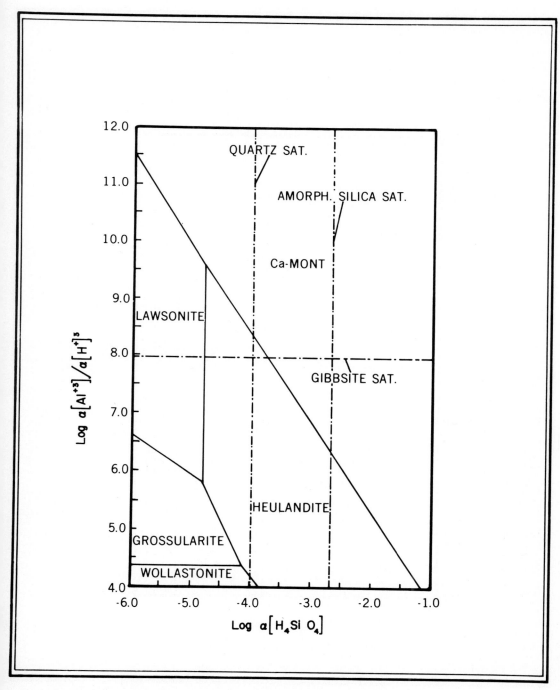

FIG. 25.—Possible phase relations in the Tertiary-Holocene volcaniclastic system, Guatemala, as a function of the Aluminum/Hydrogen ionic ratio and the Silica concentration in solution.

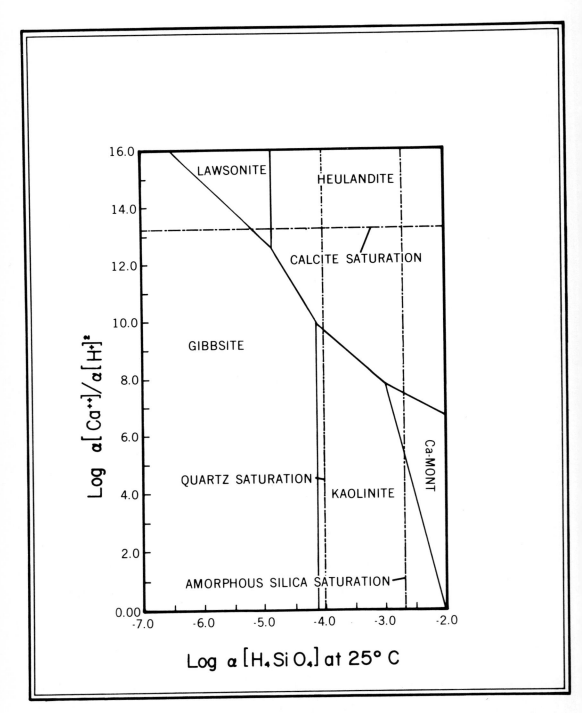

F<small>IG</small>. 26.—Possible phase relations in the Tertiary-Holocene volcaniclastic system, Guatemala, as a function of the Calcium/Hydrogen ionic ratio and the Silica concentration in solution.

TABLE 7.—WHOLE ROCK ANALYSES OF GUATAMALAN VOLCANICLASTICS

	1	2	3	4
SiO_2	58.61	63.53	60.79	60.31
TiO_2	0.83	0.75	0.68	0.59
Al_2O_3	17.70	16.01	17.75	16.81
Fe_2O_3	3.27	2.85	3.71	3.19
FeO	3.56	2.51	3.04	3.42
MgO	3.18	2.40	3.00	3.09
CaO	6.36	4.87	5.71	6.28
Na_2O	3.85	3.79	3.69	3.55
K_2O	1.74	1.34	1.49	1.69
H_2O^+	0.98	1.49	0.95	0.90
H_2O^-	0.98	0.75	0.81	0.72
MnO	0.09	0.07	0.04	0.08
P_2O_5	0.18	0.16	0.20	0.15
Total	100.35	100.52	100.11	100.78

1 = Sample L1; 2 = Sample RIP-1; 3 = Sample ADL-1; 4 = Sample AP6. SiO_2, TiO_2, Al_2O_3, MnO, + P_2O_5 determined by colorimetric methods (Shapiro and Brannock, 1962). Fe_2O_3, FeO, MgO, CaO, and Na_2O determined by atomic absorption. K_2O determined by flame photometry. H_2O^+ determined by the Penfield method. H_2O^- calculated by weight loss on heating to 105°C.

The hematite and goethite pore linings of episode I are probably the direct result of the degradation of iron rich minerals such as pyroxenes. Many ferromagnesian minerals show evidence of considerable alteration.

Continued dissolution of andesitic glass and other labile minerals results in increasing concentrations of silica, aluminum, iron and alkali earth cations in the pore fluids. When sufficient concentrations are reached, the monmorillonite of episode II begins to precipitate. It can be expected that initially almost all the silica and aluminum will be used for the formation of montmorillonite. This results in the release of hydrogen ions. However, the pore fluid pH does not increase because the amount of H^+ released is not adequate to compensate for the large amounts of hydrogen ions consumed in the hydrolysis reactions involved in the dissolution of andesite glass. Thus, the pore fluid pH continues to increase but more slowly than before the onset of montmorillonite precipitation.

As the pore fluid pH increases, the fraction of dissolved aluminum present as the aluminate ion increases. Eventually the concentration of aluminate ion and silica acid reach the point where the solution is supersaturated with respect to heulandite. Then the last diagenetic cement, heulandite, begins to precipitate.

DIAGENETIC MODEL

As ground water flows through volcaniclastic sediments, the most unstable constituents (glass, pyroxene) will dissolve, and the pore-fluids will become enriched in dissolved ionic species.

Principal dissolved ions will be silica, alumina, iron, and alkali ions. Diagenesis is considered to begin as soon as the sediment is deposited. Diagenesis may continue throughout the entire burial history of the sedimentary unit.

The specific mineral which forms at any point in the diagenetic time continuum will be a function of the chemistry of the pore-fluids. Boundaries between different diagenetic assemblages in the rocks are probably determined more by ground water chemistry and hydrology than by temperature and pressure. The chemical composition of the pore-fluids at any time is a function of (1) the length of time the pore-fluid has remained in the rock (residence time), (2) the original composition of the water, and (3) the composition of the rock. The most unstable grains will have the earliest and greatest impact on diagenesis.

As the sediment accumulates, the distance increases from the recharge area to any point within the sediment. Thus as the sediment pile thickens the pore-fluids have a progressively longer residence time within the sediment. As a direct result, the chemistry of the pore-fluids will change during the burial process. As this chemical change occurs in the pore-fluids, several minerals may form successively at any point in the system, giving rise to multiple pore-coatings. Walton (1972) indicated that for continental volcanic sediments of rhyolitic composition, the diagenetic sequence should be montmorillonite plus opal, siliceous zeolites (including clinoptilolite), quartz, and finally analcime and potassium feldspars. The Guatemalan volcaniclastics are less siliceous than the rocks studied by Walton (1972). Thus in the andesitic volcaniclastics of Guatemala the sequence is hematite-goethite, montmorillonite, and finally the aluminous zeolite, heulandite.

CONCLUSIONS

1. Volcaniclastic sediments deposited at convergent lithospheric boundaries may be deposited in small, quasi-independent basins. Southern Guatemala may be divided into three such basins, each characterized by different rates of subsidence, and sediments which may be of different compositions and textures. Exploration efforts along depositional strike may find that such forearc volcaniclastics are only correlatable over short distances parallel to depositional strike.

2. Diagenesis of Guatamalan volcaniclastics can result in almost total occlusion of original permeability within 2000 years of deposition. The chemistry of the pore-fluids is considered to be the most important control on the nature, timing, and degree of diagenesis. Temperature may be locally important, for instance in hot lahars, but it is not a major control. Depth of burial apparently plays no role in this diagenesis.

3. The diagenetic sequence I—Hematite-Goethite, II—Montmorillonite plus Hematite, III—Montmorillonite plus Heulandite is interpreted as originating through precipitation from moving ground waters. An open system diagenetic model is proposed in which unstable components (glass, pyroxene) are selectively leached from the host rocks by moving ground waters.

ACKNOWLEDGEMENTS

This study was made possible through financial support provided to Bonis and Davies by the National Science Foundation (Grant OIP-74-20040), and the Instituto Geográfico Nacional of Guatemala. Cities Service Oil Company Energy Resources Group, Exploration and Production Laboratory provided SEM and microprobe facilities together with generous technical assistance. Ig. Oscar Salazar, Chief of the Geology Section of the Instituto Geográfico Nacional of Guatemala gave invaluable logistical and administrative support of this project. Dr. K. F. Wantland of Cities Service Oil Company gave continued encouragement to this project. Archeologist Edwin Shook of Antigua Guatemala kindly dated pottery fragments collected from various locations in the Pacific coastal plain.

Field work in Guatemala was made possible through the efforts and generosity of Chiqui Bonis, Carmen Reina, Señor Fraterno Vila Betoret, Tomas Borrayo, and Daniel Gonzales. The manuscript was reviewed by Robert M. Siebert, Robert K. Park, Ted Swiderski, and Jack Thomas. We are grateful to these reviewers for their constructive comments.

REFERENCES

CARR, M. J., 1976, Underthrusting and Quaternary faulting in northern Central America: Geol. Soc. America Bull., v. 87, p. 825–829.
—— AND STOIBER, R. E., 1977, Geologic setting of some destructive earthquakes in Central America: Geol. Soc. America Bull., v. 88, p. 151–156.
——, —— AND DRAKE, C. L., 1973, Discontinuities in the deep seismic zones under the Japanese arcs: Geo. Soc. America Bull., v. 84, p. 2917–2930.
DAVIES, D. K., QUEARRY, M. W., AND BONIS, S. B., 1978, Glowing avalanches from the 1974 eruption of the volcano Fuego, Guatemala: Geol. Soc. America Bull., v. 89, p. 369–384.
DEER, W. A., HOWIE, R. A., AND ZUSSMAN, J., 1966, An introduction to the rock forming minerals; IV Tectosilicates: New York, Wiley, 528 p.
FOLK, R. L., 1968, Petrology of sedimentary rocks: Austin, Texas, Hemphills, 170 p.
HEBBERGER, J. J., 1977, Recent lahars and glowing avalanche sediments, Guatemala: M.A. Thesis, Univ. Missouri-Columbia, 117 p.
HUNTER, B. E., 1976, Fluvial sedimentation on an active volcanic continental margin: M.A. Thesis, Univ. Missouri-Columbia, 135 p.
MORGAN, J. J., 1967, Applications and limitations of thermodynamics in natural water systems, in Equilibrium concepts in natural water systems: Am. Chem. Soc. Advances in Chemistry Series, no. 67, p. 1–29.
PAINTER, J. H., 1974, Geology today: Del Mar, California, CRM Books, 527 p.
QUEARRY, M. W., 1975, Continental volcanic sediments in the region of Volcan de Fuego, Guatemala: M.A. Thesis, Univ. Missouri-Columbia, 105 p.
SILLITOE, R. H., 1974, Tectonic segmentation of the Andes: Implications for magmatism and metallogeny: Nature, v. 250, p. 542–545.
STOIBER, R. E., AND CARR, M. G., 1973, Quaternary volcanic and tectonic segmentation of Central America: Bull. Volcanol., v. 37, p. 304–325.
THARPE, L. W., 1976, Fluvial sediments of the Rio Achiquate and its tributaries, Guatemala: M.A. Thesis, Univ. Missouri-Columbia, 127 p.
WALTON, A. W., 1972, Sedimentary petrology and zeolotic diagenesis of the Vieja Group (Eocene-Oligocene), Presidio County, Texas: PhD. Diss., Univ. Texas-Austin, 265 p.

SEPM Special Publication No. 26, p. 307–317, March 1979

PETROLOGY AND DIAGENETIC EFFECTS OF LITHIC SANDSTONES: PALEOCENE AND EOCENE UMPQUA FORMATION, SOUTHWEST OREGON

LARY K. BURNS and FRANK G. ETHRIDGE
Colorado State University, Fort Collins, 80521

ABSTRACT

The Eocene and Paleocene Umpqua Formation in the southern part of the Oregon Coast Range comprises a thick sequence of lithic arenites, siltstones, mudstones, conglomerates, coals, and, in the basal part, basaltic volcanic rocks intercalated with detrital sedimentary rocks. The sediments were deposited in a basin that developed during the evolution of the Mesozoic-Cenozoic arc-trench system of western North America. Environments ranging from deltaic to moderately deep marine are reflected in the rocks.

Lithic arenites, the dominant sandstone type, have framework constituents of quartz, feldspars, micas, microfossils, plant fragments, heavy minerals, and volcanic, metamorphic and sedimentary lithic fragments. Digenetic minerals include phyllosilicates (chlorite and clay minerals), calcite, iron oxides, quartz, and zeolites.

Phyllosilicate cements occur in three varieties: clay coats on framework grains, pore-filling chlorite with a radiating habit, and chlorite as unoriented microcrystalline aggregates. The radiating chlorite is found only in the upper and middle members of the formation, and the zeolite is found in only the lower member. Sandstone porosity has been reduced by the cements and by compaction and mechanical deformation of soft grains.

A progressive sequence of diagenetic features from youngest to oldest evident in the upper and middle members is: (1) calcite pore-fill cement and the development of clay coats around framework grains, (2) precipitation of radiating pore-fill chlorite, or alteration of volcanic fragments to form unoriented microcrystalline aggregates of phyllosilicates, and (3) precipitation of silica cement in the center of pores not already completely filled. In the lower member, pore-space was not present for precipitation of the radiating chlorite. Zeolites occur in the lower member, indicating that low-grade metamorphic conditions were attained.

INTRODUCTION

The Eocene and Paleocene rock suite of the southern part of the Coast Range of Oregon was deposited in a sedimentary basin associated with a convergent plate junction along an active continental margin. The rock sequence includes great thicknesses of immature marine sandstones, siltstones, mudstones, conglomerates, and volcanic rocks. Early Eocene and Paleocene volcanics are predominately submarine tholeiitic basalts (Snavely and Baldwin, 1948; Baldwin, 1964; and Snavely et al., 1969) with minor amounts of subaerial basalts (Snavely and Wagner, 1963). The tectonic mobility of the area resulted in a variety of depositional settings ranging from deltaic to upper bathyal.

The stratigraphic framework and regional geology of southwest Oregon are summarized by Baldwin (1974). The sedimentary and tectonic history of the Klamath Mountain area south of the study area is described by Dott (1965, 1966). These studies are important because the Klamath highlands were the probable source of the Umpqua sediments. Mesozoic and Cenozoic tectonics in the Pacific Northwest are summarized by Dickinson (1976). Eocene paleogeographic reconstructions of western Oregon including the area of this study are presented by Snavely and Wagner

(1963) and Baldwin (1974). These studies provide a basic sedimentologic and tectonic framework for the present study.

The primary purpose of this study is to describe and interpret the petrography and diagenetic features of sandstones in the Eocene and Paleocene Umpqua Formation (Umpqua Group of Bladwin, 1974) as determined from studies of thin sections and heavy mineral concentrations. Rapid deposition and burial coupled with abundant labile rock fragments and heavy minerals have given rise to immature sandstones that have been subjected to pronounced diagenetic changes. The great depth of burial of the sediments in this early Tertiary basin has generated overburden pressures and resulted in elevated temperatures that reached the conditions of the zeolite facies of metamorphism (Coombs, 1961; Turner, 1968) at the bottom of the sedimentary pile, in the lower Umpqua member. Over 6400 meters (21,000 feet) of lower Tertiary sediments are known to have been deposited in the southern end of the Tertiary basin in the Coast Range of Oregon (Baldwin, 1974). The thickest section of Umpqua sedimentary rocks measured in this study is 3475 meters (11,400 feet) (location 1, fig. 1).

Tectonics.—The area was one of crustal mobility due to rafting of the sedimentary basin in

Copyright © 1979, The Society of Economic Paleontologists and Mineralogists

a Coast Range Seamount Province (Dickinson, 1976) against the continent during interaction of the spreading center off the Oregon and Washington Coast and the movement of the American Plate towards this spreading center as it overrode the Juan de Fuca Plate (Atwater, 1970). Resulting changes in water depths and depositional settings during the time of Umpqua deposition are documented by an abundance of fossils (Turner, 1938; Thoms, 1965; Baldwin, 1974). This crustal mobility is compatible with the setting of the area in terms of Eocene Plate Tectonics.

Source area.—The pre-Teritary Klamath highland to the south and southeast of the Umpqua basin was a primary contributor of detritus to the basin, and these highlands were underlain by continental crust during the time that Umpqua sediments accumulated. The Klamath highlands were probably uplifted near the end of the Mesozoic or in early Cenozoic following an extended period of orogenic activity including folding, thrust faulting, plutonism and extensive andesitic volcanism which reached a climax in the late Jurassic, between 135 and 145 m.y. ago (Dott, 1965).

The rocks of the Klamath highlands are eugeosynclinal sedimentary rocks, diorite, schist, gneiss, amphibolite, and andesite (Dott, 1965 and 1966). Ultramafic serpentinite bodies that seem to delineate shear zones are also present (Kays, 1968).

Geology and stratigraphy.—The outcrop pattern of the main rock types in the study are shown in Figure 1. The general broad syncline or synclinorium of the Cenozoic rocks in the Southern Coast Range is apparent and the location of the principal measured sections are shown in this map (Fig. 1).

The general geologic column (Fig. 2) indicates that a time span on the order of 20 million years is involved in the rocks described. The standard West Coast Stages used by Baldwin (1964), Dott (1966), Burns (1964) and others is shown on the left hand side of the figure and revised stage boundaries (Baldwin, 1974, 1975) are shown on the right hand side of this figure.

Methodology.—Samples of Umpqua sandstones and siltstones were taken from three measured sections and from other randomly selected localities. Two of the measured sections spanned most of the Umpqua Formation (loc. 1, 2, Fig. 1). The third measured section was confined to the lower member of the formation (loc. 3, Fig. 1).

Measured sections 1 and 2 (Fig. 1) are well-exposed by youthful streams that cross the formation approximately perpendicular to regional strike; fresh samples of sandstones and siltstone were collected in the stream bed. Samples were

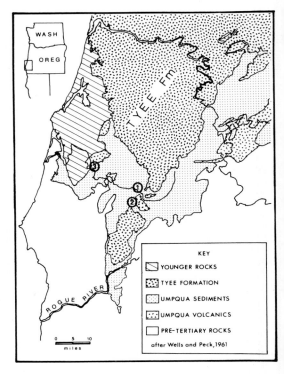

Fig. 1.—Index and lithologic map of study area in southwestern Oregon showing locations of three principal measured sections.

collected according to a stratified random sampling plan.

Fifty-one thin sections were examined for this study. Modal analyses were done on all sandstone samples by counting 200 to 400 points on each slide. The mineral composition of the plagioclase was measured using the universal stage method of Slemmons (1962), which allows both the An-content and the structural state of the plagioclase to be determined. Clay minerals from four mudstones were separated and identified using X-ray diffraction techniques on air dried, glycolated and heat treated samples (Burns, 1964).

Heavy mineral separations were made from 26 sandstone and siltstone samples. The nonmagnetic heavy mineral grains in the 2.54–4.00 phi size fraction (0.210 mm–0.625 mm) were then mounted on slides and the slides were traversed at regularly spaced intervals and all grains were counted. At least 200 grains were counted on all slides.

A semi-automatic Zeiss particle-size analyzer was used to determine grain size from photomicrographs of the thin sections. From 600 to 2,600 grains were measured on each of 23 samples,

TIME ROCK UNITS			ROCK UNITS				TIME ROCK (Baldwin, 1974)	
EPOCH	megafossils*	forams*	BALDWIN 1964	DOTT 1966	BALDWIN 1974	THIS PAPER	STAGES	EPOCH
EOCENE	Domengine	Ulatisian	TYEE FORMATION	TYEE FORMATION	TYEE FORMATION	TYEE FORMATION	Ulatisian	EOCENE
			— UNCONF. —	— ? —	— UNCONF. —	— ? —		
	Capay	Penutian	UMPQUA FORMATION — UPPER	UMPQUA FORMATION	FLOURNOY FORMATION	UPPER UMPQUA MEMBER		
			—UNCONF.—		—UNCONF.—			
			MIDDLE		LOOKINGGLASS FORMATION	MIDDLE UMPQUA MEMBER	Penutian	
			—UNCONF.—		— UNCONF. —			
			LOWER (VOLCANICS)		ROSEBURG FORMATION	LOWER UMPQUA MEMBER	Bulitian Ynezian	PALEOCENE

Fig. 2.—Summary of early Tertiary stratigraphic units in southwestern Oregon.

and the raw data for the size distributions were corrected by transforming the biased distribution from thin section data to an unbiased distribution, using the method of Greenman (1951).

Lithology.—The Umpqua Formation, for many years had been informally divided into three members on the basis of lithologic differences. These informal subdivisions roughly paralleled early field subdivisions, and Baldwin (1974) formalized the subdivisions into three separate formations.

Almost all the graded beds in the Umpqua Formation are in the lower member, which has a minimum thickness of 825 meters (2,700 feet). Conglomerates constitute about 4 percent of the member, sandstone and siltstone about 46 percent and the remaining 50 percent is mudstone and shale. The conglomerates are associated with graded beds and are mainly found in the basal part of the lower member. The pebbles and cobbles of the conglomerate include well-rounded basalt, quartzite, vein quartz, acidic volcanic rocks, plutonic rocks, schist, sandstone, shale and chert. The sandstone and siltstone beds are intercalated with mudstones, and many of them are graded. An average graded bed is about 40 cm thick. The mudstones occur at the top of graded beds as well as in separate, fairly thick, mudstone units with few sandstone interbeds. The thick sequences of tholeiitic basalts present in the eastern and western edges of the basin are not present in the axial part of the basin.

The middle member contains a basal unit consisting of sandstone and conglomerate making up 40 percent and 7 percent of the section, respectively, and an overlying mudstone unit constituting 53 percent of the section (6,000 feet) in the thickest measured section. The sandstones are thick-bedded, commonly pebbly, and better sorted than the sandstones of the lower member. No graded beds were observed in this member. Both planar and trough cross beds, cut-and-fill structures, and thin laminae of coal are found in the sandstones. A lignite bed about 3.5 meters thick is found within the sandstone portion of the middle member. It is impure and contains several shale partings, but has been mined for fuel by local residents. The mudstone portion of the middle member is about 600 meters thick and contains abundant fossil mollusks and foraminifera.

A massive basal sandstone unit with planar cross beds, cut-and-fill structures, and abundant thin lamellae of coal underlies a dark-colored mudstone and siltstone phase in the upper member. The basal sandstone unit is 425 meters (1,400 feet) thick, and the overlying mudstone unit is 365 meters (1,200 feet) thick and contains abundant pelcypods, gastropods and foraminifera.

PETROLOGY

General.—The composition of Umpqua sandstones, which make up 58 percent of all samples examined in thin sections, is summarized in Table 1. When classified according to Pettijohn *et al.* (1972), sandstones (see Fig. 3) include lithic arenites (79%), plagioclase-dominated arkosic arenites (7%), plagioclase-dominated arkosic wackes (7%), and lithic wackes (7%). Lithic arenites and lithic wackes are further classified in Figure 3, as volcanic arenites (73%), sedarenites (7.7%), phyllarenites (11.5%), and sedimentary wackes (7.7%).

Triangular plots of all sandstone compositional data show some variation among the upper, middle, and lower members, however, all members have areas of considerable overlap. Lithic fragments in the upper member are dominantly volcanics. The middle member contains almost equal amounts of sedimentary, volcanic, and metamorphic rock fragments, whereas the lower member contains almost equal amounts of sedimentary and volcanic rock fragments and lesser amounts of metamorphic rock fragments (Table 1, Fig. 3).

Composition.—Monocrystalline and polycrystalline quartz grains average 18.4 and 9.9 percent respectively of the detrital fraction (Table 1). Monocrystalline grains have straight to strongly undulose extinction and contain vacuoles and microlites in varying amounts. Some vacuoles are scattered randomly and others are aligned along fractures or incipient cleavages. Microlites are not as common as vacuoles, are generally not aligned, and their identity is usually obscured by their minute size. Most quartz grains are subangular and somewhat elongate. Polycrystalline grains have straight to strongly undulose extinction and curved to sutured boundaries between individual crystals. Polycrystalline grains tend to have few crystals with a unimodal size distribution. Many quartz grains have chlorite or calcite impinging on their boundaries, which causes the boundaries to be poorly defined.

Feldspars constitute 12.9 percent of the detrital

TABLE 1.—AVERAGE COMPOSITION OF 29 SANDSTONE SAMPLES FROM THE UMPQUA FORMATION, SOUTHWEST OREGON.

Members Umpqua Formation	QM	Qp	Q	K	P	% Detrital Fraction Frx	F	Ls	Lv	Lm	L	M	A	D	% C	Q	% QFL F	L	Ls	% L Lv	Lm
upper	20.1	10.1	30.2	2.0	12.3	4.2	18.5	4.6	30.2	8.5	43.3	5.2	2.8	84.8	15.2	33.6	20.0	46.3	9.9	69.0	21.0
middle	18.9	12.7	31.6	1.3	14.6	5.7	21.6	7.2	11.7	9.5	28.4	8.3	10.1	76.1	23.9	39.6	25.9	34.5	31.1	38.1	30.8
lower	17.4	8.6	26.0	0.4	12.5	2.0	14.9	12.6	18.1	6.7	37.4	14.3	7.4	80.1	19.9	34.4	19.6	46.0	34.8	46.7	18.5
Average	18.4	9.9	28.3	1.0	12.9	3.4	17.3	9.3	20.1	7.8	37.2	10.5	6.7	80.6	19.4	35.3	21.0	43.8	27.2	51.1	21.7

Eight samples from upper member, six from middle member, and 15 from lower member. (Qm = mono. qtz., Qp = poly. qtz., Q = total qtz., K = potash feld., P = plag. feld., Frx = feld. bearing plutonic fragments, F = total feld. plus feld. bearing plutonic fragments, Ls = sed. fragments, Lv = vol. fragments, Lm = metamorphic fragments, L = total lithic fragments, M = matrix, A = accesory minerals, D = detrital fraction, C = cement).

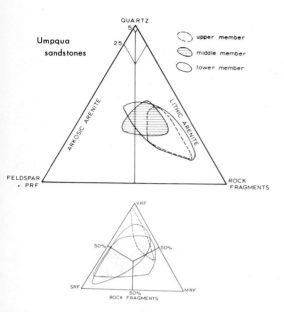

FIG. 3.—Composition of framework constituents of 29 sandstone samples from the Umpqua Formation of southwestern Oregon. Classification after Pettijohn, *et al.* (1972). Feldspar pole equals all feldspars plus feldspar-rich plutonic rock fragments.

fraction (Table 1). Plagioclase is the dominant variety in most samples. Plagioclase grains usually are fresh, but orthoclase grains commonly are extensively altered. Only 5 grains of microcline were encountered in all the samples studied. The average composition of the plagioclase is An_{32}, and most grains range from An_{27} to An_{35}, oligoclase to andesine. Those plagioclase grains for which the An content was determined are structurally plutonic (Slemmons, 1962). This suggests that most of the plagioclase occurring as individual grains was derived from metamorphic or plutonic igneous rocks rather than volcanic rocks.

Rock fragments constitute a significant proportion of the detrital fraction, averaging 37.2 percent of all sandstone samples (Table 1) and ranging up to 70 percent in some samples. Volcanic rock fragments are the dominant type in most samples. Volcanic fragments can be divided into two broad classes, one composed of fragments that contain little or no quartz (Fig. 4A, B) and the other containing abundant quartz. Quartz-poor lithic fragments generally are most abundant. Specific types of volcanic rock fragments recognized include microlitic, porphyritic, felsic, glass, and pumice. Microlitic fragments contain abundant feldspar crystals arranged so that the fabric is felty, pilotaxitic, or trachytic. Other minerals in these fragments are usually altered to chlorite

or limonitic oxides. Porphyritic fragments contain stubby, euhedral phenocrysts of plagioclase (Fig. 4B) in a fine-grained groundmass that usually has a considerable amount of chlorite. Plagioclase phenocrysts may be partially replaced by chlorite or more rarely calcite. Felsic fragments comprise intergrowths of quartz and feldspar and may be easily mistaken for chert. Devitrified volcanic glass fragments are found occasionally in some sections. Volcanic fragments, that may have been glass at one time and have been chloritized, as well as fragments of pumice with partially collapsed vesicles are present in some samples from the middle and lower members.

Sedimentary rock fragments are the second most abundant, type averaging 9.3 percent of the detrital fraction (Table 1). They include chert, mudstone (Fig. 4C), siltstone, and limestone. Limestone clasts form the dominant rock type in one sample, and mudstone forms a significant proportion of the fragments in several samples. Metamorphic rock fragments average 7.8 percent of the detrital fraction and include phyllite (Fig. 4C), schist and some nonfoliated varieties such as serpentinite and quartz-epidote fragments. Schist fragments show good foliation and commonly contain quartz, muscovite, biotite, epidote, and occasionally amphibole, chlorite, and graphite. Plutonic rock fragments form a minor proportion (3.3 percent of the detrital fraction, Table 1) of many samples and a significant proportion in only one sample in the middle member. Most plutonic fragments contain quartz and plagioclase. They are included with the feldspar pole for purposes of classification.

Both biotite and muscovite are present in minor amounts with biotite being more common. Large flakes of biotite usually are bent and commonly have been partially or totally altered to chlorite. Because of the relatively small proportion of these minerals they are included under accessories (Tables 1, 3).

The most abundant, non-opaque heavy minerals are listed in Table 2. Exclusive of the opaque minerals, the upper member is dominated by chlorite (49 percent, Table 2). The middle member is characterized by a chlorite-epidote-hornblende assemblage and the lower member contains a chlorite-epidote-garnet-olivine-zircon assemblage. All identified heavy minerals are listed in Table 3 along with their relative abundance and distribution within the Umpqua Formation. Based on the above data, it is clear that the metamorphic, volcanic, and plutonic rocks of Mesozoic age in the Klamath Highlands provided the bulk of the heavy minerals to the Umpqua sandstones and siltstones.

Matrix is present in small amounts in most sandstone samples, averaging much less than 15

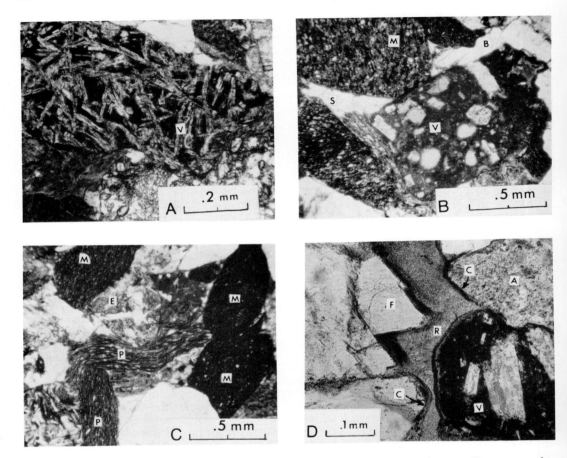

Fig. 4.—A, Volcanic rock fragment (V) of intermediate composition with intersertal texture (I): upper member. B, Porphyritic volcanic rock fragment (V) with chlorite-filled vesicles and phenocrysts of plagioclase (V); chloritized biotite fragment (B); mudstone rock fragment (M); silica and calcite cement (S): upper member. C, Example of pore space reduction by mechanical deformation of soft phyllites (P); mudstones (M); epidote-quartz metamorphic rock fragment (E): upper member. D, Clay coats (C) followed by radiating chlorite (R) filling pore space; porphyritic volcanic rock fragment with plagioclase phenocrysts in opaque glass (V); feldspar (F); acidic volcanic rock fragments (A): upper member.

percent of the detrital fraction, but it is common in siltstone samples, averaging 42 percent. Matrix percentages may even be smaller than reported in sandstone samples. The difficulty of differentiating the various types of interstitial constituents reported by Dickinson (1970) is enhanced by the advanced stages of diagenesis encountered in some samples. Matrix minerals include quartz, calcite, feldspar, epidote, clay minerals, chlorite, and sericite. Some of the matrix material is isotropic and may consist of carbonaceous matter. At least one thin section contains very thin lignite seams. A 3.5 meter lignite seam was observed in the middle member.

Clay minerals were determined for 4 mudstone samples. In two of these samples the most abun-dant clay mineral was montmorillonite. In one sample both montmorillonite and vermiculite are present, and in the last sample the most abundant clay mineral is chlorite. The most common clay mineral in one sandstone sample containing abun-dant green interstitial constituents was determined to be chlorite. Thus the mudstones appear to have a lower chlorite content than the interstitial con-stituents of sandstones. This probably results from the secondary origin of most interstitial constitu-ents as phyllosilicate cements.

Cements constitute a significant proportion of some samples, averaging 19.4 percent of the total rock and ranging up to 48 percent in some samples. At least five different types of cements are recog-nized and include phyllosilicates, calcite, iron-

TABLE 2.—AVERAGE COMPOSITION OF SELECTED HEAVY MINERALS IN THE 2.5 TO 4.0 PHI SIZE FRACTION OF 26 SANDSTONE AND SILTSTONE SAMPLES, UMPQUA FORMATION, SOUTHWEST OREGON

Members Umpqua Formation	%					
	Chlorite	Epidote	Garnet	Hornblende	Olivine	Zircon
upper (6 samples)	49.0	9.6	13.8	5.5	9.6	12.4
middle (10 samples)	25.4	35.1	8.6	17.4	7.7	5.8
lower (10 samples)	25.5	30.7	12.5	6.9	10.5	13.9
Average	30.9	27.5	11.3	10.6	9.2	10.4

oxides, silica, and zeolites (a complete discussion of these cements is found in the next section).

OBSERVED DIAGENETIC FEATURES

Most of the diagenetic features observed in thin sections of sandstone and siltstone from the Umpqua Formation are similar to those described by Carrigy and Mellon (1964), Dickinson (1970), and Galloway (1974). Diagenetic features responsible for pore space reduction can be divided into three broad categories: authigenic cements, compaction features, and replacement features.

Authigenic cements.—At least five types of authigenic cement are present in Umpqua sandstones and siltstones: phyllosilicate cement, calcite cement, iron oxide cement, silica cement, and zeolite cement. Phyllosilicate cements occur in a variety of habits including well-crystallized flakes oriented perpendicular to their substrate (radiating chlorite), unoriented microcrystalline aggregates, and as clay coats that have particles oriented parallel to the substrate. No one sample contains all five varieties: however, several samples contain as many as four varieties. Phyllosilicate cements average 13.1 percent in all sandstone samples and range from 0 to 23.7 percent. Most varieties of phyllosilicate cement are pale green to yellow-tinged green chlorite. X-ray diffraction analysis of one sandstone sample containing abundant green, interstitial constituents shows

TABLE 3.—HEAVY MINERAL DATA, UMPQUA FORMATION, SOUTHWEST OREGON. DATA OBTAINED FROM POINT COUNTS OF 26 HEAVY MINERAL SEPARATIONS.

Heavy mineral	Range in abundance in est. %	Comments
Anthophyllite	0–3	only found in two samples of middle member
Apatite	0–3	minor amounts in upper and middle members
Biotite	0–40	most common in upper member
Brookite	trace	
Cassiterite	trace	
Chlorite	2–60	abundant throughout, especially in upper member
Clinopyroxene	0–40	rare in upper member
Clinoamphibole	0–40	rare in upper member, not common, especially in upper member
Enstatite	0–5	scarce in upper member
Epidote	<1–40	common in middle and lower members
Garnet	0–20	persistent throughout only in one sample
Glaucophane	trace	
Hornblende	0–75	most probable source is amphiboite of Mesozoic age in Klamath Mountains
Hypersthene	trace	only found in 2 samples
Monazite	trace	a few grains in 2 samples
Muscovite	0–15	
Olivine	0–5	occurs persistently throughout all samples
Opaques	10–80	chromite, ilmenite, leucoxene, limonite, magnetite, pyrite
Reibeckite	very rare	
Rutile	0–3	minor amounts in middle and lower members
Titanite	trace	
Tourmaline	0–2	rare in middle and lower members
Zircon	0–5	more common in upper and lower members
Zoisite and Clinozoisite	0–10	

that a 14Å-chlorite is the dominant clay mineral. Lesser amounts of other authigenic clay minerals, including montmorillonite, are also present. However, these are not conspicuous in most thin sections. The most conspicuous variety of phyllosilicate cement occurs as well-crystallized flakes oriented perpendicular to their silicate substrate and is abundant in six sandstone samples. Radiating chlorite was not observed in silt-size samples. In many samples the radiating chlorite is separated from framework grains by a thin to thick clay coat (Fig. 4D). In some cases detrital grains form the substrate and clay coats apparently are absent. In at least two samples multiple development of radiating chlorite within the pore space is apparent (Fig. 5A). In most sandstones radiating chlorite completely fills the intergranular spaces; however, in some cases other authigenic constituents such

as silica fill the interior of pores (Fig. 5B). Pore-fill cements of this type are found only in the upper and middle members. Unoriented microcrystalline aggregates (Fig. 5C) are present in most sandstone samples from all three members. In most cases the clear, transparent nature and the absence of minute detritus or murky impurities and the obvious monomineralogy of these features serves to differentiate them from detrital matrix. Clay coats are present in all three members but are more common in the upper and lower members (Figs. 4D, 5A, 5B). These clay coats commonly are stained by unidentified iron oxide cement and are yellow brown to dark brown. When this staining is absent the flakes are either oriented parallel to the substrate or consist of randomly oriented microcrystalline grains. Calcite pore-fill cement averages 4.8 percent of all sandstone

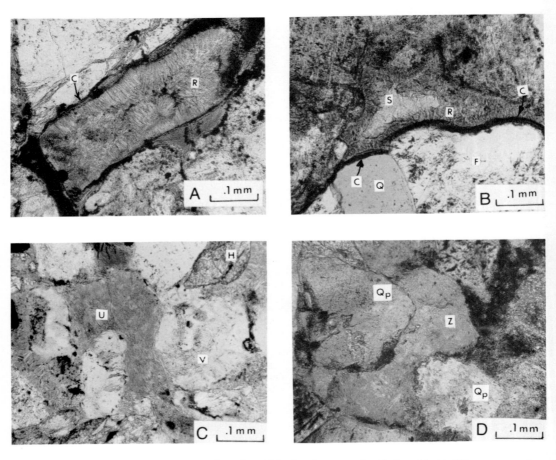

FIG. 5.—A, Pore containing clay coats (C) and multiple development of radiating chlorite (R): upper member. B, A succession of diagenetic features filling pore space including clay coats (C), radiating chlorite (R), and silica (S), feldspar (F); monocrystalline quartz (Q): upper member. C, Unoriented microcrystalline aggregates of chlorite as pore-fill material (U); clinozoisite (H); volcanic rock fragment (V): middle member. D, Zeolite pore-fill cement (Z); between two polycrystalline quartz grains (Qp): lower member.

samples and ranges widely from sample to sample from 0 to 45.3 percent. It is present in all three members but is more commonly found in samples from the lower member than from either the upper or middle members. Most calcite cement is classified as sparite. Iron oxide cement averages 2 percent of all sandstone samples and ranges from 0 to 4.3 percent. In some cases this cement may mask matrix or other forms of interstitial cements.

Silica cement is present in minor amounts and averages 0.5 percent in sandstone samples. It is present primarily in the form of microcrystalline and crystalline aggregates in pores sometimes surrounded by clay rims and only rarely forms quartz overgrowths.

Zeolite pore-fill cement is found in only four samples from the lower member (Fig. 5D). The fibrous habit, low birefringence, negative relief and small extinction angle suggest that it may be laumontite.

Compaction features.—Mechanical compaction and crushing of softer grains along with the development of various types of authigenic cement are the two most important diagenetic features responsible for loss of intergranular porosity. Mudstone, siltstone, some volcanic glass, and micritic rock fragments have all been subjected to mechanical compaction in all members of the Umpqua Formation.

Mudstone clasts are particularly susceptible to mechanical crushing and tend to form patches of pseudomatrix (Dickinson, 1970). For purposes of modal analyses these constituents have been counted as mudstones and not as matrix, based on criteria outlined by Dickinson (1970) for recognition of pseudomatrix. Orientation of rock fragments may be an important factor in mechanical deformation (Fig. 4C).

Replacement.—Replacement fabrics, while common in some sandstone samples, do not appear responsible for marked reductions in intergranular porosity. Quartz, feldspar, volcanic and plutonic rock fragments are partially replaced by calcite and chlorite in some samples from all three members. Chlorite is found as pseudomorphs after biotite. Some of these chlorite grains have retained the grain form and crystal habit of the biotite which they replace. Others seem to have replaced the biotite piecemeal with a more complex crystal habit than the original biotite, and, in addition, are grown topotaxially onto the original grain. Chlorite also impinges on and distorts grain boundaries, especially in the lower member. Several vitreous volcanic rock fragments in the lower member are totally replaced by zeolites. Complex replacement and alteration of grains in the lowermost samples from the lower member produces a fabric with indistinct grain boundaries, thus complicating the recognition of original detrital texture.

DIAGENETIC STAGES AND FACTORS AFFECTING DIAGENESIS

Introduction.—In a study of four Tertiary sedimentary basins along the Pacific continental margin of North America, Galloway (1974) recognized three stages of chemical diagenesis, in well-winnowed sandstones, based on the sequence of authigenic cements that develop. Stage 1 consists of calcite porefill cement which forms locally very early in the burial history of the sandstone. Stage 2 is characterized by authigenic clay coats and rims which form as depth of burial increases and higher temperatures and pressures become the controlling factors in the geochemical environment. Stage 3 begins at intermediate depths of burial and is characterized by a second period of cementation where the remaining open-pore spaces are filled with either well-crystallized phyllosilicate or zeolite cements. Stage 2 clay coats are usually preserved and commonly produce a halo which separates later pore-fill cement from the detrital grains. The diagenetic stages and most of the diagenetic features observed by Galloway are found in the Umpqua Formation. Some significant differences, however, are found between the diagenetic patterns in the Pacific margin basins studied by Galloway and the Oregon Coast Range basin studied here. At least one additional type of phyllosilicate cement is recognized in the Umpqua: unoriented microcrystalline aggregates of chlorite or other clay minerals. Clay coats are common in samples from the Umpqua, and well-crystallized phyllosilicate cements (radiating chlorite) and zeolites are never found in the same sample or in the same portion of the stratigraphic section.

Unoriented microcrystalline aggregates.—Unoriented microcrystalline aggregates of chlorite or other clay minerals are found in all three members and are more common in the middle and lower members. They are thought to have originated as volcanic glass or ash that has been devitrified and compacted to the extent that the chlorite now appears as a pore-fill cement. In a few instances faint ghosts of what seems to be detrital volcanic fragments were observed in the center of pores now completely filled with cement. Even if the center of the pore was occupied by a devitrified and replaced detrital fragment, some phyllosilicate material was added as cement to completely fill the pore space available.

Clay coats.—Galloway (1974) distinguished clay coats and clay rims on the basis of the orientation of the clay flakes with respect to their substrate. In clay rims the flakes are oriented perpendicular to the substrate whereas in clay coats the flakes are oriented parallel or randomly. This distinction is difficult to make optically and the general term clay coats is used here.

Galloway (1974) suggests that the clay coats and rims observed in the Tertiary basins of the northeast Pacific continental margin were formed as authigenic clays at depths between 1,000 and 4,000 feet. We do not dispute this hypothesis; however, several other possibilities must be considered with regard to time of formation and origin.

Clay coats that probably originated as authigenic clays have been observed in quartz-rich, Holocene, shoreface sediments at depths of 34 feet beneath Galveston Island off the Texas coast (Ethridge, unpublished data). Davies and Almon (this volume) also found authigenic clay coats forming in volcanoclastic sediments in Guatemala at depths of a few meters.

Walker (1976) in a study of the diagenetic origin of continental red beds suggests that clay coatings found in Cenozoic red beds from the southwestern United States originated as mechanically infiltrated clays. Although most of the Umpqua sedimentary rocks are marine, there is a possibility that some are deltaic. In the deltaic sediments an origin for clay coats similar to that proposed by Walker (1976) cannot be discounted. Mechanically infiltrated clays can only be differentiated from authigenic pore-fill clays be SEM studies of geologically young sediments (Walker, 1976). Without this type of data on samples from either the Umpqua or the rocks of the Tertiary basins studied by Galloway (1974), the exact origin of the clay coats and their time of formation cannot be accurately determined.

Well-crystallized phyllosilicate cements.—In the Umpqua Formation radiating chlorite and zeolite cements appear to be mutually exclusive diagenetic features. Well-crystallized, radiating chlorite is found only in the upper and middle members, and zeolites are found only in the lower member. Other forms of phyllosilicate cements, including chlorite, do occur in the lower member in the samples with the zeolites. The lower member which contains the zeolites was overlain by at least 2,687 m (8,600 feet) of Umpqua and could possibly have been buried to depths up to 5,937 m (19,000 feet). These depths are sufficient to encounter temperatures and pressures necessary for zeolite-facies development (Coombs, 1961; Turner, 1968).

The radiating chlorite in the middle and upper members appears to be restricted to samples that have abundant intermediate basic volcanic rock fragments which retained sufficient porosity for pore fluids to alter the volcanic fragments and transport the necessary ions. One of the main factors that inhibited the growth of radiating chlorite in the lower member as well as in many sandstones in the middle and upper members is the lack of pore space. This lack of pore space may be due to one of the following reasons: (1) the presence of soft lithic fragments, which under compaction, filled pores forming pseudomatrix; (2) early precipitation of calcite cement in pores; and/or (3) poor sorting due to the presence of substantial amounts of detrital matrix.

Based on field observations and point count data (Table 1) there does appear to be a significantly greater percentage of detrital matrix in the lower member. However, the higher matrix content of the sandstones in the lower member is related to the difference in depositional environmental between this member and the overlying Umpqua sandstones. The occurrence of graded beds, the vertical sequences of sedimentary structures, and the tectonic setting suggest that many sandstone beds in the lower member were transported and deposited by turbidity currents. The common occurrence of medium scale planar cross beds, cut and fill structures, and lignite beds suggest that many of the sandstones of the upper two members were deposited in well-winnowed shallow marine environments.

The pore space present in the winnowed sands of the upper two members was a favorable depositional site for the radiating chlorite cement and thus accounts for its presence in the middle and upper members.

CONCLUSIONS

The Paleocene and Eocene Umpqua Formation of southwestern Oregon is a thick sequence of arc-derived immature sedimentary rocks and tholeiitic basalts associated with an active, convergent continental margin. The diagenetic features observed in this formation include phyllosilicate, calcite, iron oxide, silica, and zeolite cements; compacted fine-grained rock fragments; and various types of replacement fabrics. Phyllosilicate cements occur in three varieties: clay coats on detrital framework grains, radiating chlorite filling pores, and unoriented microcrystalline aggregates replacing volcanic grains and filling pores. In the upper and middle members the order of formation of diagenetic features is interpreted as: (1) early formed calcite pore-fill cement and development of clay coats around framework grains, (2) precipitation of radiating pore-fill chlorite or alteration of volcanic fragments to form unoriented microcrystalline aggregates of phyllosilicate material, and (3) precipitation of silica cement in the center of pores not completely filled by radiating chlorite or calcite.

In the lower member, larger amounts of detrital matrix reduced porosity and precluded the development of radiating pore-fill chlorites. Depth of burial of this member, however, was sufficient to encounter temperatures and pressures adequate for the formation of zeolites.

The diagenetic features and sequence of diagenetic events observed in sandstone samples from the Umpqua Formation provide a variation to the "main stream" diagenetic sequence proposed by Galloway (1974) for sedimentary basins along active continental margins.

REFERENCES

ATWATER, TANYA, 1970, Implications of plate tectonics for the Cenozoic tectonic evolution of western North America: Geol. Soc. America Bull., v. 81, p. 3513–3536.

BALDWIN, E. M., 1964, Geology of Oregon, 2d ed.: Eugene, Oregon, Univ. Oregon Cooperative Book Store, 165 p.

——, 1974, Eocene stratigraphy of southwestern Oregon: Oregon Dept. Geology and Mineral Industries Bull. 83, 40 p.

——, 1975, Revision of Eocene stratigraphy of southwestern Oregon, in Paleogene symposium: Pacific Section, Am. Assoc. Petroleum Geologists-Soc. Econ. Paleontologists and Mineralogists-Soc. Explor. Geophysicists, Annual Meeting, p. 49–64.

BURNS, L. K., 1964, Sedimentary petrology of the Umpqua Formation in the axial part of the southern Coast Range, Oregon: M.A. Thesis, Univ. Oregon, 154 p.

CARRIGY, M. A., AND MELLON, G. B., 1964, Authigenic clay mineral cements in Cretaceous and Tertiary sandstones of Alberta: Jour. Sed. Petrology, v. 34, p. 461–472.

COOMBS, D. S., 1961, Some recent work on the lower grades of metamorphism: Australian Jour. Sci., v. 24, p. 203–215.

DICKINSON, W. R., 1970, Interpreting the detrital modes of graywacke and arkose: Jour. Sed. Petrology, v. 40, p. 695–707.

——, 1976, Sedimentary basins developed during evolution of Mesozoic-Cenozoic arc-trench system in western North America: Canadian Jour. Earth Sci., v. 13, p. 1268–1287.

DOTT, R. H., JR., 1965, Mesozoic-Cenozoic tectonic history of the southwestern Oregon coast in relation to Cordilleran orogenesis: Jour. Geophys. Research, v. 70, p. 4687–4707.

——, 1966, Eocene deltaic sedimentation at Coos Bay, Oregon: Jour. Geology, v. 74, p. 373–420.

GALLOWAY, W. E., 1974, Deposition and diagenetic alteration of sandstone in northeast Pacific arc-related basins: Implications for graywacke genesis: Geol. Soc. America Bull., v. 85, p. 379–390.

GREENMAN, N. N., 1951, The mechanical analysis of sediments from thin-section data: Jour. Geology, v. 59, p. 447–462.

KAYS, M. A., 1968, Zones of alpine tectonism and metamorphism, Klamath Mountains, southwestern Oregon: Jour. Geology, v. 76, p. 17–36.

PETTIJOHN, F. J., POTTER, P. E., AND SIEVER, R., 1972, Sand and sandstone: New York, Springer-Verlag, 618 p.

SLEMMONS, D. B., 1962, Determination of volcanic and plutonic plagioclases using a three or four-axis universal stage: Geol. Soc. America Spec. Paper 69, 64 p.

SNAVELY, P. D., JR., AND BALDWIN, E. M., 1948, Siletz River Volcanic Series, northwestern Oregon: Am. Assoc. Petroleum Geologists Bull., v. 32, p. 805–812.

——, AND WAGNER, H. C., 1963, Tertiary geologic history of western Oregon and Washington: Washington Div. Mines and Geology Rept. Inv. 22, 25 p.

——, —— AND MACLEOD, N. S., 1969, Geology of western Oregon north of the Klamath Mountains: Oregon Dept. Geology and Mineral Industries Bull., v. 64, p. 32–46.

THOMS, R. E., 1965, Biostratigraphy of the Umpqua Formation, southwest Oregon: PhD. Diss., Univ. California-Berkeley, 219 p.

TURNER, F. E., 1938, Stratigraphy and Mollusca of the Eocene of western Oregon: Geol. Soc. America Spec. Paper 10, 130 p.

TURNER, F. J., 1968, Metamorphic petrology: New York, McGraw-Hill Book Co., 403 p.

WALKER, T. R., 1976, Diagenetic origin of continental red beds, in R. Falke (ed.), The continental Permian in central, west, and south Europe: Dordrecht, Holland, D. Reidel Pub. Co., p. 240–282.

WELLS, F. G., AND PECK, D. L., 1961, Geologic map of Oregon west of the 121st meridian: U. S. Geol. Survey Misc. Geol. Inv. Map I-325.

SEPM SPECIAL PUBLICATION No. 26, P. 319–336, MARCH 1979

DEPOSITIONAL ENVIRONMENTS AND DIAGENESIS OF THE TENSLEEP SANDSTONE, EASTERN BIG HORN BASIN, WYOMING

DAVID MANKIEWICZ AND JAMES R. STEIDTMANN
The University of Wyoming, Laramie, 82071

ABSTRACT

Study of lithologies and sedimentary structures in seven surface sections and five cores indicates that the Tensleep Sandstone in the eastern Big Horn Basin was deposited in a coastal environment. The lower part of the Tensleep formed in a siliciclastic sabkha whereas the upper part represents deposition in a coastal eolian dune complex. Previous paleomagnetic and paleowind studies by others indicate that during deposition of the Tensleep Sandstone, the area lay in a trade wind belt, a setting similar to many of the major coastal sabkhas today.

Diagenesis of the Tensleep Sandstone was a function of both depositional environment and tectonic history. Early cements (anhydrite and dolomite) were, for the most part, related to the chemistry of subsurface waters in the sabkha and associated environments. However, later pre- and post-hydrocarbon entrapment cements (quartz and feldspar overgrowths and rhombic dolomite) appear to be related to episodes of tectonism (Jurassic arching and Laramide folding and faulting). Analyses of surface and subsurface waters show that calcite cement presently is stable at the surface and in the subsurface to the south. To the north, anhydrite is now stable in the subsurface.

INTRODUCTION

The complex relations among chemical, physical, and temporal factors in the depositional and post-depositional history of a sandstone often result in diagenetic patterns that are impossible to predict when unknown and difficult to interpret when identified. Textural variations in sandstone during its compaction and burial affect its porosity and permeability and thus directly influence the potential degree and distribution of cementation. These primary textural variations are in turn a function of depositional environments and thus may lend some degree of predictability to diagenetic patterns, particularly those formed during early stages. However, subsequent cementation or dissolution related to burial, tectonism, or exposure may overprint these earlier diagenetic events, destroying all or most of the evidence and the predictability related to depositional patterns. These controls are not only important because they are later in the diagenetic history but also because they may, in fact, be of more fundamental importance. Most diagenetic changes that take place in a sedimentary rock result from reactions between moving aqueous solutions and the rock itself, and the ability of the rock to transmit these fluids governs the rate and intensity of diagenesis (Blatt, et al., 1972). Cementation and dissolution are inhibited when pore fluids are static because the fluid and rock equilibrate and no further textural or compositional changes occur. This being the case, it is likely that major diagenetic events are related to changes or disruptions in the dominant hydrology of a basin, a situation logically related to periods of active tectonism. It is during these times that hydrodynamic gradients are altered, meteoric waters introduced via basin-margin subaerial exposures and cross-formational flow promoted by fracturing and faulting. It is expectable, then, that diagenetic chronologies show, at least in part, a correlation with tectonic history.

Our study of the Tensleep Sandstone is aimed both at an understanding of the control of diagenesis by individual chemical and physical processes and the resultant total diagenetic picture within the depositional and tectonic framework of the eastern Big Horn Basin (Fig. 1). This area provides an excellent opportunity to examine surface exposures and cores from nearby oil fields. Surface sections were measured and subsurface cores were logged with special attention to describing environmentally sensitive sedimentary structures and collecting representative samples. Thin-sections of samples from the surface and subsurface were examined to discriminate among primary textural attributes, grain overgrowths and pore-filling cements. The paragenetic sequence of cementation and its correlation with tectonic history was determined as closely as possible. Waters from springs, creeks, and producing wells in the Tensleep were sampled and analyzed to gain an insight into the stability of recent Tensleep cements.

STRATIGRAPHY AND DEPOSITIONAL ENVIRONMENTS

The regional stratigraphic relations among the Tensleep and its equivalents in the Weber, Quad-

Copyright © 1979, The Society of Economic Paleontologists and Mineralogists

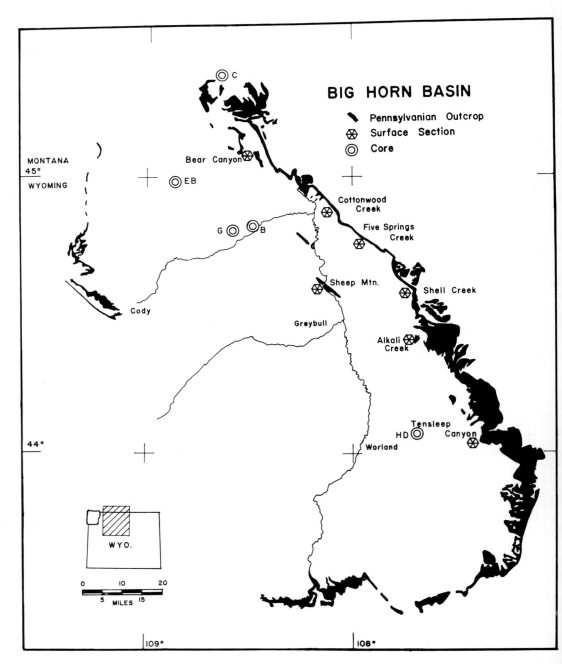

FIG. 1.—Map of Big Horn Basin showing outcrop pattern of Pennsylvanian sedimentary rocks and locations of surface and subsurface sections examined. Field name abbreviations are C (Crawford), EB (Elk Basin), G (Garland), B (Byron), and HD (Hidden Dome).

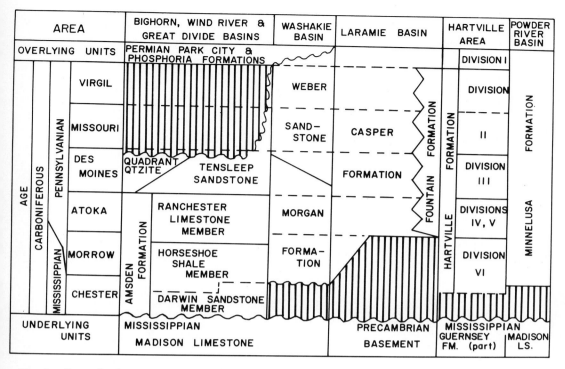

FIG. 2.—Generalized stratigraphic chart showing the relations among the Tensleep Sandstone and equivalent units (Quadrant, Weber, Casper, Fountain and Hartville) in adjacent areas (after Mallory, 1967).

rant, Casper and Minnelusa Formations are described in detail by Mallory (1967) and summarized in Figure 2. In the Big Horn Basin the Tensleep is, for the most part, Desmoinesian in age although Verville (1957) reports Wolfcampian fusulinids in the uppermost Tensleep south of our immediate study area. The Tensleep is underlain by the Ranchester Limestone Member of the Amsden Formation and overlain by Permian evaporites, siltites, and dolomites of the Phosphoria Formation. The Tensleep represents the culmination of a regressive cycle which begins with an unconformity at the karst erosional surface between the Mississippian Madison Limestone and the Darwin Sandstone Member of the Amsden Formation and ends with the unconformity at the top of the Tensleep itself.

Depositional environments represented by the Tensleep and the observed sequences of these environments in surface sections suggest a leeward eolian siliciclastic sabkha environment similar to that described by Shinn (1973) in the Persian Gulf. There, on the southeast part of the Qatar Peninsula, the coastal region is characterized by a barchanoid quartz dune complex which is rapidly migrating into the sea. The dunes migrate over an Eocene dolomite rock surface which is separated from the sea by a quartz sand sabkha or supratidal flat 40 km long and 7–10 km wide. Shinn (1973) described a regressive sequence consisting of muddy carbonate sands and stromatolitic carbonates succeeded by cross-bedded eolian sand. Similar sequences are observed in the Tensleep Sandstone of the eastern Big Horn Basin.

Orientation of eolian cross-strata in the upper Tensleep show a well-defined southwest sediment transport direction which is in accord with results reported by Opdyke and Runcorn (1960). Using paleo-pole positions determined by magnetic studies (Collinson and Runcorn, 1960), Opdyke and Runcorn (1960) placed Wyoming just north of the equator throughout the Permo-Pennsylvanian. This puts the region under the influence of an ancient tropical northeasterly wind system, a situation similar to many of the coastal sabkhas today.

Analyses of measured surface sections indicate that, for purposes of environmental interpretation, the Tensleep can be subdivided roughly into upper

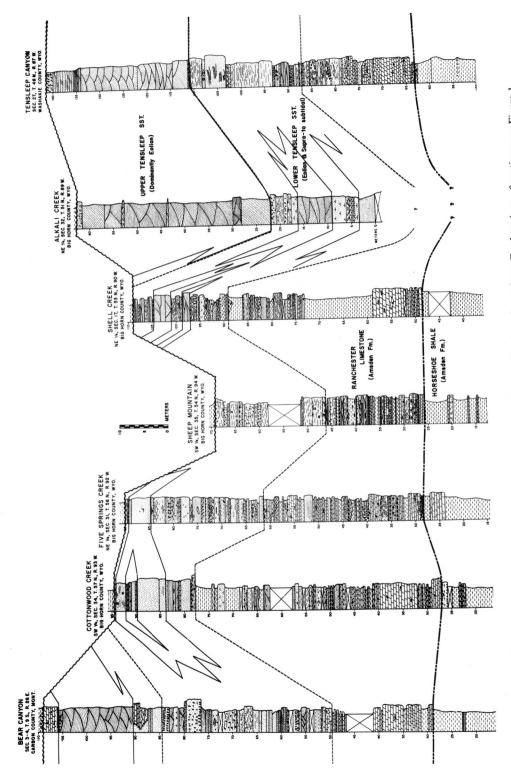

Fig. 3.—Correlation chart of surface section from the Amsden and Tensleep formations. For locations of sections see Figure 1.

and lower parts (Fig. 3). The major differences between the two relate primarily to proportions of chemical and clastic rock and to sabkha versus eolian dune depositional processes. The lower Tensleep represents deposition under primarily supratidal, intertidal, and subtidal to lagoonal conditions. Dune sand is rare and contains up to 35 weight percent detrital carbonate. Eolian cross-strata are smaller scale than those in the upper part with sets rarely exceeding 2 m in thickness. Supratidal sabkha-wind flat deposits are characterized by dolomitic and gypsiferous (anhydrite) sandstones and sandy dolomites with occasional small trough cross-stratification in sets rarely reaching 6 cm in thickness. Supratidal sandstones and dolomites generally are overlain by tidal flat or eolian dune deposits. Tidal flat sediments consist of resistant red-orange to buff dolomite with rip-up clasts, desiccation cracks (Fig. 4c) and mudcrack polygons exhibiting up-turned laminae (Figs. 4a, b). Tidal flat deposits generally are underlain by subtidal and lagoonal sediments. Subtidal and lagoonal deposits are 1–2 m thick and consist of dolomite containing fossil debris from crinoids, fusulinids, brachiopods, and pelecypods in a micrite matrix. Sandier subtidal dolomites contain tabulate and rugosan corals in apparent growth position indicating periods of normal marine salinites. Bioturbated and burrowed calcareous sandstones frequently occur throughout the lower Tensleep. Burrows are quite variable in size and morphology and usually are cemented preferentially with calcite, thereby weathering in relief. It is uncertain whether these sandstones have a subaqueous or subaerial origin.

Small scale, bi-directionally cross-stratified calcareous sandstones generally overlie tidal flat deposits and underlie eolian dune sandstones and vary from quartz calcarenites to calcareous quartz arenites. Laminae comprised of detrital carbonate grains alternate with quartz-rich laminae. They may represent either low amplitude eolian dunes migrating over a tidal flat or megaripples in tidal channels or on longshore bars. Glennie (1970) reports the common occurrence of recent eolian carbonate dunes in desert coastal environments, and warns against hastily assigning marine origin to ancient cross-bedded calcarenites.

The upper Tensleep represents deposition in eolian and associated sabkha environments (Fig. 5a). The eolian dune sand is thickly bedded but finely laminated with large-scale trough and planar tabular cross-stratification in laterally contiuous sets up to 10 m thick (Fig. 5b). Dip angles of cross-sets range from 15–31° and bedding planes occassionally contain ripples oriented down the dip of the cross-stratification, some with truncated crests. The general paucity of ripples is probably due to poor preservation of the low amplitude ripples which form under eolian conditions (Harms, 1969, p. 387). Calcite spar-filled "burrows" 5 mm in diameter and 3–7 cm long are present in some dune sands and, where abundant, disrupt or destroy continuity of lamination. These borings may represent cemented plant-root molds or burrowing by molluscs as reported by Glennie (1970, p. 128), or burrows of insects similar to those made by the sand spider in recent dunes (Alhbrandt, pers. comm.), but the exact origin is not known. Calcite cemented burrows and mounds of various dimensions also occur in the upper eolian dune sand but the origin of these has not yet been determined.

Interdunal pond and sabkha-wind flat deposits are intercalated with these eolian dune sands. The size of these deposits ranges from 1 to 1.5 m thick and up to, and occasionally exceeding 100 m in lateral extent. These lenses generally thin and pinch out in an onshore direction, often grading into horizontal truncation surfaces within the eolian dune sand. These wind flat deposits consist of parallel- to wavy-laminated dolomitic and gypsiferous (anhydrite) sandstones and sandy dolomites and occur along groundwater-controlled deflation surfaces upon which dune forms migrate (Stokes, 1968). These sediments are similar in nature to parallel- and wavy-laminated gypsiferous sediments reported by Glennie (1970, p. 65) as occurring in continental and coastal sabkha flats. Where depressions in the deflation surfaces were deep enough, algal-mat dolomites with anhydrite were formed as interdunal pond deposits.

These pond deposits consist of wavy to anastomosing, finely laminated beds of pink sandy dolomite with interweaving lentiles of sucrosic anhydrite. White to gray chert nodules are common in pond deposits, often with relict lamination intact. These deposits are similar in aspect and possibly in origin to sediments of Facies 3b described by Schreiber *et al.* (1976) in the Messinian evaporite deposits of the Sicilian Basin. Schreiber *et al.* (1976) suggest subaqueous deposition in hypersaline waters which were freshened periodically, thus allowing colonization by algae and the formation of algal mats. Deposits in the upper Tensleep probably represent hypersaline ponds occurring in deflation hollows between dune ridges. These ponds would be subject to periodic flooding during severe storms or unusually high tides. Shinn (1973) reports storm flooding of the southeast part of the Qatar Peninsula as far inland as 7–10 km.

The contact between the upper Tensleep and the overlying Phosphoria Formation is usually but

FIG. 4.—A, Underside of mudcracked polygons in intertidal dolomite of the Tensleep Sandstone. B, Cross-section of mudcracked polygon showing upturned laminae at edges. Lens cap is 6 cm in diameter. C, Shrinkage cracks in intertidal-dolomite. Lens cap is 6 cm in diameter.

FIG. 5.—*A*, Outcrop of upper Tensleep Sandstone showing pinch-out of dolomite-cemented, interdunal sediments in eolian sandstone. *B*. Large-scale trough cross-stratification of the upper Tensleep Sandstone. Rod is 1.5 m long.

not always marked by a chert and limestone pebbly sandstone up to 1 m thick. This deposit is poorly sorted and contains chert pebbles up to 1.5 cm in diameter. The poor sorting and lenticularity of this deposit suggest a fluvial origin or the reworked, deflation lag of a desert wadi environment.

TECTONIC HISTORY

Throughout the Paleozoic the area that is now the state of Wyoming lay on the western margin of the craton and was the site for deposition of shallow water shelf carbonates. Tectonic movement began during the Late Mississippian (Agatson, 1954, Mallory, 1967) with epeirogenic uplift of the Madison carbonates and consequent regional development of an erosional karst surface. Carbonates and siliciclastics of the Amsden Formation covered this irregular surface followed by the dominantly eolian sands of the Tensleep Sandstone.

During Late Pennsylvanian time a broad structural arch developed across Wyoming trending northwest-southeast, exposing older Pennsylvanian rocks on the crest and younger along the flanks (Blackstone, 1963, p. 162). Associated with this trend was a local northeast-southwest structural arch in the vicinity of the eastern Big Horn Basin and it was this high which caused the thinning by truncation of the Tensleep Sandstone from Shell Canyon northward to Big Horn Canyon (Fig. 3). The Tensleep is up to 100 m thick in the southern part of the area with a well represented upper portion of eolian sandstone which crops out as gentle dip slopes. To the north, however, the Tensleep thins to 20–30 m and crops out as narrow exposures on steeply dipping flatirons. North of the Montana line the Tensleep thickens again and retains the upper eolian section.

Tectonism continued with the emergence of the Ancestral Rocky Mountains including the Pathfinder and Front Range uplifts in Wyoming (Mallory, 1967). These structural trends established during the Pennsylvanian were precursors to comparable trends formed during Laramide tectonism (Blackstone, 1963). During Permian and Triassic time this area underwent southerly tilting followed by deposition, and truncation that resulted in a thinning of the strata from south to north. Isopachous maps of Jurassic strata (Thomas, 1965) indicate the development during this time of a structural arch of low relief which appears to be the buried northwest plunging nose of the Casper arch. Incipient basin development appears to have begun in the Upper Cretaceous with the deposition of the Frontier and Mesaverde Formations (Thomas, 1965).

Prior to Laramide time there had been minor upward movement during the Paleozoic, a major arching in the Jurassic and minor spasms of movement in the Late Cretaceous (Blackstone, 1963). During the Paleocene however, the Laramide Orogeny had its major impact and the peripheral mountain uplifts began their growth, thereby accentuating the northwest-southeast structural grain established in the Pennsylvanian. It was at this time that structural traps formed parallel and adjacent to the Big Horn Uplift. Tectonism continued into the Eocene with the unroofing of the crystalline core of the Big Horn Mountains and the deposition of gravels and conglomerates with angular discordance on older rocks (Hoppin and Jennings, 1971). From late Eocene through Pliocene time, mountain uplifts that had previously emerged were buried beneath several thousand feet of lacustrine, paludal and fluviatile sediments. Much of this infill was volcanogenic in nature as igneous activity that began in late Eocene continued and intensified in the Absaroka-Yellowstone region. Regional uplift, normal faulting, and rapid degradation that exhumed the mountains and re-excavated the basin occurred in late Pliocene and Pleistocene time (Love, McGrew, and Thomas, 1963).

PETROGRAPHY

For the most part the Tensleep Sandstone is fine to very fine grained and well sorted. Framework grains are 82–93% quartz, with the remainder mostly alkali feldspar. Rounded detrital chert grains are present but volumetrically negligable. Heavy minerals constitute only 0.2% of the grains with zircon, tourmaline, and rutile accounting for about 80% of all non-opaque heavies. The most common matrix constituent of the sandstones is dolomicrite which in places constitutes as much as 35% of the rock. These figures compare quite closely with those of Todd (1964) with the exception of feldspar content, a discrepancy which will be discussed later. The high textural maturity and predominant south to southwest transport direction (Opdyke and Runcorn, 1960), led Todd (1964) to postulate a multiple provenance for the Tensleep, probably the crystalline rocks of the Canadian Shield and the sedimentary rocks which once overlay them.

Of particular interest in our study of diagenesis are the various cements found in the Tensleep. The most common diagenetic cements are silica, anhydrite, and calcite. Dolomite, pyrite, feldspar, and kaolinite are less abundant. Silica occurs as a cement in the following ways: as quartz overgrowths on detrital grains; as chert nodules in dolomites and sandy dolomites; and as chalcedony in both radially fibrous form and pseudomorphically after anhydrite. Dust rims indicate that many of the grains were well rounded prior to formation of quartz overgrowths (Figs. 6a, b). Point counts on samples show that grain contacts average 35.4% long, 22.6% tangential, 36% concavo-convex, and 6% sutured. The paucity of sutured grain boundaries and the presence of prism faces on overgrowths suggest that much of this silica was precipitated from migrating solutions rather than as the result of local pressure solution. Many of these overgrowths show subsequent etching (Fig. 6b). Chert occurs as varicolored stringers and nodules in intertidal and subtidal dolomites, sometimes preserving fossil debris in considerable detail. Preservation of fossil debris in otherwise micritized dolomites indicates that silicification within the carbonates may have been contemporaneous with the formation of quartz overgrowths in sandstones. Chalcedony occurs pseudomorphically after gypsum-anhydrite in some shallow (150 m) subsurface samples where it exhibits a linear herringbone extinction pattern (Fig. 6c). Dead oil stain on quartz grains enclosed by this chalcedony

indicates that chalcedony followed oil accumulation (Fig. 6c). Chalcedony also occurs in a radially fibrous habit, usually concentrated along fractures in sandy dolomites at the surface. Later crosscutting fractures are filled with calcite spar which etches and replaces the radially fibrous chalcedony. Late silicification at the surface occurs extensively in outcrops to the north where steeply dipping, highly fractured Tensleep Sandstone is "case hardened" with pore-filling quartz.

Anhydrite is a conspicuous sandstone cement in the subsurface, whereas at the surface it is leached in favor of calcium carbonate. It is, however, preserved at the surface in the more impermeable algal mat and intertidal dolomites. Anhydrite occurs as fracture fillings, as poikilotopic masses enclosing and replacing detrital quartz (Fig. 7a–d), as stringers parallel to lamination and local discontinuities, as sucrosic vug and burrow fillings, and as thin wavy lenses in algal mat dolomites. Calcium sulfate may have been introduced into the sandstones during deposition of the supratidal and intertidal sediments or any-

Fig. 6.—All bar scales represent 50 microns. *A*, Photomicrograph (crossed nichols) showing quartz overgrowths with prism faces and dust rims (arrow). *B*, Scanning electron photomicrograph showing quartz overgrowths and subsequent etching (arrow). *C*, Photomicrograph (plane light) showing pseudomorphous replacement of gypsum by chalcedony. Arrows show dead oil stain. *D*, Photomicrograph (crossed nichols) showing chalcedony (ch) and later calcite (cal) pore-filling cement.

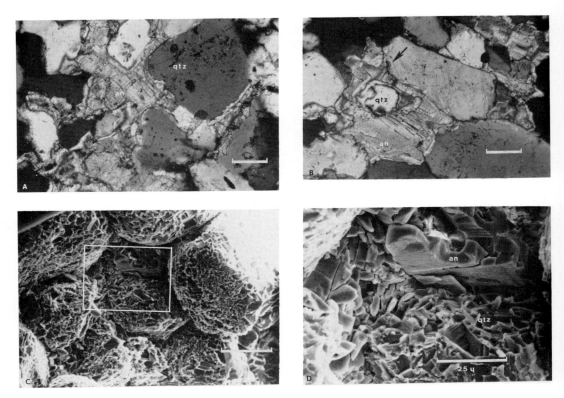

Fɪɢ. 7.—Bar scales in A, B and C represent 50 microns. *A*, Photomicrograph (crossed nichols) showing poikilotopic enclosure of quartz grains (qtz) by anhydrite (an). *B*, Photomicrograph (crossed nichols) showing replacement of quartz (qtz) by anhydrite (an). Arrow shows an abraded quartz overgrowth, *C*, Scanning electron photomicrograph of quartz grains etched by anhydrite. Box shows field of Figure 7D. *D*, Scanning electron photomicrograph showing etching of quartz (qtz) by anhydrite (an).

time during or after deposition of the Phosphoria sequence of evaporites and shales. Early anhydrite is suggested by analogy to evidence from interstitial brines in a siliciclastic sabkha on the Persian Gulf (de Groot, 1973) where both anhydrite and calcium-rich dolomite are presently forming in sediments beneath the sabkha surface. Furthermore, the involvement of these anhydrite-cemented laminae in early soft-sediment deformation attests to its early formation. However, the common occurrence of anhydrite as fracture linings suggests that at a later time fracturing allowed introduction of foreign waters into the Tensleep from the overlying evaporite beds and the precipitation of calcium sulfate.

Calcite occurs in surface rocks as sparry vug and burrow fillings, as poikilotopic masses replacing the quartz framework (Figs. 8a, b) and as fracture fillings. Calcite spar replaces anhydrite in wind flat, eolian and sabkha sediments at the surface but is rare in the subsurface, except in the south where it replaces both anhydrite and

quartz. Sparry cement in heavily burrowed dune sands results in a pocky and nubbly weathering surface. Calcite spar is also concentrated along boundaries of trough cross-stratification and weathers as resistant trough-shaped layers up to 2 cm thick. The dominance of calcite as a cement on surface exposures suggests that this is the most recent cementing event.

Secondary minerals which are somewhat less abundant than those described above but still important in the diagenetic history of the Tensleep include feldspar, dolomite, pyrite, and kaolinite. Feldspar grains with overgrowths occur as elongate rhombs and as laths with overgrowths in optical continuity with detrital host grains (Fig. 8c). Overgrowths generally are confined to the smaller detrital grains in interstices between larger framework grains. Perhaps smaller host grains made better nucleation sites for overgrowths. Where feldspars with overgrowths abut against quartz grains, boundaries are straight suggesting that the formation of feldspar and quartz over-

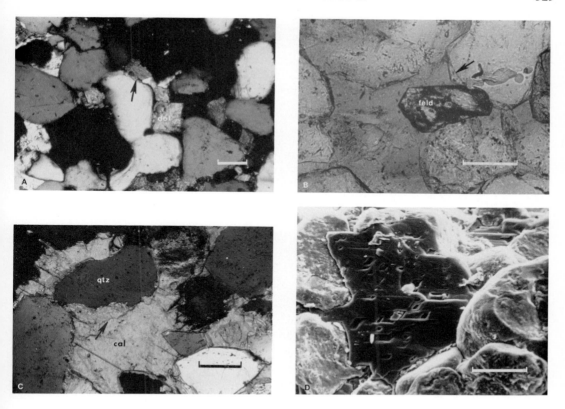

Fig. 8.—All bar scales represent 50 microns. *A*, Photomicrograph (crossed nichols) showing replacement of quartz by dolomite (arrow). *B*, Photomicrograph (plane light) showing detrital feldspar (feld) with overgrowth and prism faces. Arrow indicates quartz overgrowth. *C*, Photomicrograph (crossed nichols) showing replacement of quartz (qtz) by calcite (cal). Arrow shows ghost of former quartz rim. *D*, Scanning electron photomicrograph of calcite pore filling cement.

growths may have been comtemporaneous. Dolomite occurs as micritic blebs which probably were detrital initially and as small rhombs (Fig. 8d). Secondary conversion from micrite to mosaic microdolospar on the peripheries of detrital carbonate grains is evident in some thin sections. Dolomitization of detrital carbonate probably was early in the diagenetic history of the Tensleep Sandstone. The occurrence of recent dolomite (proto-dolomite) in the subsurface of modern sabkha environments is reported throughout the Trucial Coast in the Persian Gulf (Illing *et al.*, 1965; Shinn, 1973). In the Tensleep rhombic dolomite occurs as intergranular void-fillings anchored on adjacent quartz grains and as quartz replacement. This episode of dolomite precipitation appears to have followed the quartz overgrowths and preceded oil accumulation.

Pyrite occurs as irregular patches or stringers surrounded by anhydrite along fractures, as circular pore fillings and as framboidal clusters. Pyrite may have been early in the diagenetic history

since microbial sulfate reduction and subsequent generation of H_2S is common in recent sabkha sediments (Butler *et al.*, 1973). Breakdown of detrital ferromagnesian silicates may have provided the necessary iron for precipitation of this phase. However, high H_2S concentrations in production waters indicate that pyrite is presently stable in the subsurface. X-ray traces indicate that kaolinite is a minor constituent. It occurs as attached felted masses on feldspar grains, as dust rims on quartz grains, and rarely as intergranular pore fillings. Its presence may represent the weathering of detrital feldspars and/or clay infilling following post depositional truncation.

WATER ANALYSES

Waters were analyzed to ascertain present conditions of mineral cement stabilities. Surface waters from springs and creeks were gathered during late summer and early fall so that primarily phreatic rather than surface runoff waters were analyzed. Subsurface waters were collected at

TABLE 1.—SAMPLE LOCATIONS AND RESULTS OF CHEMICAL ANALYSES FOR SURFACE AND PRODUCTION WATERS IN THE EASTERN BIG HORN BASIN

Sample	Location	Ca^{++}	Mg^{++}	K$^+$	Na$^+$	Cl$^-$	HCO$_3^-$	SO$_4^=$	SiO$_2$	pH	H$_2$S	$\frac{IAP}{K_{cal.}}$	$\frac{IAP}{K_{gyp.}}$
						(ppm)							
surface waters													
Tensleep Creek	SEC. 27, T. 48 N., R. 87 W.	20	7	.9	1.7	.7	90.3	<24	9	8.27	—	1.06	—
Paint Rock Creek	SEC. 1, T. 49 N., R. 90 W.	107	24.2	2.5	13.6	3.8	212	200	13.9	8.45	—	12.44	.09
Shell Creek	SEC. 17, T. 53 N., R. 90 W.	25	8.5	.7	1.7	.4	115	<24	6.6	8.48	—	2.58	—
Five Springs Creek	SEC. 31, T. 56 N., R. 92 W.	52	14.3	2.6	4.2	.3	203	<24	5.8	7.66	—	1.36	—
Flat Iron Spring	SEC. 11, T. 56 N., R. 93 W.	47	18.9	.6	1.3	.6	255	<24	7.9	8.64	—	11.37	—
Cottonwood Creek	SEC. 4, T. 56 N., R. 93 W.	44	19.3	.8	1.1	.5	222	<24	8.6	8.50	—	7.95	—
Oasis Spring	SEC. 31, T. 58 N., R. 93 W.	123	38.0	1.5	12.7	5.6	146	380	24.9	7.54	—	1.16	.17
Bear Canyon Spring	SEC. 3, T. 9 S., R. 26 E.	50	15.8	.5	.9	.3	218	<24	7.4	7.52	—	1.02	—
production waters													
Nowood 1*	SEC. 9, T. 48 N., R. 90 W.	87	79	5	14	20	634	30	—	8.53	present	33.31	.01
Nowood 2*	"	98	58	5	14	36	512	47	—	8.0	"	10.46	.02
Cottonwood 1	SEC. 7, T. 47 N., R. 90 W.	180	68	14	21	.5	326	507	12.6	7.15	76	1.00	.26
Cottonwood 2	"	180	65	13	20	.3	344	504	12.4	7.13	92	.97	.26
Hidden Dome 1	SEC. 31, T. 48 N., R. 90 W.	320	117.	30	36	.8	526	865	11.3	7.1	100	2.23	.54
Hidden Dome 2	"	190	86	15	31	.2	366	577	12.6	7.25	49	1.61	.28
Bonanza 1	SEC. 26, T. 49 N., R. 91 W.	470	127	18	24	—	264	1510	9.8	7.41	50	2.60	1.09
Bonanza 2	"	410	155	24	26	—	200	1470	9.5	7.18	56	.93	.94
Sage Creek 1	SEC. 18, T. 57 N., R. 97 W.	660	135	15	7	.3	644	1670	18.1	6.7	167	1.81	1.44
Sage Creek 2	"	680	133	26	11	—	805	1630	17.0	6.6	263	1.81	1.43
Byron 1	SEC. 23, T. 56 N., R. 97 W.	630	108	55	80	.3	510	1640	23.2	6.85	106	1.96	1.40
Byron 2	"	580	87	53	164	.2	434	1650	22.4	7.00	117	1.92	1.41
Garland 1	SEC. 33, T. 56 N., R. 97 W.	540	111	106	256	1.5	680	1670	23.0	6.94	168	2.49	1.22
Garland 2	"	540	112	110	245	22.3	774	1650	24.1	6.71	164	1.84	1.20

* CHEM LAB No. 21062-2 Report no. 5-2265, 1965

the wellhead of producing Tensleep wells at Hidden Dome, Cottonwood Creek, Nowood (published data), Bonanza, Sage Creek, Byron, and Garland fields (Table 1). Special care was taken to avoid wells that were being subjected to water injection, flooding, or chemical treatment. Results of the analyses are presented in Table 1.

The chemistry of surface waters draining the western flank of the Big Horn Uplift and entering the Tensleep aquifer is influenced by weathering of lithologic units stratigraphically above and below the formation. Underlying rock units are dominantly Paleozoic limestones and dolostones which contribute most of the HCO$_3^-$, Ca^{++}, and Mg^{++} present in surface waters. The minor presence of Na$^+$ and K$^+$ may be due in part to weathering of feldspar and plagioclase from the exposed Precambrian crystalline rocks and also

to atmospheric fallout (Junge and Werby, 1958). Rock units immediately overlying the Tensleep are the Permo-Triassic red beds, carbonates, and evaporites which contribute Ca^{++}, Mg^{++}, SO$_4^=$, and HCO$_3^-$ to recharge waters.

Waters from oil field production generally reflect the mineral phases present in the rock and consequently have high concentrations of Ca^{++}, Mg^{++}, SO$_4^=$, and HCO$_3^-$. The ubiquity of H$_2$S in subsurface waters indicates probable sulfate reduction through oxidation of *in situ* hydrocarbons. H$_2$S could be a by-product of recent microbial sulfate reduction especially in shallow reservoirs that have good communication with meteoric recharge. H$_2$S might also be a remnant of previous nonmicrobial generation of hydrogen sulfide through sulfate reduction that occurred when the Tensleep was buried much deeper (Orr, 1974).

Nearly all fields sampled have low concentrations of Na^+ and K^+ except for Byron and Garland. Fields low in Na^+ and K^+ are nearer to the Tensleep outcrop and generally subject to strong downdip hydrodynamic flow (Todd, 1963; Pedry, 1975). Abnormally high concentrations of alkali metals at Byron and Garland suggest either contamination from foreign formation waters or lack of communication with meteoric recharge. Higher total dissolved solids in waters at Sage Creek Field compared with other fields exhibiting a strong water drive might be explained by the high degree of fracturing and faulting of the Tensleep reservoir in this area.

Results of water analyses were subjected to WATEQ, a computer technique for calculating chemical equilibria of natural waters (Truesdell and Jones, 1974). This program calculates ionic strength, activity coefficients, aqueous complexes and saturations of various mineral phases. Chemical equilibria for calcite and gypsum from water samples are represented as saturation indices, defined as:

$$\text{for calcite,} \quad S = \frac{IAP}{K_{eq}} = a_{Ca^{++}} \cdot a_{CO_3^{=}} / K_{cal}$$

where IAP is the ion activity product and K is the equilibrium constant for the reaction.

if: $S > 1.0$ supersaturated

$S = 1.0$ saturated

$S < 1.0$ undersaturated

The results are summarized in Table 1. Gypsum saturation indices are given over those of anhydrite since at the temperature analyzed ($22°$ C) the hydrated form is the more stable phase. Fields to the north (Byron, Garland, Sage Creek, and to a lesser extent Bonanza) have a high dissolved sulfate content and are super saturated with respect to both gypsum and calcite ($S > 1.0$), and core samples show a dominance of anhydrite and dolomite in this part of the basin. To the south, however, waters are more dilute and undersaturated with respect to gypsum while supersaturated with respect to calcite. Core samples from Hidden Dome field show replacement of both quartz and anhydrite by late calcite. Dilute formation waters in the south are due to high porosity and permeability of the upper Tensleep, wide outcrop exposures, and a continuous relatively unbroken or faulted aquifer of high transmissibility.

Encroachment by meteoric waters into shallow hydrocarbon bearing sands in the south has several consequences. First, simple dilution of oil-field waters dissolves anhydrite. Secondly, sulfate reduction increases bicarbonate alkalinity according to the following relationship (Berner, 1971):

$$2\,CH_2O + SO_4^{=} \dashrightarrow 2HCO_3^{-} + H_2S$$
$$2\,HCO_3^{-} + Ca^{++} \dashrightarrow 2CaCO_3 + 2H^{+}.$$

Increased HCO_3^{-} concentrations coupled with high Ca^{++} concentrations from anhydrite dissolution increase the ion activity product (IAP) for calcite, thus favoring it over anhydrite as a mineral cement.

Although all waters sampled were supersaturated with respect to dolomite, sluggish kinetics of precipitation of this phase and the necessity for high Mg^{++}/Ca^{++} ratios preclude the possibility of dolomite precipitating as a recent cement.

PH values of waters from springs and creeks (Table 1) are neutral to slightly alkaline, ranging from 7.52 to 8.64. Surface waters have pH values that average 8.33, suggesting that the hydrogen ion concentration in these waters is controlled by carbonate equilibria. Garrels and Christ (1965) estimate that water in contact with pure calcite and in equilibrium with atmospheric carbon dioxide should have a pH of about 8.4. The presence of minerals other than pure calcite plus local variations in the partial pressure of carbon dioxide probably accounts for the variability in pH values observed. Production waters, on the other hand, are neutral to slightly acid with pH values ranging from 6.6 to 7.25 and averaging 7.0. The apparent controlling relationship here is the disassociation of hydrogen sulfide which tends to increase hydrogen concentration and lower the pH according to:

$$H_2S \rightleftharpoons H^{+} + HS^{-} \quad pK_{eq} = 7.0$$

If disassociation of H_2S is the only controlling factor in determining hydrogen concentration then pH values would be about 7.0. Variations from this "ideal" value may be the result of interaction between carbonate and sulfide equilibria and possible variations in pK_{eq} with total concentration of dissolved solids (Goldhaber and Kaplan, 1975).

All analysed waters (surface and subsurface) plot in the kaolinite region of the stability field diagram in the system $K_2O\text{-}Al_2O_3\text{-}SiO_2\text{-}H_2O$ (Fig. 9). Subsurface waters cluster closer to the feldspar field than do surface waters indicating a longer rock residence time and a higher content of dissolved silica. Increased K^+ in subsurface waters compared to surface waters is counterbalanced by increases in hydrogen concentration due to H_2S disassociation. This may resolve in

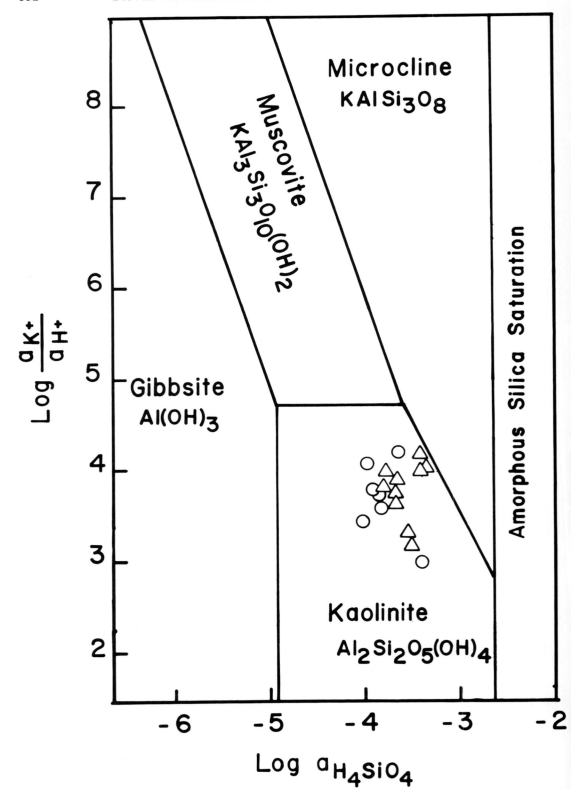

part the discrepancy of reported feldspar content in the Tensleep Sandstone. Surface waters are dilute and may be weathering feldspars to kaolinite on outcrop whereas in the subsurface increased K^+ and SiO_2 increases the stability of potassium feldspar. Thus estimates of feldspar content in surface rocks alone may be low.

In summary, the waters on the surface and those in the near basin flank subsurface are all supersaturated with calcite, which dominates as the present stable phase at the surface and in the subsurface to the south. In the north however, the subsurface waters are supersaturated with regard to gypsum and apparently this prohibits the replacement of anhydrite-gypsum by calcite. High concentrations of H_2S in production waters indicate that pyrite is presently stable in the subsurface.

CEMENT CHRONOLOGY AND CORRELATION WITH TECTONIC HISTORY

A summary of the sequence of diagenetic events and the inferred correlation of these events with the tectonic history of the eastern Big Horn Basin is shown in Figure 10. For the most part, the chronologic sequence of cements comes directly from petrographic evidence whereas its correlation with the tectonic history is based on less direct lines of evidence. Textural criteria alone, are in some cases not sufficient to decipher the puzzles of cement paragenesis. Precipitation events are most definitive especially when they

are accompanied by pseudomorphous replacement. However, dissolution events, such as the development of secondary porosity, are rarely obvious and some, if not all previous cementation events may be obliterated. Timing of cementation events in reservoir rock is in part controlled by migration and accumulation of hydrocarbons. In this regard, we are using Stone's 1967 hypothesis for a common pool of Phosphoria-derived hydrocarbons in the Tensleep resevoir by end of Jurassic time and surely by early Cretaceous time.

Anhydrite cement appears to both precede and follow oil accumulation. Most of the anhydrite probably was a primary precipitate in algal mats and sabkha-flat sediments and a secondary precipitate in root and burrow fillings. It is also found as a poikilotopic cement in eolian dune sands where it must have had a gypsum precursor.

De Groot (1973) reports salinities above halite saturation from interstitial brines in buried eolian sand of the Persian Gulf, and Glennie (1970) reports gypsum-cemented dunes and anhydrite-filled burrows and root molds in modern sabkha environments. Some of the early anhydrite in the Tensleep may have been dissolved during post depositional truncation as fresher waters flushed the early-cemented sands.

A second episode of anhydrite cementation took place during or shortly after the Laramide Orogeny. The common occurrence of anhydrite-filled fractures suggests the introduction of foreign waters during Laramide disruption. Formation

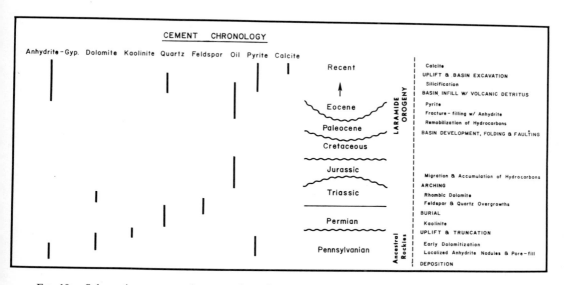

FIG. 10.—Schematic summary of cement chronology and its probable correlation with tectonic history.

FIG. 9.—Stability field diagram for common minerals in the system $K_2O-Al_2O_3-SiO_2-H_2O$ (modified from Berner, 1971). Circles represent surface waters, triangles represent production waters.

waters from the overlying evaporite facies of the Phosphoria are much higher in sulfate content than Tensleep waters, and may have provided sufficient precipitate for this fracture filling. Pyrite generally is associated with the early anhydrite-cemented sandstones and even replaces quartz framework-grains in some instances. This pyrite must have formed shortly after deposition in the reducing environment provided by bacterial reduction of sulfate in the sabkha sediments. Isotopic analysis of sulfates in recent sabkha sediments (Butler *et al.*, 1973) indicates active sulfate reduction in these environments.

Pyrite also occurs in the fractures filled by late anhydrite suggesting that it is also related to sulfate reduction following hydrocarbon entrapment. The presence of H_2S in production waters indicates that pyrite presently is a stable mineral.

The precipitation of quartz and feldspar overgrowths and the formation of kaolinite are the first major diagenetic events, but their order of occurrence is unclear. We propose the diagenetic sequence of kaolinite, followed by feldspar and then quartz, inasmuch as this follows a silica enrichment trend such as that depicted by moving from left to right on Figure 9. It should be pointed out, however, that kaolinite may have formed through degradation of detrital feldspars or it may have been an infilling during deposition of the Tensleep or during postdepositional truncation. However, though ubiquitous, kaolinite is not particularly abundant, and its presence can be accounted for by degradation of feldspar above.

Feldspar overgrowths are uncommon and generally are restricted to the smaller framework host grains in interstices bounded by larger quartz grains. Quartz overgrowths are very common and occur on very well rounded quartz grains. In some cases they show prism faces, indicative of growth into void space rather than replacement or xenomorphic control. Not all quartz overgrowths are authigenic however. Detrital grains from recycled sediments are evidenced by abraded quartz overgrowths. Quartz also occurs as pore fillings which exhibit no dust rims or prism faces and may have formed as a replacement of some mineral-cement precursor. Where kaolinite and feldspar grains abut against quartz framework-grains, quartz overgrowths do not occur. Both feldspar and quartz overgrowths apparently follow kaolinite and it is likely that quartz overgrowths and quartz pore-fillings (replacement?) followed precipitation of feldspar overgrowths.

After the precipitation of quartz overgrowths, small rhombs of dolomite formed across both overgrowth and detrital quartz-grain boundaries. Any remaining primary aragonitic or high magnesian calcitic sediments probably were dolomitized at this time but most carbonate sediments, especially those of the intertidal and supratidal origin,

may have been dolomitized prior to burial. Precipitates of calcium-rich dolomite (proto-dolomite) are reported from recent siliciclastic sabkhas (Shinn, 1973; de Groot, 1973). The formation of rhombic dolomite is the last pre-oil diagenetic event observed in the sandstones. A similar interpretation is reported by Fox *et al.* (1975) and Todd (1963).

Precipitation of (or transformation into) rhombic dolomite was followed by development of secondary porosity as evidenced by the presence of pore spaces larger than framework grains and etching of quartz overgrowth. Subsequently, hydrocarbons migrated up the shelf edge from the west and into large gentle warps and swells, accumulating as a common pool by the end of the Jurassic (Stone, 1967). Locally in the Big Horn Basin, hydrocarbons accumulated into broad structural warps that developed during tectonic arching in the Jurassic (Blackstone, 1963; Thomas, 1965).

The latest cementing events to occur are pore-filling and replacement by both silica and calcite. Late silicification is for the most part, confined to highly disrupted areas where it fills fractures and pore spaces and replaces anhydrite. Pseudomorphous replacement of anhydrite-gypsum by chalcedony and the presence of dead oil stain around detrital quartz grains affected by this silicification indicate that this episode of cementation followed oil accumulation. This silicification followed Laramide deformation and probably was related to basin filling by volcanogenic sediment (Love, McGrew and Thomas, 1963) which provided silica-enriched waters.

Calcite was introduced after silicification and therefore probably later than Pliocene. It is the latest Tensleep cement in most of the southern part of the eastern Big Horn Basin where it replaces almost all other cements and grains. Analyses of surface and subsurface waters in this part of the basin indicate that calcite presently is the stable phase. Here the thick, porous, eolian upper part of the Tensleep is extensively exposed in wide outcrops of beds with low dips, and surface waters have ample opportunity to invade the formation, dissolve anhydrite, and cause large-scale calcification. In the north, however, the eolian upper portion of the Tensleep is absent because of postdepositional removal and the dips on the basin flank are much steeper. Apparently this has prevented the large scale recharge by surface waters, and anhydrite remains the youngest stable cement in the subsurface.

SUMMARY OF CONCLUSIONS

The Tensleep Sandstone in the Eastern Big Horn Basin was deposited in a coastal environment. The lower portion of the formation represents deposition in the various subenvironments of a clastic sabkha whereas the upper part was deposited as a coastal eolian-dune complex. Early diagenesis of the Tensleep occurred shortly after deposition and, for the most part, is evidenced by gypsum-anhydrite and dolomite cementation from recharge waters in the sabkha subsurface. Later cementation by silica and dolomite preceded oil accumulation and probably was related to changes in basin hydrology during regional warping in the Jurassic. Major hydrocarbon entrapment occurred during Laramide folding and was followed by very late calcite pore-fillings and anhydrite and silica fracture fillings. Analyses of surface and subsurface waters indicate that calcite presently is the stable phase at the surface and in the subsurface to the south where down-dip flow of surface waters occurs in the eolian upper Tensleep sand. To the north, however, anhydrite presently is stable in the subsurface where the upper Tensleep is missing by truncation and little meteoric recharge occurs.

The above interpretations indicate that diagenesis of the Tensleep Sandstone was in part controlled by depositional environment. Early cementation was a function of the subsurface water chemistry common to the sabkha setting and later cementation was, in part, a function of recharge in the porous and permeable eolian sand. However, tectonism exerted more important controls on diagenesis when, in the Jurassic and later during Laramide deformation, dominant basin hydrology was disrupted and cementation patterns were altered.

ACKNOWLEDGEMENTS

We acknowledge Marathon Research Center, Denver, the Spear Foundation, University of Wyoming, and Sigma Xi honorary society for financial support of this project and we thank J. I. Drever for his assistance and helpful discussions concerning the water geochemistry.

REFERENCES

AGATSON, R. S., 1954, Pennsylvanian and Lower Permian of northern and eastern Wyoming: Am. Assoc. Petroleum Geologists Bull., v. 38, p. 508–583.

BERNER, R. A., 1971, Principles of chemical sedimentology: New York, McGraw-Hill, 240 p.

BLACKSTONE, D. L., 1963, Development of geologic structure in Central Rocky Mountains: Am. Assoc. Petroleum Geologists Mem. 2, p. 160–179.

BLATT, H., MIDDLETON, G. AND MURRAY, R., 1972, Origin of sedimentary rocks: Englewood Cliffs, New Jersey, Prentice-Hall, 634 p.

BUTLER, G. P., KROUSE, R. H., AND MITCHELL, R., 1973, Sulfur-isotope geochemistry of an arid, supra-tidal evaporite environment, Trucial Coast, *in* B. H. Purser (ed.), The Persian Gulf: New York, Springer-Verlag. p. 453–462.

COLLINSON, D. W., AND RUNCORN, S. K., 1960, Polar wandering and continental drift: Evidence from paleomagnetic observations in the United States: Geol. Soc. America Bull., v. 71, p. 915–958.

DE GROOT, K., 1973, Geochemistry of tidal flat brines at Umm Said, SE Qatar, Persian Gulf, *in* B. H. Purser (ed.), The Persian Gulf: New York, Springer-Verlag, p. 377–394.

FOX, J. E., LAMBERT, P. W., MAST, R. F., NUSS, N. W., AND REIN, R. D., 1975, Porosity variation in the Tensleep and its equivalent, the Weber Sandstone, western Wyoming; a log and petrographic analysis, *in* D. W. Bolyard (ed.), Deep drilling frontiers of the central Rocky Mountains: Denver, Colorado, Rocky Mountain Assoc. Geologists, p. 185–216.

GARRELS, R. M., AND CHRIST, C. L., 1965, Solutions, minerals, and equilibria: New York, Harper, 450 p.

GLENNIE, K. W., 1970, Desert sedimentary environments: Amsterdam, Elsevier, 222 p.

GOLDHABER, M. B., AND KAPLAN, I. R., 1975, Apparent dissociation constants of hydrogen sulfide in chloride solutions: Marine Chemistry, v. 3, p. 83–104.

HARMS, J. C., 1969, Hydraulic significance of some sand ripples: Geol. Soc. America Bull., v. 80, p. 363–396.

HOPPIN, R. A., AND JENNINGS, T. V., 1971, Cenozoic tectonic elements, Big Horn Mountain region, Wyoming-Montana: Wyoming Geol. Assoc. Guidebook 23d Ann. Field Conf., p. 39–47.

ILLING, L. V., WELLS, A. J., AND TAYLOR, J. C. M., 1965, Penecontemporary dolomite in the Persian Gulf, *in* L. C. Pray and R. C. Murray (eds.), Dolomitization and limestone diagenesis: Soc. Econ. Paleontologists and Mineralogists Spec. Pub. 13, p. 89–111.

JUNGE, C. F., AND WERBY, R. T., 1958, The concentration of chloride, sodium, potassium, calcium, and sulfate in rain water over the United States: Jour. Meteorology, v. 15, p. 417–425.

LOVE, J. D., McGREW, P. O., AND THOMAS, H. D., 1963, Relationship of latest Cretaceous and Tertiary deposition and deformation to oil and gas in Wyoming: Am. Assoc. Petroleum Geologists Mem. 2, p. 196–208.

MALLORY, W. W., 1967, Pennsylvanian and associated rocks in Wyoming: U. S. Geol. Survey Prof. Paper 554-G, 31 p.

OPDYKE, N. D., AND RUNCORN, S. K., 1960, Wind direction in the western United States in the late Paleozoic: Geol. Soc. America Bull., v. 71, p. 959–971.

ORR, W. L., 1974, Changes in sulfur content and isotopic ratios of sulfur during petroleum maturation—Study of Big Horn Basin Paleozoic oils: Am. Assoc. Petroleum Geologists Bull., v. 58, p. 2295–2318.

PEDRY, J. J., 1975, Tensleep Sandstone stratigraphic-hydrodynamic traps, northeast Big Horn Basin, Wyoming: Wyoming Geol. Assoc. Guidebook 27th Ann. Field Conf., p. 117–128.

SCHREIBER, B. C., FRIEDMAN, G. M., DECIMA, A., AND SCHREIBER, E., 1976, Depositional environments of Upper Miocene (Messinian) evaporite deposits of the Sicilian Basin: Sedimentology, v. 23, p. 729–760.

SHINN, E. A., 1973, Sedimentary accretion along the leeward, SE coast of Qatar Peninsula, Persian Gulf, *in* B. H. Purser (ed.), The Persian Gulf: New York, Springer-Verlag, p. 199–210.

STOKES, W. L., 1968, Multiple parallel-truncation bedding planes—A feature of wind deposited sandstone formations: Jour. Sed. Petrology, v. 38, p. 510–515.

STONE, D. S., 1967, Theory of Paleozoic oil and gas accumulation in the Big Horn Basin, Wyoming: Am. Assoc. Petroleum Geologists Bull., v. 51, p. 2056–2114.

THOMAS, L. E., 1965, Sedimentation and structural development of the Big Horn Basin: Am. Assoc. Petroleum Geologists Bull., v. 49, p. 1867–1877.

TODD, T. W., 1963, Post-depositional history of Tensleep Sandstone (Pennsylvanian), Big Horn Basin, Wyoming: Am. Assoc. Petroleum Geologists Bull., v. 47, p. 599–616.

——, 1964, Petrology of Pennsylvanian rocks, Big Horn Basin, Wyoming: Am. Assoc. Petroleum Geologists Bull., v. 48, p. 1063–1090.

TRUESDELL, A. H., AND JONES, B. F., 1974, WATEQ, a computer program for calculating chemical equilibria of natural waters: U. S. Geol. Survey Jour. Research, v. 2, p. 233–248.

VERVILLE, G. J., 1957, Wolfcampian fusulinids from the Tensleep Sandstone in the Big Horn Mountains, Wyoming: Jour. Paleontolgy, v. 31, p. 349–352.

SEPM Special Publication No. 26, p. 337–378, March 1979

DIAGENESIS OF FRONTIER FORMATION OFFSHORE BAR SANDSTONES, SPEARHEAD RANCH FIELD, WYOMING

RODERICK W. TILLMAN and WILLIAM R. ALMON
Cities Service Oil Company, Tulsa, Oklahoma 74150

ABSTRACT

Diagenesis and physical and biological reworking of the sandstones at Spearhead Ranch Field control the entrapment of oil. The major producing facies is at the top of a sandstone interpreted to be a reworked offshore marine bar.

Mineralogically the reworked facies differ from the underlying non-reworked facies; the reworked facies is high in chert and quartz and low in plagioclase feldspar. The non-reworked bar facies is somewhat lower in chert and quartz and high in plagioclase. Diagenesis of the two mineralogic suites has contributed to preservation of a good reservoir in the reworked facies and destruction of the reservoir in the underlying facies.

Nearly twice as much chlorite is present in the reworked facies as the non-reworked facies. The percent chlorite has a negative correlation (0.7) with quartz in the reworked reservoir facies. Apparently the growth of chlorite grain-coatings has impeded growth of quartz overgrowths and thereby maintained primary porosity and permeability in the reworked facies. Quartz overgrowths have almost completely eliminated porosity and permeability in the non-reworked bar facies. Porosity and permeability calculated from core plugs in the reworked facies average 5.6% and 3.5 md respectively, while comparative values in the non-reworked facies are 4.4% and 0.3 md. The percentages of illite and montmorillonite are also significantly different in the two facies probably resulting from contrasting origins. In the reworked bar facies below the topmost sandstone, calcite cement has in some areas degraded the potential reservoirs.

Results of this study are based on interpretation of three slabbed and polished cores (116 to 150 feet in length) taken by Mountain Fuel (Nos. 2, 3, 4 Spearhead Ranch). Scanning electron microscope analyses, X-ray diffraction analyses and petrographic laboratory studies were carried out on samples from the cores.

Four "stacked" upward-coarsening sequences, up to 70 feet thick, were interpreted from analyses of sedimentary structures and vertical sequences of lithologies and facies. Discriminant analysis of the X-ray diffraction results of 36 reworked and non-reworked facies sandstones yields nearly perfect separation (97%) of the two facies.

INTRODUCTION

Initial production from Spearhead Ranch Field was begun in May, 1973, when the Mountain Fuel Supply Company No. 1 MF Anadarko Fox drilled into the First Frontier Sandstone at 12,583 feet and it "blew out" due to high formation pressures. The twin (relief) well, the Spearhead Ranch No. 1A (SENW Sec. 13, T39N, R75W), drilled 170 feet northwest of the discovery was completed in November, 1973. By mid-1976, eleven wells were completed and produced from the First Frontier Sandstone. Due to economics and the depths required to reach production, the field was developed on 640-acre spacing. Initial potential in most of the producing wells averaged 1000 BOPD and 2 MMCFGPD.

Spearhead Ranch Field lies near the southwestern corner of the Powder River Basin in Wyoming (Fig. 1) and near the maximum subsea depths in the Basin on the top of the First Frontier Sandstone (Fig. 2). The field is located just east of the synclinal axis where the relatively uniform regional dip is to the southwest. The field, as presently outlined, appears to be entirely a stratigraphic trap with producing intervals lying at the very top of the uppermost First Frontier Sandstone. The overlying black marine shelf of the Cody (Carlile) forms the reservoir seal.

The producing sandstones in the field are a series of laterally discontinuous lenses of sand enclosed by shales. Reservoirs within the field are thin and commonly are less than five feet thick. Several laterally discontinuous sand pods occur within the field area (Fig. 3) and some of these are productive.

This study is based primarily on the study of three slabbed and polished subsurface cores taken by Mountain Fuel Oil Company in the early development of the field. The wells are the No. 2, No. 3, and No. 4 Spearhead Ranch located in T39N and R74 and 75W. All cores began in the Carlile Shale which overlies the reservoir. The lengths of cores recovered are 147.3, 116 and 121.5 feet respectively. The deepest core penetration into the First Frontier is in the No. 2 well, 133 feet. The cores are presently part of the collection at the Colorado School of Mines.

Following slabbing and polishing all the core slabs were photographed and major depositional units were designated. Recognition of individual units was based on lithology, sedimentary structure associations and specific inferred environ-

Copyright © 1979, The Society of Economic Paleontologists and Mineralogists

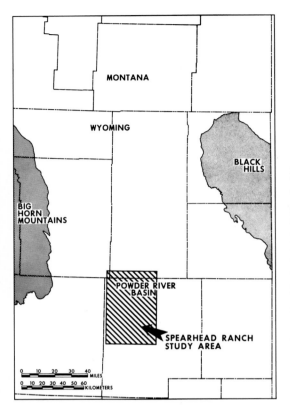

Fig. 1.—Location of Spearhead Ranch study area, Converse County, Wyoming.

submerged marine-bar sandstone, reworked marine-bar sandstone and interbar shales and sandstones. The reworked marine-bar facies, where present, is the uppermost sand in the sequence. When it is sufficiently thick and directly overlies a submerged bar, it usually is productive. Within the reworked bar sequence at the top of the First Frontier, initial porosities were apparently sufficient to constitute a reservoir. A series of diagenetic events has preserved the porosity and permeability.

In the non-reworked submerged marine-bar facies, commonly located below the reworked bars (Fig. 4), initial porosity and permeability have been almost entirely plugged by secondary growths of quartz. Reworked bars such as Unit 6B (Well No. 2), (Fig. 4) and Unit 1C (Well No. 4) (Fig. 5) located below the top of the First Frontier, do not produce. The upper sequence of submerged marine bars prograded southward(?) over highly bioturbated silty shallow marine shelf shales. As indicated in Figures 3 and 7, individual bars did cover the whole area. The easternmost edge of the uppermost sandstones in the First Frontier Sandstones can be mapped east of the field, (Slack 1974, personal communication and Prescott Fig. 2, 1975). The First Frontier Sandstones apparently extend no further than 30 miles east of the Spearhead Ranch Field at the latitude of the field.

FACIES ANALYSIS

In addition to the sandstones of the reworked and non-reworked bar facies, sandstones were also deposited in an interbar facies and a foreshore subhorizontally laminated facies. Sub-sand size facies include marine shelf shales, tidal flat silty shales, shelf siltstones and lagoonal(?) siltstones. The nearshore facies, beach (upper foreshore), lower foreshore, lagoon and tidal flat facies are limited to deposits below the interpreted lower unconformity at 12,382.8 feet (MFSR No. 2), and similar deposits at the base of MFSR No. 4 (Figs. 5, 22B). All the deposits above the unconformity are interpreted to be offshore marine bar and offshore shelf siltstones and shales.

Submerged marine bars.—This facies usually is composed of 40% or more fine-grained sandstones; siltstone, and shale lenses and clasts comprise the remainder, (Fig. 8). Physical structures comprise 70–90% of the facies. The remaining 10—30% is burrowed by 1/8" to 1/4"—diame-

ments of deposition. Two unconformities were identified in wells No. 2 and 4. These are indicated in well No. 2 at 12,408.5 and 12,482.8 feet (Fig. 4) and in No. 4 at 12,534.9 and 12,602.5 feet (Fig. 5). In well No. 3 an unconformity occurs below the upper sand at 12,772.7 feet (Fig. 6). Well No. 3 did not penetrate deeply enough to encounter the second unconformity (Fig. 6).

Production in the field seems to be limited by facies defined on the basis of environment and process of deposition, and by stage and type of secondary diagenesis. The first portion of the study deals with analysis of environments of deposition of the upper part of the First Frontier Sandstone. All of the sandstones are facies which are within or closely associated with offshore-bar sand deposition. The bar-related facies include

Fig. 2.—First Frontier Sandstone structure map, Spearhead Ranch Field area. Wells numbered 1, 2, 3, 4, 5 on map correspond to Mountain Fuel Spearhead Ranch wells numbered 1A, 2, 3, 4, and 5, respectively.

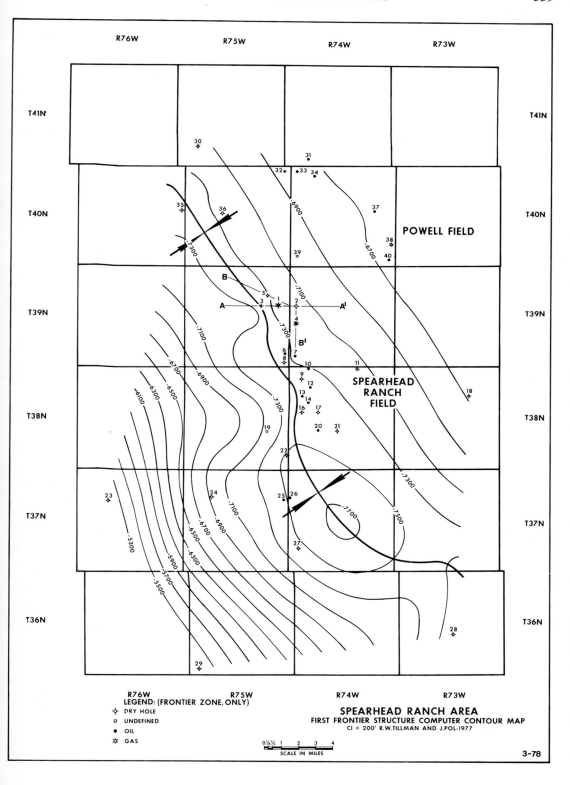

LEGEND: (FRONTIER ZONE, ONLY)
- ✧ DRY HOLE
- ○ UNDEFINED
- ● OIL
- ✦ GAS

SPEARHEAD RANCH AREA
FIRST FRONTIER STRUCTURE COMPUTER CONTOUR MAP
CI = 200' R.W.TILLMAN AND J.POL-1977

SCALE IN MILES

3-78

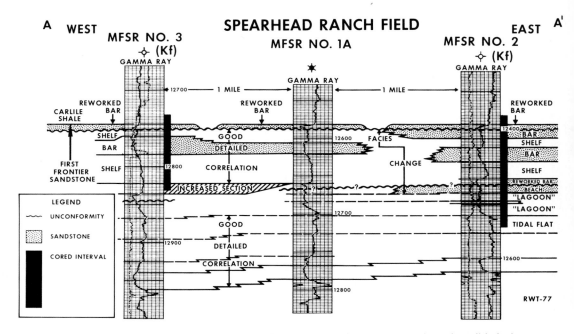

FIG. 3.—Stratigraphic cross-section across Spearhead Ranch Field. Gamma ray logs show lithologic contacts observed in cores. Good detailed correlations are suggested between MFSR No. 3 and 1A. Only between 12,819–34 feet is an increased thickness of shallow marine siltstones suggested when compared to MFSR No. 1A. The detailed correlation between MFSR No. 3 and 1A at the base of the marine bar suggests that it is a single bar which thins eastward. The base of the partially equivalent non-reworked bar in MFSR No. 2 is lower and presumably formed at a different (earlier?) time.

Well MFSR No. 1A produces from the First Frontier Sandstone, the other two wells produce only from the Dakota and/or Lakota Sandstones.

A westward slope of the markers is indicated below 12,700 feet in the MFSR No. 1A.

ter oblique and horizontal burrows. *Asterosoma* may form up to 2% by volume of the facies (Figs. 9A, B, D).

The predominant physical structures are moderate to high-angle trough cross-bedding (Figs. 9B, C). Troughs form 25–75% of the facies. Ripples and ripples on troughs (Figs. 9E, F) form up to 20% of the facies. Interbedded shales may form up to 5% of the unit (Fig. 9A). Vertical sequence associations typically indicate this bar overlies the bioturbated shelf siltstone, (Figs. 4, 6) or interbar facies (Figs. 5, 6). This facies is most commonly overlain by a reworked marine facies (Figs. 4, 5). It may also be overlain by the bioturbated shelf siltstone facies.

This facies is lower in percentage of chert and quartz than the reworked marine-bar facies with which it is commonly in contact, and it is higher in feldspar content than the reworked facies.

Reworked marine-bar facies.—This facies differs from the submerged marine-bar facies in several respects. It is predominantly medium grain size and is commonly almost totally physically and biogenically reworked (non-laminated), (Figs.

10A, B). Mineralogically it is high in chert and quartz and low in plagioclase feldspar.

Typically, the facies contains 60% or more sandstone and where structures are visible they are characteristically moderate and high angle cross-bedded troughs (Fig. 11). The high percentage of trough cross-beds suggests the deposition from currents was responsible for deposition of the reworked bar facies. Locally, areas of biologic reworking by burrowers are observed but volumetrically biological reworking is much less important than physical processes. The amount of reworking varies from 18 to 80%. The percentage of burrowing is variable, ranging from 2 to 16%.

The upper and lower contacts are sharp (Figs. 10D, F; 12). The base is interpreted to be unconformable wherever observed in the cores. Typically, in vertical sequence, the reworked sandstones overlie a non-reworked bar facies (Figs. 3, 7), or they may overlie a shelf siltstone (MFSR No. 3), (Fig. 3). Near the edges of the bar complex in MFSR No. 5, no reworked sandstone is observed (Fig. 7). Reworked bars occur below the

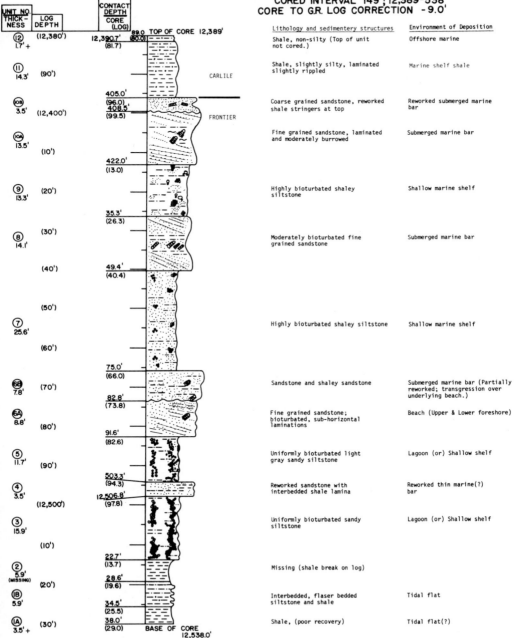

FIG. 4.—Core facies description and interpretation, Mountain Fuel Spearhead Ranch No. 2. Core depths are indicated; log depths are in parentheses. Units numbered A and B are interpreted to be very specifically genetically related. The major sedimentary features are indicated. Location of well shown in Figure 2.

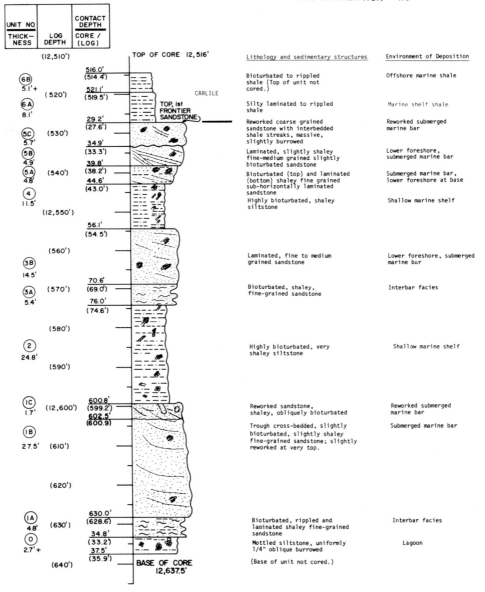

MOUNTAIN FUEL NO. 4, SPEARHEAD RANCH
SE NW SEC. 19 T·39·N R·74·W
CONVERSE COUNTY, WYOMING

CORED INTERVAL 121.5'; 12,516-637.5'
CORE TO G.R. LOG CORRECTION -1.6'

| UNIT NO. | | CONTACT DEPTH | | | |
| THICK-NESS | LOG DEPTH | CORE / (LOG) | | Lithology and sedimentary structures | Environment of Deposition |

TOP OF CORE 12,516'

6B 5.1'+	(520')	516.0' (514.4') 521.1' (519.5')	CARLILE	Bioturbated to rippled shale (Top of unit not cored.)	Offshore marine shale
6A 8.1'			TOP, 1st FRONTIER SANDSTONE	Silty laminated to rippled shale	Marine shelf shale
5C 5.7'	(530')	29.2' (27.6') 34.9'		Reworked coarse grained sandstone with interbedded shale streaks, massive, slightly burrowed	Reworked submerged marine bar
5B 4.9'		(33.3') 39.8'		Laminated, slightly shaley fine-medium grained slightly bioturbated sandstone	Lower foreshore, submerged marine bar
5A 4.8'	(540')	(38.2') 44.6' (43.0')		Bioturbated (top) and laminated (bottom) shaley fine grained sub-horizontally laminated sandstone	Submerged marine bar, lower foreshore at base
4 11.5'	(12,550')			Highly bioturbated, shaley siltstone	Shallow marine shelf
3B 14.5'	(560')	56.1' (54.5')		Laminated, fine to medium grained sandstone	Lower foreshore, submerged marine bar
3A 5.4'	(570')	70.6' (69.0') 76.0' (74.6')		Bioturbated, shaley, fine-grained sandstone	Interbar facies
2 24.8'	(580') (590')			Highly bioturbated, very shaley siltstone	Shallow marine shelf
1C 1.7'	(12,600')	600.8' (599.2') 602.5' (600.9')		Reworked sandstone, shaley, obliquely bioturbated	Reworked submerged marine bar
1B 27.5'	(610') (620')			Trough cross-bedded, slightly bioturbated, slightly shaley fine-grained sandstone; slightly reworked at very top.	Submerged marine bar
1A 4.8'	(630')	630.0' (628.6') 34.8' (33.2')		Bioturbated, rippled and laminated shaley fine-grained sandstone	Interbar facies
0 2.7'+	(640')	37.5' (35.9')		Mottled siltstone, uniformly 1/4" oblique burrowed	Lagoon

BASE OF CORE 12,637.5'

(Base of unit not cored.)

FIG. 5.—Core facies description and interpretation, Mountain Fuel Spearhead Ranch No. 4. Core depths are indicated; log depths are in parentheses. Units numbered A, B, and C interpreted to be specifically genetically related. The lithologies and major sedimentary features are indicated. Location of well shown in Figure 2.

MOUNTAIN FUEL NO.3, SPEARHEAD RANCH (FIELD)
FRONTIER FM. (UPPER CRETACEOUS)
SENW SEC.14 T·39·N R·75·W
CONVERSE CO., WYOMING
CORED INTERVAL 116'; 12,733-849'
CORE TO G.R. LOG CORRECTION -19.0'

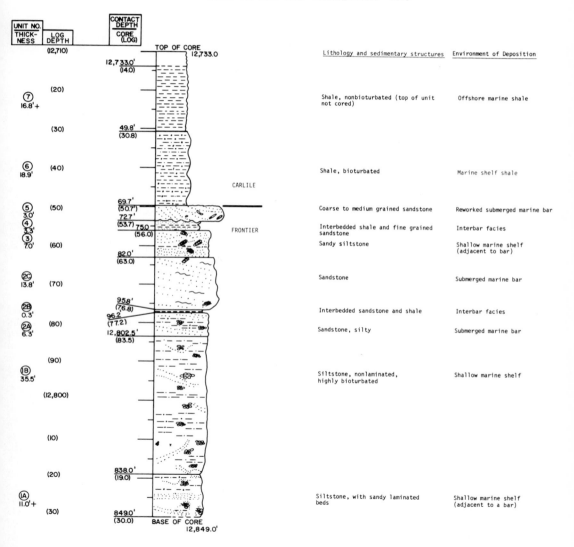

		Lithology and sedimentary structures	Environment of Deposition
⑦ 16.8'+		Shale, nonbioturbated (top of unit not cored)	Offshore marine shale
⑥ 18.9'		Shale, bioturbated	Marine shelf shale
⑤ 3.0'		Coarse to medium grained sandstone	Reworked submerged marine bar
④ 1.3'		Interbedded shale and fine grained sandstone	Interbar facies
③ 7.0'		Sandy siltstone	Shallow marine shelf (adjacent to bar)
②C 13.8'		Sandstone	Submerged marine bar
②B 0.3'		Interbedded sandstone and shale	Interbar facies
②A 6.3'		Sandstone, silty	Submerged marine bar
①B 35.5'		Siltstone, nonlaminated, highly bioturbated	Shallow marine shelf
①A 11.0'+		Siltstone, with sandy laminated beds	Shallow marine shelf (adjacent to a bar)

Fig. 6.—Core facies description and interpretation, Mountain Fuel Spearhead Ranch No. 3. Core depths are indicated; log depths are in parenthesis. Units numbered A, B, and C are interpreted to be specifically genetically related. The lithology and major sedimentary features are indicated. Location of well shown in Figure 2.

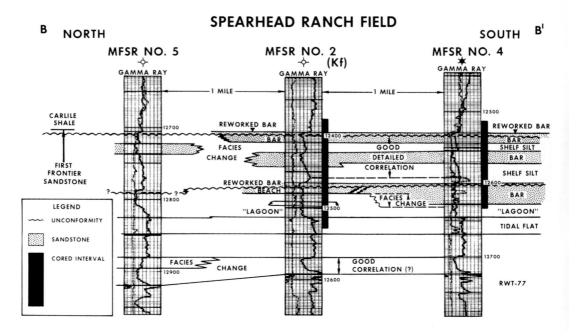

FIG. 7.—Stratigraphic cross-section Spearhead Ranch Field. Gamma Ray logs show lithologic contacts observed in cores. Good detailed correlations are observed above 12,460 feet (MFSR No. 2) and MFSR No. 4. The upper reworked bar facies in MFSR No. 4 produces. In MFSR No. 5, the reworked bar facies is very thin to absent and the single marine bar is at a different position than the bars in the other two wells. Below 12,475.0 feet abrupt facies changes occur between MFSR No. 2 and No. 4. The thin "lagoon" thick marine bar sequence apparently grades to the north into a thick "lagoon" and thin beach facies. The tidal flat facies cored in MFSR No. 2 apparently correlates with both of the other wells. Location of the cross-section is given in Figure 2.

uppermost sandstones but they less commonly succeed these slightly older non-reworked bars. Where present, the uppermost reworked bar sandstone is succeeded by a silty shale facies of the Cody (Carlile) Shale. Reworked bars below the topmost sandstone are succeeded by bioturbated shelf siltsone (Fig. 10E).

In the only cored well that produces from the Frontier (the MFSR No. 4), the pay zone is largely concentrated in the reworked facies which is 5.7 feet thick (Fig. 5). At this location, it overlies a non-reworked bar which contributes a minor amount of production. In the MFSR No. 2, the same vertical sequence is encountered in the uppermost sandstone but the reworked facies is too thin (3.5 feet), (Fig. 4), for economic production. In the MFSR No. 3 (Fig. 6), the reworked sand does not overlie a non-reworked bar and again is thin (3.0 feet).

Upper and lower foreshore sandstone.—In the zone below low tide and above storm-wave base, several predominantly wave-swash deposited sandstones are observed in the cores (Figs. 13A, B, C). Thicknesses of this facies range from 5–9 feet. Commonly, the subhorizontally laminated

laminasets are up to 1.5 feet thick and comprise from 25–90% of the unit. Moderately dipping (10–20°) planar laminae may form up to 25% of the unit (MFSR No. 2, Unit 6A). Ripples form up to 15% of the facies and up to 2% moderate size troughs are observed. Rip-up shale clasts may be distributed randomly in the sandstone (Fig. 13D). About 75% of the facies are physical structures; up to 25% of the units are burrowed. Horizontal 1/4 to 1/2 inch diameter burrows occur in amounts up to 20% by volume. Five percent vertical burrows are observed (Figs. 13E, F). *Asterosoma* are present in amounts up to 2% (Fig. 13E). Trace amounts of 1/8 inch diameter horizontal burrows are also present.

In addition to the intervals interpreted as foreshore in several of the non-reworked bars, sets of subhorizontal laminae are sparsely interbedded with trough cross-beds in some non-reworked bar facies.

The best developed foreshore facies occurs in Unit 6A in MFSR No. 2 and it overlies what is interpreted as a uniformly bioturbated lagoon (?) facies. The top of the facies in this well is interpreted to be unconformable. In Unit 5A of

SUBMERGED MARINE BAR NON-REWORKED (K_f)

Mountain Fuel #2
Spearhead Ranch Field
Converse County, Wyoming

Columnized Data Format:
    %/Max. set thickness/Additional notes

(R. W. Tillman 3-75, 1-78)

Unit 10A
Core Depth: 12,408.5-22.0'(13.5')
(Log Depth :   12,399.5-13.0')

Lithology
1. Sandstone (%) — 40%/0.2'
2. Siltstone (%) — 35%/0.2'
3. Shale (%); a) Laminated; b) Clasts — 25%/0.05/a,tr-b

Physical Structures — 73%/0.3'
1. High angle cross-bedding (20°+); a) Troughs; b) Planar — tr/0.2'/a
2. Moderate angle cross-bedding (10-20°) a) Troughs; b) Planar — 13%/0.2'/a
3. Subhorizontal to low angle bedding; a) Trough; b) Planar — 7%/0.3'/b
4. Horizontal laminations — -
5. Rippled: a) Sandstone; b) Shale — 35%/0.2'
6. Rippled interbedded sandstone and shale — 25%/0.2'
7. Ripples superimposed on troughs — -
8. Reworked: a) By waves & currents; b) Bedding destroyed, massive; c) By bioturbation — 17%/0.3'/10%a

Biogenic Sedimentary Structures — 27%/0.2'
1. Identified burrows; d) "Donut burrows"; t) Teichichnus; a) Asterosoma; c) Chrondrites — 2%-a, tr-c
2. Distinct burrows; aa) <1/8"; a) 1/8" - 1/4"; b) 1/4" - 1/2"; c) >1/2"; d) silt filled; e) Clay filled; f) Sand filled; g) Silt lined; h) Clay lined; i) Spreiten; j) Vertical; k) Oblique; l) Horizontal — 4% - c, f, k / 4% - b, d, l / 2% - b, d, k / 10% - b, d, k / tr-c,f,j tr-c,f,l
3. Bioturbated — 2%
4. Total interval burrowed (%,footage) — 1.4'
5. Diversity (Number of burrow types; 3-low, 7-moderate, 10-high.) — 8-moderately high

Fig. 8.—Non-reworked marine bar components, Unit 10A, Mountain Fuel Spearhead Ranch No. 2, SENW, Sec. 18, T39N, R74W, Converse County, Wyoming.

Note that the "Lithology" percentages, sandstone, siltstone and shale total 100%. The physical plus biologic components also total 100%. The components (not accompanied by vertical black bar) total the percent within each of the major categories (physical or biological). The percentages in lines having black vertical bar along margin do not contribute to the 100% total but instead are descriptors of subcomponents. On the chart, the percentage, by volume, is given first followed by the maximum set thickness (in feet) for each component.

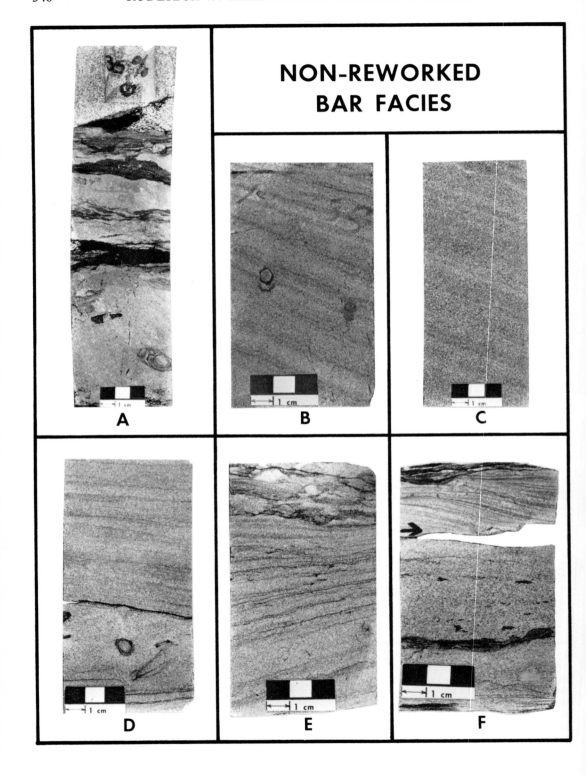

NON-REWORKED
BAR FACIES

MFSR No. 4, the foreshore lamination occurs at the base of the uppermost sandstone (Unit 5A). There it overlies a shelf siltstone and is succeeded by trough-bedded facies of a non-reworked bar facies.

Interbar facies.—The interbar facies is transitional in characteristics between submerged non-reworked bar and bioturbated shelf siltstone. It contains more shale interbedded with the sandstones and siltstones than do the bar facies. Thicknesses of this facies range from 0.3 to 5.4 feet.

Physical structures range from 35–95% by volume of the facies. Ripples form 15–95% of the structures and in all but one core (MFSR No. 4, Unit 3A) form over half of the facies. Interbedded rippled sand and shale are common (Figs. 14A, C). Thin units with trough cross-bedding are locally interbedded and irregularly laminated zones of deformed soft sediment (partially reworked?) occur (Fig. 14B). Burrowing in the interbar facies ranges up to 60%. Mottling occurs in some zones. Horizontal and oblique 1/8 to 1/4 inch diameter burrows predominate (Figs. 14B, C).

Shelf siltstone facies.—The shelf siltstone facies differ from all other facies in that they are predominantly (50–90%) siltstone and in all units burrowing exceeds 55% by volume. Very fine-grained sandstone occurs in amounts from a trace to 30%. Shales are silty and commonly are interbedded with siltstones and rarely with thin sandstone laminasets (Fig. 15A). Most of the burrowed portions are bioturbated and show a mottled appearance. Quarter-inch diameter horizontal to oblique burrows can be distinguished in most of the mottling (Fig. 15E). Slightly larger (1/2 inch) and smaller (1/8 inch diameter) burrows can also

be distinguished in lesser amounts. Silt-lined shale-filled burrows occur in amounts up to 17% by volume (Fig. 15D). Shale-lined burrows are present in trace amounts (Fig. 15A). *Teichichnus* (Fig. 15B) and *Asterosoma* (Fig. 15C) are observed in trace amounts. In all facies designated as shelf siltstones, 88% or more of the total vertical section includes one or more burrows.

Physical structures in this facies range from 10–50%. Subhorizontal laminae of sandstone and siltstone are the most abundant bedding type. Ripples of both symmetrical (wave) and asymmetrical (current?) types are also observed in zones which were not highly bioturbated. Interbedding of lithologies on a very fine scale is common (Fig. 15F). The thickest sets in the facies were about 0.2 foot.

Lagoon (or shallow shelf) siltstone.—Lagoonal sediments differ from those interpreted as shelf siltstones because of their uniform light gray color and bioturbation in excess of 95% in all three units cored (Fig. 16). The very uniformly mottled appearance resulting from almost total bioturbation by predominantly horizontal, 1/4 inch diameter, burrows (Figs. 17A, B) is the most characteristic feature. Up to 5% vertical burrows of 1/4 inch diameter also occur (Fig. 17C). The burrows are universally filled by silt and very fine-grained sand, but locally dark shale occurs between burrows. No microfauna were recovered in samples from this facies (D. Dailey, personal communication), and all palynologic material was of too poor quality for recognition of genus or species (R. Bergad, personal communication). The number of individual palynomorphs observed was very small. It appears that little, if any, additional information could be obtained from this facies to further substantiate a lagoon origin for these

FIG. 9.—*A*, Contact between medium grained reworked marine bar and fine-grained non-reworked bar. Typical interbedded shale and rippled sandstone. Concentrically shale-laminated. *Asterosoma* burrow near base. Slabbed core. Units 10A and 10B, MFSR No. 2, 12,408.4 feet. *B*, Uppermost bed of non-reworked submerged marine bar. Overlying this core slab is reworked bar facies. Note thinning of several laminasets toward left near top; thinning is typical of troughs (as contrasted with planar laminasets). Bedding produced by strong unidirectional current. Clay-lined sand filled burrows resembling *Asterosoma* and suggestive of deposition in water depths *in excess* of 30 feet. See Figure 12 for location of this core slab in sequence. Unit 5B, MFSR No. 4, 12,535.1 feet. *C*, Large scale trough with high angle sub-parallel cross-laminations. This type of bedding is formed by high energy unidirectional currents and represents the highest energy constructional feature of the bar complex. Initial porosities in this type of bedding were high; porosity now is 7.5%, which is moderately high for the field. Slabbed core. Non-reworked submerged marine bar. Unit 2C, MFSR No. 3, 12,785.8 feet. *D*, Low amplitude trough cross-bedding. *Asterosoma*, concentric clay laminae surrounding sand filled 1 cm diameter burrow, also *Asterosoma* at 45°. Non-reworked submerged marine bar. Slabbed core, Unit 2A, MFSR No. 3, 12,801.6 feet. *E*, Slightly rippled subhorizontal sheaves of wave and low velocity bottom-current deposited laminasets overlain by bioturbated ripples. Lower foreshore bar. Facies overlying facies interpreted as lagoon. Unit 6A, MFSR No. 2, 12,485.3 feet. *F*, Current rippled interlaminated sandstone and shale overlying low amplitude trough cross-bedding with shale rip-up clasts. Slabbed core. Non-reworked submerged marine bar, Unit 2A, MFSR No. 3, 12,802.2 feet.

REWORKED BAR FACIES

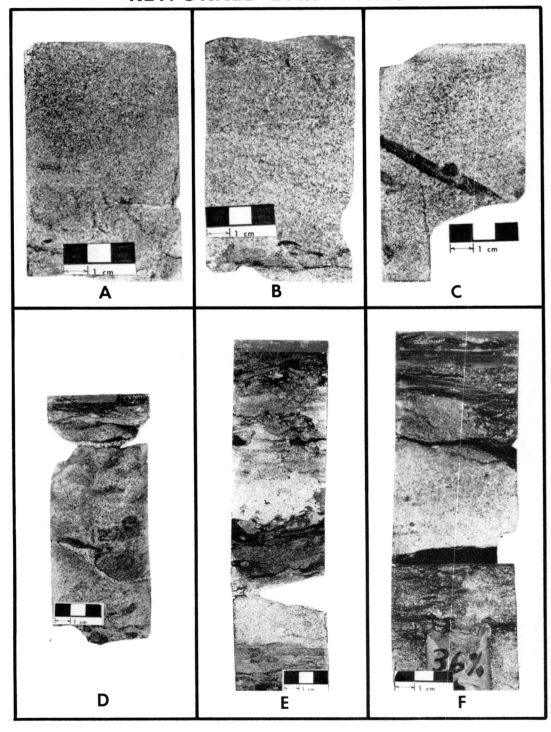

units. The association with what are interpreted as tidal flat deposits below in MFSR No. 2 (Units 1A and 1B), and foreshore deposits (Unit 6A) above suggests a very shallow water affinity for this facies (Fig. 4). The association with interbar deposits in MFSR No. 4 (Unit 1A) is not necessarily contradictory to a very shallow water origin for Unit 0, (Fig. 5).

Tidal flat shales.—The two lowermost units in MFSR No. 2 are interpreted to be tidal flat deposits. The units differ from other sub-sandstone size units in the cores in that they are predominantly physically bedded (65–95%) (Fig. 18). Ripples strongly dominate the bedding (56–85%) and flaser and lenticular bedding (Reineck and Singh, 1975, p. 97) are observed in amounts up to 15% (Figs. 17D, E). Subhorizontal to slightly wavy laminasets (Fig. 17F) form about 10% of the units.

Burrowing ranges from 5 to 35% in the two units studied. Silt-filled 1/8–1/4 inch diameter horizontal burrows dominate the biological structures (Figs. 17D, F). No vertical burrows were observed.

A wholly agglutinated fauna of low species diversity and high faunal dominance suggests a stress environment in samples from Units 1A and 1B in MFSR No. 2. The dominant form present is *Haplophragmoides gilberti* which generally is reported from environments shunned by the vast majority of Foraminifera "such as shallow brackish environments (tidal flats) and deeper bathymetric levels of the ocean." (D. Dailey, personal communication).

Marine shelf shales.—In the cores studied, shales were limited to the tops of the cores where they directly overlie the reworked bar sandstone facies. This unit is the Carlile (Cody) Shale. It differs significantly from the tidal flat facies of the First Frontier in its silt content, fossil content, and scale of physical sedimentary structures.

Typically, the unit contains from 2 to 10% silt. The silt is disseminated and also forms ripple laminae and subhorizontal laminations (Figs. 14, D, E, F). Where a thick section of the Cody was cored, a contrast in the amount of silt was observed. In MFSR No. 3, the lower 20 feet of the Cody contains significantly more silt than the overlying shale. Physical structures range from 55 to 75%. Burrows form a sort of mottling and unless studied in detail are not readily observed. Most of the bioturbation is the result of horizontal to oblique 1/8 inch diameter burrows. Typically, less than 10% of the burrows are individually recognizable. Traces of white, silt-lined "donut burrows" were observed.

Microfauna observed in these shales suggest an open ocean central (to outer) shelf deposition according to D. Dailey (personal communication), (Fig. 19A). Shales examined in MFSR No. 3 represent a sequence from late middle Cenomanian (Unit 1B) to late Cenomanian (Units 6 & 7) to "no younger than middle *Turonian*" at the top of Unit 7, (Figs. 6 and 19B).

According to Merewether *et al.* (1976, p. 44) the Wall Creek Sandstone Member in the type locality contains fossils of late *Turonian* age (Table 1, zone 16). He also states that southwest of Tisdale Mountain (in Section 35, T39N, R83W) the Wall Creek (First Frontier) Sandstone is overlain by a sandstone that contains younger fossils (Table 1, zone 18). Using electric logs, Merewether, *et al.* claim that "the fossiliferous beds in the lower part of the Cody Shale can be traced from Tisdale Mountain to Spearhead Ranch oil field" and that the "petroleum bearing sandstone can be correlated with the shale in the Cody that contains fossils from zone 18."

Merewether had no samples from Spearhead Ranch Field and relied on subsurface log markers for his correlation from the outcrop section (zone 18) to the subsurface. Samples from the Mountain Fuel No. 2, No. 3, and No. 4 cores were examined and "the youngest micro-fossils found were middle *Turonian*" (Dailey, personal communication). This suggests that the sandstones at the outcrop (zone 18) are younger than those at Spearhead Ranch Field. Dailey's evidence suggests that possibly the lowermost 36 feet of Cody Shale at Spearhead Ranch are no younger than zones

---

Fig. 10.—*A*, Typical "massive appearing" medium-grained sandstone. Salt and pepper appearance, cherty. Reworked marine bar facies; *reservoir sandstone*. Uppermost sandstone of First Frontier Sandstone. Unit 5C, MFSR No. 4, 12,532.1 feet. *B*, Medium-grained sandstone with abundant black chert grains. Typical "massive appearance." 3.5 feet thick uppermost First Frontier Sandstone, reworked submerged marine bar. Unit 10B, MFSR No. 2, 12,406.2 feet. *C*, *Asterosoma* burrow, concentric clay laminated at a typical angle of 45° from horizontal. Part of a 3 feet thick medium-grained sandstone at top of First Frontier Sandstone. Reworked submerged marine bar, Unit 5, MFSR No. 3, 12,771.7 feet. *D*, Bioturbated medium-grained sandstone at top of First Frontier Sandstone. Contact with subhorizontally laminated Cody (Carlile) Shale at top of core slab. Reworked marine bar facies, Unit 5, MFSR No. 3, 12,769.7 feet. *E*, Physically and biologically reworked sandstone at the top of the bar. Contact with shelf siltstone (Unit 7) near top of core slab. Reworked submerged marine bar. Unit 6B, MFSR No. 2, 12,474.8 feet. *F*, Cody (Carlile) Shale (upper 4 cm) lying on top of medium-grained physically reworked marine bar sandstone. Units 10B and 11, MFSR No. 2, 12,404.8 feet. Porosity at base of core slab 3.6%.

REWORKED SUBMERGED MARINE BAR (K$_f$)

              Mountain Fuel #2
              Spearhead Ranch Field
              Converse County, Wyoming

Columnized Data Format: (R. W. Tillman 3-75, 1-78)
  %/Max. set thickness/Additional notes   Unit 10B
                                          Core Depth: 12,405-8.5' (3.5')
                                          (Log Depth : 12,396.0-99.5')
Lithology
1. Sandstone (%) | 60%/0.5' |
2. Siltstone (%) | 15%/0.1' |
3. Shale (%); a) Laminated; b) Clasts | 25%/0.05'/a, tr-b |

Physical Structures | 98%/0.5' |
1. High angle cross-bedding (20°+); a) Troughs;
    b) Planar | 10%/0.2/b? |
2. Moderate angle cross-bedding (10-20°)
    a) Troughs; b) Planar | 60%/0.5/b? |
3. Subhorizontal to low angle bedding; a) Trough;
    b) Planar
4. Horizontal laminations | 10%/0.2/a |
5. Rippled: a) Sandstone; b) Shale
6. Rippled interbedded sandstone and shale
7. Ripples superimposed on troughs
8. Reworked: a) By waves & currents; b) Bedding
    destroyed, massive; c) By bioturbation | 18%/0.5/a |

Biogenic Sedimentary Structures | 2%/0.1'/in sh |
1. Identified burrows; d) "Donut burrows";
    t) Teichichnus
                                                         | tr - a,f,1 |
2. Distinct burrows; aa) <1/8"; a) 1/8" - 1/4"; b) 1/4" - 1/2"; | tr - a,f,k |
    c) >1/2"; d) Silt filled; e) Clay filled;
    f) Sand filled; g) Silt lined; h) Clay lined;
    i) Spreiten; j) Vertical; k) Oblique; l) Horizontal

3. Bioturbated | - |

4. Total interval burrowed (%,footage) | 9%/0.3' |

5. Diversity (Number of burrow types; 3-low, | 2 - low |
    7-moderate, 10-high).

Fig. 11.—Reworked marine bar components for Unit 10B, Mountain Fuel Spearhead Ranch No. 2 well. Note that the "Lithology" percentages for sandstone, siltstone and shale total 100%. The physical plus biologic components also total 100%. The components (not accompanied by vertical black bar) total the percentage within each of the major categories (physical or biological). The percentages in lines having black vertical bar along margin do not contribute to the 100% total but instead are descriptors of subcomponents. On the chart, the percentage by volume is given first followed by the maximum set thickness (in feet) for the component.

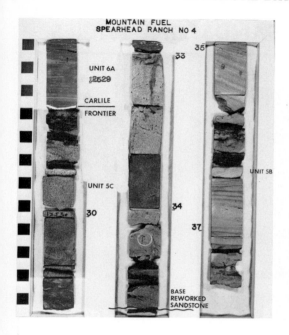

Fig. 12.—Uppermost sandstone in First Frontier Sandstone, Mountain Fuel Spearhead Ranch No. 4. The reworked marine bar facies, (12,529.2–34.9 feet, Unit 5C) is productive. Physically reworked, medium-grained, slightly burrowed (oblique and vertical). The non-reworked bar facies (12,534.9–39.8 feet, Unit 5B) contains moderate to high angle cross-bedding with thin intensely bioturbated zones. *Asterosoma* is at 12,535.2 feet. Cody Shale (Unit 6A) above 12,529.2 feet contains abundant silty laminations and is sparsely burrowed. Slabbed core; scale to left in inches.

13 to 15 (Merewether *et al.*, 1976, Table 1, p. 38).

TRACE FOSSILS

Burrowing ranges from a minimum of 2% in some reworked bar facies and ranges to as high as 98% in the facies interpreted as lagoonal. The predominant identifiable burrow in the various facies is *Asterosoma*. It appears inclined at a characteristic 45° angle in the reworked bar facies (Fig. 10C), in the non-reworked bar facies where its concentric clay linings are prominent (Figs. 9A, D), and in lower foreshore sandstones (Figs. 13E, 20E). In the shelf siltstones, bioturbation is common and some of the burrows can be recognized as *Asterosoma* (Fig. 15C). Traces of *Teichichnus* burrows are observed in the shelf siltstone (Fig. 15B).

In the shelf siltstone, slightly flattened "donut burrows" are recognized by a burrow lining of white, very fine-grained sand (Fig. 20G). These burrows are similar to Howard's (1966) "plural

curving tubes" but, in contrast to Howard's description, they seldom if ever occur in pairs.

Most of the burrows observed in all facies in the cores were horizontal to low angle oblique. Occasional vertical burrows were encountered but only in the foreshore facies. *Asterosoma*-type concentrically clay-lined vertical burrows (Fig. 13E) and medium-grained sand-filled (Fig. 13F) vertical burrows were also observed in the foreshore deposits. Several types of vertical burrows were observed in the foreshore facies. Nearly vertical to vertical burrows filled with sand of the same size as in the surrounding sandstone also were observed in the foreshore facies (Figs. 20A, B). Other vertically oriented asymmetrical burrows were observed in the foreshore (Fig. 20C). A trace of very ornate vertical sand-, silt- and shale-filled burrows were observed in the shelf siltstone (Fig. 20D). In the lagoon facies scattered vertical burrows identical in appearance to the predominantly horizontal 1/4 inch-diameter horizontal burrows were observed (Figs. 17C).

Burrows that had silt linings with slightly finer grained filling were abundant in the shelf siltstones (Figs. 15D and 20F). Silt and very fine-grained sand-filled burrows comprise the 95 to 98% bioturbated lagoon facies (Fig. 21 and Figs. 17A, B). This facies is distinguished by its light color and its uniform and thorough bioturbation. Locally, the material between burrows is shale (Fig. 21).

Burrowing in units interpreted as tidal flat facies was limited to 1/8 to 1/4 inch horizontal burrows. Vertical and U-shaped burrows were absent.

FIRST FRONTIER FACIES DISTRIBUTION

Regional studies of the Frontier were done by Barlow and Haun (1966) and Goodell (1962). Hose (1955) mapped the Frontier in the Crazy Woman Creek outcrop area west of Spearhead Ranch and Lange (1976) cited production statistics on Spearhead Ranch Field.

In wells utilized in this study, the SP-Induction log character of MFSR No. 2 and No. 4 as indicated in Figure 22A appears to be very similar; however, as can be seen in Figure 22B this is not true below the unconformity at 12,482.8 feet. Foreshore (beach) sandstones in MFSR No. 2 grade laterally into non-reworked bar sandstones in MFSR No. 4. The lower portion of MFSR No. 2 grades laterally from the totally bioturbated lagoon to predominantly physically bedded barrier(?) bar sandstone in MFSR No. 2.

The good detailed correlation between MFSR No. 2 and No. 4 above the lower unconformity (Figs. 7, 23) is attributed to the fact that these wells lie along the north-south depositional trend of the field. However, below the unconformity a change in the trend of the facies is inferred.

In the west-east stratigraphic section (Fig. 23)

LOWER FORESHORE SANDSTONE FACIES

wells lying approximately normal to the field axis show significant lateral changes above the unconformity at 12,482.8 feet. In MFSR No. 3, a shelf siltstone (and interbar) facies lies below the reworked bar facies at the top of the First Frontier Sandstone in contrast to the vertical succession of reworked bar over non-reworked bar in the MFSR No. 2. None of the non-reworked marine bars in the MFSR No. 3 and MFSR No. 2 can be correlated between the two cored wells. The bar in MFSR No. 3 at 12,782.0 feet can be correlated with a thick sand in MFSR No. 1A but it "pinches out" to the east. Both bars in MFSR No. 2 "pinch out" to the west.

The core in MFSR No. 3 does not go deep enough to give exact data for correlation of individual facies below the lower unconformity at 12,482.8 feet in MFSR No. 2, but the beach facies in MFSR No. 2 apparently pinches out east of MFSR No. 1A and the reworked bar facies is either absent or lower in the section in MFSR No. 3.

The rapid changes in facies in an east-west direction above the lower unconformity suggest that individual sands within the field are not laterally continuous for great distances in an east-west direction. Correlation in a north-south direction is somewhat better in the uppermost First Frontier (Fig. 22B) but, where three wells on a north-south trend are correlated (Fig. 7), facies changes and "pinch out" of sandstones occur between MFSR No. 2 and MFSR No. 5. This lack of continuity, especially in an east-west direction, suggests possible limited reservoirs.

SANDSTONE DIAGENESIS

Superimposed on the physically deposited spectrum of facies are secondary diagenetic effects which have substantially altered the pore systems. Several aspects of the facies seem to control the occurrence and relative amounts of diagenesis. Grain size varies substantially and mineralogy slightly between the reworked bar facies and the non-reworked bar and foreshore facies.

PARAGENETIC SEQUENCE

Textural relationships within the Frontier Formation of Spearhead Ranch Field indicate that the paragenetic sequence is:

1. Chlorite development
2. Quartz cementation
3. (A) Feldspar leaching
   (B) Smectite/Illite development
4. Calcite development
5. Hydrocarbon emplacement

In the most porous and permeable zones within the Frontier Formation of Spearhead Ranch Field, chlorite pore-linings are the only diagenetic phase that has developed (Figs. 24, 25, and 26). The very best development of these chlorite pore-linings is within the coarsest portions of the reworked bar facies (Fig. 27).

Chlorite pore-linings are less well developed in the finer grained portions of the reworked bar facies and are most poorly developed in the non-reworked bar and foreshore facies (Figs. 28, 29, 30). This variation in chlorite development probably reflects variations in depositional texture and as a result the degree to which pore waters had access to the various portions of the sand bodies. There is a striking contrast in grain size between the reworked and non-reworked facies. The reworked facies has a consistent maximum grain size of about 1 mm (coarse sand) while in the non-reworked facies the maximum quartz grain size is about 0.5 mm, medium sand. A qualitative analysis suggests that for each facies, the mean size is about half that of the maximum size; medium and fine grained sandstone respectively.

In those areas of the sand bodies where chlorite pore-linings are non-existent or poorly developed a second generation diagenetic mineral is extensively developed (Fig. 31). This second generation is quartz cement (Figs. 32 and 33) which has

←

Fɪɢ. 13.—*A,* Subhorizontal wave (swash) deposited parallel laminated sandstone; truncated and rippled above. Subtidal foreshore bar. Slabbed core. Unit 6A, MFSR No. 2, 12,490.1 feet. *B,* Subhorizontal laminations typical of the lower portion of several of the non-reworked submerged marine bars. Dark grains are chert; fine to medium grain size. Contact with laminated shale at top of interbar facies, near base of photo. Units 1A and 1B, MFSR No. 4, 12,629.6 feet. *C,* Several sets of subhorizontal wave (swash) deposited laminae interbedded with slightly bioturbated shale. 1 cm diameter horizontal burrows near top. Non-reworked submerged marine bar. Slabbed core. Unit 10A, MFSR No. 2, 12,417 feet. *D,* Subhorizontal laminated sandstone with abundant rip-up shale clasts at top of non-reworked submerged marine bar. No reworked bar facies is deposited above this bar. Slabbed core. Unit 8, MFSR No. 2, 12,435.3 feet. *E,* Near vertical and oblique *Asterosoma*-type concentrically clay-lined burrows. Vertical trail of "pellets" mark additional vertical burrows. Subtidal foreshore. Slabbed core. Unit 6A, MFSR No. 2, 12,483.0 feet. *F,* Vertical 1 cm diameter, 12 cm long, sand-filled burrow (far right) in horizontally burrowed, subhorizontally laminated and rippled swash and current deposited sandstone. Subtidal foreshore. Slabbed core. Unit 6A, MFSR No. 2, 12,485.3 feet.

INTERBAR FACIES

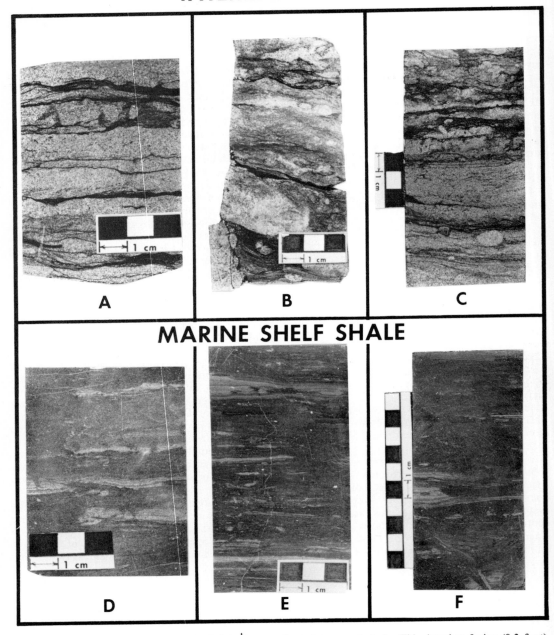

MARINE SHELF SHALE

FIG. 14.—*A*, Rippled interlaminated, slightly burrowed sandstone and shale. Thin interbar facies (0.3 foot). Slabbed core. Unit 2B, MFSR No. 3, 12,795.8 feet. *B*, Interlaminated shale, sandstone and siltstone. 30% bioturbated by 1/4–1/2 cm diameter horizontal burrows. Interbar facies sandwiched between overlying reworked bar and non-reworked bar. Slabbed core. Unit 4, MFSR No. 3, 12,772.8 feet. *C*, Interlaminated silty shale and very fine-grained sandstone. Bioturbated at top; 1/4–3/4 cm diameter horizontal burrows near base. Flattened silt-lined "donut burrows" near top. Interbar facies, Unit 3A, MFSR No. 4, 12,575.8 feet. *D*, Wispy siltstone layers in silty shale, slightly rippled. Immediately overlies sandstone of reworked bar facies; two feet above top of First Frontier Sandstone. Cody (Carlile) Shale. Marine shelf shale. Unit 6, MFSR No. 3, 12,767.4 feet. *E*, Cody (Carlile) Shale one foot above top of reworked bar sandstone facies. Note subhorizontal parallel silty laminations with only minor burrowing. Current ripples are very minor to absent. Marine shelf shale. Slabbed core. Unit 6A, MFSR No. 4, 12,529.0 feet. *F*, Burrowed silty shale. Silty laminae subhorizontal to low amplitude rippled. Marine shelf shale, Unit 11, MFSR No. 2, 12,397.7 feet.

SHELF SILTSTONE FACIES

FIG. 15.—*A*, Thin subhorizontal laminated storm(?) deposited sandstone, interbedded with bioturbated shaley siltstone. Note dark shale-lined silt-filled burrow near base. Shelf siltstone facies. Slabbed core. Unit 1B, MFSR No. 3, 12,815.0 feet. *B*, Vertically nested spreite of *Teichichnus* burrows in shaley sandy siltstone. Shelf siltstone facies. Slabbed core. Unit 1A, MFSR No. 3, 12,847.9 feet. *C*, Bioturbated siltstone. Note shaliness associated with burrows of *Asterosoma* type; 90% bioturbated. Shelf siltstone facies. Slabbed core. Unit 4, MFSR No. 4, 12,546.7 feet. *D*, Silt-lined (upper right) and shale-lined burrows in shaley siltstone. 95% bioturbated by 1/8–2 cm diameter burrows. Shelf siltstone facies. Slabbed core. Unit 3, MFSR No. 3, 12,776.5 feet. *E*, Highly bioturbated (75%) shaley siltstone. Shelf siltstone facies. Slabbed core. Unit 9, MFSR No. 2, 12,427.8 feet. *F*, A typical physically bedded portion of shelf siltstone facies. Only rarely are thin zones such as this non-burrowed in this facies. Unit 1A, MFSR No. 3, 12,846.9 feet.

```
LAGOON
                        Mountain Fuel #2
                        Spearhead Ranch Field
                        Converse County, Wyoming

                                    MFSR#2          MFSR#2
 CORE NUMBER:
 UNIT THICKNESS                     11.7'           15.9'

 R. W. Tillman, 2-75                Unit 5          Unit 3
                                    (12,482.6-94.3')  (12,497.8-513.7')
 Columized data format:             12,491.6-503.3'   12,506.8-22.7'
   %/Max. set thickness/Additional notes
```

Lithology

1. Sandstone (%)	tr	tr
2. Siltstone (%)	90%/1.0	94%/1.5
3. Shale (%)	9%/0.5	5%/0.05

Physical Structures

	3%/0.1	2%/0.05
1. Ripples, shaley	3%/0.1	2%/0.05

Biologic Structures

	97%/1.0	98%/1.5
1. Mottling	97%/1.0	98%/1.5
a) 1/4" burrows (horizontal)	80%/0.05	85%/1.5
b) 1/4" burrows (vertical)	5%/1.0	10%/0.7
c) 1/4" burrows (oblique)	10%/0.1	2%/0.1
d) 1/4" shaley, silt lined	90%/1.0	70%/1.5
e) 1/4" shale lined	tr	-
f) shale filled	tr/1.0	-
2. Total interval burrowed (% - footage)	97%/11.3'	98%/15.6'

Comments

Mottling not as uniform as Unit 3.

"Type example"

Fig. 16.—Lagoon (or Shallow Marine) components, Units 3 and 5, Mountain Fuel Spearhead Ranch No. 2. Note that the "Lithology" percentages, sandstone, siltstone and shale total 100%. The physical plus biologic components also total 100%. On the chart, the percentage by volume is given first followed by maximum set thickness (in feet) for the component.

Fig. 17.—*A*, Totally bioturbated. Uniformly burrowed by 0.5 cm diameter horizontal to oblique burrows. Very light gray siltstone to very fine-grained sandstone. Lagoon (or shallow shelf?). Slabbed core. Unit 3, MFSR No. 2, 12,512.3 feet. *B*, Totally bioturbated by 0.5–1 cm diameter horizontal to oblique burrows. Very light gray siltstone to very fine-grained sandstone. Lagoon (or shallow marine?). Slabbed core. Unit 5, MFSR No. 2, 12,497.3 feet. *C*, Vertical burrows (2) with spreite (arrows and outline) in totally horizontally bioturbated (0.5 cm diameter) light gray siltstone to very fine-grained sandstone. Lagoon (or shallow shelf?). Slabbed core. Unit 3, MFSR No. 2, 12,519.0 feet. *D*, Flaser-bedded, rippled, interbedded shale and sandstone. Current rippled. Abundant 0.25 cm horizontal burrows. Tidal flat facies. Slabbed core. Unit 1B, MFSR No. 2, 12,531.0 feet. *E*, Flaser-bedded and interbedded laminated sandstone and shale, silt and sandstone. Thin subhorizontal bedded sandstone and rippled sandstone. Scattered throughout burrows. Tidal flat facies. Slabbed core. Unit 1B, MFSR No. 2, 12,530.5 feet. *F*, Laminated and rippled (flaser bedded), silty sandstone and shale. Tidal flat facies. Unit 1A, MFSR No. 2, 12,534.5 feet.

LAGOON FACIES

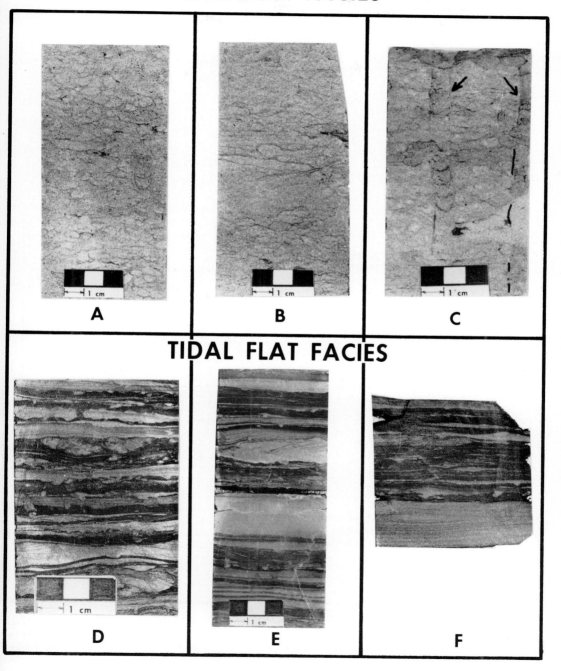

TIDAL FLAT FACIES

TIDAL FLAT (Kf)

Mountain Fuel #2
Spearhead Ranch Field
Converse County, Wyoming

	MFSR#2	MFSR#2
CORE NUMBER:		
UNIT THICKNESS:	6.8'	10.5+'
(R. W. Tillman, 2-75)	Unit 1B	Unit 1A
	(12,518.7-25.5')	(12,525.5-36.0'+)
Columized data format:	12,527.7-34.5'	12,534.5-38'+
%/Max. set thickness/Additional notes		

Lithology

1. Sandstone (%)	tr	tr
2. Siltstone (%)	60%/0.5	34%/0.03
3. Shale (%)	40%/0.3	65%/0.05
a) Interbedded sandstone and shale	-	-
b) Interbedded siltstone and shale	100%/0.05	100%/0.05

Physical Structures

1. Subhorizontal to horizontal lamina	68%/0.1	97%/0.3
	12%/0.1	11%/0.05
a) Laminated (non-rippled)	2%/0.1	tr
b) Slightly rippled	10%/0.05	10%/0.05
c) Alternating shale & sandstone	8%/0.05	-
2. Ripple bedding	88%/0.04	85%/0.05
a) Alternating sandstone & shale	-	-
b) Alternating siltstone & shale	50%/0.05	40%/0.05
3. Flaser bedding	17%/0.3	tr/0.3
a) < 60% sand (silt)	10%/0.3	-
b) Equal sand and shale	5%/0.3	-
c) < 60% shale	2%/0.05	tr/0.3

Biological Structure

1. Horizontal burrows	32%/0.05	3%/0.03
	32%/0.05	3%/0.03
a) Silt filled 1/8" diameter	30%/0.05	3%/0.03
b) Silt filled 1/4" diameter	-	-
c) Shale filled 1/2" diameter	2%/0.03	-
2. Mottled (bioturbation)	-	-
3. Total interval burrowed (%-Footage)	32%/2.2'	3%/0.3'

Fig. 18.—Tidal flat facies, components Units 1A and 1B, Mountain Fuel Spearhead Ranch No. 2. Note that the "Lithology" percentages, sandstone, siltstone and shale total 100%. The physical plus biologic components also total 100%. On the chart, the percentage by volume is given first for each component. The percentage is followed by the maximum set thickness (in feet) for the component.

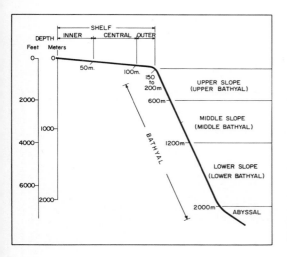

FIG. 19A.—Shelf and slope model with appropriate boundary depths. Shelf deposition from 5 to 10 meters down to 50 meters. Bathyl extends from 150 to 200 meters down to 2000 meters. Abyssal deposits lie below 2000 meters (Dailey, personal communication).

APPROX. AGE MILLION YEARS	EUROPEAN STANDARD AMMONOID STAGE	WESTERN INTERIOR MEGAFOSSIL ZONES	WESTERN INTERIOR REFERENCE SECTION	POWDER RIVER BASIN			
				N W	N E	S W	S E
85							
	CONIACIAN	*Scaphites depressus*	NIOBRARA FM. — SMOKY HILL CHALK	NIOBRARA FORMATION	NIOBRARA FORMATION	NIOBRARA FORMATION	NIOBRARA FORMATION
		Scaphites ventricosus					
90		*Inoceramus* diformis / aff. perplexus / erectus	FORT HAYS LS.				
		Scaphites corvensis	SAGE BREAKS SH.	CARLILE SH.	SAGE BREAKS SH. MBR.	CARLILE SH.	SAGE BREAKS SH. MBR.
		Prionocyclus wyomingensis	TURNER SS.		TURNER SS. MBR.	1st. FRONTIER SS.	TURNER SS. MBR.
95	TURONIAN	*Prionocyclus hyatti*	BLUE HILL SH.		POOL CREEK SH. MBR.	LOCAL SS. SHALE	UNNAMED SHALE MEMBER
		Collignoniceras woollgari	FAIRPORT SH.				SHALE
		Inoceramus labiatus	PFEIFER SH.	FRONTIER FORMATION	GREENHORN FORMATION	2nd. FRONTIER SS.	GREENHORN FORMATION
100			JETMORE CHK.				
		Sciponoceras gracile / *Dunveganoceras albertense* / *Dunveganoceras conditum*	HARTLAND SH.			SHALE	
		Dunveganoceras pondi	LINCOLN LS.			3rd. FRONTIER SS.	
105	CENOMANIAN	*Plesiacanthoceras wyomingense*	BELLE FOURCHE SHALE		BELLE FOURCHE SHALE	SHALE	BELLE FOURCHE SHALE
		Acanthoceras amphibolum					
		Calycoceras sp.					
110		*Neogastroplites sp.*	MOWRY SHALE	MOWRY SHALE	MOWRY SHALE	MOWRY SHALE	MOWRY SHALE

FIG. 19B.—Correlation of a portion of the Cretaceous in the Powder River Basin.

TRACE FOSSILS

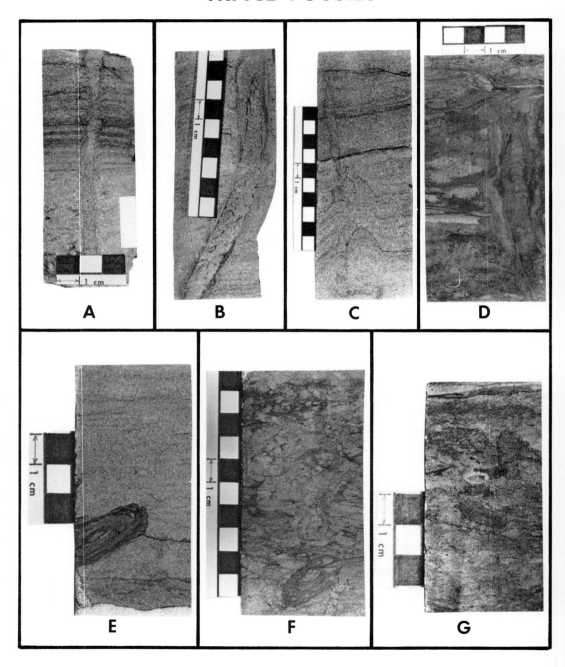

MOUNTAIN FUEL
SPEARHEAD RANCH NO 2

12521

LAGOON
UNIT 3

22

22.8

12528.6

TIDAL FLAT
UNIT 1B

32

30

FIG. 21.—Typical highly bioturbated lagoon (or shallow shelf) siltstone (Unit 3, 12,506.8–22.7 feet). Uniformly light gray, burrowed by 0.5 cm horizontal to oblique burrows. Uniformity of color and light gray color characteristic of this facies. Detailed descriptions of unit given in legend for Fig. 16. Interbedded sandstone and shale (Unit 1B, 12,528.6–34.5 feet) containing *Haplophragmoides gilberti* (D. Dailey, personal communication). Sandstones rippled and subhorizontal laminated tidal flat facies. Detailed description of unit given in legend for Fig. 18.

developed as syntaxial overgrowths on the numerous silicic grains and as silica cement. Syntaxial overgrowths have locally engulfed the poorly developed chlorite pore-linings (Figs. 28 and 29). Thus, in the non-reworked bar facies quartz overgrowths occlude most of the porosity.

In the reworked bar facies, the dense chlorite pore-linings have inhibited the development of large syntaxial quartz overgrowths. However, conditions were favorable for quartz cement precipitation as evidenced by the presence of small euhedral quartz crystals within the pore system of the reworked bar facies (Figs. 33, 34). These diagenetic quartz crystals have developed partially or entirely on top of the earlier chlorite pore-linings and have grown until they encounter the pore linings on the opposite side of the pore. At this time growth ceased as is clearly seen in Figure 34 where the quartz crystal has grown until it engulfed portions of the chlorite pore-linings in each end of the crystal. Further growth was prevented by physical blocking of growth sites.

The third stage of diagenesis involved the alteration of feldspars (Fig. 30). Some change in the pore-fluid chemistry caused feldspars to become unstable in the diagenetic environment and they began to alter (Figs. 35, 36) to one of the clay minerals, illite or smectite. The mineral that developed probably depended upon local variations in the $Na+$ and $K+$ concentration in the pore fluid. Smectite is developed locally on the altering sodic feldspar surfaces (Fig. 37). Smectite and illite are also developed as partial pore-linings within the reworked bar facies (Fig. 38). Some of the partial illite/smectite pore-linings are developed on top of pre-existing chlorite pore-linings (Fig. 38) and, therefore, most have formed more recently than the chlorite pore-linings (Fig. 30).

It should be noted that this third diagenetic stage is more extensive in the reworked bar facies

←

FIG. 20.—*A*, Long vertical sand-filled burrow (12+ cm) in subhorizontally laminated (wave swash deposited) sandstone. Subtidal foreshore facies. Unit 6A, MFSR No. 2, 12,490.2 feet. *B*, Long partially oblique to vertical 1.3 cm diameter sand-filled burrow in subhorizontal laminated sandstone. Subtidal foreshore facies. Unit 6A, MFSR No. 2, 12,489.3 feet. *C*, Deformed low amplitude trough cross-bed. Deformation the result of slightly oblique to vertical burrow. Wave swash and current deposited subtidal foreshore facies. Unit 3B, MFSR No. 4, 12,570.0 feet. *D*, Ornate 3 cm diameter vertical burrow showing a variety of different concentrically laminated filling materials: sand, silty sand, shale, and silty shale. Marine shelf siltstone, Unit 2, MFSR No. 4, 12,594.7 feet. *E*, *Asterosoma*, characterized by its obliquely oriented and concentrically layered clay laminations. Subtidal foreshore sandstone facies, Unit 6A, MFSR No. 2, 12,488.0 feet. *F*, Highly (80%) bioturbated siltstone including *Asterosoma* concentrically-clay-laminated burrow at base. Note silt and shale linings of many burrows. Bioturbated shelf siltstone interbedded with subhorizontally laminated sandstone above and below photo. Unit 5A, MFSR No. 4, 12,540.6 feet. *G*, "Donut burrow"; horizontal to oblique sand-lined, silt-filled burrow, approximately 0.75 cm in diameter. Note flattening due to compaction of associated shale. Marine shelf siltstone, Unit 7, MFSR No. 2, 12,471.8 feet.

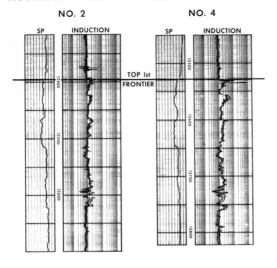

MOUNTAIN FUEL SPEARHEAD RANCH FIELD

NO. 2   NO. 4

FIG. 22A.—SP-induction logs for Mountain Fuel Spearhead Ranch No. 2 and No. 4. At first glance, it appears that the section above 12,514 feet (MFSR No. 2) can be readily correlated between wells. As can be seen in Figure 22B, the facies sequences below 12,466 feet is not the same in both wells. From the base to the top in MFSR No. 2, a sequence of lagoon, reworked bar, lagoon, beach, is partially equivalent to a sequence of lagoon, interbar, submerged bar, reworked bar in MFSR No. 4. This points out the difficulty of making *detailed* log correlations in this field.

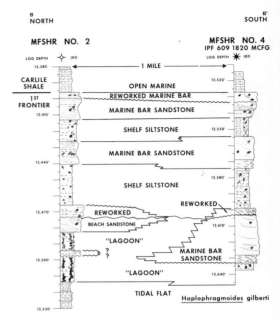

FIG. 22B.—North-south stratigraphic cross-section, Spearhead Ranch Field, Mountain Fuel Spearhead Ranch No. 2 and No. 4. No. 4 is the only cored well among those studied that was completed in the First Frontier Sandstone. No. 2 was completed in the Dakota. The location of the wells is shown in Fig. 2. The section above 12,466 feet (MFSR No. 2) is apparently more continuous along this section than in an east-west direction (Fig. 23). On this basis, a north-south lineation of the bars is suggested. The processes that formed the unconformity at 12,499.5 feet (log depth) in MFSR No. 2 is of major importance in forming the reservoir in MFSR No. 4 as is discussed in the text.

Light gray, uniformly bioturbated, 0.25 inch diameter burrowed siltstones are observed in both wells. Samples processed for foraminifera and palynomorphs yielded no fossils in this facies. Based on limited data, this facies is interpreted as "Lagoonal." The units in MFSR No. 2 below 12,513.7 feet are interpreted as tidal flat based on the abundance of flaser bedding, abundant burrowing and the presence of *Haplophragmoides gilberti*.

than in the non-reworked bar facies (Fig. 30). The difference in degree of development of feldspar alteration between reworked and non-reworked facies probably reflects the difference in the degree of access of pore fluids to the feldspar grains. In the reworked facies where pore fluids had easy access to the feldspar grains, almost all feldspar grains show some signs of alteration.

In the non-reworked facies feldspar alteration is minor. Fresh feldspar grains are commonly seen isolated within quartz cement (Fig. 39). Most commonly where the pores are entirely filled with quartz cement the feldspars are fresh. This indicates that feldspar alteration is dependent on exposure to pore fluids and that quartz cementation predates feldspar alteration. Thus, feldspars are common and relatively fresh in those zones where quartz cementation is extensive.

The last diagenetic mineral to develop was calcite (Figs. 40, 41). Calcite cement has reduced the porosity and permeability of many zones which could otherwise serve as reservoir rocks. Calcite has developed as a pore-filling cement

which is more recent than the development of quartz cement as can be seen in Figure 40 where calcite occludes a pore which contains partial euhedral quartz overgrowths.

Diagenesis in the Frontier sandstones of Spearhead Ranch Field was presumably terminated by the emplacement of hydrocarbons (Fig. 30) in those portions of the sandstone bodies which still remained porous and permeable after the earlier diagenetic stages. Thus, the major reservoirs at Spearhead Ranch Field are the reworked bar facies where the first diagenetic stage, chlorite

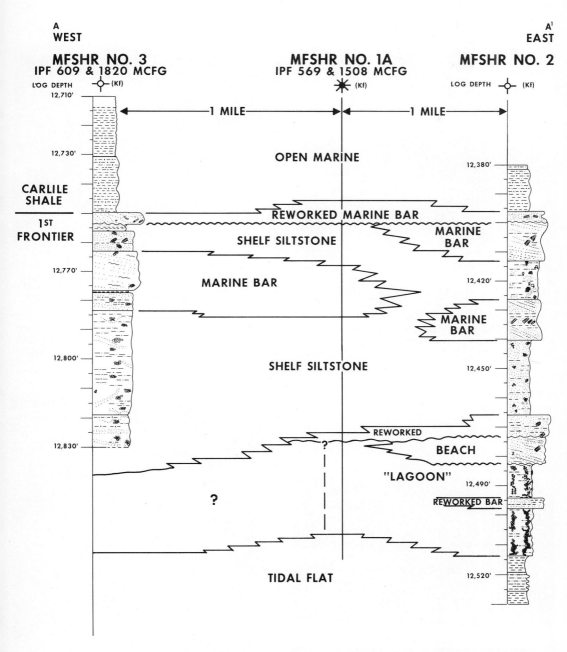

F IG. 23.—East-west stratigraphic cross-section, Spearhead Ranch Field. Log depths indicated. Mountain Fuel Spearhead Ranch wells Nos. 1A, 2, and 3. Well MFSR 1A was the twin to the discovery well. The individual environments in No. 2 and No. 3 were interpreted based on observations of physical and biologic sedimentary structures and the lithology of continuous sections of slabbed and polished core. The section is hung on the upper unconformity and on log markers which parallel it below the cored interval. Facies changes are over relatively short distances above 12,440 feet (MFSR No. 2) suggesting that the marine bar facies are of limited lateral extent. The location of the wells is given in Fig. 2.

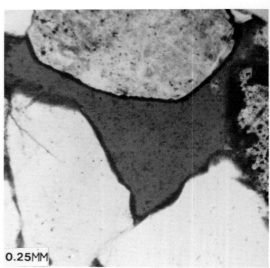

FIG. 24.—Porosity (black) in quartz and chert rich reworked facies, Frontier Formation, Reworked Marine Bar, MFSR No. 3, 12,770.6 feet. Crossed polarizers.

FIG. 25.—Open pores in reworked bar facies (dark gray). Quartz and chert grains. Pores lined with thin continuous chlorite clay coating (black). MFSR No. 4, 12,532.1 feet. Plane light.

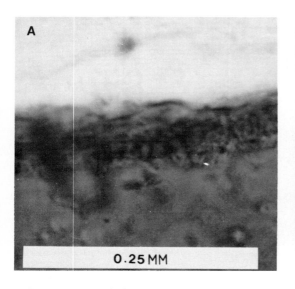

FIG. 26.—"Radial" fabric of chlorite pore lining of quartz grain. Reworked Marine Bar, MFSR No. 4, 12,532.1 feet. Plane light. B, Pore lining composed of well-formed individual chlorite crystals growing perpendicular to the grain surface. Quartz grain surface to which chlorite is attached oriented parallel to page. MFSR No. 4, 12,532.1 feet. SEM photomicrograph.

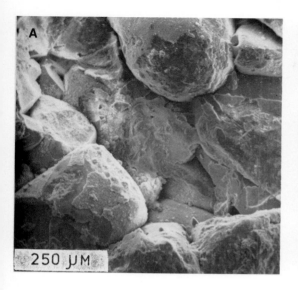

FIG. 27.—Only very small quartz overgrowths occur on the surfaces of these chlorite-lined pores. Chlorite pore-linings have prevented major quartz overgrowths. MFSR No. 4, *A*, 12,534.0 feet. *B*, 12,532.1 feet. SEM photomicrographs.

pore-linings, prevented the development of extensive quartz overgrowths. The preservation of initial porosity and permeability allowed pore fluids to attack feldspar grains and produce some secondary porosity which in turn was partially clogged by clay pore-fillings. The resulting porosity and permeability was incompletely destroyed by carbonate cementation (calcite) before the emplacement of hydrocarbons terminated diagenesis.

QUANTITATIVE ANALYSIS

Recognition in a qualitative way has yielded a usable paragenetic sequence which allows some predictability as to the quality of the reservoir to be expected. The next section will be an effort to understand in a more quantitative way the probable variations in reservoir quality between the reworked bar and non-reworked bar facies.

Detailed x-ray diffraction analysis was done on 36 samples almost evenly distributed between the reworked and non-reworked bar facies. Quantitative estimates of the relative amounts of the clay minerals chlorite, illite, and montmorillonite were made. Estimates of relative amounts were based on diffraction peak heights and area under the peak. In addition, the relative amounts of quartz, calcite, and plagioclase in the less than 5 microns size fraction were determined (Table 1). Using these quantitative estimates, ratios were calculated to include several of the minerals: illite/montmorillonite, chlorite/quartz and plagioclase/illite. As can be seen (Table 2) the mean values for illite/montmorillonite are similar in both facies. This similarity will be referred to later. The values for chlorite/quartz do not appear to be highly different between the facies, but this ratio is very useful in the discrimination of the

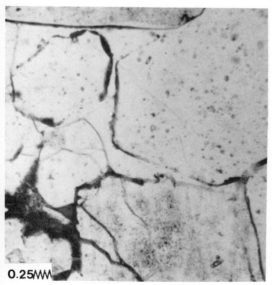

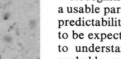

FIG. 28.—Non-reworked bar facies in which porosity has been occluded by major syntaxial quartz overgrowths. Grain boundaries marked by "dust" rims. MFSR No. 3, 12,785.2 feet. Plane light.

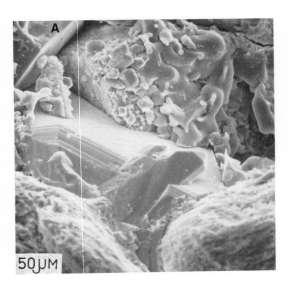
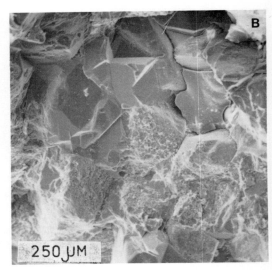

FIG. 29.—Quartz pore filling in non-reworked facies. Crystals have partially (*A*) to totally (*B*) filled pore. Quartz overgrowths have engulfed the "dust rims" (immature chlorite pore linings) on the quartz and chert grains (Fig. 28) in the non-reworked bar facies. *A*, MFSR No. 2, 12,407.5 feet. *B*, MFSR No. 3, 12,782.0 feet.

PARAGENETIC SEQUENCES
FIRST FRONTIER FORMATION SANDSTONES, SPEARHEAD RANCH FIELD

	REWORKED MARINE BAR FACIES					NON REWORKED MARINE BAR FACIES				
DIAGENETIC STAGE	CHLORITE	QUARTZ	FELDSPAR LEACHING	ILLITE/ SMECTITE	CALCITE	CHLORITE	QUARTZ	FELDSPAR LEACHING	ILLITE/ SMECTITE	CALCITE
I	▮					▮	▮			
II		▮					▮			
III			▮	▮				▮	▮	
IV					▮					▮
V	HYDROCARBON EMPLACEMENT IN RESERVOIRS									

0.25MM

FIG. 31.—Second generation diagenetic quartz cement in non-reworked bar facies. Quartz overgrowths have isolated a feldspar grain (arrow) and totally filled pores. MFSR No. 3, 12,785.2 feet. Crossed polarizers.

FIG. 32.—Abundant chert grains (up to 25% by volume) in non-reworked bar facies cemented by quartz cement. MFSR No. 2, 12,486.0 feet. Crossed polarizers.

25 μM

FIG. 33.—Dense well-developed chlorite pore-lining in reworked bar facies. Note absence of chlorite lining where grain was broken away (lower right). Small euhedral quartz crystals developed within the pores isolated from any host grains by the thick chlorite grain coatings, (see also Fig. 34). These isolated crystals do not significantly reduce porosity. Small droplets presumed to be oil are covered by conductive coating material. MFSR No. 4, 12,534.0 feet. SEM photomicrograph.

FIG. 30.—Comparison of the paragenetic sequence for the reworked facies and non-reworked facies. Diagenetic stage and relative abundance of diagenetic components specified by length and width of bars respectively. Compare the relative amounts of chlorite and quartz in the two facies. The earlier occurrence of abundant chlorite deterred formation of extensive quartz overgrowths in the reworked facies; the absence of extensive chlorite pore-linings in the non-reworked facies allowed extensive pore-filling by quartz overgrowth and/or cement.

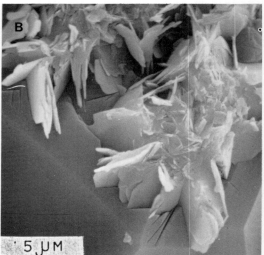

FIG. 34.—Small doubly terminated quartz crystals in the pore system of reworked bar facies (A). Quartz crystal has grown until the end(s) encountered the pore lining of the opposite side(s) of the pore. Figure B is a close-up of Figure A; chlorite was partially engulfed. Imperfections in quartz crystal in lower left where chlorite has been broken off. MFSR No. 4, 12,532.1 feet. SEM photomicrographs.

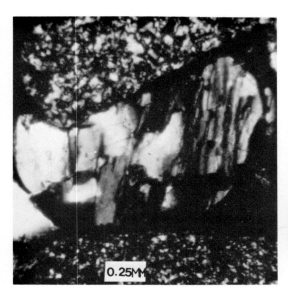
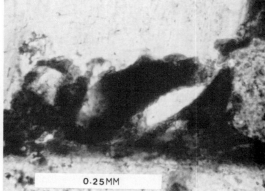

FIG. 35.—Altered feldspar grain sandwiched between chert grains. Note clay replacement parallel to cleavage. In the reworked bar facies, feldspar grains are commonly partially altered to illite/smectite. MFSR No. 2, 12,408.0 feet. Crossed polarizers.

FIG. 36.—Corroded feldspar grain margins. This close-up of Figure 12 reveals that the grain margin is altering to illite/smectite. MFSR No. 2, 12,408.0 feet. Crossed polarizers.

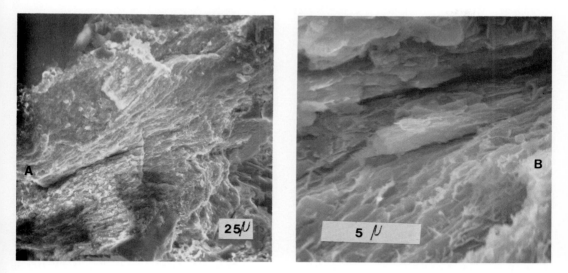

FIG. 37.—Feldspar crystal altering along cleavage traces. The alteration product is illite/smectite, as shown in close-up (Fig. B). Reworked bar facies, MFSR No. 3, 12,772.0 feet. SEM photomicrograph.

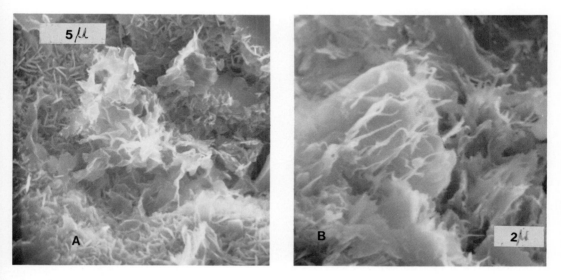

FIG. 38.—Secondary illite/smectite developed as partial pore linings within the reworked bar facies. These illite/smectite pore linings are developed on top of chlorite pore linings (upper right). Indicates paragenetic sequence (Fig. 30) is chlorite followed by illite/smectite. MFSR No. 2, 12,407.3 feet. SEM photomicrographs.

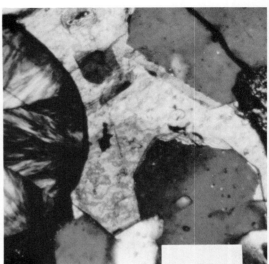

Fig. 39.—Unaltered feldspars in the non-reworked bar facies. These feldspars commonly are surrounded by quartz overgrowths from neighboring grains. MFSR No. 4, 12,604.7 feet. Crossed polarizers.

Fig. 40.—Calcite mosaic-cement pore-filling in non-reworked bar facies (Fig. 30). Calcite is the last cement to appear in the non-reworked zone; commonly it surrounds partial quartz overgrowths. MFSR No. 3, 12,785.2 feet. Crossed polarizers.

Fig. 41.—Poikilotopic calcite cement in reworked bar facies. Calcite cement in this facies may be the result of an early syndepositional redistribution of shell carbonate. The cement is poikilotopic and patchy and the included grains are loosely packed and display neither quartz overgrowths nor chlorite clay-linings. MFSR No. 2, 12,476.5 feet. Crossed polarizers.

reworked and non-reworked bar facies. Plagioclase / illite ratios are consistently lower in samples from the reworked facies when compared to the non-reworked facies (Tables 1, 2).

Among the mean values for x-ray diffraction measurements, significant differences can be seen between the two facies for chlorite, illite, montmorillonite, calcite, and plagioclase (Table 2).

Correlation coefficients.—Correlation coefficients were calculated for all the x-ray diffraction measurements and ratios as well as for the production parameters which will be discussed later. Correlation coefficients were calculated for the total suite of bar samples (Table 3), the reworked bar samples (Table 4) and the non-reworked bar samples (Table 5).

Among the correlation coefficients for the whole sample only three were 0.5 or greater: quartz vs. illite, $-.66$; quartz vs. chlorite, $-.60$; and illite vs montmorillonite, 0.50 (Table 3). Many more high correlation coefficients were observed when only the reworked bar facies samples were considered. Chlorite had high correlations with quartz ($-.72$), illite (.66) and plagioclase (.60). Illite had high correlations with quartz ($-.78$), plagioclase (.75), and montmorillonite (.59). Montmorillonite had high correlations with illite (.59) and plagioclase (.54), (Table 4). The only other high correlation was calcite vs. plagioclase ($-.56$).

A strong contrast in the number of high correlation coefficients is observed between the minerals in the reworked bar (8) listed above and the very low number of high correlation values for the non-reworked facies (2). Only illite vs. montmorillonite (.51) and illite vs. quartz ($-.55$) exceed

TABLE 1.—Less than 5 micron mineral percentages for reworked bar and non-reworked bar sandstone facies, MFSR 2, 3 and 4. Values reflect x-ray diffraction peak height and area under peaks. The last four columns are from Core Laboratory Inc. standard tests.

Well	Footage	% <5μ	Chlorite	Illite	Montmor-illonite	Illite Montmor-illonite	Quartz	Calcite	Plagio-clase	Chlorite/Quartz	Plagio-clase/Illite	Perme-ability (md)	% Porosity	% Oil Saturation	% Water Saturation	Core: Well-Unit No.
REWORKED(CENTRAL)BAR																
2	12,405.5	16.4	14.0	15.0	9.0	1.66	60.0	0.00	3.00	0.23	0.20	22.0	3.6	0.0	30.6	
2	12,407.5	7.1	21.0	4.0	3.0	1.3	70.0	0.00	3.00	0.30	1.33	2.5	9.9	10.1	19.2	2-10B
2	12,408.0	9.9	14.0	3.0	2.0	1.5	77.0	0.00	3.00	0.18	1.00	1.4	3.5	8.6	40.0	
2	12,476.5	8.6	45.0	20.0	5.0	4.0	25.0	0.00	5.00	1.8	0.25	3.7	6.4	9.4	57.8	
2	12,480.5	20.0	27.0	13.0	9.0	1.4	38.0	9.00	5.0	0.71	0.38	1.8	3.9	2.6	79.6	2-6B
2	12,482.3	20.7	32.0	13.0	9.0	1.4	35.0	7.00	3.0	0.91	0.23	1.2	7.0	0.00	70.1	
2	12,482.7	9.8	45.0	25.0	5.0	5.0	20.0	0.00	5.0	2.25	0.20	1.2	7.00	0.00	70.1	
2	12,503.6	7.4	45.0	20.0	10.0	2.0	20.0	0.00	5.0	2.25	0.25	1.6	4.00	15.0	22.6	2-4
3	12,770.6	10.1	8.0	9.0	5.0	1.8	30.0	47.00	1.0	0.26	0.11	0.2	2.4	0.00	41.7	
3	12,772.4	10.0	5.0	9.0	5.0	1.8	77.0	8.00	2.0	0.07	0.22	0.1	3.2	0.00	34.4	3-5
4	12,530.5	9.8	21.0	4.0	3.0	1.3	71.0	.00	2.0	0.29	0.50	2.0	5.6	12.5	28.6	
4	12,532.1	10.1	21.0	4.0	3.0	1.3	56.0	16.00	1.0	0.37	0.25	12.0	14.5	7.6	38.7	
4	12,533.5	4.2	10.0	15.0	10.0	0.66	55.0	5.00	1.0	0.18	0.33	0.42	5.0	10.0	50.0	4-5C
4	12,534.0	11.8	25.0	4.0	3.0	1.3	57.0	10.0	1.0	0.43	0.25	-	-	-	-	
4	12,534.4	4.9	21.9	14.4	6.4	2.2	52.8	0.00	4.3	0.41	0.29	0.23	3.3	12.1	51.5	
4	12,600.9	6.5	20.0	10.0	10.0	1.0	20.0	35.00	5.0	1.00	0.50	-	-	-	-	4-1C
NON-REWORKED BAR																
2	12,409.5	5.00	15.0	25.0	5.0	5.0	40.0	0.00	15.0	0.37	0.60	0.31	5.00	10.0	52.0	
2	12,410.2	10.7	10.0	12.0	8.0	1.5	67.0	0.00	3.0	0.14	0.25	0.22	5.30	15.1	43.5	2-10A
2	12,412.0	6.5	10.0	20.0	15.0	1.33	45.0	0.00	10.0	0.22	0.50	0.40	3.10	3.2	51.7	
2	12,435.4	8.3	20.0	30.0	15.0	2.00	25.0	0.00	10.0	0.80	0.33	2.7	5.3	0.00	62.2	
2	12,446.8	10.2	15.0	35.0	25.0	1.40	10.0	0.00	15.0	1.50	0.42	1.10	4.10	0.00	68.3	2-8
2	12,486.0	8.9	10.0	20.0	15.0	1.33	35.0	0.00	20.0	0.28	1.0	0.05	4.30	0.00	76.8	
2	12,488.5	9.9	20.0	25.0	15.0	1.66	20.0	10.00	10.0	1.00	0.40	0.04	2.5	0.00	84.0	2-6A
3	12,785.2	5.5	15.0	20.0	15.0	1.33	40.0	0.00	10.0	0.37	0.50	0.25	5.6	16.1	16.1	
3	12,791.2	7.4	15.0	20.0	15.0	1.33	35.0	0.00	15.0	0.42	0.75	0.07	7.2	12.5	23.6	3-2C
3	12,796.7	6.1	15.0	20.0	15.0	1.33	40.0	0.00	10.0	0.37	0.50	0.08	4.5	15.6	40.0	3-2A
3	12,801.4	9.6	10.0	25.0	15.0	1.66	30.0	0.00	20.0	0.33	0.80	0.01	2.3	0.00	87.0	
4	12,535.1	6.7	15.0	20.0	15.0	1.33	35.0	0.00	15.0	0.42	0.75	0.10	3.9	5.2	69.6	
4	12,536.9	8.3	10.0	25.0	15.0	1.66	30.0	0.00	15.0	0.33	0.80	0.05	3.8	5.2	57.9	
4	12,538.8	7.8	15.0	20.0	15.0	1.33	35.0	0.00	15.0	0.42	0.75	0.03	3.7	2.7	73.0	4-5B
4	12,542.3	6.0	5.0	5.0	5.0	1.00	20.0	55.0	10.0	0.25	2.0	0.02	1.3	0.00	69.2	
4	12,544.0	6.3	10.0	20.0	10.0	2.0	40.0	0.00	20.0	0.25	1.00	0.03	4.4	0.00	77.4	4-5A
4	12,556.0	5.9	10.0	15.0	15.0	1.0	50.0	0.00	10.0	0.20	0.66	0.74	7.50	1.30	52.0	
4	12,561.4	6.5	20.0	15.0	10.0	1.5	40.0	0.00	15.0	0.50	1.00	0.17	5.6	7.2	55.2	4-3B
4	12,570.0	6.9	20.0	15.0	10.0	1.5	40.0	0.00	15.0	0.50	1.00	-	-	-	-	
4	12,604.7	9.0	20.0	20.0	15.0	1.33	30.0	0.00	15.0	0.66	0.75	0.12	5.4	1.9	75.90	4-1B
Range		16.5	40.0	37.0	28.0	4.5	67.0	55.00	19.0	2.25	2.00	22.0	13.2	16.1	70.9	
Mean		8.8	18.2	16.3	9.9	1.72	40.8	5.6	9.0	0.58	0.53	1.7	4.9	5.5	53.6	
Std. Deviation		3.6	10.2	8.6	6.4	1.1	17.1	13.1	6.3	0.60	0.43	4.2	2.4	5.7	20.1	

0.5 (Table 5). It should be noted that in the above discussion only correlation coefficients for pairs of single minerals were considered.

As might be expected, significant differences between correlation coefficients for the same pair of variables exist between the reworked and non-reworked bar. A predictable contrast exists between the correlation coefficients for quartz and chlorite. A bivariate plot of the values for individual samples is Fig. 42. The reworked bar has a much stronger negative correlation than does the non-reworked bar. Illite and chlorite have a much stronger positive correlation in the reworked bar as seen by the distribution of values in Figure 42. A strong contrast in correlation coefficients also exists between the chlorite/quartz ratio and plagioclase (Fig. 43). A slightly stronger correlation coefficient exists for chlorite/quartz vs. illite (Fig. 43).

The major point to be considered is the fact that in all these pairs there is a significant difference in correlations *between* the two facies.

Discriminant analysis.—In order to determine rigorously whether the ten variables we have calculated are sufficient to separate the reworked and non-reworked bars we used discriminant analysis. By using the technique described by Klovan and Billings (1967), we can determine if the *within* group variation for each group of samples is sufficiently small and if the *between* group variation is sufficiently great to allow separation *between* the two facies. A discriminant score for each sample was calculated and plotted (Fig. 44). The mean discriminant score for the reworked bar was −3.2 and the mean for the non-reworked bar was −1.8. Clustering of individual sample discriminant scores around these two means allowed the correct discrimination of all but one of the thirty-six samples; one non-reworked bar sample was grouped with the reworked bar facies. In addition to the discriminant scores, probabilities of group membership were calculated for

TABLE 2.—Tabulation of mean and standard deviations of x-ray diffraction mineral percentages for reworked and non-reworked bar sandstone facies.

	VARIABLE	MEANS REWORKED	MEANS NON-REWORKED	STANDARD DEVIATIONS REWORKED	STANDARD DEVIATIONS NON-REWORKED
1	%<5μ	10.64	7.61	5.01	1.73
2	CHLORITE	23.56	13.68	13.69	4.35
3	ILLITE	12.02	22.47	6.87	6.76
4	MONTMORILLONITE	6.02	14.63	2.85	5.99
5	ILLITE/MONTMORIL.	1.73	1.72	1.28	1.05
6	QUARTZ	48.62	35.10	20.28	12.30
7	CALCITE	6.57	3.42	12.64	12.69
8	PLAGIOCLASE	3.37	13.57	1.51	4.59
9	CHLORITE	.63	.45	.87	.33
10	PLAGIOCLASE/ILLITE	.30	.71	.39	.40
11	MAX. PERMEABILITY	3.59	.34	6.08	.63
12	PERMEABILITY @90°	3.09	.10	4.99	.20
13	POROSITY	5.66	4.46	3.25	1.55
14	RESID. OIL SATURATION	6.27	5.05	5.57	5.91
15	WATER SATURATION	45.34	59.75	18.64	19.30

TABLE 3.—Correlation coefficients for combined bar facies. Variables 1–10 are derived from calculations of less than five micron mineral percentages. Variables 11–15 are from Core Laboratory Inc. standard tests. High correlations are underlined.

REWORKED AND NON-REWORKED BAR FACIES

VARIABLE	1	2	3	4	5	6	7	8	9	10	11	12	13	14	15
1	1.00														
2	.08	1.00													
3	.02	.46	1.00												
4	.25	.09	.50	1.00											
5	-.11	.34	.26	-.47	1.00										
6	-.15	-.60	-.66	-.33	-.38	1.00									
7	.01	-.35	-.14	-.29	.24	-.27	1.00								
8	-.02	.12	.21	.32	.00	-.31	-.26	1.00							
9	.10	.87	.67	.28	.41	-.80	-.19	.20	1.00						
10	-.34	-.15	-.30	-.33	.06	.13	.26	.27	-.21	1.00					
11	.28	-.09	.00	.04	.01	.12	-.07	-.09	-.18	-.19	1.00				
12	.25	-.22	-.12	-.02	-.06	.31	-.13	-.06	-.29	.04	.81	1.00			
13	-.07	.23	-.22	-.17	-.08	.17	-.24	-.12	-.03	-.10	.23	.00	1.00		
14	-.45	.15	-.06	-.17	-.14	.33	-.31	-.26	-.07	.01	-.15	-.10	.24	1.00	
15	.40	.19	.23	.21	.13	-.46	.12	.40	.33	-.01	-.16	-.19	-.26	-.68	1.00

Column variable labels: 1 = %<5μ, 2 = CHLORITE, 3 = ILLITE, 4 = MONT-MORILLONITE, 5 = ILLITE/MONT, 6 = QUARTZ, 7 = CALCITE, 8 = PLAGIO-CLASE, 9 = CHLORITE, 10 = QUARTZ PLAG./ILLITE, 11 = MAX. PERM., 12 = PERM.@90°, 13 = POROSITY, 14 = RESID. OIL SATUR., 15 = WATER SATUR.

TABLE 4.—Correlation coefficients for reworked bar sandstone. Variables 1–10 are derived from calculations of less than five micron mineral percentages. Variables 11–15 are from Core Laboratory Inc. standard tests.

CORRELATION MATRIX REWORKED

VARIABLE	1	2	3	4	5	6	7	8	9	10	11	12	13	14	15
1 %<5μ	1.00														
2 CHLORITE	.07	1.00													
3 ILLITE	.00	.66	1.00												
4 MONT-MORILLONITE	.30	.17	.59	1.00											
5 ILLITE/MONT	-.04	.57	.68	-.07	1.00										
6 QUARTZ	-.14	-.72	-.78	-.45	-.59	1.00									
7 CALCITE	.10	-.39	-.23	-.08	-.06	-.22	1.00								
8 PLAGIO-CLASE	-.10	.60	.75	.54	.31	-.46	-.56	1.00							
9 CHLORITE/QUARTZ	.05	.92	.83	.35	.67	-.83	0.28	.70	1.00						
10 PLAG./ILLITE	-.40	-.06	-.47	-.55	-.24	.54	-.41	-.02	-.24	1.00					
11 MAX. PERM.	.30	-.11	-.03	.09	.02	.17	-.10	-.23	-.22	-.25	1.00				
12 PERM.@90°	.27	-.24	-.21	-.05	-.09	.39	-.20	-.20	-.32	.08	.81	1.00			
13 POROSITY	-.04	.22	-.24	-.36	-.01	.06	-.07	-.24	-.02	.06	.25	-.00	1.00		
14 RESID. OIL SATUR.	-.64	.21	-.12	-.11	-.31	.15	-.41	.26	.06	.59	-.20	-.15	.13	1.00	
15 WATER SATUR.	.46	.34	.46	.30	.25	-.50	.04	.44	.42	-.44	-.25	-.30	-.06	-.43	1.00

TABLE 5.—Correlation coefficients for non-reworked bar sandstone. Variables 1–10 are derived from calculations of less than five micron mineral percentages. Variables 11–15 are from Core Laboratory Inc. standard tests.

CORRELATION MATRIX NON-REWORKED

VARIABLE	1	2	3	4	5	6	7	8	9	10	11	12	13	14	15
1 %<5μ	1.00														
2 CHLORITE	.13	1.00													
3 ILLITE	-.07	.23	1.00												
4 MONT-MORILLONITE	.43	.10	.51	1.00											
5 ILLITE/MONT	-.31	-.18	-.10	-.70	1.00										
6 QUARTZ	-.21	-.24	-.55	-.35	-.07	1.00									
7 CALCITE	-.16	-.41	-.07	-.38	.51	-.34	1.00								
8 PLAGIO-CLASE	.11	-.07	.11	.30	-.08	-.37	-.22	1.00							
9 CHLORITE/QUARTZ	.40	.59	.56	.41	-.10	-.76	-.07	.08	1.00						
10 PLAG./ILLITE	-.37	-.43	-.18	-.28	.33	-.33	.73	.38	-.22	1.00					
11 MAX. PERM.	.01	.32	.32	.11	-.03	-.21	-.14	-.26	.42	-.35	1.00				
12 PERM.@90°	.12	.32	.30	-.01	.18	-.18	-.11	-.22	.32	-.34	.92	1.00			
13 POROSITY	-.20	.31	-.23	-.12	-.20	.46	-.54	-.14	-.09	0.38	.24	.08	1.00		
14 RESID. OIL SATUR.	-.27	.10	-.01	-.20	-.01	.55	-.24	-.40	-.34	-.37	-.23	-.20	.43	1.00	
15 WATER SATUR.	.42	-.02	.06	.20	.03	-.45	.17	.44	.27	.28	-.03	.03	-.60	-.84	1.00

all samples. For the 16 samples in the reworked bar facies the probability that individual samples belonged to that facies ranged from 69% to 100% with a mean of 96%. In the non-reworked bar, 19 of the 20 samples were correctly classified with probabilities ranging from 99–100%. The lone incorrectly discriminated sample had a probability of only 2%. These discrimination results (scores and probability values) indicate how distinctly different the two facies are.

In doing the discrimination all 10 values derived from x-ray diffraction data were utilized. A tab-ulation of the relative importance of the discriminating ability of the variables is given in Table 6. Based on the relationships we've seen, it is no surprise that quartz and chlorite values form three of the first four variables. Slightly surprising is the fact that the percentage of material in each sample that is less than five microns in size, contributes so little to the discrimination. This suggests that it is not so important how much clay and matrix is present as it is to recognize the distribution within the pores and the variation in mineralogies.

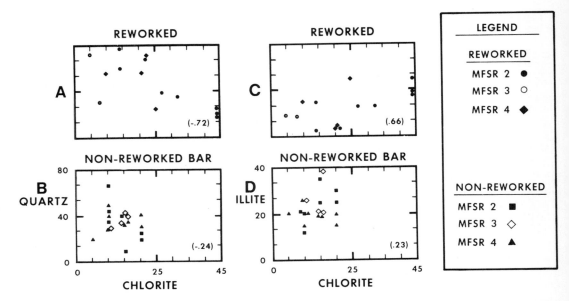

FIG. 42.—Plots of chlorite versus quartz and illite, Mountain Fuel Spearhead Ranch, Nos. 2, 3, 4 cores, reworked and non-reworked submerged marine bar facies. Correlation given in parentheses. Note strong contrast between values for correlation of reworked and non-reworked facies. *A*, The strongest negative correlation occurs in the reworked facies where there are the fewest overgrowths and where chlorite is most abundant. In the non-reworked facies (*B*) the correlation between quartz and chlorite is weak. Chlorite and illite tend to be positively correlated in the reworked facies (*C*) while there is little correlation in the reworked facies (*D*). Chlorite is nearly twice as abundant in the reworked facies as in the non-reworked facies. Illite is approximately half as abundant in the reworked facies compared to the non-reworked. The relative abundance of the two mineral types also reverses between the two facies (Tables 1 and 2).

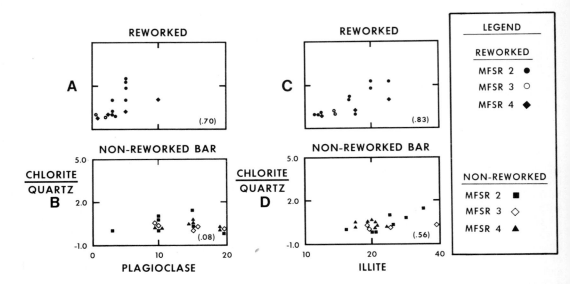

FIG. 43.—Plots of chlorite/quartz ratio vs plagioclase and illite. Note the strong contrast in correlation coefficient values between the reworked and the non-reworked bar samples; (.70) vs (.08), and (.83) vs (.56).

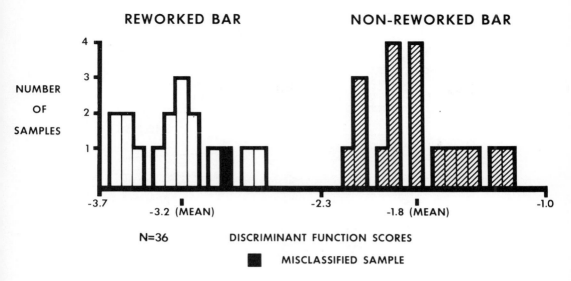

FIG. 44.—Discriminant score plot for reworked and non-reworked submerged marine bar facies, Spearhead Ranch Field core samples. Ten less than five microns X-ray diffraction variables. 36 MFSR 2, 3 and 4 samples. Mean discriminant scores: Non-reworked bar = −1.8; Reworked bar = −3.2. 35 of 36 samples correctly discriminated. Misclassified sample is MFSR No. 2, 12,410.2 feet.

TABLE 6.—Less than 5 microns x-ray diffraction variables listed in order from most to least discriminating ability at 95% probability level.

DISCRIMINATING ABILITY OF VARIABLES

1. QUARTZ	6. ILLITE/MONTMORILLONITE
2. CHLORITE/QUARTZ	7. MONTMORILLONITE
3. CALCITE	8. PLAGIOCLASE
4. CHLORITE	9. ILLITE
5. PLAGIOCLASE/ILLITE	10. % <5 MICRONS

SHRF-7A;95%

HYDROCARBON DISTRIBUTION

Until now the major discussion has been related to variations in facies and diagenetic patterns between the reworked bars and the non-reworked bars and foreshore deposits. As can be seen in MFSR No. 4 (Fig. 45) which is the only producing well among the three cores studied, the percentage of oil saturation is significantly less in the bar (non-reworked bar) than in the overlying reworked bar at the top of the First Frontier Sandstone. In the non-reworked bar facies, permeability is 0.1 md or less throughout and porosity is less than 6%. In this well, the reworked bar at the top of the First Frontier is productive because

of sufficient thickness (6 feet), porosity ($\bar{X} =$ 8.3%), permeability ($\bar{X} = 7$ md) and oil saturation ($\bar{X} = 10$%).

None of the facies below the top reworked bar in the MFSR No. 4 produce; the reworked bar facies at 17,600.8 feet (Fig. 5) is too thin (1.7 feet) and too calcite-cemented (Table 1) to yield much production.

In MFSR No. 2, encouraging values for oil saturation, porosity and permeability were recorded ($\bar{X} = 10.5$%, 6.1%, 6.2 md respectively), for Unit 6B (Fig. 4) but it did not yield economic production even though it is 7.8 feet thick. The distribution of porous and permeable streaks in this facies may be significant since only two thin porous streaks have values exceeding the mean values in the production facies (Unit 5C) in the MFSR No. 4; the remainder of the unit has low values. Lack of economic production in MFSR No. 3 is probably related to the thinness and calcite cementation of the reworked bar facies at the top of the First Frontier Sandstone. No oil saturation was recorded in Unit 5C. Oil saturation was recorded on Unit 2C, the non-reworked bar ($\bar{X} = 13.3$ feet), however, permeability values averaged only 0.6 md (Fig. 45).

Correlation coefficients; production parameters.—In the reworked bar facies, only three correlation coefficients involving production parameters exceeded 0.5 (Table 4). Oil saturation had a −.64 correlation with % < 5μ and .59 with

MFSR NO. 4 Kf

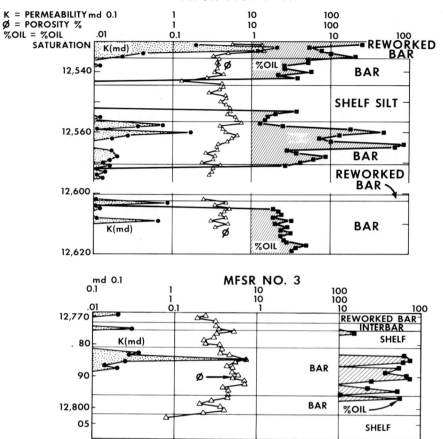

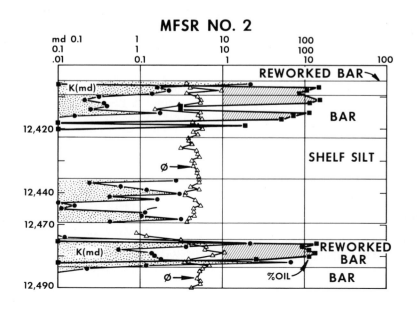

SPEARHEAD RANCH FIELD

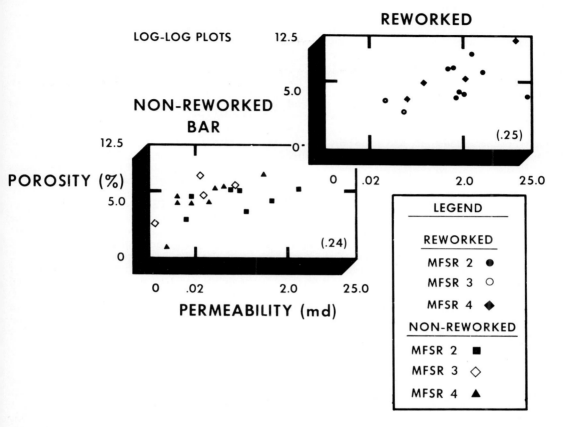

FIG. 46.—Log-log plot of porosity versus permeability. Mountain Fuel Spearhead Ranch Nos. 2, 3, 4 cores; reworked and non-reworked submerged marine bar facies. In the reworked bar the respective range and mean of porosities and permeabilites are: 2.4–14.50%, $\bar{x} = 5.6\%$, 0.1–22 md, $\bar{x} = 3.6$ md. In the non-reworked bar the respective range and mean of porosities and permeabilities are: 1.3–7.5%, $\bar{x} + 4.5\%$, 0.01–2.7 md, $\bar{x} = 0.34$ md. The correlation coefficients given in parentheses suggest that in these facies there is very little correlation with porosity and permeability. This lack of correlation emphasizes the need for core data.

FIG. 45.—Plots of permeability, porosity and percent oil saturation with depth in the First Frontier Sandstone. Mountain Fuel Spearhead Ranch Nos. 4, 3 and 2. In MFSR No. 4 permeability exceeds 2 md only in the reworked bar facies at the top (12,529–35 feet). Porosity exceeds 8% only in the reworked bar facies. Oil saturation exceeds 10% both in the reworked bar facies and in the middle marine (non-reworked) bar. (Neither the MFSR No. 2 or 3 were completed in the Frontier.) In the MFSR No. 4 production comes almost entirely from the upper reworked bar facies. This facies is thick enough (6 feet) and porous enough, 8.3% and permeable enough, 7 md, to yield production. In MFSR No. 3 Permeability exceeds 2 md only at 12,785 feet in the non-reworked bar facies. Porosity does not exceed 8% anywhere in the cored interval. In the Mountain Fuel Spearhead Ranch No. 2. Permeability exceeds 2 md only in parts of the upper and lower reworked bar facies. In both reworked bars combined less than 2 feet exceed 10 md permeability. Porosity exceeds 8% in very thin stringers in both reworked bars. Percent oil saturation never exceeds 12% in any of the facies. This well does not produce in the First Frontier Sandstone. The higher permeability streaks are too thin, the porosity is below 8% in the sandstones, the oil saturation is too low, and the reworked sandstone too thin or calcite plugged to produce.

the plagioclase/illite ratio. Water saturation had a 0.5 correlation with quartz. Interestingly, oil saturation and water saturation had only a weak negative correlation $(-.43)$ in this facies.

In the non-reworked facies, oil saturation has a strong negative correlation $(-.84)$ with water saturation. Oil saturation and quartz have a .55 correlation. Porosity has a $-.60$ correlation with water saturation and a $-.54$ correlation with calcite.

The negative correlation of water saturation and calcite is reflected, especially in the calcite pore-filling in MFSR No. 3, Unit 5, at the top of the First Frontier Sandstone, and in MFSR No. 4, Unit 1C well below the top of the First Frontier Sandstone.

Where subsurface log data are the only data available, problems arise in estimating which (if any) of the units in the Spearhead Ranch Field might produce hydrocarbons. In the reworked bar facies only 25% of the time is there a 0.5 or greater correlation between porosity and permeability (Table 4; Fig. 46). Only 24% of the time are there 0.5 or better correlations between porosity and permeability in the non-reworked facies (Table 5; Fig. 46). Since only porosity values, and not permeability values, can be derived from logs, core data are almost mandatory to evaluate potentially productive zones in the First Frontier Sandstone in Spearhead Ranch Field.

SUMMARY

Production in Spearhead Ranch Field is from reworked marine bar sandstones at the top of the First Frontier sandstone of late Cenomanian to middle Turonian age. The field is located near the deepest portion of the Powder River Basin and produces at depths of nearly 13,000 feet. Non-reworked marine bar sandstones associated with the reworked facies contribute only minor amounts of production. All bar sandstones below the top of the First Frontier are non-productive. Lower foreshore (subtidal), intertidal and probably lagoonal sandstones are identified below an unconformity in the cores.

Chlorite clay rims, recognized in thin section and with the scanning electron microscope, suppress growth of excessive quartz pore-filling material and as a result the reworked bar facies, which contains almost twice as much chlorite as the non-reworked facies, has maintained porosity and permeability. Quartz overgrowths have almost entirely filled the original porosity in the non-reworked bar facies. Calcite has plugged original porosity in most of the marine bar facies located below the top of the First Frontier Sandstone.

Statistical analysis consisting of correlation coefficients and discriminant analysis of the reworked and non-reworked bar facies supports the contrasting diagenetic changes that have taken place in the two bar facies. These diagenetic changes in large part control the distribution of permeability and porosity in the reworked and non-reworked facies of the First Frontier Sandstones. Discriminant analysis of X-ray diffraction mineralogic data yields an almost perfect separation between reworked and non-reworked bar sandstones.

ACKNOWLEDGEMENTS

Thanks are due to Bob Weimer for providing cores from the Colorado School of Mines collection and for reading the manuscript, to Paul Slack for discussion on the geology of the field during its early development, to Don Dailey for his analysis and interpretation of the microfauna, and to Fred Mason for his diligence in core photography.

REFERENCES

BARLOW, J. A., JR., AND HAUN, J. D., 1966, Regional stratigraphy of Frontier Formation and relation to Salt Creek Field, Wyoming: Am. Assoc. Petroleum Geologists Bull., v. 50, p. 2185–2195.

GOODELL, H. G., 1962., The stratigraphy and petrology of the Frontier Formation of Wyoming: Wyoming Geol. Assoc. Guidebook 17th Ann. Field Conf., p. 173–210.

HOSE, R. K., 1955, Geology of the Crazy Woman Creek area, Johnson County, Wyoming: U.S. Geol. Survey Bull. 1027-B, p. 33–117.

HOWARD, J. D., 1966, Characteristic trace fossils in Upper Cretaceous sandstones of the Book Cliffs and Wasatch Plateau: Utah Geol. and Mineralog. Survey Bull. 80, p. 35–53.

KLOVAN, J. E., AND BILLINGS, G. K., 1967, Classification of geological samples by discriminant-function analysis: Bull. Canadian Petroleum Geology, v. 15, p. 313–330.

LANGE, ALAN U., 1976, Spearhead Ranch Field: Wyoming Geol. Assoc. Guidebook 28th Ann. Field Conf., p. 175–178.

MEREWETHER, E. A., COBBAN, W. A., AND SPENCER, C. W., 1976, The Upper Cretaceous Frontier Formation in the Kaycee-Tisdale Mountain area, Johnson County, Wyoming: Wyoming Geol. Assoc. Guidebook 28th Ann. Field Conf., p. 33–44.

PRESCOTT, MAX, 1975, Spearhead Ranch Field, Converse Co., Wyoming, in D. W. Bolyard (ed.), A symposium on deep drilling frontiers in the Central Rocky Mountains: Denver, Colorado, Rocky Mountain Assoc. Geologists, p. 239–244.

REINECK, H. E., AND SINGH, I. B., 1975, Depositional sedimentary environments: New York, Springer-Verlag, 439 p.

SEPM Special Publication No. 26, p. 379–400, March 1979

REGIONAL DIAGENETIC TRENDS IN THE LOWER CRETACEOUS MUDDY SANDSTONE, POWDER RIVER BASIN

WILLIAM R. ALMON AND DAVID K. DAVIES

Cities Service Oil Company, Tulsa, Oklahoma 74150, and Texas Tech University, Lubbock, 79409

ABSTRACT

Lower Cretaceous sandstones of the Muddy Formation have produced a number of significant hydrocarbon reservoirs in the Powder River Basin. These reservoir sandstones accumulated in a variety of fluvial, deltaic, and shallow marine environments. The porosity and permeability of Muddy sandstones are affected significantly by the amount and composition of diagenetic clay minerals. Diagenetic clay mineral assemblages within the Muddy are time controlled. Oldest Muddy sandstones (sedimentologic zones 5 and 6) are characterized by a Kaolinite-Chlorite-Illite-Quartz assemblage with some smectite. Intermediate Muddy sandstones (sedimentologic zones 3 and 4) are characterized by an Illite-Smectite assemblage with sporadic Chlorite, Quartz and Kaolinite. Youngest Muddy sandstones (sedimentologic zones 1 and 2) are characterized by a Kaolinite-Quartz assemblage. This diagenetic time-trend is matched by a change in the composition of detrital components. Older Muddy sandstones are more feldspathic, contain more rock fragments and less quartz than the younger sandstones.

Well stimulation and completion treatments should take into account the diagenetic assemblages present in the reservoir sandstones. In the oldest Muddy sandstones, the rocks will tend to be acid sensitive, occasionally fresh water sensitive, and there will be migration of fines. In the younger Muddy sandstones, the principal problem will be the migration of fines and the stabilizing of the kaolinite.

INTRODUCTION

The presence of diagenetic minerals in a sandstone may have profound effects on many rock properties. Even a few percent of a diagenetic mineral can greatly reduce permeability, increase acid or fresh water sensitivity, totally alter the electric log response characteristics, or increase irreducible water saturations. Diagenetic minerals are an important control on reservoir quality because they develop within the pore system, reduce pore-throat size, and increase the surface area of the pores.

Of particular importance are chemically precipitated clay minerals. These develop within sandstone pores, either as pore-coatings on top of framework grains, or as loose, pore-filling aggregates. The presence and composition of such clay minerals play an important role in reservoir engineering. Clay pore-linings receive the greatest exposure to drilling, treatment, and completion fluids, and thus they control reservoir sensitivity (Almon, 1977).

The Muddy Formation in the Powder River Basin (Fig. 1) contains a number of well developed sandstones which may be divided into six zones (Fig. 2) (Berg, 1976; Stone; 1972). Sandstones in each of these zones contain clay minerals which are of both detrital and diagenetic origin. Diagenetic clays line or fill pore-spaces in each of the 800 Muddy sandstone samples analyzed for this study. Some 500 of these samples were collected from Bell Creek, Rocky Point and Recluse Fields (Figs. 1, 2). Remaining samples were

collected from outcrops and wells scattered throughout the Powder River Basin. All six Muddy zones were sampled.

The widespread occurrence of diagenetic clays in the pores of Muddy sandstones is of significance to reservoir engineering efforts. The clay minerals vary in composition within the 150 ft of the Muddy Formation. Fortunately this variation appears to be vertical, systematic, and consistent over most of the basin. Drilling and completion efforts should take into account in which zone the target sands are likely to occur, for different zones have different fluid sensitivities. This is a direct result of the vertical variation in the composition of diagenetic clay minerals.

MUDDY FORMATION

The Muddy Sandstone in the Powder River Basin consists of 150 ft of interbedded sandstones, siltstones and shales. Muddy sandstones were deposited in a variety of depositional environments ranging from marine to nonmarine. The composition of detrital components varies among zones and environments (Davies and Ethridge, 1973). Generally, the lowest zones (5 and 6) contain highest percentages of unstable components (feldspars, rock fragments), while the highest zones (1 and 2) are the most mature (Table 1, Fig. 3). The amount of clay matrix in the sandstones varies with zone, reflecting both changes in depositional environment and diagenesis.

Copyright © 1979, The Society of Economic Paleontologists and Mineralogists

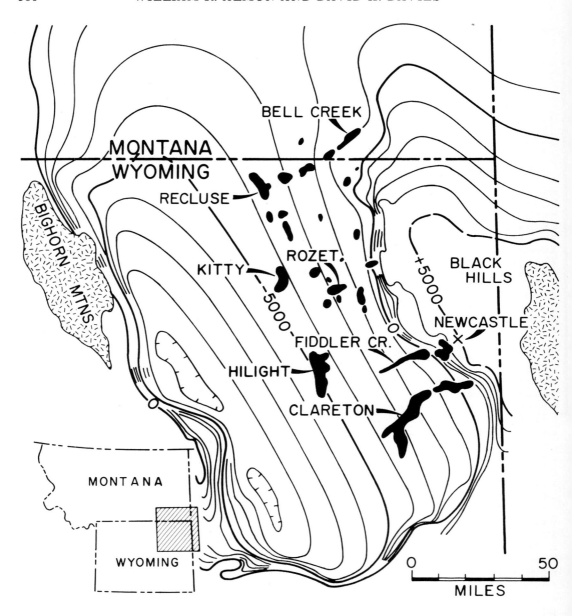

FIG. 1.—Index map of Powder River Basin, Wyoming and Montana, showing principal oil fields in Muddy sandstones. Structure contours are on top of Lower Cretaceous Dakota Sandstone. Contour interval 1000 ft.

DIAGENETIC ZONES

General statement.—Muddy sandstones in the Powder River Basin may be divided into three diagenetic zones. These zones are recognized on the basis of analyses of the clay size fraction (Table 2), and SEM observations of more than 800 samples. These diagenetic zones may be related to the sedimentologic zonation of the Muddy Formation (Table 3, Fig. 4). Diagenetic zone A is equivalent to sedimentologic zones 1 and 2; diagenetic zone B is equivalent to sedimentologic zones 3 and 4; diagenetic zone C is equivalent to sedimentologic zones 5 and 6 (Tables

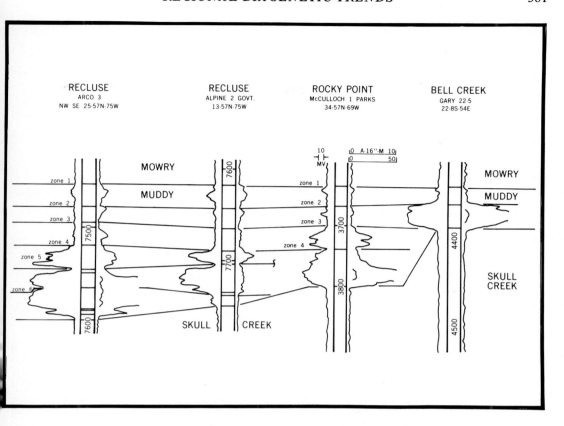

Fig. 2.—Correlation of Muddy sedimentologic zones 1 through 6 from Bell Creek to Recluse Field, illustrating variable development of lenticular sandstones within the Muddy Formation (Modified from Berg, 1976).

2, 3; Fig. 4). Each diagenetic zone contains a different assemblage of authigenically precipitated clays. The clays occur as pore-linings and pore-fills. Distinction between different diagenetic zones is based on the composition of the authigenic clays present in the pores of any sandstone unit. Each diagenetic zone also contains authigenically precipitated calcite. However, calcite cement is not indicative of any specific zone.

Diagenetic zone A.—Diagenetic zone A is characterized by the development of secondary kaolinite and quartz overgrowths in sedimentologic zones 1 and 2 (Figs. 4, 5). Kaolinite occurs as loose pore-fills which are composed of numerous booklets, each composed of individual kaolinite crystals (Fig. 6). Individual crystals show pseudo-hexagonal outlines. Occasionally the kaolinite booklets are partially enclosed by quartz overgrowths (Fig. 7). Booklets can be very large, reaching 100 μ in length, and lie in the pores with no apparent relationship to each other or to surrounding grains.

This kaolinite is interpreted as originating through precipitation from pore-fluids. The secondary, authigenic, origin of the clay is suggested by the good crystal outlines, and large size of individual booklets (too large to pass through pore-throats as detrital particles). The kaolinite may arise from the alteration of feldspars in the Muddy Formation, as kaolinite can be observed developing in cracks in partially leached, potassium feldspar grains. The silica for the quartz overgrowths may be derived from the same source. The transformation of feldspar to kaolinite involves liberation of excess silica which is used to form secondary silica overgrowths.

Secondary kaolinite and quartz overgrowths occur in reservoir sandstones at Bell Creek Field (Figs. 1, 3A, 3B). These sandstones can be very porous (>30 percent) and permeable (>13000 md), with the exception of a thin, but well developed low permeability horizon referred to as a "tight-streak." This tight-streak results from extensive development of kaolinite in pores at this level

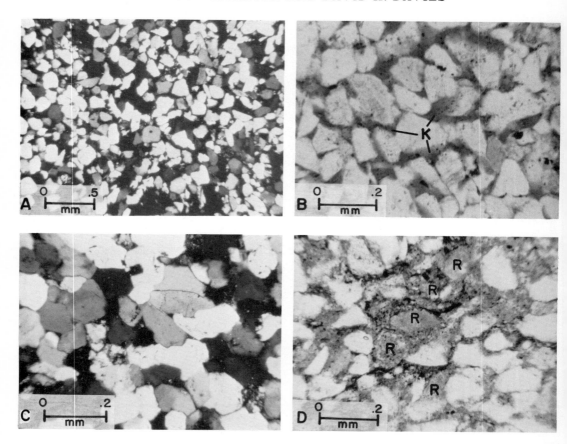

FIG. 3.—Petrography of Muddy sandstones. *A*, Field view of Muddy sandstone from Bell Creek Field (diagenetic zone A, sedimentologic zone 2) illustrating quartzose, well sorted nature of the sand. (Crossed nicols). *B*, Kaolinite pore-fill in diagenetic zone A of the Muddy Sandstone. Sample taken from "tight" streak in Well B-13-15 at Bell Creek Field. (Plain polarized light). *C*, Quartz overgrowths in diagenetic zone A of the Muddy sandstone, Wildcat, southeastern Montana (Crossed nicols). *D*, Rock fragments in Muddy sandstone (R) sedimentologic zone 5.

TABLE 1.—ENVIRONMENTS, GRAIN SIZE, AND COMPOSITION OF SANDSTONES AS A FUNCTION OF SEDIMENTOLOGIC ZONE IN THE MUDDY FORMATION, POWDER RIVER BASIN

Zones	Field	Environment	Mean Quartz Size (mm)	Composition Stables %	Unstables %	Matrix %
1 and 2	Bell Creek	Barrier	0.16	91	3	6
	Kitty	Barrier	0.20	92	Trace	7
	Wildcat	Delta	0.24	89	6	5
3 and 4	Recluse	Delta-destruc. bar.	0.17	79	3	18
	Wildcat	Delta-destruc. bar.	0.15	44	8	48
5 and 6	Recluse	Fluvio-Deltaic	0.28	62	10	28
	Kitty	Fluvio-Deltaic	0.18	44	12	44
	Wildcats (3)	Fluvio-Deltaic	0.17	35	18	47

Note: Stables = Monocrystalline quartz and polycrystalline quartz with 5 or less crystals per grain.
Unstables = Feldspar, micas, and rock fragments, including polycrystalline quartz with more than 5 crystals per grain.
Matrix = Material with grain size of less than 20 μ.

TABLE 2.—ENVIRONMENTS AND COMPOSITION OF LESS THAN 5 μM SIZE FRACTION OF SANDSTONES AND SHALES AS A FUNCTION OF ZONE IN THE MUDDY FORMATION, POWDER RIVER BASIN

Zone	Field	Environment	Composition				
			Illite	Montmoril-lonite	Kaolinite	Chlorite	Quartz
1 and 2	Bell Creek (Sandstone)	Barrier	—	5	30	—	65
	Kitty (Sandstone)	Barrier	—	—	35	—	65
	Wildcat (Sandstone)	Delta	—	—	40	—	60
3 and 4	Recluse (Sandstone)	Delta-destruc. bar.	4	6	20	5	65
	Wildcat (Sandstone)	Delta-destruc. bar.	5	4	19	8	64
5 and 6	Recluse (Sandstone)	Fluvio-Deltaic	10	5	20	18	47
	Kitty (Sandstone)	Fluvio-Deltaic	7	5	25	12	51
	Wildcats (3) (Sandstone)	Fluvio-Deltaic	12	6	24	14	44
	Bell Creek (Shales)		5	55	—	—	40
	Wildcat (Shales)		trace	63	5	—	32

TABLE 3.—DIAGENETIC ZONATION OF MUDDY SANDSTONE, POWDER RIVER BASIN

Diagenetic Zone	Diagenetic Mineralogy	Sedimentologic Zone
A	kaolinite + quartz	1 + 2
B	kaolinite + illite-smectite + traces chlorite	3 + 4
C	kaolinite + chlorite (high iron) + ferrigenous illite-smectite	5 + 6

in the reservoir. We suggest this may represent an old oil-water contact developed early in the history of the filling of this prolific reservoir.

Diagenetic zone B.—Diagenetic zone B embraces sedimentologic zones 3 and 4 (Figs. 2, 8). This diagenetic zone is marked by the development of illite and smectite as major diagenetic phases. Minor amounts of iron-rich chlorite, kaolinite, and silica overgrowths also occur. The illite-smectite clay minerals occur as well developed pore-linings (Figs. 9, 10). Individual groups of crystallites form a cornflake-like structure which engulfs pre-existing kaolinite booklets (Fig. 9C). Scattered chlorites often have pseudo-hexagonal outline, and are oriented perpendicular to the surface of the host grain (Fig. 10). Microcrystalline quartz may be observed on top of pre-existing kaolinite, and illite-smectite (Fig. 10F).

The delicate structure, the orientation and sequential arrangement of the kaolinite, illite-smectite, and chlorite suggest that these clay minerals are of diagenetic origin. The microcrystalline quartz appears to be the final diagenetic phase developed.

Diagenetic zone B is represented by the reservoir sandstone at Rocky Point and Recluse Field (Fig. 8).

Diagenetic zone C.—Diagenetic zone C includes sedimentologic zones 5 and 6 (Figs. 2, 11). Chlorite is a major constituent of the clay mineral assemblage, and occurs as isolated rosettes either dispersed throughout an illite-smectite pore-lining or completely covering it. Individual chlorite crystals comprising the rosettes have pseudo-hexagonal outlines (Figs. 12, 13). Quartz overgrowths also occur. Feldspars in this zone are severely leached (Fig. 12) but do not appear to be altering to kaolinite.

The pore-lining illite-smectite, and later chlorite rosettes are interpreted as diagenetic clays precip-

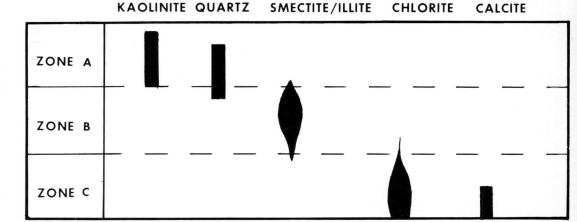

Fig. 4.—Sequence of formation for diagenetic minerals associated with each of the three diagenetic zones in the Muddy Formation.

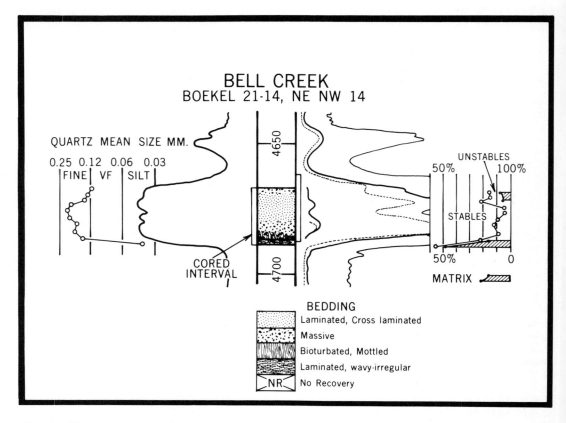

Fig. 5.—Electric log, compositional, and textural characteristics of Muddy Sandstone at Bell Creek Field (diagenetic zone A; sedimentologic zone 2).

FIG. 6.—SEM's of Muddy Sandstones at Bell Creek Field illustrating kaolinite development in diagenetic zone A. *A,* General view of diagenetic kaolinite pore fill. Note good porosity and euhedral overgrowths on some quartz grains. B marks position of magnified shot 6B. *B,* Close inspection of kaolinite pore-fill reveals that it is formed of closely packed kaolinite booklets of varying size. *C,* At higher magnification, extensive porosity is visible in kaolinite pore-fill. *D,* General view of excellent porosity in sandstones containing upwards of 10% kaolinite. *E,* Delicate structure of diagenetic kaolinite masses may lead to production problems if they are disturbed by fluid flow during production. *F,* Delicate structure of kaolinite booklets indicating diagenetic origin.

itated within the pore space of the sandstones. This diagenetic zone is well represented by the lower sands at Recluse Field (Fig. 11).

Calcite cement.—Calcite occurs in all zones of the Muddy Formation. Two generations may be recognized:

1. Early generation calcite, resulting from the solution and reprecipitation of shells. This is relatively minor in terms of total abundance.

2. Late generation calcite which occurs as a pore-fill cement. This cement can be locally abundant (up to 30 percent in some Bell Creek sandstones). It is considered to represent a late phase in the diagenesis of these sandstones, and is probably related to the reduction of organics and iron in the sandstones and associated shales. This reaction results in excess CO_2 which would encourage the precipitation of late stage calcite.

WILDCAT EXAMPLE

One of our wildcat wells contains two well developed sandstones representing sediment zones 3 and 6. These sandstones are separated by approximately 30 feet of shale and a 3 foot sand representing zone 4. The well-developed sandstones contain diagenetic mineral suites typical of diagenetic zones B and C (Figure 14).

The upper sandstone contains booklets of diagenetic kaolinite (Fig. 15), many of which are engulfed by later quartz overgrowths. Ferrous illite-smectite pore-linings overlap and partially cover earlier kaolinite booklets and quartz overgrowths. Minor amounts of high iron chlorite are present in the sand, and feldspar grains show signs of leaching. Secondary minerals in this upper sandstone are characteristic of diagenetic zone B.

The lower sandstone in this well contains a diagenetic clay suite which is characteristic of diagenetic zone C (Figure 16). Chlorite is abundant as pore-linings, which occasionally may be continuous. Kaolinite and illite-smectite underlie the chlorites. The feldspars in this sand zone commonly are leached and microcrystalline quartz

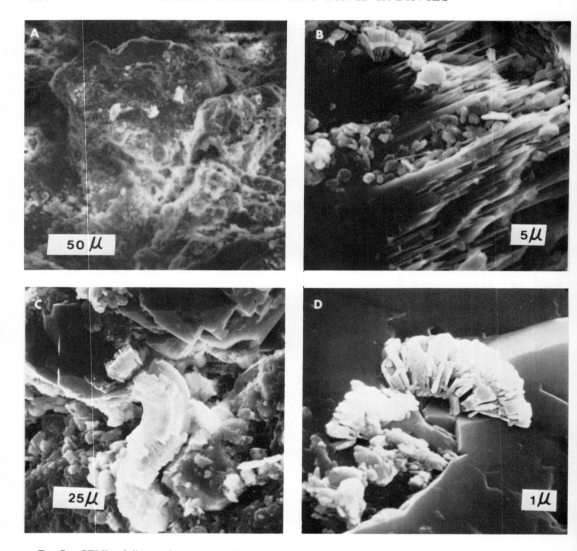

FIG. 7.—SEM's of diagenetic zone A. *A,* Some pores completely occluded by diagenetic kaolinite. *B,* Feldspar grains altering to kaolinite. This alteration involves dissolution of the feldspar and reprecipitation of kaolinite. It is not the result of incongruent dissolution of feldspar leaving a kaolinite residue. *C,* Some kaolinite booklets are > 100 μ in length. *D,* Kaolinite booklets engulfed by later development of quartz overgrowths.

occasionally is developed on top of the chlorite pore-linings.

The occurrence of two diagenetic zones in two distinct sandstones within a single well reduces the probability that the diagenetic zonation is a result of random differences between sands developed in different portions of the basin. This wildcat example strongly suggests that diagenetic zones in the Muddy Formation are arranged vertically in the rock sequence.

DEVELOPMENT OF DIAGENETIC SYSTEM

Two facts are important in understanding the development of the diagenetic system within the Muddy Formation:

1. Authigenic clay minerals are developed sequentially within the pores. Thus, where more than one authigenic clay mineral occurs, the clays are not arranged randomly. For example, in diagenetic zone B detrital grains are lined first with kaolinite, which is itself overlapped or covered

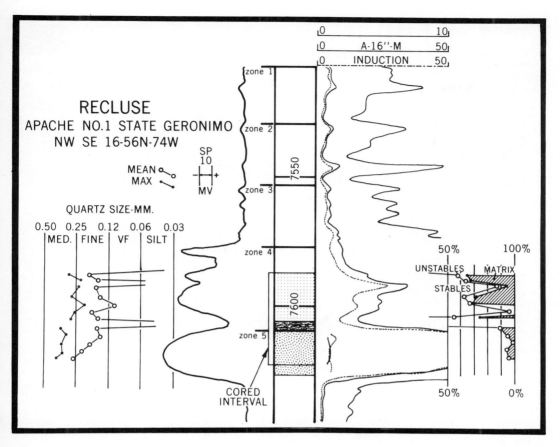

FIG. 8.—Electric log, compositional, and textural characteristics of Muddy Sandstone at Recluse Field (Diagenetic zone B; sedimentologic zone 4).

with a halo of illite-smectite. Chlorite and micro-crystalline quartz are then superimposed upon the illite-smectite halo. Thus each later zone shows the inheritance of previous stages.

2. The diagenetic zones are arranged vertically within the Muddy Formation and appear to be independent of sandstone facies.

Diagenetic clays in the pores of Muddy sandstones are considered to have originated by precipitation from moving pore-fluids. The sequential nature of the authigenic pore-fill clays indicates that these fluids were moving either continually or in pulses through the Muddy Formation during diagenesis. Without motion and evolution of the pore-fluids the authigenic clays would be randomly, not sequentially arranged in the pores.

The vertical arrangement of diagenetic zones suggests that the diagenetic system was an open system, and that the moving fluids were principally ground-water derived. Ground water flowing

through a sediment pile may be expected to dissolve the more labile grains and become enriched in dissolved ionic species. This process of dissolution will continue until the composition of the fluid becomes supersaturated with a mineral which then begins to precipitate. Ions not involved in the precipitation reaction will continue to increase their concentration in the fluid until the solution is in equilibrium with another mineral, which is then precipitated. It is theoretically possible for diagenesis to begin as soon as sediments start to accumulate, and it may continue throughout the history of a large stratigraphic unit or an entire basin. Figure 17 is a generalized model. In this model, pore fluids with abundant dissolved ion species move into a porous rock. Depending on the chemistry of the fluid and concentrations of the ions, two or more ions may combine to form a cement which may be precipitated in the pore. Temperature and pressure, while important

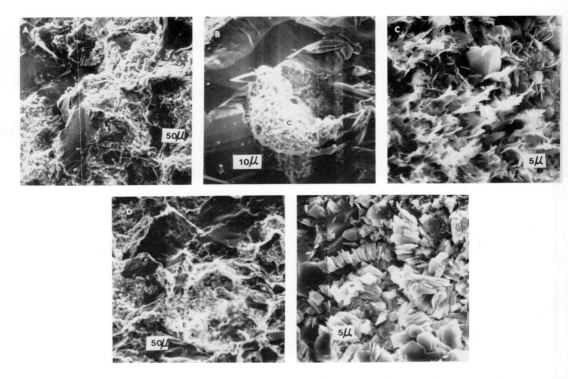

FIG. 9.—SEM's of Muddy Sandstones at Recluse Field indicate that sedimentologic zone 4 is characterized by development of illite-smectite and traces of chlorite. *A*, General view of extensive diagenesis occluding many pores. *B*, Pore blocked by kaolinite, illite-smectite, and quartz overgrowths. *C*, Flame-like illite-smectite developed over earlier kaolinite and quartz. *D*, Many pores in diagenetic zone B are blocked by diagenetic kaolinite pore fills. *E*, Kaolinite booklets within the pore-fill show excellent development and extensive micro-porosity.

in this process, are not the major control.

The direction of fluid flow is determined by the hydraulic potential gradient. For a given potential gradient, the permeability distribution exercises control over the rate of flow and the distribution of flow lines. Thus the direction of ground water flow may be controlled by the orientation of the most permeable layers within a sedimentary accumulation. In such instances, boundaries between diagenetic mineral assemblages may be parallel to or subparallel to the boundaries of the more permeable zones. This parallelism may result from the fact that in undisturbed laminated reservoirs, fluid flow rates are greater in a horizontal than a vertical direction, in all except basin margin areas. (At the basin margins, there should be a strong vertical component of flow as fluids enter or leave the system). Over much of the basin, therefore, the boundaries between different diagenetic assemblages precipitated from moving fluids may cross stratigraphic boundaries at a low angle, except near the margins of the basin.

The composition of ground water in a diagenetic system is a function of (1) the length of time the water has been in contact with the rock, (2) the initial composition of the water when it enters the system, and (3) the composition of the rock, with the least stable grains having the most rapid and greatest impact. As the sediment pile becomes thicker during the course of basin development, the water must flow further from the recharge area to any fixed point in the sediment pile (Fig. 18). This increases the residence time of the fluid in the sediment allowing more of the rock constituents to be dissolved. This tends to increase the concentration and amount of dissolved solids in the water. The chemical composition of the water will change during the progressive burial of a sediment pile as a result of changing concentrations and reactions. As the composition of the water changes during the burial history (or diagenetic history) of the basin, several minerals may form successively in the system, either forming in voids or replacing other minerals.

Diagenesis in an open system may produce

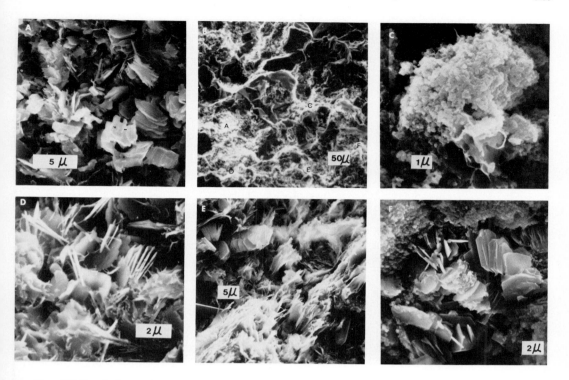

FIG. 10.—SEM's of diagenetic zone B. *A*, Many pores blocked by loose kaolinite masses. *B*, General view revealing numerous pore-fill cements shown in micrographs 10C, D, E and F. *C*, Microcrystalline quartz precipitated on diagenetic illite-smectite. *D*, Platy chlorite crystals occur infrequently among illite-smectite growths. *E*, Flame-like illite-smectite developed on top of earlier kaolinite booklets. *F*, Microcrystalline quartz masses precipitated within the micro-porosity of kaolinite booklets.

several zones in which the various diagenetic mineral assemblage zones cross time stratigraphic boundaries at low angles in the direction of ground water flow. Because ground water hydrology is an important aspect of the system, permeability should be a major control on diagenetic mineral development (von Engelhardt, 1967).

These theoretical considerations match our observations of regional diagenesis in the Muddy sandstones of the Powder River Basin. The diagenetic zones observed in Muddy sandstones in the area of this investigation are parallel or subparallel to the boundaries of the most permeable layers. Thus different diagenetic zones embrace different sedimentologic zones (Fig. 2), and are arranged vertically within the Muddy Formation (Fig. 14). The six sedimentologic zones of the Muddy Formation are a series of overlapping sand accumulations. Thus, the apparent vertical stacking of diagenetic zones may also represent down-dip diagenetic zonation of a bulk sand unit composed of partially overlapping sub-units.

PRODUCTION AND COMPLETION PROBLEMS RELATED TO DIAGENETIC ZONES

General statement.—The mineralogy of authigenic pore-fills in the Muddy varies between each of the three diagenetic zones. Thus production and completion problems will be different in each diagenetic zone. Problems encountered vary from the relatively minor one of migrating fines, to severe acid and fresh-water sensitivity. Awareness of the diagenetic mineralogy in a potential reservoir or target sandstones allows for successful design of drilling and completion systems.

Diagenetic zone A.—If specific sands of interest are located in diagenetic zone A (sedimentologic zones 1 and 2) well completion techniques should take into account that loose kaolinite booklets are abundant in pores of this zone. The main engineering problem is the migration of kaolinite. This migration may cause productivity problems as an individual field is developed. When fluid flow in the pore-system is turbulent, the loose

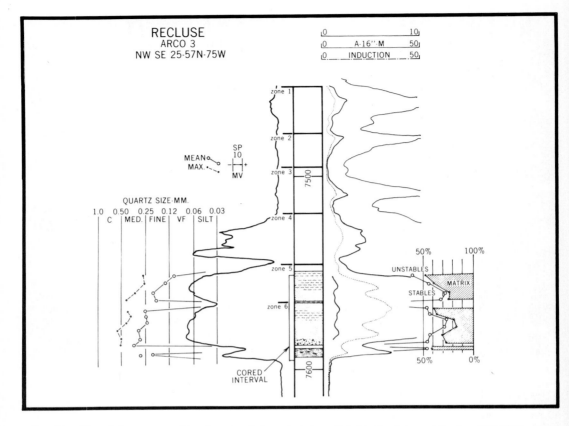

F$_{IG}$. 11.—Electric Log, compositional, textural characteristics of Muddy Sandstone at Recluse Field (Diagenetic zone C; sedimentologic zones 5 and 6).

booklets of kaolinite will migrate. These kaolinite booklets are larger than the pore throats, and thus will lodge in the throats acting as check valves, thereby reducing permeability. This problem is easily solved with any of the clay stabilization systems (such as polyhydroxy aluminum) as long as the treatment is carried out at an early stage in the history of a well.

Diagenetic zone B.—Diagenetic zone B includes sedimentologic zones 3 and 4. Sandstones in this interval are characterized by illite-smectite pore-coatings which largely cover earlier kaolinite. These illite-smectite coats act to naturally stabilize the kaolinite, in much the same way as an artificial polyhydroxy aluminum treatment. However, illite-smectite in zone B contains up to 80 percent expandable layers, and is fresh-water sensitive. Introduction of fresh-water into zone B will cause the illite-smectite pore-coating to break down, and may result in a secondary problem of illite-smectite and kaolinite migration.

Engineering problems in this zone can be avoided by the use of oil-base or KCl drilling and

completion systems. Permeability in reservoirs of zone B may be improved by acidization with weak HF systems which will dissolve both the kaolinite and illite-smectite clays. In reservoirs containing calcite or dolomite, a chelating agent may be necessary to prevent precipitation of CaF_2 in the pores—and resulting loss of permeability.

Diagenetic zone C.—The development of extensive chlorite pore-linings marks diagenetic zone C and introduces a possible severe problem of acid sensitivity. The diagenetic chlorite in this zone is iron rich and, if exposed to acid treatment, will dissolve and then precipitate as $Fe(OH)_3$ when the acid has spent. This possible iron precipitation problem can be avoided if an oxygen scavenger and an iron chelating agent are added to the acid, and care is taken to recover all the acid introduced into the well.

The diagenetic minerals in zone C are dominantly pore-lining minerals which have a drastic effect in reducing permeability. The permeabilility of the reservoir system in zone C may be improved if these pore-lining minerals are dissolved. A good

Fig. 12.—SEM's of diagenetic zone C revealing extensive diagenetic chlorite. *A*, General view of good porosity and abundance of diagenetic minerals. *B*, Extensive leaching of feldspars. *C*, Pores (D) completely blocked by diagenetic minerals. *D*, Diagenetic chlorite rosette completely blocking pore marked D in 12C. *E*, Diagenetic chlorite displaying well developed pseudo-hexagonal outlines.

method will be a mixed system of hydrochloric acid and hydrofluoric acid with the proper chelating agents and oxygen scavengers. Such a system has successfully been used to treat reservoirs similar to those in Muddy zone C.

GEOCHEMICAL CONSIDERATIONS

General statement.—The development of sequential pore filling clay cements in the Muddy Sandstone is a strong argument in favor of an open diagenetic system. The ions necessary for the late stage cements could not have arisen from detrital grains in the local vicinity of the pore, otherwise these cements would have been incorporated in the earlier generations of cement. Early pore-linings are considered to have coated the detrital grains, and effectively removed them from reactions with the pore-fluids. The development of an open diagenetic system, introduces a caveat into applications of thermochemical calculations.

Thermochemical calculations are based on the assumption of equilibrium states which describe closed systems. In these systems, all spontaneous reactions have proceeded to completion and all unstable phases are replaced by stable phases

(Curtis, 1978). In this state, the distribution of chemical species in the solution phase and its composition must reflect all the solids present. Thus in closed systems the activities of the chemical species in solution are determined by the composition and amounts of solids present. In open, non-equilibrium systems (such as here proposed for the Muddy Formation) the solids present are controlled by the activities of the chemical species present in solution.

Nonetheless, "equilibrium" thermochemical calculations are of great value in identifying both potentially unstable phases (which may react and serve as source materials) and stable phases (which may precipitate). It is essential to qualify such statements as these with the word "may" because total equilibrium is seldom approached during diagenesis. It is clear, however, that sediment diagenesis must be controlled by reactions involving the decomposition of unstable minerals within the sediment system and by the actual amounts of these minerals involved. These controls must be identified and assessed.

According to Curtis (1978), an overall view of sediment composition suggests that muds and silts

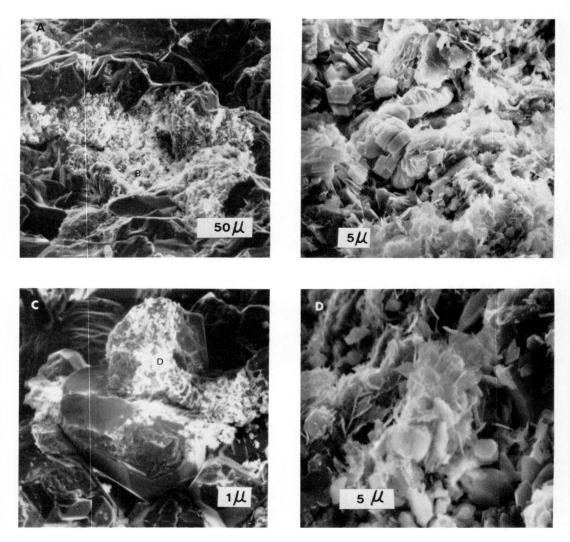

FIG. 13.—SEM's of diagenetic zone C. *A*, Diagenetic kaolinite, illite-smectite play an important role in occluding porosity in Zone C. *B*, Well developed kaolinite booklets showing excellent crystallographic development. Illite-smectite infills around much of the kaolinite. *C*, Well developed quartz overgrowths with euhedral faces. *D*, Quartz overgrowths engulfing previously developed kaolinite and illite-smectite pore-fills.

are the likeliest source of material to form diagenetic cements. Sands largely consist of mineral detritus which has survived the weathering environment. The clay fraction, on the other hand,

represents breakdown products formed in an oxygen-rich, low ionic strength environment. Early during diagenesis, reactions between these constituents are most likely to generate cement-

→

FIG. 15.—SEM's of diagenetic zone B in upper sand (sedimentologic zone 3) of Wildcat "A" (Figure 14). *A*, General view of excellent porosity, quartz overgrowths and kaolinite pore-fills. *B*, Kaolinite pore-fill partially engulfed by syntaxial quartz overgrowths. *C*, Quartz overgrowths engulfing kaolinite pore-fills and illite-smectite pore linings. *D*, Some pores are totally occluded by interlocking quartz overgrowths. (See also figure 3C). *E*, Pore almost completely blocked by quartz overgrowths, kaolinite pore-fill and illite-smectite. *F*, Pores blocked by diagenetic kaolinite.

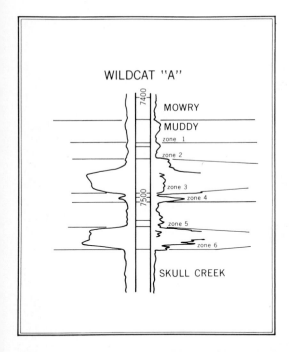

FIG. 14.—Electric Log of Wildcat "A" indicating good sand development in sedimentologic zones 3 and 6.

forming chemical species in aqueous solution. The coarser grained, less reactive minerals of the sand fraction are much less likely to enter into reaction. At the higher temperatures and pressures of deeper burial, the sand-size minerals will begin to react. Unstable minerals will break down and contribute solutes to the pore-water phase.

Diagenetic reactions.—The major diagenetic reactions involved in the alteration of the Muddy Formation are shown in Table 4. These reactions can account for almost all of the alteration observed. From textural considerations, the paragenetic sequence of cements within the Muddy Sandstone can be determined, but there is no clear relationship between this textural sequence and the thermodynamics of the various reactions. Consideration (Fig. 19) of the molar free energy of reaction (ΔG_r) would seem to indicate the sequence: kaolinite, smectite, quartz, and chlorite, as one progresses from the most negative free energy of reaction (the reaction most likely to occur) to the most positive free energy (the reaction least likely to occur).

Such a trend is not in agreement with the observed sequence. However, as Curtis (1976) pointed out in his discussion of weathering reactions, the free energy changes for a reaction are affected by the sizes of the molecular formulae. Chemical formulae and equations express only

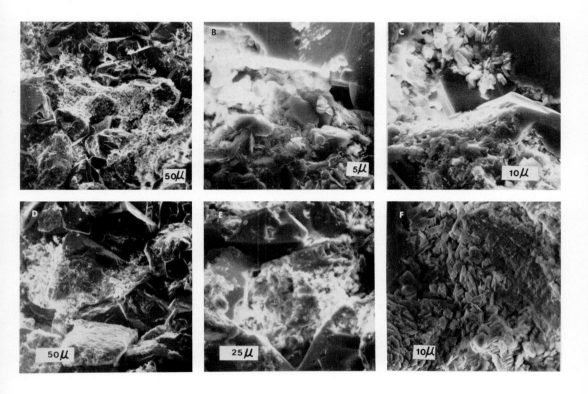

Fig. 16.—SEM's of diagenetic zone C in lower sand (sedimentologic zone 6) of Wildcat "A" (Figure 14). A, Fair original porosity remains in this zone. Secondary porosity introduced by leaching of feldspar grains. B, Illite-smectite and kaolinite are developed in many pores. C, Microcrystalline quartz developed in some illite-smectite pore coatings. D, Syntaxial quartz overgrowths. E, Extensive development of chlorite pore-linings. F, Individual chlorite crystals displaying pseudo-hexagonal crystal outlines.

the relative numbers of atoms within them and may be multiplied or divided by any factor. Thus, comparisons between different chemical equations are different. The simplest method of correcting this problem is to restate the values on a gram-atom basis by dividing the molar free energy by the number of atoms involved in the reaction. The resultant comparison will be between the amounts of energy liberated for a given number of product atoms. If diagenesis is linked to energy liberation, high negative values of ΔG_r° indicate favorable reactions at relatively low temperature and pressure conditions. Less negative, or slightly positive values would indicate reactions requiring higher temperatures and pressures. Highly positive values of ΔG_r° would indicate diagenetic reactions which occur when high temperatures are available to drive the reaction. Actually the ΔG_r at the temperature of interest is much more revealing than those calculated at the standard state of 25° C and 1 atmosphere total pressure, but thermodynamic data for many minerals is unavailable for any state other than the standard state.

As a first approximation, the silica concentration in solution will be maintained at approximately $10^{-4.0}$ by equilibrium with quartz precipitation. However, there is non-limiting control on the aluminate ion concentration in solution. As a result, the concentration of aluminate ion may continue to increase until the point is reached at which illite-smectite may begin to precipitate (pH 6 to 7, log $[Al(OH)_4^-] = -3.5$ to -3.0). This assumes that the magnesium ion concentration has reached approximately log $[Mg^{++}] = -5.0$.

When illite-smectite precipitation begins, it will be controlled by concentration of silica in solution, because 3.8 silicon atoms are incorporated into the precipitate for every 2.0 aluminum atoms. Thus if silica and aluminate ions are added to the pore fluids at approximately equal rates from surrounding shales or from dissolution of unstable detrital sand-sized grains, the concentration of aluminate ion will continue to increase as the pH gradually increases. This is due to the consumption of hydrogen ions during the precipitation of illite-smectite. Assuming that the concentration of ferrous and magnesium ions each has risen

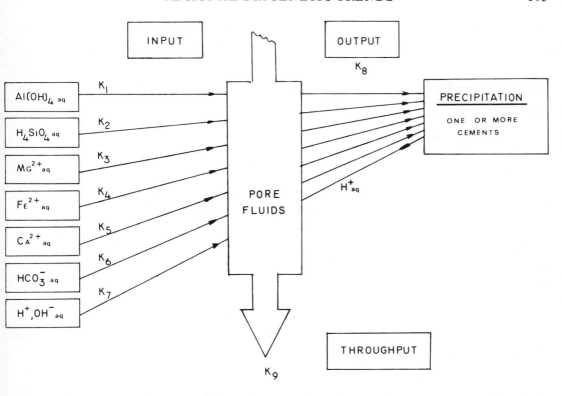

Fig. 17.—Rate of diagenesis is controlled by dynamics of fluid flow and the chemical composition of the pore fluid. These, in turn, are controlled by the rate at which fluid flows through the system (K9), the rates at which dissolved solids enter the pore fluid (K1 through K7), and the rate of precipitation of various cements (K8).

to log $[Fe^+] = -5.0$ and log $[Mg^{++}] = -5.0$ chlorite should begin to precipitate when the log $[Al(OH)_4^-]$ has risen to approximately -2.5 at pH = 7. Consideration of the free energy of reaction, on a gram-atom basis for these reactions indicates the diagenetic sequence in the Muddy Formation should be: kaolinite, quartz or smectite, and calcite or chlorite. If one considers the necessity of building up the concentration of various reactants the series becomes: kaolinite, quartz, smectite, and calcite and chlorite.

Solution-mineral equilibria.—Thermochemical equilibrium calculations are of great value in identifying stable phases which may precipitate from solution and making an approximation of the conditions under which such precipitation may occur. According to Figure 20 kaolinite would be the first mineral to precipitate in the system under discussion. Kaolinite could begin to precipitate at values of log $[Al(OH)_4^-]$ as low as -10 if log $[H_4SiO_4]$ approximated -4.0 under slightly acid conditions (pH ≈ 6). Such conditions might exist in a ground-water derived from the surficial weathering of a slightly feldspathic rock and its

associated soils. Such water introduced into an aquifer could begin to precipitate kaolinite in the pore spaces of the sandstone. Augmented by waters derived from the shallow compaction of the enclosing shales, the original water would become increasingly enriched in silica and alumina. Eventually, dissolved silica would begin to form syntaxial overgrowths on the host quartz grains. This essentially simultaneous precipitation of quartz and kaolinite would cause a gradual buildup of alumina in solution and a very gradual increase in pH (See Table 4, Equation I).

The precipitation of chlorite is the first reaction in this series to decrease the pH. In fact the precipitation of chlorite produces eight moles of hydrogen ion for every mole of chlorite formed. This production has a pronounced effect on the reduction of iron in the sands and adjacent shales and silts.

In the pH range of interest (pH between 5 and 9) ferric iron occurs as $Fe(OH)_2^+$ and ferrous iron as Fe^{++} (Stumm and Morgan, 1970) thus the equilibrium equation for iron reduction can be written:

$$8Fe(OH)_2^+ + CH_4 \rightleftarrows 8Fe^{++} + CO_2$$
$$+ 8OH^- + 6H_2O$$

The production of hydrogen ion by the precipitation of chlorite and the incorporation of ferrous iron into chlorite will serve to drive this reaction in the direction of ferrous iron. That this may have occurred in the case of the Muddy Formation is illustrated by three factors: (1) the chlorite in zone C is iron rich, (2) the illite-smectite associated with zone C has a higher ferrous iron content

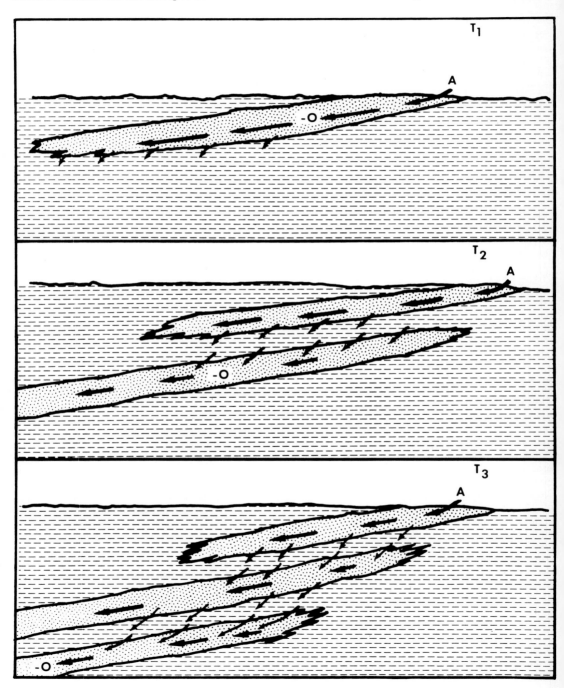

TABLE 4.—POSSIBLE DIAGENETIC REACTIONS OCCURRING IN MUDDY SANDSTONE POWDER RIVER BASIN

Equation I

$$2Al(OH)_{4\ (aq)}^{-} + 2H_4SiO_{4(aq)} + 2H^+ \rightleftharpoons \overset{kaolinite}{Al_2Si_2O_5(OH)_{4(s)}} + 7H_2O_{(l)}$$

$\Delta G_r = -52.23$ kcal/mole

$\Delta G_r = -1.374$ kcal/gm-atom.

Equation II

$$2Al(OH)_{4\ (aq)}^{-} + 3.8H_4SiO_{4(aq)} + 1/2Mg_{(aq)}^{++} + H^+ \rightleftharpoons$$

$$\overset{smectite}{Mg_{.5}Si_{3.8}Al_{2.0}O_{10}(OH)_{2(s)}} + 11.2H_2O_{(l)}$$

$\Delta G_r = -40.41$ kcal/mole

$\Delta G_r = -0.749$ kcal/gm-atom.

Equation III

$$2Al(OH)_{4\ (aq)}^{-} + 3H_4SiO_{4(aq)} + 4mg_{(aq)}^{++} + Fe_{(aq)}^{++} \rightleftharpoons$$

$$\overset{chlorite}{Fe^{II}Mg_4Al_2Si_3O_{10}(OH)_{8(s)}} + 2H_2O_{(l)} + 8H^+$$

$\Delta G_r = +32.96$ kcal/mole

$\Delta G_r = +0.659$ kcal/gm-atom.

Equation IV

$$H_4SiO_{4(aq)} \rightleftharpoons \overset{quartz}{SiO_{2(s)}} + H_2O_{(l)}$$

$\Delta G_r = -5.08$ kcal/mole

$\Delta G_r = -0.56$ kcal/gm-atom.

Equation V

$$Ca_{(aq)}^{++} + HCO_{3\ (aq)}^{-} \rightleftharpoons CaCO_{3(s)} + H^+$$

$\Delta G_r = +2.78$ kcal/mole

$\Delta G_r = +0.463$ kcal/gm-atom.

than that in zone B, and (3) there is significantly greater calcite cementation in shales associated with zone C than in the shales associated with zone A or B.

The increase in the reduction of iron in the diagenetic system may also be associated with the emplacement of hydrocarbons into the sand bodies. This would introduce a plentiful source

FIG. 18.—Schematic diagram of Muddy Formation diagenetic system.

At time 1 (T_1) the sediment pile begins to accumulate in successive layers of high and low permeability. Ground water preferentially enters the most permeable horizons (A) and begins to dissolve the most unstable grains building up a concentration of dissolved solids (C_1) at observation point O.

At time 2 (T_2) burial has proceeded. Most fluid flow is along permeable layers with some infiltration into less permeable layers. The concentration of dissolved solids (C_2) at observation point O is greater than C_1, as the water has been in contact with the sediment for a longer time because the distance between A and O has increased due to the continued build-up of the sediment pile.

At T_3 the burial and dissolution processes continue. The concentration of dissolved solids (C_3) has increased, $(C_3 > C_2 > C_1)$. Diagenesis will progress as observation point O is exposed to increasingly more concentrated solutions of dissolved solids.

PRECIPITATION MAY BE EXPLAINED BY THE
GIBBS FREE ENERGY OF REACTION

$$\Delta G = \Delta H - T \Delta S$$

ΔH = ENTHALPY

T = TEMPERATURE

ΔS = ENTROPY

EQUILIBRIUM CONSTANT MEASURES THE EXTENT
TO WHICH REACTION WILL PROCEED

$$\Delta G = -R\,T\,Ln\,K$$

R = UNIVERSAL GAS CONSTANT

K = EQUILIBRIUM CONSTANT

THE MORE NEGATIVE ΔG,
THE MORE FAVORABLE THE REACTION

ie. $\Delta G = -1.0$ Kcal/ gram atom   FOR REACTION 1

and $\Delta G = -0.50$ Kcal/ gram atom FOR REACTION 2

REACTION 1 IS MORE LIKELY TO OCCUR
THAN REACTION 2
AND MAY PROCEED MORE RAPIDLY

Fig. 19.—Precipitation of diagenetic minerals in Muddy Sandstone may be explained by Gibbs Free Energy of Reaction.

Fig. 20.—Diagenetic reactions in Muddy Sandstone may be followed on a plot of aluminate ion concentration versus pH, assuming minimal concentrations of ferrous iron and magnesium; solid line = amorphous silica saturation, dashed line = quartz saturation.

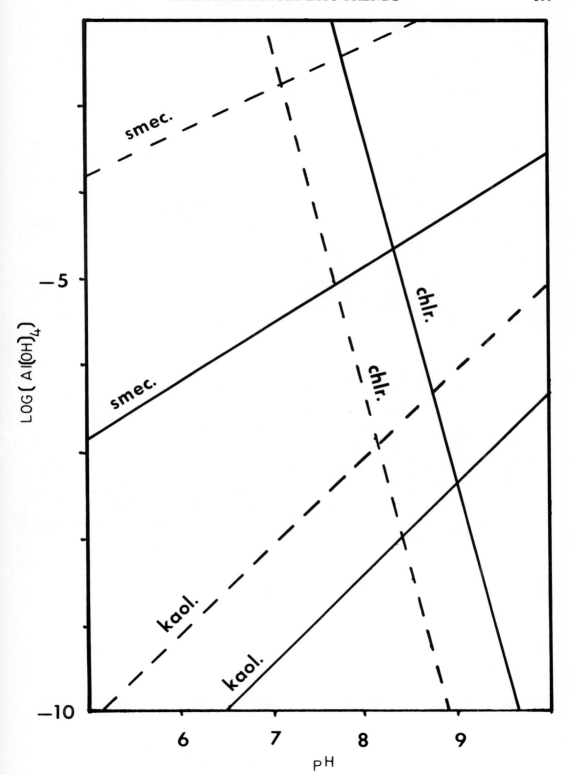

of carbon to act as the reducing agent. The emplacement of hydrocarbons into the reservoir sandstones may be considered the last step in their diagenesis since this greatly reduced the access of water to the formation and greatly reduced any chemical precipitation from aqueous solution.

in the Muddy Formation enables delineation of the production and completion problems which may be encountered at different levels in the formation. An understanding of sandstone diagenesis is of direct practical importance, as well as being of theoretical importance in understanding hydrocarbon generation and entrapment.

CONCLUSIONS

In this paper we have attempted to construct a rational scenario of diagenesis for a large multi-sand-body, multi-facies rock system. Beginning with the classical petrographic-textural observations of a series of sand bodies we have been able to define zones of different diagenetic intensity, based on the degree of development of various authigenic pore-fill minerals. Diagenetic zones have been equated to specific, equivalent sedimentological units within a depositional basin. Furthermore, a model of a hydrochemcial system has been constructed which may explain the diagenesis in the Muddy Formation from the time of deposition, through burial until the time of hydrocarbon emplacement.

An understanding of the diagenetic zonation

ACKNOWLEDGEMENTS

This research was made possible through support provided by Cities Service Oil Company, Energy Resources Group, Exploration and Production Laboratory. We wish to express our gratitude to Dr. K. F. Wantland for his continued encouragement of this project.

Cores, samples, and logs were provided by many individuals and companies. In particular we express our gratitude to Robert R. Berg, the late C. A. Biggs, Alexander McGregor, Samuel Gary, Juliana Waring, R. S. Agatson, M. McBrayer, and J. M. Parker. The manuscript was reviewed by John M. Sharp, Jr., Robert M. Siebert, Robert K. Park, Ted Swiderski, and Jack Thomas. We are grateful to these reviewers for their constructive comments.

REFERENCES

ALMON, W. R., 1977, Sandstone diagenesis as a factor in stimulation design: Texas Tech Univ, 27th Ann. Petroleum Short Course, p. 1–7.

BERG, R. R., 1976, Trapping mechanisms for oil in Lower Cretaceious Muddy Sandstone at Recluse Field, Wyoming: Wyoming Geol. Assoc. Guidebook 28th Ann. Field Conf., p. 261–272.

CURTIS, C. D., 1976, Stability of minerals in surface weathering reactions: A general thermochemical approach: Earth Surface Processes, v. 1, p. 63–70.

——, 1978, Possible links between sandstone diagenisis and depth related geochemical reactions occurring in enclosing sandstones: Geol. Soc. London, Diagenesis symposium.

DAVIES, D. K., AND ETHRIDGE, F. G., 1973, Sandstone composition and depositional environment: Am. Assoc. Petroleum Geologists Bull, v. 59, p. 239–264.

STONE, W. D., 1972, Stratigraphy and exploration of the Lower Cretaceous Muddy Formation, northern Powder River Basin, Wyoming and Montana: Mountain Geologist, v. 9, p. 355–378.

STUMM, W., AND MORGAN, J. J., 1970, Aquatic chemistry: New York, Wiley-Interscience.

VON ENGELHARDT, W., 1967, Interstitial solutions and diagenesis in sediments, in G. Larsen and G. W. Chilingar (eds.), Diagenesis in sediments: Amsterdam, Elsevier.

SEPM SPECIAL PUBLICATION No. 26, P. 401–423, MARCH 1979

EARLY DIAGENESIS OF HIGH PLAINS TERTIARY VITRIC AND ARKOSIC SANDSTONE, WYOMING AND NEBRASKA

K. O. STANLEY AND L. V. BENSON

The Ohio State University, Columbus, 43210, and The University of California, Berkeley, 94720

ABSTRACT

The Cenozoic High Plains sequence is a semiarid alluvial and eolian complex in which low temperature diagenetic processes were primarily the result of reactions of unconsolidated sediment and dilute aqueous solutions. Post-depositional modifications of arkosic and vitric sandstone include intrastratal alteration and dissolution of chemically unstable grains and the precipitation of cement in pore space. These processes, however, have only slightly altered the original fabric and mineralogy of High Plains sandstone, although chemically unstable heavy minerals and volcanic glass are abundant. Thermochemical calculations suggest that present-day groundwater is in possible equilibrium with calcite, montmorillonite, kaolinite, and a silica phase. Cement in sandstone is commonly montmorillonite, but can be calcite, opal, chert, and rarely clinoptilolite. Most sandstone is friable and cemented with montmorillonite. Interspersed in this sandstone are calcite concretions; opal and chert cemented sandstone occurs sporadically in High Plains rocks on Cretaceous shale and associated with old land surfaces in the Tertiary rocks. Commonly, the order of precipitation of cement is calcite, montmorillonite, and opal. All cemented sandstone shows some dissolution of grain surfaces, but only friable sandstone shows extensive intrastratal dissolution of grains, peripheral alteration of pyroxene and amphibole grains, and hollow montmorillonite coatings where chemically unstable grains were dissolved. These montmorillonite coatings are up to 100 micrometers thick and consist of a reticulate arrangement of relatively porous clay particles oriented normal to the grain's surface. Most of the cements and intrastratal alteration features can be explained by pedogenic processes, evaporative concentration of groundwater in the capillary zone, or by groundwater reaction with sediment.

INTRODUCTION

Incipient diagenetic alteration of the Middle and Upper Tertiary High Plains sequence (Fig. 1) demonstrates that vitric and arkosic sandstone can persist for tens of millions of years in a semiarid eolian-alluvial depositional-hydrologic system without significant modification to texture, fabric or composition. The persistence of chemically unstable grains, the preservation of porosity, and the lack of significant amounts of cement reflect an environmental and climatic setting that strongly inhibited the interaction of interstitial fluids and sediment. That this sandstone is rich in chemically unstable grains and has not undergone significant diagenetic alteration bears directly on our thinking about the evolution of porosity and authigenic mineralogy of continental sandstones, which is of consequence to the exploration for economically important minerals precipitated or trapped in the rock.

East of the Rocky Mountains, Cenozoic continental deposits occupy a similar cratonic setting and were deposited in similar environments from the Texas coastal plain northward into Canada, but they show different amounts of alteration, types of diagenetic products, and kinds of economic mineral resources. The High Plains sequence east of the Laramie Range in Wyoming and Nebraska represents one end-member of these deposits. Other sequences in Texas, New Mexico and Kansas show more extensive grain alteration,

cementation, and concentration of uranium ores (McBride *et al.*, 1968; Walton, 1975; Walker, 1976; Berendsen, 1977; Galloway *et al.*, 1977). However, unlike many other sedimentary basins, the High Plains depositional basin provides a unique opportunity to examine early diagenesis of vitric and arkosic sandstones in a setting where many components of the depositional-diagenetic system have remained nearly constant. The most important of these components are: hydrologic limits and tectonic framework of the basin, types of sandstone deposited in the basin, environments of deposition, climate, and pressure-temperature history.

The importance of early diagenesis in determining the ultimate compositional and textural properties of continental sandstone sequences has been stressed by Walker (1967; 1976) for arid region redbeds, and by Hay (1970, 1976) and others for alluvial and saline alkaline lake deposits. Early diagenetic modifications to the texture, fabric, and composition of a sandstone are important factors which determine the ability of a clastic reservoir to act as a petroleum sink. These modifications may also play an important role in concentrating ores of uranium and other authigenic minerals. In the continental facies of sedimentary basins, the early phase of post-depositional modification is commonly a consequence of chemical reactions between interstitial fluids and sediment at low temperatures (10°–30° C) and

Copyright © 1979, The Society of Economic Paleontologists and Mineralogists

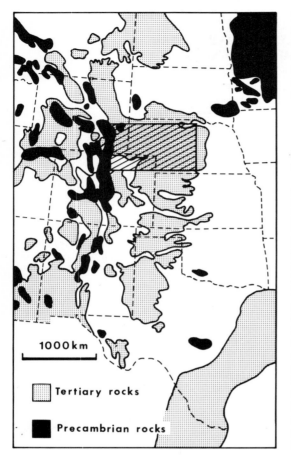

FIG. 1.—Distribution of Tertiary rocks in mid-continent United States of America showing the location of the High Plains sequence (heavy lined rectangle) in relation to other Tertiary rock units in the Rocky Mountains, plains, and coastal plain.

Laramie Range (Fig. 1); clay, silica, and carbonate mineral equilibria in modern groundwater of this region; and what this information tells us about the reactions of fluids and sediment in a temperate semiarid grassland plain where environmental and compositional controls on diagenesis can be evaluated.

DEPOSITIONAL SYSTEM

The depositional system responsible for aggradation of up to 630 m of vitric and arkosic sedimentary rocks east of the Laramie Range (Fig. 1) was strongly influenced by the semiarid climate, and the tectonic stability of the region during Oligocene, Miocene, and Pliocene time. The flat-lying post-orogenic High Plains sequence was built-up by (1) airfall accumulation of pyroclastic material from outside of the hydrographic basin, and to a lesser amount by (2) supply of epiclastic detritus from Precambrian crystalline rocks and Paleozoic-Mesozoic sedimentary rocks in the Laramie and Front Ranges and Hartville uplift (Stanley, 1976). The depositional system is thus an eolian-fluvial system constructed by airfall accumulation of vitric detritus with (1) smaller contribution by streams supplying material from adjacent mountains, and includes more importantly, (2) the reworking of sediment by streams headed on the plains and by winds blowing across the plains (Fig. 2). The High Plains of Nebraska is the modern expression of this depositional system. Today, this region is characterized by major rivers flowing eastward from the Rocky Mountains that are separated by vast expanses

pressures (about 1 bar). Relationships between sediment composition, the rate of movement and composition of interstitial fluids, and the interaction of the solid and fluid phase therefore, must be characterized in terms of different tectonic, environmental, and climatic settings in order to generate diagenetic models that can be used to predict the timing and degree of alteration. In addition, a more complete understanding of mass transfer in the diagenetic system is necessary to generate predictive models for cements and porosity distributions based on sediment composition and textural properties. Our concern in this paper is the nature and variability of diagenetic alterations in Oligocene through Pliocene vitric and arkosic alluvial, eolian, and lacustrine sandstones of the High Plains sequence east of the

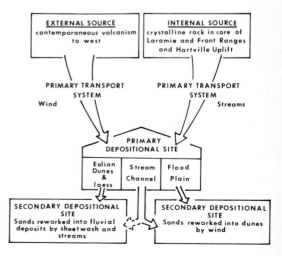

FIG. 2.—Schematic flow-diagram of sources and depositional processes and sites of sandstone of the High Plains sequence east of the Laramie Range in Wyoming and Nebraska.

of eolian dune fields and loess with small lakes and streams. These major rivers are fed by watersheds in the Rocky Mountains and by groundwaters on the plains.

Today, the High Plains is characterized by a semiarid temperate continental climate with variability and seasonability of precipitation and temperature that grade eastward to a subhumid climate. Annual precipitation ranges from 35 to 50 cm per year in western and central Nebraska and up to 80 cm in easternmost Nebraska (Elder, 1969, p. 5). Natural vegetation of this region is a "mixed prairie" grassland on featureless prairie between streams with a gallery of deciduous trees along their banks. Valleys where groundwater is within reach of plant roots sustain tall grasses, whereas valleys and hills where groundwater is beyond the reach of roots support stands of short grasses (Elder, 1969). Evidence from fossil grass seeds (Elias, 1942; Elias and Lugn, 1939), fossil trees (Wanless, 1923), mammalian faunas (Matthew, 1901; Clark *et al.*, 1967), Oligocene and Pliocene caliche profiles (Swineford *et al.*, 1955; Lillengraven, 1970), and sediments (Lovering, 1929; Stanley, 1976) all suggest that a semiarid grassland prevailed during deposition of the High Plains sequence. In addition, arid conditions are suggested during deposition of the upper part of the White River Group and the lower part of the Arikaree Group by extensive sand-dune and massive loesslike deposits, mammalian faunas (Schultz and Falkenbach, 1968), and the absence of fossil grasses.

Geographic and textural distribution of Oligocene and Miocene eolian and alluvial rocks conform to depositional patterns described by Garner (1959) for sedimentation under arid and semiarid climate conditions. Fanglomerates in the Oligocene White River and Oligocene-Miocene Arikaree Groups are restricted to areas adjacent to the Laramie Range and Hartville uplift. More than 20 km from the mountains small and volumetrically unimportant, coarse-grained fluvial sandstone composed of arkosic detritus is intercalated in fine-grained eolian and alluvial material which is in large part pyroclastic material comprising from 50 to 90 percent of the sequence (Fig. 2). Adjacent to the Hartville uplift, beds of Arikaree vitric arenite abut against Precambrian hornblende schist with little contribution from the uplift; and only local and sparse breccias composed of schist are intercalated in the volcaniclastic sandstone. The dominance of pyroclastic detritus requires airfall as the principal mechanism of sediment supply during deposition of the White River and Arikaree Groups. This pattern of sedimentary facies requires a sufficient volume of water to periodically carry large quantities of coarse detritus a short distance from the mountains as well

as sparse vegetation and rainfall on the plains so that sand dunes and loess developed away from the mountains.

Arkosic material in the Miocene-Pliocene Ogallala Group reflects a regime in which greater material was supplied from the Rocky Mountains, but pyroclastic material, including ash falls, is also an important component. This phase of sedimentation reflects a time of regional uplift and expansion of the drainage basin that drastically influenced the ability of streams to carry detritus away from the mountains (Stanley, 1971; 1976).

NORTHERN HIGH PLAINS SEDIMENTARY
PETROLOGIC PROVINCE

Tectonic setting and stratigraphy.—East of the Laramie Range, the High Plains sequence consists of a wedge of Oligocene through Pliocene fluvial, eolian, and lacustrine rocks that extends several hundred kilometers from the mountain front (Fig. 1). The sequence is represented by the Oligocene White River, Oligocene-Miocene Arikaree, Miocene Hemingford, and Miocene-Pliocene Ogallala Groups (Stanley, 1976). These are post-orogenic sedimentary rocks subjected only to epirogenic movements (Stanley, 1971; Stanley and Wayne, 1972). In eastern Wyoming and adjoining Nebraska, these rocks rest unconformably on gently folded Cretaceous rocks, and locally, on a late Eocene lateritic paleosol developed on Cretaceous rocks (Pettyjohn, 1966). Adjacent to the mountains they abut against upturned Paleozoic and Mesozoic strata and rest on Precambrian crystalline rocks that form the core of the Laramie and Front Ranges and Hartville uplift (Darton, 1899, 1903; Darton *et al.*, 1910; Denson and Botinelly, 1949). Stratigraphic evidence indicates that the relationship of the sedimentary basin of the High Plains sequence to adjacent uplifts has not changed greatly either physiographically or structurally since the onset of continental sedimentation during the earliest Oligocene (Denson and Bergendahl, 1961; Clark *et al.*, 1967; Stanley, 1971).

Interpretation of the stratigraphic framework of the High Plains sequence and of the stratigraphic position of sandstone sample localities is based on published geologic maps. Stratigraphic position of sandstone sample localities is based on published geologic maps, stratigraphic sections, and land-mammal ages established during a century of study by paleontologists and stratigraphers (Clark *et al.*, 1967; Condra and Reed, 1943; Darton, 1899; 1903; Darton *et al.*, 1910; Elias, 1942, Lugn, 1939; McGrew, 1963; 1967a–d; McGrew, 1953; Schlaikjer, 1935; Schultz and Stout, 1955; 1961; Vondra *et al*, 1969). Although disagreements exist about subdivision of the High

Plains sequence, the major lithostratigraphic units are mapped units whose biostratigraphic range, isotopic age, and lithologic boundaries are well established in Nebraska and adjoining Wyoming.

Sandstone composition and provenance.— Sandstone and siltstone in the High Plains sequence consists of pyroclastic detritus derived from distant volcanic eruptions and of epiclastic fragments eroded from Precambrian crystalline rocks, Paleozoic and Mesozoic sedimentary rocks, and Cenozoic volcanic rocks exposed in the Laramie and Front Ranges, Hartville uplift, and Black Hills (Wanless, 1922; 1923; Sato and Denson, 1967; Stanley, 1976). Modal analyses of detrital mineralogy of High Plains sandstones indicate that it is immature with a large proportion of chemically unstable framework constituents, angular to subangular grains, poor sorting, and a "matrix" that ranges in amount from a trace to 15 percent (Stanley, 1976). All sandstone is arkose and vitric litharenite (after Folk, 1968) and these compositions also characterize siltstone.

Four distinct natural populations of detrital minerals are recognized in the High Plains sequence. These mineralogies constitute the following sandstone petrofacies, which are independent of grain-size and biostratigraphic position: (1) volcaniclastic sandstone, (2) plagioclase sandstone, (3) feldspathic sandstone, and (4) rhyolite-bearing feldspathic sandstone (Table 1). Each petrofacies contains a unique assemblage of light and heavy minerals and lithic fragments, which can be related to a specific source terrane (Stanley, 1976).

East of the Laramie Range, volcaniclastic rocks are siltstone, mudrock, and very fine-grained to fine-grained vitric litharenite, which together comprise the main body of the rocks of the Arikaree Group; vitric siltstone and mudrock dominate the White River Group (Table 2). These lithologies contain 40 to 80 percent rhyolitic shards, which exhibit bubble-wall junctures, rod shapes, or are pumiceous. Pyroclastic material was probably ejected from volcanoes west of the High Plains. Similar Middle Tertiary pyroclastic-rich rocks are common in the Wind River basin of central Wyoming (van Houten, 1957) and in Browns Park basin in northwestern Colorado, suggesting a volcanic source further to the west. The volcaniclastic sandstone of the High Plains and in the intermontane basins to the west were deposited contemporaneously with an episode of immense volcanic activity in the eastern Great Basin of Nevada and Utah (Armstrong, 1968), which is the most likely source of the rhyolitic glass in sandstone and ash beds.

The source of major constituents in the plagioclase sandstone petrofacies shown in Table 1 is the Laramie anorthosite complex in the central Laramie Range where norite, anorthosite, and hypersthene syenite are the dominate lithologies (Stanley, 1976). Minerals and lithic fragments that make up the feldspathic sandstone petrofacies, however, are comparable to minerals in granitic

TABLE 1.—AVERAGES (MEANS) AND STANDARD DEVIATIONS (SQUARE ROOT OF VARIANCE) OF RESULTS OF POINT COUNTS ON THIN SECTIONS OF SANDSTONE IN THE HIGH PLAINS SEQUENCE AND OF SANDS OF MODERN STREAMS

Petrofacies	Modern stream sand and sandstone of High Plains sequence	N	Q	F	L	Heavy minerals	P/F	V/L	Amphibole Pyroxene
Plagioclase sandstone	Chugwater Creek	5	24 ± 7	52 ± 9	17 ± 6	7 ± 3	0.7 ± 0.2	0	<0.2
	Ogallala Group	20	20 ± 6	52 ± 7	15 ± 5	13 ± 3	0.8 ± 0.1	0	<0.1
	Arikaree Group	83	27 ± 6	57 ± 10	11 ± 4	5 ± 2	0.7 ± 0.2	0	<0.3
	White River Group	100	28 ± 5	56 ± 6	10 ± 5	6 ± 3	0.8 ± 0.2	0	<0.3
Feldspathic sandstone	Lodgepole Creek	3	50 ± 9	30 ± 5	16 ± 3	4 ± 2	0.4 ± 0.1	0	>1
	Arikaree Group	30	50 ± 8	23 ± 10	14 ± 5	13 ± 7	0.5 ± 0.1	0	>1
	White River Group	60	48 ± 6	21 ± 8	17 ± 4	14 ± 6	0.5 ± 0.1	0	>1
Rhyolite-bearing feldspathic sandstone	North Platte River	4	58 ± 10	24 ± 5	17 ± 4	1	0.4 ± 0.1	<0.1	>1
	Ogallala Group	50	51 ± 6	23 ± 4	20 ± 3	6 ± 4	0.4 ± 0.2	<0.4	>1
Volcaniclastic sandstone	Arikaree Group	110	23 ± 12	18 ± 10	52 ± 25	7 ± 4	0.4 ± 0.2	>0.8	>1

Note: Procedures of modal analyses, sample localities, and textural properties of sandstone are reported by Stanley (1976). N is the number of thin sections counted. Values for quartz (Q), Feldspar (F), lithic and granitic fragments (L), and heavy minerals are volumetric percentages of the total framework. Values of P/F, V/L, and amphibole/pyroxene are decimal fractions. P is plagioclase; V is volcanic lithic fragments or pyroclastic material.

TABLE 2.—DEPOSITIONAL SYSTEM OF HIGH PLAINS SEQUENCE

	Eolian Deposits		Stream Channel Deposits		Flood Plain Deposits	
	E	I	E	I	E	I
Ogallala Group	S	S	S	D	S	C
Arikaree Group	C	S	C	C	C	S
White River Group	C	S	S	C	D	S

E = External source of sediment (volcanism); I = Internal source of sediment (crystalline rock in Laramie and Front Ranges and Hartville uplift); D = Dominant lithology; C = Common lithology; S = Sparse lithology.

and metamorphic rocks in the Hartville uplift and in the Laramie and Front Ranges. Source rocks for the petrofacies range from quartz syenite to granodiorite and include the Sherman batholith south of the Laramie anorthosite complex and metamorphic rocks of amphibolite facies, principally hornblende gneiss and schist, biotite gneiss, and quartz-feldspathic gneiss (Denson and Botinelly, 1949; Osterwald and Dean, 1957; Smithson and Hodge, 1972). The rhyolite-bearing feldspathic sandstone petrofacies contains constituents derived from plutonic and metamorphic rocks in the front of Laramie Range and Tertiary volcanic fields on the west side of the Front Range in North Park basin, Colorado. This is the dominant rock type in the Ogallala Group (Table 2).

DIAGENETIC FEATURES

Fabric.—Porosity and permeability are the most important bulk properties of potential fluid reservoirs. Post-depositional chemical and mechanical alteration of rock fabric usually reduces porosity and permeability, but can enhance these properties of the sediment. As noted by Walker (1967, 1976) the fabrics of continental sands commonly are significantly altered during early diagenesis. The fabric of sandstone in the High Plains sequence shows no stratigraphic or geographic variations, and detectable modifications of original depositional fabric are restricted to porosity reduction by cementation, minor porosity enhancement by dissolution of chemically unstable detrital grains, and crushing and bending of some mica grains at grain-to-grain contacts. The volumetric percentage of cement and void space in High Plains sandstones, determined in thin section, ranges from 25 to 42 percent, reflecting the very loose packing that developed under eolian and alluvial conditions of deposition. Silica and calcite cements fill most intergranular space whereas montmorillonite and (or) zeolite cements that volumetrically range up to 27 percent of the

rock seldom fill more than 45 percent of the intergranular space. Scanning electron microscopy indicates that these cements not only reduce pore space, but also inhibit fluid flow through the sediment by reducing the size and number of interconnecting holes. Thin section analysis of cement-free sands and those with only thin (less than 10 microns) clay and zeolite coatings indicates about 30 percent porosity, nearly all of which is intergranular porosity, related to packing of grains (Fig. 3). Similar porosities were obtained by thin-section analysis of Quaternary alluvial sands. The types of contacts between grains in sandstone of the High Plains sequence reflect the loose packing of the grains and the lack of compaction of the sediment (Fig. 3). Taylor (1950) recognized four possible types of grain-to-grain contacts for sandstone: tangential and long contacts that reflect depositional fabrics and packing, and concavoconvex and sutured contacts that reflect pressure solution at grain-to-grain contacts during more intense compaction of the sand with burial. In the High Plains sequence sandstone fabrics are characteristically tangential and long grain-to-grain contacts (Fig. 3). Only locally are biotite grains crushed and bent between other detrital grains. Mudrock, glass shards, and carbonate grains are not crushed and their grain-to-grain contacts are tangential or long, again reflecting the dearth of compaction alteration in the sediment (Fig. 3).

Alteration of detrital grains.—Alteration of detrital grains in the High Plain sequence and in overlying Quaternary sediments is related (1) to weathering with formation of soils (Fig. 4) and (2) to intrastratal solution. Weathering resulted in formation of soil horizons that display highly variable alteration of detrital grains and mineral associations. In hardpan calcrete, calcified sand, and surfaces of weathering, which may or may not include root horizons, detrital grains exhibit the most intense alteration, and in some calcrete

0.1mm

FIG. 3.—Fine-grained volcaniclastic sandstone of the basal Arikaree Group from Scotts Bluff, Nebraska, showing the open packing and porosity that are common in sandstones of the High Plains sequence. Sand grains are coated with montmorillonite cement 4 micrometers thick.

horizons only quartz remains of the original detrital modes. Caliche and root horizons show calcite replacement of feldspar, alteration of glass to montmorillonite, root casts filled with montmorillonite, fibrous sepiolite and palygorskite after montmorillonite (in Ogallala profiles), and variable amounts of alteration of heavy minerals.

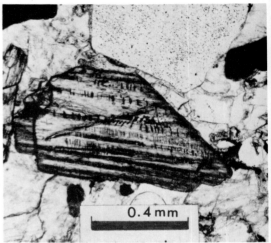

0.4 mm

0.4 mm

FIG. 4.—Paleosol profile in upper part of the Arikaree Group, near Agate, Nebraska, showing root zone developed in alluvial sandstone below an ancient "land surface." Pervasive argillization of vitric components in the original volcaniclastic sandstone characterize the root horizon, whereas very fine- and fine-grained volcaniclastic sandstone below the root horizon is coated with montmorillonite.

FIG. 5.—Photomicrographs of calcite cemented plagioclase sandstone of the Ogallala Group adjacent to the Laramie Range Anorthosite complex showing the lack of intrastratal alteration of chemically unstable non-opaque heavy minerals. *Top*, Hypersthene grain showing only slight oxidation of the grain surface. *Bottom*, Olivine grains (O) with iron oxide rims and fracture fillings.

Intrastratal solution, which involves the dissolution of grains during early diagenesis, is more uniform and resulted in a general sequence in the kind and degree of alteration. Most chemically unstable grains in High Plains sandstone and siltstone indicate incipient intrastratal solution and alteration (Fig. 5, 6). Olivine grains, the most unstable mineral in the sandstones, exhibit iron oxide rims and fracture fillings in calcite-cemented rocks, but are otherwise unaltered (Fig. 5). This early calcite cementation of sandstone probably inhibited further dissolution and alteration (Fig. 5). Olivine in porous and friable sand, however, is altered to iddingsite and locally, the grains are partly or wholly (?) removed by dissolution. The only other mineral to show extensive alteration is hypersthene, which is the principal non-opaque

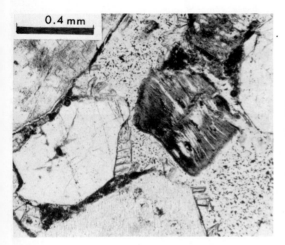

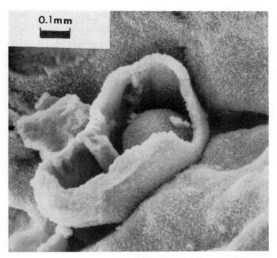

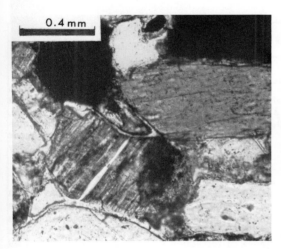

Fig. 6.—Photomicrographs of friable plagioclase sandstone showing intrastratal alteration and cement types of sandstone not cemented by calcite. *Top,* Friable sand collected adjacent to the calcite cemented sandstone shown in Figure 5, showing intrastratal alteration of hypersthene and cement, which is montmorillonite (dark material) and clinoptilolite crystals. *Bottom,* White River Group plagioclase sandstone near Scotts Bluff, Nebraska, with unaltered hornblende adjacent to strongly altered hypersthene; all grains are coated with a thick montmorillonite cement.

Fig. 7.—Scanning electron micrographs of montmorillonite cemented sandstone of the plagioclase sandstone (top) and volcaniclastic sandstone (bottom) petrofacies showing hollow clay coatings where detrital grains were removed by intrastratal dissolution.

FIG. 11.—Photomicrograph of channel sandstone (Eocene?) east of Valentine, Nebraska, showing detrital quartz grains, kaolin cement and replacement of grains, and large vermicular kaolinite crystals developed authigenically after deposition. This sandstone appears to pre-date the High Plains sequence and may be related to the Slim Buttes Formation of South Dakota.

tal alteration of chemically unstable minerals (e.g. olivine and hypersthene) within concretions (Fig. 5). The absence of montmorillonite, kaolinite, silica, and zeolite pore-filling cement in Quaternary alluvial and eolian sediments, together with

They must represent a different hydrochemical system operative in the depositional basin before the Oligocene.

Four different mineral cements occur in the High Plains sequence as three different cement assemblages: (1) calcite and montmorillonite with only local trace amounts of kaolinite (Figs. 7, 10), (2) zeolite and montmorillonite with calcite or silica, and (3) silica with or without authigenic fibrous clays (sepiolite or palygorskite?). In addition, silica or calcite cement is locally present without significant amounts of other diagenetic minerals. Where more than one cement phase is present, the chronology of cement precipitation is calcite, montmorillonite, silica, and finally zeolite (Fig. 12). Late calcite or silica cement also may be locally significant. Early calcite cement forms concretions composed of sparry calcite pore filling of large (up to 2 cm diameter) sand-calcite crystals. That these concretions formed shortly after deposition of alluvial and eolian sands is indicated by (1) the presence of water-worn concretions as clasts in penecontemporaneous fluvial channels, a relationship first described by Schultz (1941), and by (2) the paucity of intrastra-

dissolution of grains in Quaternary volcanic ash layers, suggests that these cements are Tertiary in age. Stratigraphic distributions of cement types imply that the cements, except for late calcite and silica, are all probably related to the early post-depositional history of fluids of each rock stratigraphic unit (Fig. 10).

Opal with a disordered tridymite or cristobalite structure (based on x-ray diffraction analysis; Mitchell and Tufts, 1973) is the most common silica cement (Fig. 13). In the Ogallala Group friable- and opal-cemented sands contain fibrous authigenetic clay minerals that impart a greenish color to the rocks. X-ray diffraction analysis and dispersive X-ray analysis with scanning electron microscopy indicate that these authigenic clays are either sepiolite and (or) palygorskite. Frye *et al.* (1974) report this mineral association below calcrete horizons in the Ogallala Formation of New Mexico and infer it to be related to alteration of montmorillonite to opal and fibrous clay by pedogenic processes. However, some opal cements in the Ogallala and in the White River and Arikaree Groups of Nebraska and Wyoming do not occur with fibrous clays (Fig. 13). Pre-Ogallala silica cements also are locally crystalline quartz, chert, and (or) chalcedony that may or may not occur with opal.

The only zeolite species recognized in the High Plains sequence of Wyoming and Nebraska is clinoptilolite (Fig. 8, 12), which was confirmed by x-ray analysis using the heat treatment method described by Boles (1972). The zeolite was found in coarse friable sandstone of the plagioclase sandstone petrofacies growing on opal-and montmorillonite-coated grains (Fig. 8, 12). The zeolite occurs in the lower part of the Ogallala Group, a relationship also noted by Frye *et al.* (1974) for heulandite in the Ogallala Formation of New Mexico, and in White River Group sandstones below the Ogallala. The zeolite cement is progressively more abundant toward the base of Ogallala sandstone beds and is rare in underlying White River sandstone. This relationship implies that zeolites in the White River sandstone may reflect percolation of waters from the Ogallala into older beds. Recently, the Nebraska State Conservation

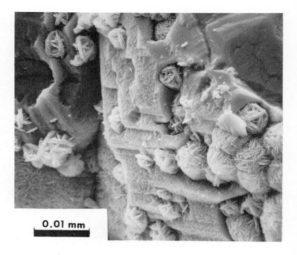

Fig. 13.—Opal cement in feldspathic sandstone of the White River Group near Torrington, Wyoming. *Top,* feldspar grain showing surface etching and dissolution with authigenic opal-tridymite growing in pits dissolved in the grain. *Bottom,* thick coating of authigenic opal on the surface of a quartz grain. The crystal habit of the surface of the opal cement is characteristic of tridymite.

Fig. 12.—*Top,* Clinoptilolite crystals resting on an earlier phase of montmorillonite cement that coats grains in the sandstone. Plagioclase sandstone from the Ogallala Group near Farthing, Wyoming. *Bottom,* Clinoptilolite crystals resting on opal cement coating sand grains, White River Group sandstone below the Ogallala Group near Farthing, Wyoming. The zeolite post-dates the formation of both the montmorillonite and opal cement. Samples were collected within a distance of 1 km.

and Survey Division of the University of Nebraska has also identified clinoptilolite in lacustrine rocks of northwestern Nebraska, perhaps related to alkaline lakes (Boellstorff, oral communication, 1976).

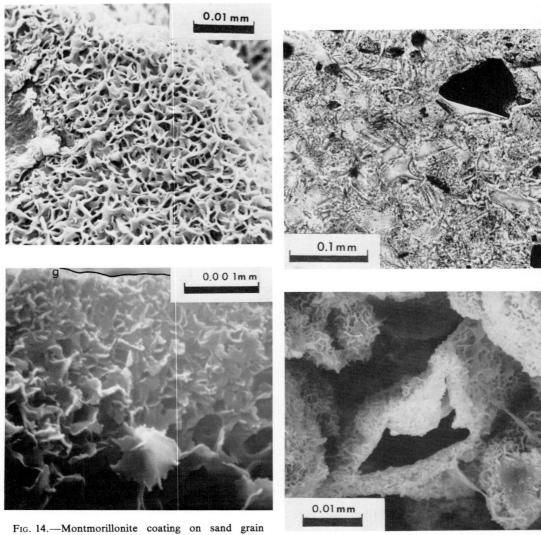

FIG. 14.—Montmorillonite coating on sand grain showing the fabric of authigenic montmorillonite. *Top,* montmorillonite-coated surface of a sand grain. *Bottom,* Cross-section of thicker cement coating showing montmorillonite "cornflake-like" particles that increase in size away from the grain surface (g).

FIG. 15.—Vitric siltstone of the White River Group at Scotts Bluff, Nebraska, showing rhyolitic glass shards with development of montmorillonite cement. *Top,* photomicrograph of vitric siltstone showing bubble-wall and rod-shaped shards, biotite with attached glass, and clay filling voids between grains that is difficult to interpret as either detrital or authigenic in thin section. *Bottom,* scanning electron micrograph of the above sample showing that clay is well developed authigenic montmorillonite growing on grain surfaces. No detrital clay is present, although size analysis of this samples indicates about 25 percent clay-size material.

Montmorillonite cement in High Plains sandstone and siltstone consists of coatings on grains up to 0.1 millimeters thick, which consist of a reticulate arrangement of relatively porous clay (Figs. 7, 14, 15, 16). Individual particles and their reticulate arrangement are similar to montmorillonites grown in the laboratory by Demirel, Erol, and Lohnes (1975). Individual particles in the coatings are up to 4 micrometers across and less than 0.3 micrometers thick. Most coatings are less than 4 micrometers thick and are made up of one layer of particles arranged normal to the grain surface (Fig. 14, 15). Thicker cements consist of more randomly oriented particles that increase in size away from the grain surface;

particle size ranges from 0.5 micrometers to 3 micrometers across (Fig. 7, 16). The identification and the nature of interstratification of the montmorillonites was determined from power diffraction patterns of oriented ethylene glycol treated samples (Fig. 17), microprobe analyses, and qualitative elemental analyses using energy dispersive x-rays on the scanning electron microscope (Fig. 18). The analyses indicate no detectable variation in montmorillonite with different grain sizes of sediment, depositional settings, or sandstone petrofacies. All montmorillonite is a dioctahedral aluminosilicate with variable amounts of exchangeable ions, but with magnesium, calcium, and iron the major cations. Most of the analyzed montmorillonites exhibited x-ray diffraction profiles like that shown in Figure 17. Only a few samples contain kaolinite in addition to montmorillonite. By comparison with x-ray diffraction profiles reported by Reynolds and Hower (1970), the amount of interstratification in the montmorillonites appear to be small with greater than 70 percent montmorillonite layers in the interstratified clay structure (Fig. 17).

Fig. 16.—Intrastratally altered hypersthene grain from sandstone shown in Figure 6 from the White River Group. *Top,* Hypersthene grain and montmorillonite cement. *Bottom,* Montmorillonite filling dissolved parts of the hypersthene grain. Crystals of montmorillonite are oriented normal to the walls of the dissolution cavities.

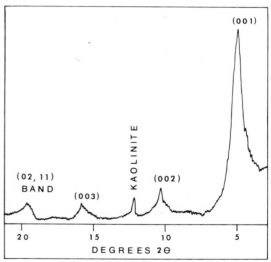

Fig. 17.—X-ray diffraction pattern of montmorillonite cement coating sand grains in the High Plains sequence. The interlocking arrangement of clay crystals in the cement (Fig. 14) inhibits good preferential alignment of the clay particles in oriented-power preparations for x-ray analysis, and consequently, the resulting x-ray diffraction patterns are difficult to evaluate in terms of the illite mixed layered illite-montmorillonite, and montmorillonite patterns described by Reynolds and Hower (1970). Nevertheless, sufficient information is available to indicate a montmorillonite with little mixed layering.

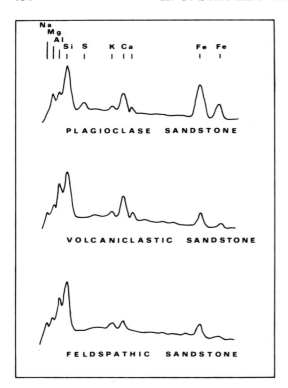

Fig. 18.—Qualitative elemental analyses of montmorillonite cement in the plagioclase, volcaniclastic, and feldspathic sandstone petrofacies showing the peak intensities of the major elements in the montmorillonite using energy dispersive x-rays on the Cambridge Scanning Electron Microscope; 170,000 to 200,000 counts were made so that peak intensity is a semiquantitative estimate of abundance.

PETROLOGIC VARIATIONS IN DIAGENESIS

In many continental and marine sedimentary sequences, significant differences in the style of diagenetic alteration can be equated with texture, environment of deposition, and (or) composition. In the High Plains sequence, these possible controls on dissolution and cementation can be evaluated for a semiarid climatic regime because of the unique association in which eolian, alluvial, and lacustrine rocks compose the plagioclase, volcaniclastic and feldspathic sandstone petrofacies shown in Table 1. As noted previously, dissolution is selective and favors specific chemically unstable detrital grains so that the amount of dissolution in a sandstone can be related to composition of detrital modes. The plagioclase sandstone petrofacies shows the most grain destruction with varying amounts of dissolution and alteration of olivine, hypersthene, and labradorite

(Fig. 16). Volcaniclastic sandstone exhibits a lesser amount of dissolution which is commonly confined to removal, etching, and pitting of rhyolitic glass and rare hypersthene grains (Figs. 7, 16). Total removal of glass resulting in hollow clay coatings (Fig. 7) appears to be more prevalent in vitric siltstone than in sandstone and is the only textural influence recognized on the dissolution of grains in the sequence (Fig. 15). Feldspathic sandstone shows the least amount of dissolution with only minor surface etching of feldspar and amphibole grains.

In general, the amount of clay and (or) zeolite cement in sandstone correlates with the intensity and amount of intrastratal dissolution of grains. For example, the Ogallala sandstone petrofacies adjacent to the Laramie Range are contemporaneous alluvial rocks whose diagenetic alterations, exclusive of paleosol horizons, are markedly different. Rhyolite-bearing feldspathic sandstone shows only minor etching of grain surfaces and no clay cements, whereas plagioclase sandstone only a few kilometers away shows extensive alteration of hypersthene and olivine, minor dissolution of labradorite, and montmorillonite and zeolite pore-filling cement up to 0.1 mm thick. Similarly, grains in Arikaree eolian dune sandstone of the volcaniclastic sandstone petrofacies east of Chugwater, Wyoming, exhibit montmorillonite coatings that commonly are less than 4 micrometers thick (Fig. 7), whereas similar Arikaree dune sandstone of the plagioclase sandstone of the petrofacies less than 3 km away have montmorillonite coatings from 10 to 100 micrometers thick (Fig. 7). In both of these cases, and indeed in all comparisons where the environment of deposition is a constant, composition is the major factor that controls the amount of dissolution and cementation. Comparisons of rocks deposited in different environments show the same compositional influence, but differences in dissolution and cementation in rocks of the same petrofacies are insignificant. The only exception to these relations is zeolitic alteration of lacustrine sandstone that is presently being studied by workers from the University of Nebraska Conservation and Survey Division (Boellstorff, oral communication, 1976), where alteration is probably related to saline alkaline lake conditions.

Montmorillonite, calcite, and silica are the most common cements in the High Plains sequence and occur in all sandstone petrofacies; in alluvial, eolian, and lacustrine rocks; and in siltstone to conglomeratic sandstone. Kaolinite occurs only with montmorillonite in coarse-grained sandstone implying a textural control on the sparse occurrence of kaolinite in the High Plains sequence. As noted above, montmorillonite shows no detectable difference in the amount of mixed-layering. Qualitative elemental analysis of the montmorillonite coating suggests some minor variations in the exchangable cations of the clay structure, depending on the sandstone composition (Fig. 18). Counts for iron, sodium, potassium, and calcium, which are crude semiquantitative estimates of abundance, are shown in Figure 18 by peak intensities. They suggest more iron in cements of the plagioclase sandstone petrofacies, and more importantly, the presence of sulfur suggests that finely disseminated iron sulfides might be associated with the montmorillonite cement in these rocks. The high iron content of these cements also could reflect derivation of the clay from solution and alteration of iron-bearing silicates, a relationship noted by Walker, Ribbe, and Honea (1967) for clay which replaces hornblende in redbeds of Baja, California. Sodium, potassium, magnesium, and calcium also seem to be selectively distributed relative to sandstone composition, again suggesting a possible control on clays by the composition of the sandstone.

Although textural properties and environments of deposition have locally affected some diagenetic alterations of the High Plains sequence, the principal factors that controlled dissolution and cementation is the mineralogic composition of the rocks. Nevertheless, cement types are ubiquitous, and only changes in abundance and (or) minor changes in chemistry can be equated with composition.

STRONTIUM IN THE DIAGENETIC SYSTEM

The $^{87}Sr/^{86}Sr$ ratio for detrital grains in sandstone and for their parent crystalline source rocks of the High Plains depositional basin is determined by the composition, magmatic history, and age of these materials. Continental crust is enriched in ^{87}Sr relative to the mantle, and therefore, rocks formed by melting, metasomatism, or assimilation of continental crustal materials will have a higher $^{87}Sr/^{86}Sr$ ratio than uncontaminated rocks derived from the mantle by fractionation (Faure and Powell, 1972). In addition, the $^{87}Sr/^{86}Sr$ ratio is determined by the radioactive decay of ^{87}Rb to ^{87}Sr so that older rocks will have a higher $^{87}Sr/^{86}Sr$ ratio than younger rocks. Where a considerable difference in age and (or) magmatic history can be ascribed to potential source materials for sandstone, the relative contribution of the different sources of sand grains can be calculated from the $^{87}Sr/^{86}Sr$ ratio. More importantly for our purpose in this paper, the $^{87}Sr/^{86}Sr$ ratio of interstitial fluids and diagenetic mineral phases in sediment should be controlled by the $^{87}Sr/^{86}Sr$ ratio of ions from the solids that were dissolved, transported, and precipitated in the sediment. Therefore, the isotopic composition of strontium in interstitial fluids can be regarded as a mixture

of different isotopic varieties of strontium derived from weathering and (or) intrastratal dissolution of rocks through which the fluid passed. Strontium in sandstone of the High Plains sequence is from three potential sources: (1) Precambrian crystalline rocks of the cores of uplifts and detritus derived from these rocks in sandstone on the plains; (2) late Paleozoic carbonate rocks on the eastern flank of the uplifts; and (3) Tertiary airfall rhyolitic glass in sandstones and ash layers.

Precambrian crystalline rocks in the Front Range have been studied by Hills *et al.* (1968) and Peterman and Hedge (1968), who report a wide range of $^{87}Sr/^{86}Sr$ ratios of from 0.7060 to 1.128. Late Paleozoic marine carbonate rocks around the world, like modern ocean waters, appear to be isotopically homogeneous at any given time, but vary with time; the late Paleozoic published values for the $^{87}Sr/^{86}Sr$ ratio range from 0.7070 to 0.7090 (Peterman, Hedge, and Tourtelot, 1970). Rhyolitic glass in Ogallala ash beds on the High Plains has a strontium isotopic ratio of 0.7143 (Table 3).

Strontium isotopic ratios for montmorillonite, calcite, and zeolite cements in sandstones show little variation and range from 0.7103 to 0.7113, although these cements occur in plagioclase, feldspathic, and volcaniclastic sandstone (Table 3). Strontium in these cements must have been equilibrated with strontium in the interstitial waters when cement was precipitated. The slight variation in $^{87}Sr/^{86}Sr$ ratios of cements suggests a homogeneous water relative to strontium. The

TABLE 3.—STRONTIUM ISOTOPIC COMPOSITION FOR DETRITAL SANDSTONE AND CEMENT IN THE HIGH PLAINS SEQUENCE

	$^{87}Sr/^{86}Sr$
Feldspathic Sandstone Petrofacies	
Calcite cement	0.7112
Sandstone	0.7491
Plagioclase Sandstone Petrofacies	
Calcite cement	0.7113
Zeolite cement	0.7110
Sandstone	0.7065
Sandstone with Components of both the Feldspathic and Plagioclase Sandstone Petrofacies (Intercalated in rocks of the volcaniclastic sandstone petrofacies)	
Montmorillonite cement	0.7103
Sandstone	0.7103
Volcaniclastic Sandstone Petrofacies	
Calcite cement	0.7103
Rhyolitic glass (Ogallala Group, age 7 m.y.)	0.7143

dissimilarity of the $^{87}Sr/^{86}Sr$ ratios for cement and sandstone shown on Table 3 requires a hydrochemical system in which solutes in pore waters were not controlled locally by the isotopic composition of adjacent sand grains. A homogeneous and open hydrochemical system is indicated with water moving rapidly through large volumes of sediment or rapid diffusion rates relative to rates of precipitation. A nearly homogeneous water relative to strontium isotopic ratios can be explained by relatively rapid mixing of strontium from different sources of strontium in the system and (or) by dissolution of large volumes of material with an isotopic composition similar to that of the water. Dissolution and mixing of strontium from Paleozoic limestone and (or) rocks of the plagioclase sandstone petrofacies with strontium from rocks of the feldspathic sandstone petrofacies is one possible explanation for the isotopic composition of cements. Such mixing requires that most of the strontium was derived from Paleozoic limestone ($^{87}Sr/^{86}Sr$ 0.7070) or rocks of the plagioclase sandstone petrofacies ($^{87}Sr/^{86}Sr$ 0.7065). A second plausible explanation for the strontium isotopic composition of cements is strontium derivation from rhyolitic glass, which has an isotopic composition similar to that of the cement (Table 3). However, vitric material contains small amounts of strontium (Fig. 19) which would require that glass dissolution was the major source of solutes in the fluids. Analysis of strontium and rubidium in sandstone and rhyolitic glass shown in Figure 19 support the derivation of strontium from Precambrian detritus in sandstone and not from rhyolitic glass. Sandstone contains 12 to 16 times more strontium than glass, and the amount of strontium is directly proportional to the amount of feldspar, particularly plagioclase, in the sediment, so that dissolution of feldspar is believed to be a probable important source of strontium in the hydrochemical system (Fig. 19). Available information cannot be used to discriminate between these possible sources of strontium, but it does indicate that strontium in cement can be explained by a hydrochemical system similar to that of today in which rainwater falls on the plains, infiltrates the sediment, percolates to the zone of saturation, and moves to a site of discharge into streams or lakes (Fig. 20).

INTERSTITIAL WATER AND MINERAL EQUILIBRIA

Hydrology and hydrochemistry of subsurface water.—Present-day groundwater and its movement through Tertiary and Quaternary sediments of Nebraska and adjacent Wyoming is perhaps a modern analogue of the ancient hydrochemical system that precipitated cements in the High Plains sequence (Figure 20). The concentration and composition of these groundwaters is a func-

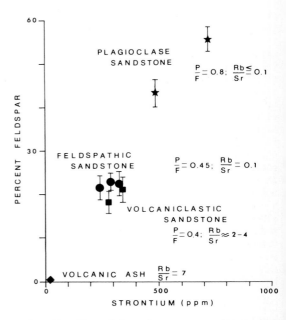

FIG. 19.—Plot of Strontium concentration against percent feldspar. Also shown are the correlation between sandstone type, plagioclase to total feldspar ratio (P/F), and the rubidium to strontium ratio (Rb/Sr). The near linear correlation between feldspar content, particularly plagioclase, and strontium content indicates that the major source of strontium in the sandstone is the feldspar. Pure volcanic glass in ash beds has less than 25 ppm strontium.

tion of rates of fluid movement in the sediment coupled with the kinetics of mineral dissolution and cement precipitation. These processes are time and space dependent. In the Sand Hills of Nebraska, groundwaters of the Elkhorn River drainage basin probably exemplify the interaction of water and sediment with an increase in dissolved solids along the regional hydrodynamic gradient (west to east) and with depth in the zone of saturation (Bentall, 1971). The zone of saturation in the Sand Hills and in Tertiary rocks in western Nebraska is commonly within 30 m of the surface and the direction of groundwater movement is toward sites of discharge at the land surface (Fig. 20). The rate of lateral movement in the Sand Hills region ranges up to 90 cm per day in major perched and shallow aquifers, but may be only a small fraction of this rate in deeper or less porous aquifers (Bentall, 1971). The fraction of precipitation that becomes part of the groundwater system is highly variable. In areas of sand or friable sandstone the fraction of precipitation that infiltrates the soil but is not taken up by plant roots or returned to the atmosphere

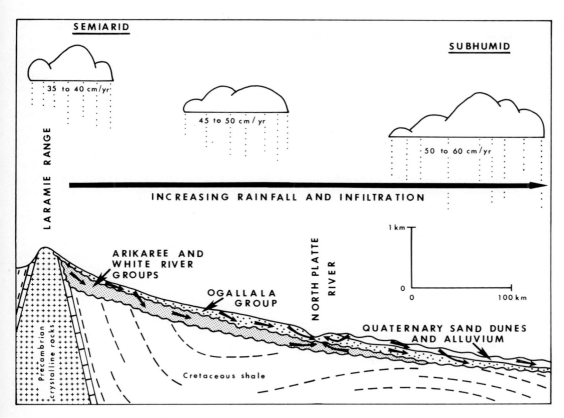

FIG. 20.—Schematic diagram of the present-day High Plains east of the Laramie Range showing sedimentary rock sequences and the circulation of hydrologic system.

by evaporation is up to 25 percent (McGinness, 1963; Bentall, 1971; Keech and Bentall, 1971; Rahn and Paul, 1975). Where clay, silt, or caliche are the surface material, little or no water is infiltrated to the zone of saturation (Rahn and Paul, 1975). Much of the discharge from the zone of saturation in Nebraska is due to evapotranspiration in places where the water table is within the reach of roots; the remainder occurs as seepage into lakes and streams and constitutes the principal regional surface water source (Bentall, 1971; Rahn and Paul, 1975). This hydrologic system is a consequence of the regional physiography, semiarid climate, grassland vegetation, and sediment types; factors that were all similar during the deposition of the High Plains sequence (Fig. 20). Because the modern groundwaters are dilute solutions with a short residence time in contact with sediment before discharge into streams, they can be considered as precursors of interstitial waters from which cements would be precipitated. Such solutions and their cement phases should be analogous to the Tertiary hydro-

chemical system that deposited cements in the pores of High Plains sequence sandstone.

For several decades the United States Geological Survey has monitored the properties and dissolved solids in surface and subsurface waters of Nebraska and adjacent Wyoming. Several hundred analyses are now published in water quality reports (Wenzel *et al.*, 1946; Babcock and Visher, 1952; Bradley, 1956; Rapp *et al.*, 1957; Sniegocki, 1959; Lowry and Crist, 1967). Most of the subsurface water data are from wells that supply potable water to ranches and towns; this is a sample bias against more saline waters in less porous rocks. In addition, constraints are placed on the significance of mineral equilibria and saturation calculation for these waters, because many properties, such as pH, were measured in the laboratory after collection.

Two subsurface water masses are present in western Nebraska and adjoining Wyoming (Fig. 21): (1) sodium bicarbonate waters that characterize Cretaceous sandstone and shale, and, locally, basal sandstones of the High Plains sequence,

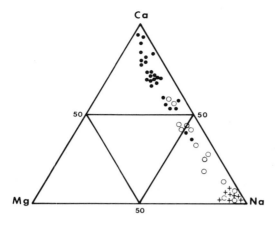

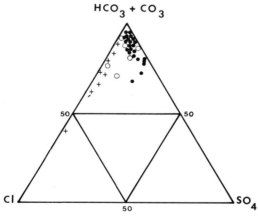

•— Ogallala and Arikaree Groups
◦— White River Group
+— Cretaceous shale

FIG. 21.—Triangular percentage plots showing graphically the fields of present-day well waters in western Nebraska and adjoining Wyoming in terms of the major cations and anions in solution and the rock unit at the bottom of the well. Two water masses have been recognized in southwestern Nebraska by Smith and Souders (1975): calcium bicarbonate waters in Arikaree, Ogallala and Quaternary rocks, and sodium bicarbonate waters in Cretaceous sandstones and shales and some basal White River rocks. A mixture of these waters is suggested for waters in some White River rocks.

and (2) calcium bicarbonate waters in the High Plains sequence and Quaternary sediments (Smith and Souders, 1975). Dilute sodium bicarbonate waters contain two to four times the total dissolved solids of calcium bicarbonate waters, and also contain more chlorine, boron, iron and sulfate

(Smith and Souders, 1975). Calcium bicarbonate waters usually contain more than 200 to 350 ppm total dissolved solids. The sodium bicarbonate waters seem to reflect movement through the marine Cretaceous sandstones and shales, whereas calcium bicarbonate waters characterize water moving through Tertiary continental rocks.

Mineral equilibria.—The present-day High Plains is an open and semiconfined groundwater flow system in which possible mineral equilibria, saturation, and precipitation can be considered in terms of water composition data reported by the United States Geological Survey (e.g. Wenzel *et al.*, 1946; Babcock and Visher, 1952; Bradley, 1956; Smith and Souders, 1975). Previously, we proposed that the same diagenetic processes have been taking place on the High Plains since the Eocene or during the past 37 million years. To demonstrate that the same chemical reactions are possible today, the mineral equilibria states of waters from 113 wells bottomed in White River, Arikaree, or Ogallala rocks have been calculated with respect to the principal authigenic mineral phases. The thermodynamic data used in the calculations were taken from Aagaard *et al.* in prep.

Carbonate mineral equilibria in the groundwaters can be determined by comparison of mean activity products of mineral species in the aqueous phase with their solubility products, and by the scatter of water data on the activity diagram for the system $CaO-Mg-OH_2O-CO_2$. For the High Plains groundwaters analyzed the mean activity product of calcite normalized to 25° C is identical to the solubility product of calcite of $10^{-8.5}$. It appears, therefore, that High Plains well waters are in general equilibrium with calcite, the pervasive carbonate cement in the High Plains sequence. However, the mean activity product for stoichiometric dolomite is $10^{-17.1\pm0.7}$; this value is similar to the mean activity value of $10^{-16.9}$ reported by Langmuir (1971) for groundwater presumed to be in equilibrium with a carbonate terrain. This indication of possible equilibrium with both carbonate phases is also suggested by the distribution of water composition data on the activity diagram for the system $CaO-MgO-H_2O-CO_2$ (Fig. 22). The data shown on Figure 22 form a cluster of points that define a linear trend that is parallel to the calcite-dolomite equilibrium lines.

Mineral equilibria in the multicomponent aluminosilicate system are not as well known as those of the carbonate system, and therefore, saturation and equilibrium are more difficult to predict for different mineral phases. With respect to the clay system, conventional activity diagrams such as those published by Norton (1974) and Tardy (1971) suggest that many well waters are in equilibrium with montmorillonite (Ca- or Na-montmorillonite) and (or) kaolinite. However, clay mineral crystalline solutions have been treated in these activity diagrams as if they are pure one component phases or as if they are solid solutions of fixed composition. The lack of accurate data on aluminum species in the aqueous phase prohibits the explicit calculation of activity products, and in addition, clay minerals such as montmorillonite and illite generally occur in nature as crystalline solid-solutions and not as pure one-component phases. Although these problems are by necessity partly ignored in construction of activity diagrams, the best available consideration of activities for clay mineral species is provided by ideal site theory. Helgeson *et al.* (in prep.) and Benson and Aagaard (in prep.) have applied an ideal site mixing model to clay minerals which allows their representation as solid solutions in activity space. Figure 23 is a two-dimensional representation of the system $K_2O\text{-}Al_2O_3\text{-}SiO_2\text{-}H_2O$ projected through an aluminum-bearing component space. The construction and interpretation of this diagram is discussed in detail by Benson and Aagaard (in prep.). The compositions of the 113 well waters plotted in Figure 23 suggest that most present-day fluids are in equilibrium with montmorillonite. Several fluids appear to be in equilibrium with kaolinite and a few fluids are inferred to be in equilibrium with a mixed-layer illite-montmorillonite or an illite phase. The activity of aqueous silica ranges from about $10^{-3.8}$ to $10^{-3.0}$. This range of values is

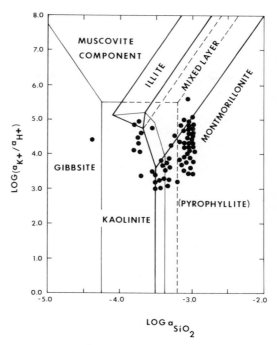

FIG. 23.—Activity diagram for the aluminosilicate system showing stability fields of naturally-occuring clay mineral groups. Mixed-layer refers to illite-montmorillonite solid-solutions. Also shown by solid dots are the plots of water analyses of 113 shallow wells from western Nebraska and eastern Wyoming that indicate equilibrium with montmorillonite for the majority of well waters.

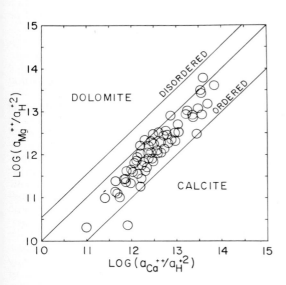

FIG. 22.—Activity diagram for the system $CaO\text{-}MgO\text{-}CO_2\text{-}H_2O$ showing the plot of water well analyses from 113 wells in Nebraska and adjacent Wyoming. Water analyses are shown by open circles.

interpreted to indicate equilibrium with a silica phase of variable crystallinity such as opal CT. The value of $10^{-3.0}$ suggests an upper activity limit buffered by the solubility of β-crystobalite.

The available data indicate that groundwaters of the High Plains sequence and Quaternary sediments in western Nebraska and adjoining Wyoming are in equilibrium with observed authigenic mineral phases. This suggests that present-day diagenetic processes are similar to past processes, a relationship that supports a persistent depositional-hydrologic history for the depositional basin in the middle and late Cenozoic.

INTERPRETATIONS AND SUMMARY

Vitric and arkosic sandstone in continental facies of sedimentary basins are generally assumed to undergo extensive early diagenetic alteration of fabric and composition; and indeed, some Tertiary arid and subhumid alluvial sequences of the mid-continent do show great amounts of alteration of chemically unstable grains and pervasive cements (Walker, 1967, 1976; McBride *et al.* 1968; Galloway *et al.*, 1977). The pastel browns and greens and absence of hematite cement distinguish the High Plains sequence from arid red beds of the Rio Grande Rift, 2000 km to the south in New Mexico (Walker, 1976). Color of the High Plains sequence is similar to that of the subhumid Catahoula Formation of south Texas (3000 km to the south), which, however, displays more extensive alteration of grains and cementation (McBride et al., 1968). The semiarid High Plains sequence, therefore, displays some of the same gross diagenetic features as the arid and subhumid sequences, but it is distinct because of the incipient development and lack of some features. These differences between rocks deposited in different climatic settings reflect slightly different hydrochemical systems that appear in turn to be strongly influenced by the composition of the sediment, the amount and movement of interstitial fluids, and perhaps vegetation.

Post-depositional changes in mineralogy and fabric of the High Plains sequence are related to (1) weathering and soil forming processes that operated during deposition of the stratigraphic sequence, and (2) the interaction of interstitial fluids of open and semiconfined ground water systems with sediment. Pedogenic horizons occur throughout the High Plains sequence, but calichification of eolian and alluvial sandstone and mudrock are most common in the Ogallala Group. Pre-Ogallala rocks exhibit soil horizons that are distinguished by surfaces with discoloration, pervasive root casts, and abundant clay in underlying rocks (Fig. 4). All of these soil profiles are characterized by calichification, silicification, and (or) argillization that have partly or wholly destroyed grains, rhyolitic glass altered to montmorillonite or silica (opal), grains replaced by silica or calcite, and pore space filled with varying amounts of cement. These horizons are discontinuous, only a few meters thick, and less porous than underlying or overlying rocks.

The lack of alteration of sandstone and siltstone between paleosol horizons requires that these sediments have persisted for long intervals of time in the zone of infiltration and capillary-assisted evaporation below the soil horizon and above the zone of water saturation. Preservation of vitric siltstone with only minor hydration and dissolution of glass requires a paucity of interstitial fluids that could react with unstable mineral species, and just as importantly, dilute waters of about neutral pH. The grassland vegetation that covered areas between streams and lakes may have played an important role in this diagenetic system by (1) reducing the infiltration of waters to the water table through rapid evapotranspiration by short-lived annuals, and by (2) lowering the pH of percolating fluids. Diagenesis of sediment in the zone of aeration and capillary-draw of interstitial

waters probably includes formation of calcite concretions, many of which are calcite-sand crystals several centimeters in diameter, and may also include montmorillonite coatings precipitated from solutions concentrated by the evaporation. These two types of cement occur in many sandstones with calcite precipitated before montmorillonite. Calculations of cement-mineral saturation for present-day dilute groundwaters, if concentrated, indicate precipitation of a similar sequence of mineral phases. Open and semiconfined ground water flow systems in sandstones could also explain petrographic evidence for undersaturation and saturation of waters: dissolution of grains, zeolitization, and formation of some calcite, silica, and clay cements. Clinoptilolite is the only zeolite species we recognized; crystals apparently were precipitated on sand grains already coated with silica or montmorillonite (Fig. 12). The solution from which clinoptilolite was precipitated probably was groundwater of alkaline composition formed by interaction of semiconfined interstitial water and chemically unstable grains of plagioclase and (or) volcaniclastic sandstone.

Unlike many continental deposits rich in ferromagnesium minerals, alteration of sandstone in the High Plains sequence has not led to formation of iron oxide cements. Present-day groundwaters commonly contain less than 0.2 ppm dissolved iron (Smith and Sounders, 1975), which must be combined in silicate or sulfide authigenic mineral phases or removed from the system. Montmorillonite contains iron, and locally, in some cements rich in iron, sulfur has been identified, which suggests the possible presence of iron sulfide minerals.

The interaction of interstitial waters and sediment has resulted in varying amounts of intrastratal alteration of the most chemically unstable grains, but only surface etching and dissolution of amphiboles, rhyolitic glass, micas, and feldspars. Dissolution and alteration of olivine and hypersthene, and locally glass, has resulted in removal of some grains and intensely dissolved cockscomb features of others. Because this intrastratal alteration is mineralogically selective, the amount of post-depositional alteration in the High Plains sequence favors specific sandstone petrofacies shown in Table 1. Plagioclase sandstone displays the most intense alteration with dissolution and alteration of olivine and hypersthene, and etching and minor dissolution of the surface of labradorite grains. Volcaniclastic sandstone shows less alteration of grains with only minor pitting and dissolution of the surface of glass, amphibole, and feldspars, and locally, removal of glass and hypersthene grains. Feldspathic sandstones show the least alteration with only surface etching of grains. Types of cements produced by the interaction of interstitial waters and sediment are ubiquitous and their presence is independent of sandstone type, environment of deposition, and fabric and texture of the rock. The amount of montmorillonite cement, however, does seem to correlate with the amount of intrastratal alteration of the sandstone so that plagioclase sandstone tends to have the thickest montmorillonite coating cement on grains (up to 100 micrometers) whereas volcaniclastic sandstone commonly has a thin coating (less than 4 micrometers) and feldspathic sandstone only sparce and thin coatings, if present. The strontium isotopic composition of cements reflects either (1) the isotopic composition of strontium in rhyolitic glass, or (2) the mixture of strontium of variable isotopic composition from feldspathic and plagioclase sandstones and Paleozoic limestone. Strontium in the system is probably controlled by dissolution of feldspars, which contain the most strontium, but also could reflect dissolution of large volumes of glass in the sediment. Preliminary microprobe analyses of the montmorillonite coatings suggest that the major exchangeable ions in this authigenic mineral are

calcium, iron, and magnesium; cations more likely were derived from dissolution of feldspar and heavy minerals in sandstone than from rhyolitic glass.

The available data suggest that groundwaters of the High Plains and Quaternary sediments in central and western Nebraska and adjoining Wyoming are in equilibrium with montmorillonite, kaolinite, illite, mixed layer illite-montmorillonite, opal CT, calcite, and possible a disordered dolomite. Some of these are also the most common mineral phases found as cement in rocks of the High Plains sequence.

ACKNOWLEDGEMENTS

We are grateful to James W. Collinson and Charles H. Summerson who reviewed an earlier version of the manuscript and made helpful suggestions for improvement. Thanks also are extended to Theodore R. Walker for his helpful discussion of diagenesis while in the field with Stanley, and to Gunter Faure who determined the isotopic composition of High Plain sequence sandstones, volcanic ash, and cements.

REFERENCES

ARMSTRONG, R. L., 1968, Sevier orogenic belt in Nevada and Utah: Geol. Soc. America Bull., v. 79, p. 429–458.

BABCOCK, H. M., AND VISHER, F. N., 1952, Reconnaissance of the geology and groundwater resources of the Pumpkin Creek area, Morrill and Banner Counties, Nebraska: U.S. Geol. Survey Circ. 156, 30 p.

BENTALL, RAY, 1971, Water supplies and the land—The Elkhorn River Basin of Nebraska: Univ. Nebraska Conservation and Survey Div. Resources Atlas no. 1, 51 p.

BERENDSEN, PIETER, 1977, Anomalous uranium concentrations related to paleo-drainage system in the Pliocene Ogallala Formation in southwestern Kansas [abs.]: Geol. Soc. America Abs. with Programs, v. 9, p. 708.

BOLES, J. R., 1972, Composition, optical properties, cell dimensions, and thermal stability of some heulandite group zeolites: Am. Mineralogist, v. 57, p. 1463–1493.

BRADLEY, E., 1956, Geology and groundwater resources of the upper Niobrara River Basin, Nebraska and Wyoming: U.S. Geol. Survey Water-Supply Paper 1368, 70 p.

CLARK, J., BEERBOWER, J. R., AND KIETZKE, K. K., 1967, Oligocene sedimentation, stratigraphy, paleoecology and paleoclimatology in the Big Badlands of South Dakota: Fieldiana-Geology, v. 5, p. 5–158.

CONDRA, G. E., AND REED, E. C., 1943, The geological section of Nebraska: Nebraska Geol. Survey Bull. 15A, 82 p.

DARTON, N. H., 1899, Preliminary report on the geology and water resources of Nebraska west of the one hundred and third meridian: U.S. Geol. Survey Prof. Paper 19, p. 1–69.

——, BLACKWELDER, E., AND SIEBENTHAL, C. E., 1910, Laramie-Sherman, Wyoming: U.S. Geol. Survey Folio 173, 18 p.

DEMIREL, T., EROL, O., AND LOHNES, A., 1975, Fabric of sodium montmorillonite as shown by stereo micrographs [abs.]: Geol. Soc. America Abs. with Programs, v. 7, p. 1049–1050.

DENSON, N. H., AND BERGENDAHL, N. H., 1961, Middle and Upper Tertiary rocks of southeastern Wyoming and adjoining areas: U.S. Geol. Survey Prof. Paper 424-C, p. 168–172.

——, AND BOTINELLY, T., 1949, Geology of the Hartville Uplift, eastern Wyoming: U.S. Geol. Survey Oil and Gas Inv. Prelim. Map 102.

ELDER, J. A., 1969, Soils of Nebraska: Univ. Nebraska Conservation and Survey Div. Resources Rept. 2, 60 p.

ELIAS, M. K., 1942, Tertiary prairie grasses and other herbs from the High Plains: Geol. Soc. America Spec. Paper 41, 176 p.

—— AND LUGN, A. L., 1939, Late Tertiary environment in a portion of the High Plains: Geol. Soc. America Bull., v. 50, p. 1907–1908.

FAURE, G., AND POWELL, J. L., 1972, Strontium isotope geology: New York, Springer-Verlag, 188 p.

FOLK, R. L., 1968, Petrology of sedimentary rocks: Austin, Texas, Hemphill's, 170 p.

FRYE, J. C., GLASS, N. D., LEONARD, A. B., AND COLEMAN, C. D., 1974, Caliche and clay mineral zonation of Ogallala Formation, central-eastern New Mexico: New Mexico Bur. Mines and Mineral Resources Circ. 144, 16 p.

GALLOWAY, W. E., MURPHY, T. D., BELCHER, R. C., JOHNSON, B. D., AND SUTTON, S., 1977, Catahoula Formation of the Texas coastal plain: Depositional systems, composition, structural development, ground-water flow history, and uranium distribution: Texas Univ. Bur. Econ. Geology Rept. Inv. 87, 59 p.

GARNER, H. F., 1959, Stratigraphic-sedimentary significance of contemporary climate and relief in four regions of the Andes Mountains: Geol. Soc. America Bull., v. 70, p. 1327–1368.

HAY, R. L., 1970, Silicate reactions in three lithofacies of a semi-arid basin, Olduvai Gorge, Tanzania: Mineralog. Soc. America Spec. Paper 3, p. 237–255.

——, 1976, Geology of the Olduvai Gorge: Berkeley, California, Univ. California Press, 203 p.

HILLS, F. A., GAST, P. W., HOUSTON, R. S., AND SWAINBANK, I. G., 1968, Precambrian geochronology of the Medicine Bow Mountains, southeastern Wyoming: Geol. Soc. America Bull., v. 79, p. 1757–1784.

KEECH, C. F., AND BENTALL, RAY, 1971, Dunes on the plains, the Sand Hills region of Nebraska: Univ. Nebraska Conservation and Survey Div. Resources Rept. 4, 18 p.

LANGMUIR, D., 1971, The geochemistry of some carbonate ground-waters in central Pennsylvania: Geochim. et Cosmochim. Acta, v. 35, p. 1023–1045.

LILLENGRAVEN, J. A., 1970, Stratigraphy, structure and vertebrate fossils of the Oligocene Brule Formation, Slim Buttes, northwestern South Dakota: Geol. Soc. America Bull., v. 81, 831–850.

LOVERING, T. S., 1929, The geologic history of the Front Range, Colorado: Colorado Sci. Soc. Proc., v. 12, p. 59–111.

LOWRY, M. E., AND CHRIST, M. A., 1967, Geology and ground-water resources of Laramie County, Wyoming: U.S. Geol. Survey Water-Supply Paper 1834, 71 p.

LUGN, A. L., 1939, Classification of the Tertiary System in Nebraska: Geol. Soc. America Bull., v. 50, p. 1245–1276.

—— AND LUGN, R. V., 1956, The general Tertiary geomorphology and sedimentation in Nebraska and the northern Great Plains: Compass, v. 33, p. 98–114.

MATTHEW, W. D., 1901, Fossil mammals of the Tertiary of northeastern Colorado: Am. Museum Natural History Mem. 1, p. 355–447.

McBRIDE, E. F., LINDEMANN, W. L., AND FREEMAN, P. S., 1968, Lithology and petrology of the Gueydan (Catahoula) Formation is south Texas: Texas Univ. Bur. Econ. Geology Rept. Inv. 63, 122 p.

McGREW, L. W., 1963, Geology of the Fort Laramie area, Platte and Goshen Counties, Wyoming: U.S. Geol. Survey Bull. 1141-F, p. F1–F39.

——, 1967a, Geologic map of the Natwick SW Quadrangle, Platte County, Wyoming: U.S. Geol. Survey Geol. Quad. Map GQ-623.

——, 1967b, Geologic map of the Natwick Quadrangle, Platte County, Wyoming: U.S. Geol. Survey Geol. Quad. Map GQ-624.

——, 1967c, Geologic map of the Richeau Hills Quadrangle, Platte County, Wyoming: U.S. Geol. Survey Geol. Quad. Map GQ-625.

——, 1967d, Geologic map of the Wheatland NE Quadrangle, Platte County, Wyoming: U.S. Geol. Survey Geol. Quad. Map GQ-628.

McGREW, P. O., 1953, Tertiary deposits of southeastern Wyoming: Wyoming Geol. Assoc. Guidebook 8th Ann. Field Conf., p. 61–64.

McGUINNESS, C. L., 1963, The role of groundwater in the national water situation: U.S. Geol. Survey Water-Supply Paper 1800, 1121 p.

MITCHELL, R. S., AND TUFTS, SUSAN, 1973, Wood opal—A tridymite-like mineral: Am. Mineralogist, v. 58, p. 717–720.

NORTON, D., 1974, Chemical mass transfer in the Rio Tanama system, west-central Puerto Rico: Geochim. et Cosmochim. Acta, v. 38, p. 267–277.

OSTERWALD, F. W., AND DEAN, B. G., 1957, Preliminary tectonic map of northern Colorado and northeastern Utah showing distribution of uranium deposits: U.S. Geol. Survey Mineral Inv. Map MF-130.

PETERMAN, Z. E., AND HEDGE, C. E., 1968, Chronology of Precambrian events in the Front Range, Colorado: Canadian Jour. Earth Sci., v. 5, p. 749–756.

——, —— AND TOURTELOT, H. A., 1970, Isotopic composition of strontium in sea water throughout Phanerozoic time: Geochim. et Cosmochim. Acta, v. 34, p. 105–120.

PETTYJOHN, W. A., 1966, Eocene paleosol in the northern Great Plains: U.S. Geol. Survey Prof. Paper 550-C, p. 61–65.

RAHN, P. H., AND PAUL, H. A., 1975, Hydrology of a portion of the Sand Hills and Ogallala aquifer, South Dakota and Nebraska: Groundwater, v. 13, p. 428–437.

RAPP, J. R., VISHER, F. N., AND LITTLETON, R. T., 1957, Geology and ground-water resources of Goshen County, Wyoming: U.S. Geol. Survey Water-Supply Paper 1377, 145 p.

REYNOLDS, R. C., JR., AND HOWER, JOHN, 1970, The nature of interlayering in mixed-layer illite-montmorillonites: Clays and clay minerals, v. 18, p. 25–36.

SATO, Y., AND DENSON, N. H., 1967, Volcanism and tectonism as reflected by the distribution of nonopaque heavy minerals in some Tertiary rocks of Wyoming and adjacent states: U.S. Geol. Survey Prof. Paper 575-C, p. 42–54.

SCHLAIKJER, E. M., 1935, Contributions to the stratigraphy and paleontology of the Goshen Hole area, Wyoming: Harvard Univ. Museum Comparative Zoology Bull., v. 76, p. 71–189.

SCHULTZ, C. B., 1941, The pipy concretions of the Arikaree: Nebraska Univ. State Museum Bull., v. 2, p. 69–82.

——, 1961, Field conference on the Tertiary and Pleistocene of western Nebraska: Nebraska Univ. State Museum Spec. Pub. 2, 55 p.

SMITH, F. A., AND SOUDERS, V. L., 1975, Groundwater geology of Banner County, Nebraska: Univ. Nebraska Conservation and Survey Div., 96 p.

SMITHSON, S. B., AND HODGE, D. S., 1972, Field relations and gravity interpretations in the Laramie anorthosite complex: Wyoming Univ. Contr. Geology, v. 11, p. 43–59.

SNIEGOCKI, R. T., 1959, Geologic and groundwater reconnaissance of the Loup River drainage basin in Nebraska: U.S. Geol. Survey Water-Supply Paper 1493, 106 p.

STANLEY, K. O., 1971, Tectonic implications of Tertiary sediment dispersal on the Great Plains east of the Laramie Range: Wyoming Geol. Assoc. Guidebook 23d Ann. Field Conf., p. 65–70.

——, 1976, Sandstone petrofacies in the Cenozoic High Plains sequence, eastern Wyoming and Nebraska: Geol. Soc. America Bull., v. 87, p. 297–309.

—— AND WAYNE, W. J., 1972, Epeirogenic and climatic control of early Pleistocene fluvial sediment dispersal in Nebraska: Geol. Soc. America Bull., v. 83, p. 3675–3690.

SWINEFORD, ADA, FRYE, JOHN, AND LEONARD, A. B., 1955, Petrography of the late Tertiary volcanic ash falls in the central Great Plains: Jour. Sed. Petrology, v. 25, p. 243–261.

TARDY, Y., 1971, Characterization of the principal weathering types by the geochemistry of waters from European and African crystalline massifs: Chem. Geology, v. 7, p. 253–271.

TAYLOR, J. M., 1970, Pore-space reduction in sandstone: Am. Assoc. Petroleum Geologists Bull., v. 34, p. 701–716.

VAN HOUTEN, F. B., 1957, Tertiary rocks of southern Wind River Basin area, central Wyoming: Wyoming Geol. Assoc. Guidebook 12th Ann. Field Conf., p. 79–88.

VONDRA, C. F., SCHULTZ, C. B., AND STOUT, T. M., 1969, New members of the Gering Formation (Miocene) in western Nebraska, including a geological map of Wildcat Ridge and related outliers: Nebraska Geol. Survey Paper, sec. 2, no. 18, 18 p.

WALKER T. R., 1967, Formation of red beds in modern and ancient deserts: Geol. Soc. America Bull., v. 78, p. 353–368.

——, 1976, Diagenetic origin of continental red beds, *in* H. Falke (ed.), The continental Permian in central, west, and south.Europe: Dordrecht, Holland, D. Reidel Pub. Co., p. 240–282.

——, RIBBE, P. H., AND HONEA, R. M., 1967, Geochemistry of hornblende alteration in Pliocene red beds, Baja California, Mexico: Geol. Soc. America Bull., v. 78, p. 1055–1060.

WALTON, A. W., 1975, Zeolitic diagenesis in Oligocene volcanic sediments, Trans-Pecos Texas: Geol. Soc. America Bull., v. 86, p. 615–624.

WANLESS, H. R., 1922, Lithology of the White River sediment: Am. Philos. Soc. Proc., v. 61, p. 184–203.

——, 1923, The stratigraphy of the White River beds of South Dakota: Am. Philos. Soc. Proc., v. 62, p. 190–269.

WENZEL, L, K., CADY, R. C., AND WAITE, H. A., 1946, Geology and groundwater resources of Scotts Bluff County, Nebraska: U.S. Geol. Survey Water-Supply Paper 943, 150 p.

SEPM Special Publication No. 26, p. 425–443, March 1979

PARAGENESIS OF DIAGENETIC MINERALS IN THE ST. PETER SANDSTONE (ORDOVICIAN), WISCONSIN AND ILLINOIS

I. EDGAR ODOM, TIMOTHY N. WILLAND AND RICHARD J. LASSIN

Northern Illinois University, DeKalb, 60115

ABSTRACT

Mineralogical analyses of the silt- and clay-size fractions and detailed SEM studies of whole rock samples show that diagenetic minerals in the St. Peter Sandstone formed in essentially five separate stages. The first stage, beginning after compaction, involved the precipitation of K-feldspar in selected pore spaces, and the precipitation of quartz as a thin, conformable envelope on quartz grain surfaces not in contact with other grains. During the second stage illite and locally smectite and chlorite were precipitated, sometimes with dolomite and calcite. A mixed layer clay, which is occasionally present, is believed to be an alteration product of illite. The third stage is marked by development of terminated (euhedral to subhedral) quartz overgrowths. Faces of terminated overgrowths are nearly always free of clay minerals, dolomite and calcite. The fourth stage is the formation of pyrite. The fifth stage is the development of kaolinite which does not appear to have formed directly from the alteration of K-feldspar.

The authigenic mineral suite and paragenetic sequence record a pronounced change in the chemistry of the pore fluids through time. The early precipitation of K-feldspar and quartz indicates that the pore fluids had a high K/H ratio and silica content. The K/H ratio decreased through time to bring the pore fluid chemistry in equilibrium with illite, smectite, and chlorite. A high silica concentration in the pore fluids, not attributable to pressure solution, existed after the illite stage. The ionic content of these pore fluids was higher than that of fresh water because terminated quartz overgrowths and pyrite, both of which were precipitated from these fluids, occur where the St. Peter presently contains saline pore fluids. Diagenetic kaolinite is observed only where fresh water has invaded the St. Peter.

Most, if not all, of the authigenic minerals in the St. Peter were precipitated from migrating pore fluids. The source of cations may be related to high salinity conditions during the deposition of overlying and underlying carbonates, the dissolution of silica during carbonate diagenesis, and the later *in situ* alteration of potassium silicates.

INTRODUCTION

The senior author's interest in the diagenetic history of the St. Peter Sandstone was aroused in 1971, upon discovery that K-feldspar was a frequent component of the silt-size and sometimes the clay-size fractions and that the clay mineral composition was recognized as quite variable from place to place. To date, detailed mineral analyses and SEM studies have been made on more than 30 outcrop and subsurface sections, and additional work is in progress. This paper reports some of the initial results and interpretations.

Diagenetic minerals form in sandstones from either the alteration of pre-existing minerals or the direct precipitation from connate or migrating pore fluids. In immature sandstones it is often difficult to determine paragenetic relations between diagenetic phases, and whether cations were derived from unstable minerals, pore fluids or both. The "clean", mature nature of the St. Peter Sandstone, however, is well known, and the formation is an important source of flint-grade glass sand. This sandstone is usually white, well sorted, fine- to medium-grained and friable, with a primary mineralogy of >99% quartz. The virtual absence of detrital, unstable minerals requires that

the cations for at least the early-formed authigenic minerals now present in the St. Peter be derived from connate or migrating pore fluids.

The St. Peter Sandstone outcrops over a wide area of western Wisconsin, eastern Minnesota, and northeastern Iowa, and isolated exposures occur in central Missouri and northern Illinois. The St. Peter and equivalents extend in the subsurface from Michigan to Oklahoma and eastward to Virginia. The regional stratigraphy and texture of the St. Peter have been described by Lamar (1928) and Dapples (1955). The detailed stratigraphy of the St. Peter and intertonguing Glenwood Formations in Illinois and Wisconsin have been described in detail by Templeton and William (1963) and Fraser (1976). In Illinois and Wisconsin, the formation is divided into three members which are, in ascending order, the Kress (Readstown in Wisconsin), Tonti, and Starved Rock. The Starved Rock Member occurs primarily in Illinois where the Glenwood Formation is absent.

The objectives of this study are to determine the paragenesis of authigenic minerals present in the St. Peter and to attempt to reconstruct, from the diagenetic mineral suite and the paragenetic

Copyright © 1979, The Society of Economic
Paleontologists and Mineralogists

sequence, the geochemical nature of pore fluids through time. To our knowledge, this is the first attempt to make paragenetic interpretations of a large authigenic mineral suite and to attempt to relate paragenesis to pore fluid geochemistry.

METHODS OF STUDY

Five hundred to 1000 grams of each sample were disaggregated with an ultrasonic probe, and the combined silt- and clay-size fractions were removed by sedimentation procedures. The silt (<44 microns) and clay (<2 microns) fractions were then separated, also by sedimentation. Core samples were evaluated to be certain that no drilling mud had penetrated the portion of the core studied. The mineralogy of each size fraction was determined by X-ray diffraction methods. Sedimented slides were prepared of the clay-size fraction and placed in an ethylene glycol atmosphere for 60 hours prior to X-ray examination. An X-ray powder pattern was run on the silt-size fraction after grinding to a suitable fineness.

The relative abundance of clay minerals was evaluated by a procedure modified from Grim, Bray, and Bradley (1937), which expresses the abundance of each clay mineral in terms of its contribution to the total diffraction effects. This procedure does not express the volume percent of an individual clay mineral. For example, the kaolinite that occurs in St. Peter Sandstone is very well crystallized. Although the illite is also well crystallized, a relatively larger volume of illite is required to produce the same diffraction effects as the kaolinite. The relative abundance of feldspar in the silt faction was evaluated by comparing the intensity of the strongest feldspar line occurring between 3.24 Å and 3.28 Å to the (100) quartz peak. This ratio (F/Q) is shown in subsequent illustrations as is the intensity of the strongest feldspar line (F).

The X-ray analyses were used to select samples for further study with a scanning electron microscope to determine paragenetic relations. An approximately 1 cm square fragment was mounted on a brass stud, coated with a gold palladium alloy and examined with a JOEL JXA-50A scanning electron microscope. The chemical composition of the feldspar in a few samples was determined with an electron microprobe.

RESULTS

The outcrop and core sections discussed in this paper are those that best illustrate our present understanding of the mineralogy, mineral paragenesis, and diagenetic history of the St. Peter Sandstone (Fig. 1). In the following descriptions, the term neoformation refers to mineral formation

by precipitation from pore fluids, whereas the term transformation refers to mineral formation resulting from the chemical and structural alteration of a pre-existing mineral. The term encrusting is used to describe a thin coating of authigenic quartz, whereas the term incipient is used to describe the development of very small crystal faces on the encrusting quartz. Quartz overgrowths showing well developed rhombohedral crystal faces are referred to as terminated. Mixed-layer material refers to a regular, interstratified illite-smectite with a basal spacing of approximately 11.5 Å after glycol saturation. Authigenic jarosite, alunite, gypsum and lepidocrocite which are found occasionally in outcrop sections are not discussed because their origin is related to modern weathering.

OUTCROP SECTION, HANOVER, WISCONSIN

At Hanover, Wisconsin about 90 feet of the St. Peter are exposed in an active silica sand quarry (Fig. 2). The St. Peter is overlain by a few feet of Glenwood Shale, which is overlain in turn by the Platteville Dolomite. The St. Peter section includes 85 feet of the Tonti Member which is underlain by 5–6 feet of interbedded

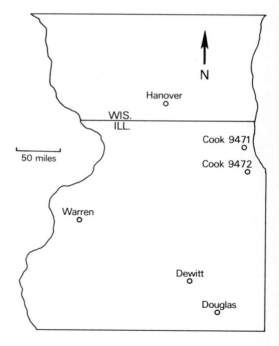

Fig. 1.—Location of described outcrop and core samples.

siltstone, sandstone and shale assigned to the Readstown Member.

Mineralogy of the Tonti Member.—The Tonti is composed of >99% detrital quartz. The authigenic minerals present are K-feldspar, illite, kaolinite, and quartz. The outstanding feature of the

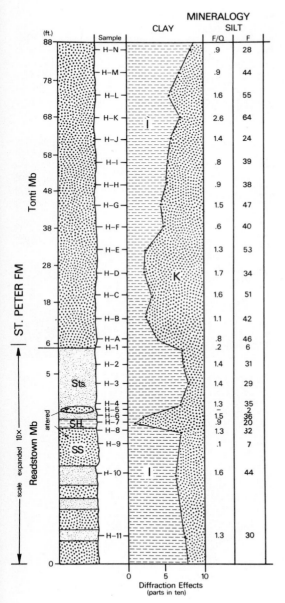

FIG. 2.—Mineralogy of the silt and clay size fractions from the St. Peter at Hanover, Wisconsin. I = illite; K = kaolinite.

Hanover section is that the silt fraction of the Tonti and especially the siltstones in the Readstown contain a large amount of authigenic K-feldspar (Fig. 2).

Throughout the Tonti, K-feldspar occurs as euhedral to subhedral crystals ranging from 5 to 100 microns in size. The crystal form is often modified by concave outlines and impressions where crystals are in contact with quartz grains (Fig. 3A). These characteristics, which are identical at all localities studied, indicate that the feldspar developed epigenetically. The feldspar crystals have a monoclinic morphology—the monoclinic structure is verified by X-ray diffraction data. The crystals grew most rapidly in the c and a axial directions, and a,b, and c pinacoids are usually well developed (Fig. 3B). The 101 and 10$\bar{1}$ faces, when developed, have an etched appearance (Fig. 3B), but this characteristic is believed to be a growth feature unrelated to solution. All feldspar crystals show some degree of dissolution and transformation to illite (illitiation). The solution is most pronounced in the a–b crystallographic plane (Fig. 3B). The amount of feldspar transformed to illite is greatest in the upper part of the Tonti where the amount of illite is greatest. Small amounts of diagenetic illite also occur along the contacts between quartz grains (Fig. 3C).

In the Tonti Member, kaolinite occurs entirely as euhedral crystal groups (Fig. 3D). Unlike illite, the kaolinite distribution does not seem related to any particular mineralogical or physical feature (Fig. 4D).

Quartz overgrowths are abundant throughout the Tonti. Encrusting and incipient overgrowths occur on the surfaces of all grains (Fig. 3E, F) and are solely responsible for the frosted appearance of St. Peter sand grains. Terminated quartz overgrowths are also common in some samples and often engulf feldspar crystals (Fig. 4A). The quartz overgrowths are not interlocking; thus the St. Peter Sandstone at Hanover is quite friable. The faces of terminated overgrowths are free of mineral material, except where overlapped by the edges of kaolinite crystals (Fig. 4B). There has been only a small amount of pressure solution at quartz-grain contacts (Fig. 3C).

Paragenesis of authigenic materials in the Tonti Member.—Feldspar appears to be the first authigenic mineral to form in the Tonti. The reason that feldspar crystals developed in selected pore spaces is not apparent, although some crystals are sufficiently large to suggest that they formed on a detrital feldspar. Although some illite has formed around pressure-solution features, the primary development of the illite now present occurred when the pH and chemical composition

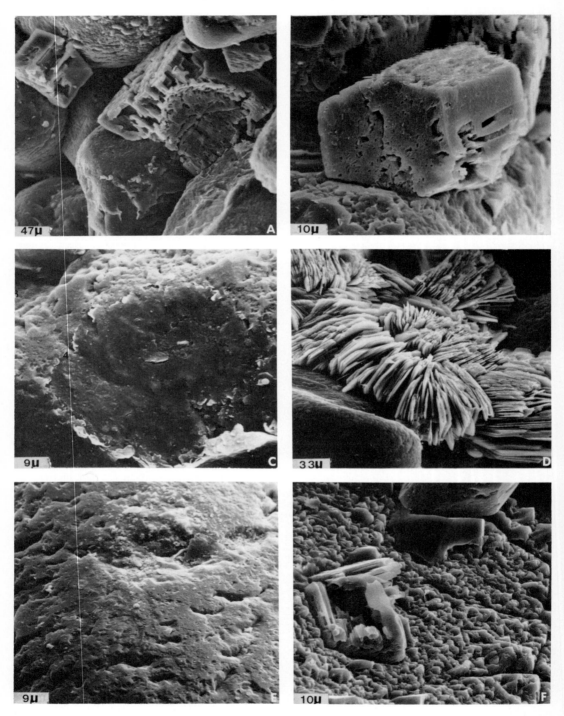

Fig. 3.—SEM photomicrographs showing authigenic minerals in the St. Peter (Tonti Member) at Hanover, Wisconsin. *A*, Feldspar crystal showing impression of neighboring quartz grain; *B*, feldspar crystal showing euhedral form and roughness of 101 face; *C*, illite around pressure solution pit; *D*, Euhedral kaolinite; *E*, nature of encrusting quartz overgrowth; *F*, nature of incipient overgrowths and lineage boundary intersecting quartz-grain surface (lower right).

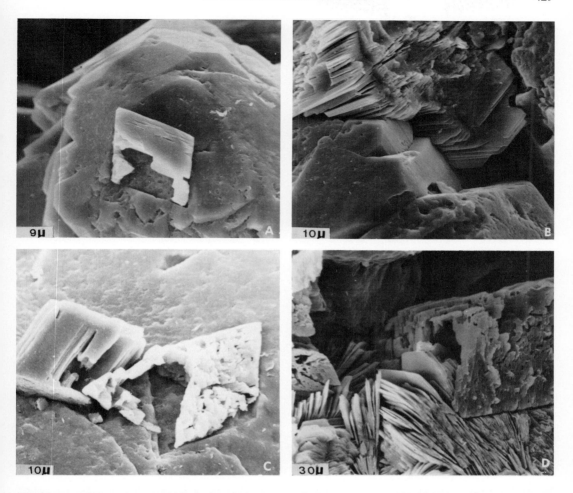

FIG. 4.—SEM photomicrographs showing authigenic minerals in St. Peter (Tonti Member) at Hanover, Wisconsin. *A,* Terminated quartz overgrowth engulfing partially dissolved feldspar crystal; *B,* kaolinite overlapping terminated quartz overgrowth; *C,* thickness of encrusting quartz overgrowth; *D,* kaolinite developed around K-feldspar.

of the pore fluids permitted K-feldspar alteration. The nature of illite occurrence in subsurface sections described later suggests that some illite has been dissolved from this outcrop section. The time of formation of the encrusting quartz overgrowths cannot be precisely established other than that it superceded the initial phase of K-feldspar formation (Fig. 3F) and preceded the neoformation of illite around pressure solution features (Fig. 3C). In most cases, the terminated quartz overgrowths formed before kaolinite (Fig. 4B).

It is especially noteworthy that in no case is kaolinite observed to be forming on the surface of, or at the site of, altered K-feldspar. Although kaolinite has developed near, beside, or even partially surrounding K-feldspar (Fig. 4D), there is no evidence of the formation of kaolinite from an alumina-silica residue derived from the weathering of K-feldspar. Illite that is forming on the surface of feldspar appears to be metastable—it is being dissolved rather than altering to kaolinite.

Mineralogy of the Readstown Member.—The Readstown beds at Hanover contain one of several known occurrences of large amounts of K-feldspar directly below the quartz sandstones of the Tonti Member (Fig. 2). The Hanover K-feldspar occurrence was first described by H. H. Woodard (1972). Although the ratio of quartz to feldspar in the silt fraction from this sequence is similar to that in the overlying Tonti, the total volume

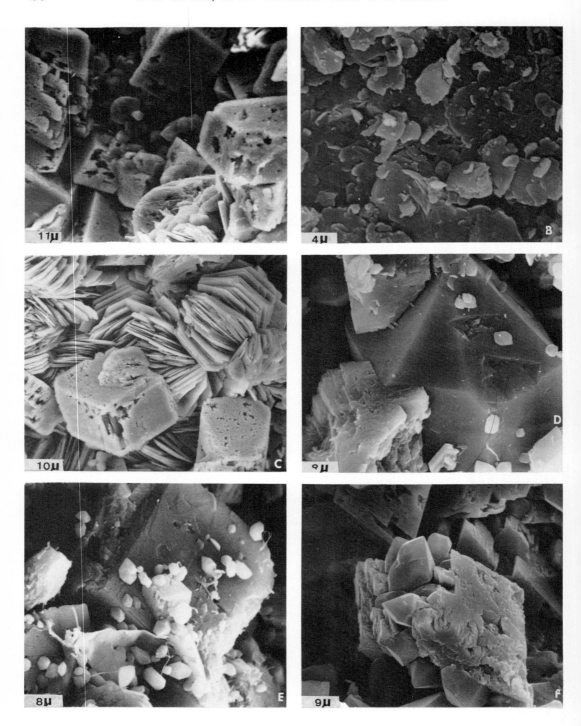

F<small>IG</small>. 5.—SEM photomicrographs of authigenic minerals in the St. Peter (Readstown member), Hanover, Wisconsin. *A*, Euhedral K-feldspar; *B*, kaolinite in shale unit; *C*, euhedral kaolinite and K-feldspar; *D*, authigenic K-feldspar formed after terminated quartz overgrowth; *E*, slightly illitized K-feldspar; *F*, doubly terminated quartz crystals developed within partially dissolved K-feldspar.

of feldspar in the siltstone units is at least 50 percent (Fig. 2).

The upper 2.5 feet of the Readstown consists of pinkish siltstone with sandstone lenses increasing toward the bottom. These siltstones contain ripple marks, slickensides, and soft-sediment deformation structures. The upper siltstone sequence is underlain by a few inches of laminated shale. Sandstones immediately above and for 1.5 feet below the shale are contorted and locally altered to soft, powdery silica. This altered zone is underlain by approximately 2 feet of alternating sandstone and highly feldspathic siltstone.

Most of the feldspar in this sequence shows a moderate degree of solution (Fig. 5A), and in some zones the feldspar is appreciably illitized. Kaolinite crystals are present in both siltstones and sandstones, but again their occurrence is not directly associated with altered feldspar (Fig. 5C). The thin shale unit contains a large amount of kaolinite, but the crystals are irregular (Fig. 5B). Large terminated overgrowths and numerous small, doubly terminated quartz crystals are dispersed through the feldspathic siltstones and sandstones (Fig. 5D). The quartz sandstones in the altered zone contain many small, doubly terminated quartz crystals (Fig. 5E).

Paragenesis of authigenic minerals in the Readstown Member.—The paragenetic sequence in the Readstown is (1) K-feldspar, (2) encrusting and terminated quartz overgrowths, (3) K-feldspar, (4) illitization of feldspar, (5) kaolinite and (6) small euhedral quartz crystals. The second phase (3) of feldspar formation (Fig. 5) is believed to coincide with the initial alteration of the interbedded sandstones. It is interesting that thin laminae of K-feldspar present in the altered sandstones are only partially illitized. Although illitic shales are common elsewhere in the Readstown, no other kaolinitic shales have been observed. This and its irregular crystal morphology suggest that the kaolinite is the thin shale associated with the altered sandstones formed from the alteration of illite.

CORES 9471 AND 9472, COOK COUNTY, ILLINOIS

Mineralogy.—Although these two cores are just 25 miles apart, they are very different in mineralogy. Core 9471 (Fig. 6), the northernmost of the two, includes a sandstone at the top with bimodal grain-size distribution and believed to be the Starved Rock Member. It contains illite throughout, kaolinite near the top and smectite and mixed layer material in lower part (Fig. 6). Clusters of pyrite crystals are present throughout. Dolomite is present in sample 794.5 (Fig. 6). Feldspar is abundant in the Starved Rock but is absent in the Tonti (Fig. 6).

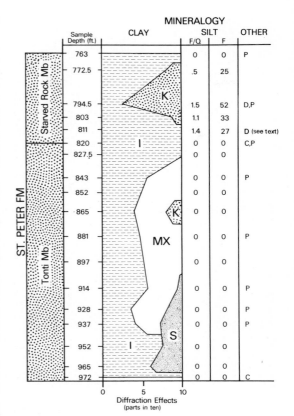

FIG. 6.—Mineralogy of the silt and clay size fractions from the St. Peter Sandstone-Core 9471, Cook County, Illinois. I = illite; K-kaolinite, MX = mixed-layer; S = smectite; P = pyrite; D = dolomite; C = calcite.

In core 9472 (Fig. 8) much kaolinite is associated with illite, smectite, and mixed-layer material throughout. Feldspar was detected only in the upper three samples, being most abundant in sample 862. Clusters of pyrite occur throughout the core.

Paragenesis of authigenic materials in core 9471.—Feldspar was the first authigenic mineral to form, but it is restricted to the Starved Rock Member. Illite has formed around pressure-solution features (Fig. 7F), on the surface of quartz grains (Fig. 7C), and through the illitization of feldspar (Fig. 7D). The kaolinite in samples 772.5–803 occurs as distinct crystal clusters (Fig. 7E) as it does in the Hanover section, and again it is not directly associated with feldspar or other clay minerals. It is not clear whether the smectite in samples 914–965 is neoformed or is the result of illite alteration, however, the nearly complete collapse of the mixed-layer material on potassium saturation suggests that it is a product of illite

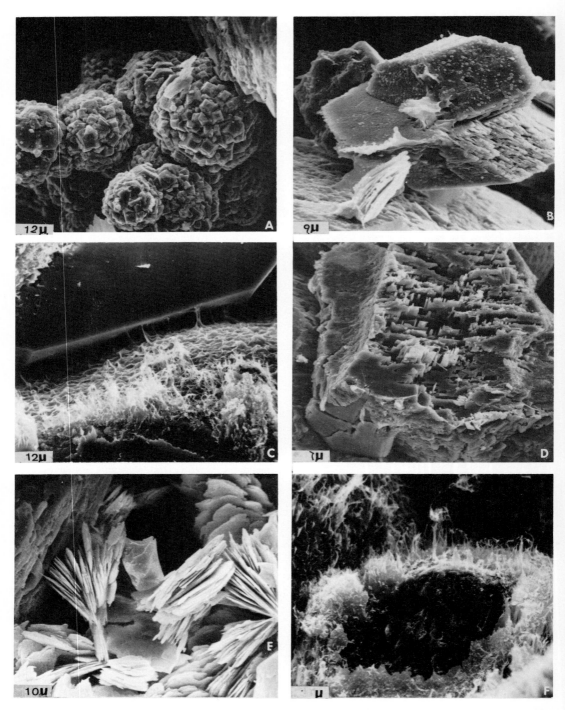

Fɪɢ. 7.—SEM photomicrographs of authigenic minerals in Core 9471, Cook County, Illinois. *A*, Samll kaolinite crystals on authigenic pyrite; *B*, K-feldspar, kaolinite and incipient quartz overgrowths; *C*, filament-like illite around pressure-solution pit, on surface of encrusting quartz overgrowth, and bridging to terminate overgrowth; *D*, partially illitized and dissolved F-feldspar with quartz-grain impression on left; *E*, euhedral kaolinite; *F*, illite formed around pressure-solution pit.

alteration. The dolomite in sample 794.5 is associated with illite, and we assume that they formed essentially simultaneously. The detrital quartz grains all contain some degree of encrusting and incipient overgrowth development (Fig. 7B). The encrusting overgrowths are often coated with illite (Fig. 7C). Terminated quartz overgrowths are abundant only in samples 974.5 and 865 and are without clay coatings. Figure 7C shows a rare instance of illite bridging to a terminated quartz overgrowth.

Evidenced that pyrite in core 9471 formed before kaolinite is shown by the presence of kaolinite on pyrite crystals (Fig. 7A).

The proposed paragenetic sequence in core 9471 is (1) K-feldspar, (2) encrusting quartz overgrowths, (3) illite-smectite-dolomite, (4) terminated quartz overgrowths, (5) pyrite and (6) kaolinite. The mixed-layer material and possibly smectite may be transformation products from illite. Some illite, mixed-layer material or smectitie continued to form after the euhedral quartz developed (Fig. 7C).

Paragenesis of authigenic minerals in core 9472.—The feldspar grains observed near the top of the core formed first and in general are more illitized than in core 9471 (Fig. 9A). We were not able to differentiate between illite, mixed-layer material, and smectite in the SEM studies, so that their exact paragenetic relation is inconclusive. These clay minerals occur as coatings on

encrusting overgrowths and bridge between quartz grains (Fig. 9B). In sample 862, kaolinite occurs in euhedral crystal clusters (Fig. 9c), but in stratigraphically lower samples it also occurs as vermicular-shaped crystals within masses of illite and smectite (Fig. 9D). The vermicular form of kaolinite is rare. In some cases, what appears to be filament-like illite occurs on the kaolinite (Fig. 9E).

Encrusting and incipient overgrowths occur on all quartz grains (Fig. 9F) and terminated quartz overgrowths are abundant in samples with low clay content. The faces of terminated quartz overgrowths are usually free of mineral material (Fig. 9D). Pyrite is observed resting on the terminated quartz overgrowths, and kaolinite is observed resting on pyrite crystals. The proposed paragenetic sequence in core 9472 is (1) K-feldspar, (2) encrusting quartz overgrowths, (3) illite-smectite, (4) euhedral quartz overgrowths, (5) pyrite, (6) kaolinite and (7) illite (?). It is probable that the mixed-layer material is a transformation product from illite. Although some illite formed through the illitization of feldspar, most is neoformed as are the quartz overgrowths, pyrite and kaolinite. The apparent illite which formed after the development of terminated overgrowths and kaolinite (Fig. 9E) may be related to potassium released during feldspar alteration.

CORE 6251, DEWITT COUNTY, ILLINOIS

Mineralogy.—The DeWitt core is notable because it contains abundant illite as well as smectite and chlorite. There is no kaolinite, practically no mixed-layer material, and feldspar is also not very abundant (Fig. 10). There is no evidence that detrital clay minerals were initially present. The K-feldspar present has undergone considerable solution and illitization (Fig. 11A). Neoformed illite and presumably smectite and chlorite occur around pressure-solution features (Fig. 11B), lining pores (Fig. 11C), and on the surface of encrusting overgrowths (Fig. 11D), but most terminated overgrowths are free of mineral material (Fig. 11C). Pyrite is randomly distributed but is most abundant near the top and bottom of the section.

Paragenesis of authigenic materials.—As in other core and outcrop sections, K-feldspar was the initial authigenic mineral formed, followed by encrusting quartz overgrowths. Most of the illite and presumably smectite and chlorite formed after the feldspar and encrusting overgrowths but before terminated quartz overgrowths. Illite, dolomite, calcite, smectite and chlorite appear to have formed simultaneously. Pyrite is the last authigenic mineral formed, although illite is transformed from K-feldspar. Minor illite crystal

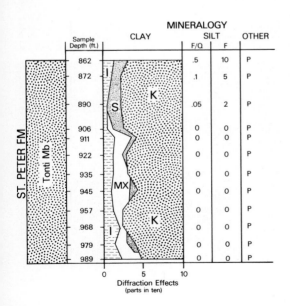

FIG. 8.—Mineralogy of silt-and clay-size fractions from the St. Peter Sandstone-Core 9472, Cook County, Illinois. I = illite; K = kaolinite; MX = mixed-layer material; S = smectite; P = pyrite.

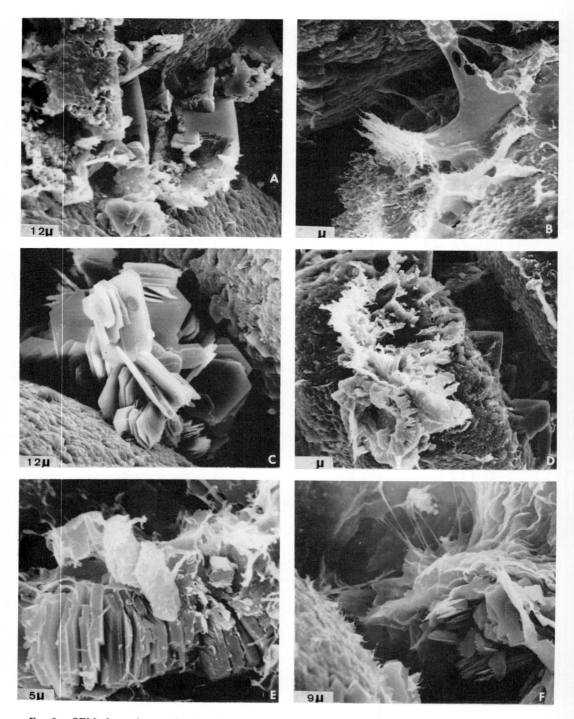

FIG. 9.—SEM photomicrographs of authigenic minerals in Core 9472, Cook County, Illinois. *A*, Illitized and dissolved K-feldspar; *B*, illite on encrusting quartz overgrowths and around pressure-solution pit; *C*, euhedral kaolinite on incipient quartz overgrowths; *D*, vermicular kaolinite associated with illite-smectite and "clean", terminated quartz overgrowths; *E*, vermicular kaolinite developed within illite (?); *F*, kaolinite associated with filament-like illite.

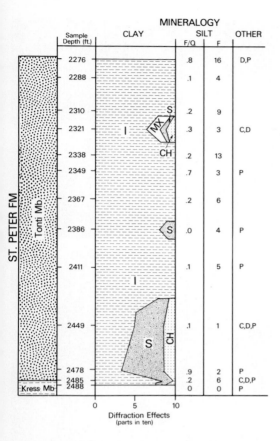

FIG. 10.—Mineralogy of silt- and clay-size fractions from the St. Peter Sandstone-DeWitt County, Illinois. I = illite; MX = mixed-layer material; CH = chlorite; S = smectite; P = pyrite; D = dolomite; C = calcite.

growth continued after the development of terminated overgrowths (Fig. 11D).

CORE 4218, DOUGLAS COUNTY, ILLINOIS

Mineralogy.—Although illite is the dominant clay mineral throughout the core, small amounts of smectite and chlorite occur near the bottom (Fig. 12). The chlorite and smectite occur only in samples containing calcite, whereas most samples contain dolomite. Feldspar is very abundant in the upper half of the core but significantly decreases in the zone containing smectite and chlorite. Pyrite is also present in small amounts in all samples.

Samples below 1556 are typical, white, St. Peter Sandstone, whereas sample 1556 and those above contain detrital illite (Fig. 13A), indicated by the presence of clay laminae in the core. Encrusting overgrowths are present on most quartz grains,

but incipient and terminated overgrowths are only sparingly abundant in samples 1509, 1533, and 1556 (Fig. 13A). This core shows evidence that detrital and authigenic clay coatings tend to inhibit terminated quartz overgrowth development (Fig. 13E). The faces of terminated overgrowths are again free of mineral material (Figs. 13B and E).

Paragenesis of authigenic materials.—Feldspar was the first authigenic mineral formed (Fig. 13C). Some of the feldspar crystals grew in pore spaces containing detrital illite which appears to have been incorporated into the feldspar (Fig. 13D). Some neoformed illite has developed in pores and on the surface of quartz grains (Fig. 13F). Feldspar shows various degrees of solution and illitization (Fig. 13C). Dolomite is always associated with illite. The chlorite and smectite near the bottom of the core could not be positively differentiated from illite in the SEM photomicrographs.

The paragenetic sequence of authigenic minerals in the Douglas County core is believed to be (1) K-feldspar, (2) encrusting quartz overgrowths, (3) illite-smectite-chlorite-dolomite-calcite, (4) terminated quartz overgrowths, and (5) pyrite. On the basis of the absence of mixed-layer material, we conclude that smectite and chlorite are neoformed as are feldspar, quartz overgrowths, and pyrite. Illite is detrital, neoformed, and transformed feldspar alteration.

CORE 7215, WARREN COUNTY, ILLINOIS

The St. Peter Sandstone in the Warren County core (Fig. 14) contains only a moderate amount of K-feldspar but appreciable amounts of illite, smectite and chlorite. A small amount of kaolinite might be present in a few samples, but it could not be clearly identified in either the X-ray or SEM studies. There is no evidence of detrital feldspar or clay minerals except at the base in sample 1166, which is a green shale containing lenses of siltstone. The shale contains only illite, whereas the siltstone contains illite and considerable euhedral, unaltered feldspar (Fig. 15A). All samples contain dolomite (Fig. 15B) and most contain calcite (Fig. 14).

Illite, smectite and chlorite could not be positively differentiated in the SEM photomicrographs. They occur around pressure-solution features (Fig. 15C), as branching forms on and between quartz grains and silt-size feldspar crystals, and on encrusting overgrowths. Terminated quartz overgrowths are so abundant in this core that the St. Peter is moderately cemented. Many feldspar grains have been nearly engulfed by these overgrowths (Fig. 15D).

Paragenesis of authigenic minerals.—As in other sections, K-feldspar formed first and was immediately followed by encrusting quartz-overgrowth development. Throughout this core there

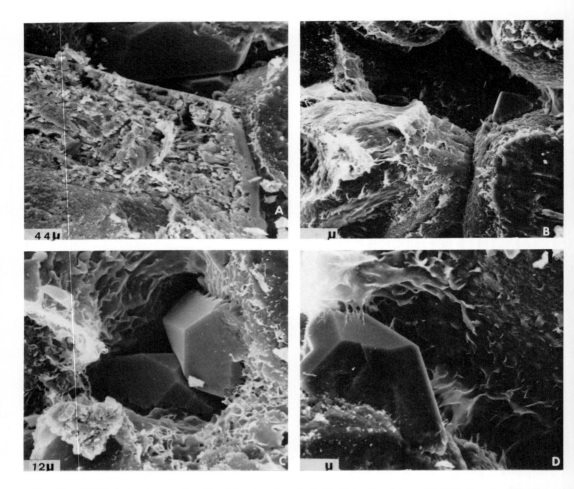

Fig. 11.—SEM photomicrographs of authigenic minerals in St. Peter Sandstone, DeWitt County, Illinois. *A,* Partially illitized and dissolved K-feldspar; *B,* illite developed on encrusting overgrowths and around pressure-solution pit; *C,* illite surrounding a pore containing "clean" terminated quartz overgrowths; *D,* illite apparently bridging to terminated overgrowth.

is evidence that illite, smectite and chlorite tend to inhibit the development of terminated quartz overgrowths (Fig. 15E). Since there is no mixed-layer phase, we make the assumption that all clay minerals are neoformed as are feldspar, quartz overgrowths, pyrite, dolomite and calcite. Feldspar shows evidence of solution and some illitization (Fig. 15F). The paragenetic sequence is (1) K-feldspar, (2) encrusting quartz overgrowths, (3) illite-smectite-chlorite-dolomite-calcite, (4) terminated quartz overgrowths, and (5) pyrite.

DISCUSSION

K-feldspar.—The amount of authigenic feldspar in the St. Peter, except locally in the Readstown, is small in amount compared to that in

Cambrian strata of the upper Mississippi Valley, but the bulk of the Cambrian authigenic feldspar occurs as overgrowths on detrital feldspar grains (Odom, 1975). Although there are small amounts of detrital feldspar in some samples of the St. Peter (Odom, Doe, and Dott, 1976), most of the K-feldspar crystals described in this study are believed to be without detrital nuclei. If nuclei are present, they are too small to be observed microscopically, and efforts to identify them by microprobe methods have proven inconclusive.

The pattern of feldspar dissolution also argues that detrital nuclei are not generally present. The dissolution is most rapid in the plane of the a–b crystallographic direction (Fig. 3B), and it is believed that this dissolution pattern would be

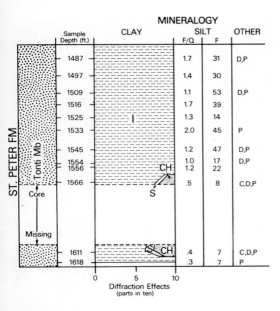

MINERALOGY

FIG. 12.—Mineralogy of silt- and clay-size fractions from the St. Peter Sandstone, Douglas County, Illinois. I = illite; S = smectite; CH = chlorite; P = pyrite; D = dolomite; C = calcite.

disrupted by detrital nuclei unless there were perfect crystallographic continuity. The overgrowths observed on detrital feldspar in the St. Peter and in the Cambrian strata are never in perfect optical continuity.

The authigenic feldspar in the St. Peter is potassium-rich (approximately 16% K_2O). There is no detectable Na or Ba. The feldspar has an adularia-like (monoclinic) morphology. Both the morphology and composition are identical to the authigenic feldspar that occurs so abundantly as overgrowths in Cambrian strata.

Quartz overgrowths.—In the St. Peter, it is apparent that an early silica phase was precipitated as a thin coating on exposed quartz-grain surfaces. The surface of this quartz has a botryoidal appearance. This early silica phase partially engulfs feldspars (Fig. 4C) and is present beneath coatings of diagenetic illite (Fig. 7C). With further silica precipitation, small projections begin to develop locally and the morphology (Fig. 3F) becomes similar to the incipient-type overgrowths described by Waugh (1970) and Pittman (1972). The presence of a thin, enveloping silica coating on grains in some West Virginia sandstones was noted by Heald (1950). The encrusting silica coating on St. Peter quartz grains is responsible for their frosted appearance, which has been cited previously as evidence for wind abrasion.

The amount of terminated quartz overgrowth development is clearly hindered by the presence of detrital clay minerals and by coatings of authigenic illite, smectite, and chlorite where these are abundant. (Fig. 15E). For terminated overgrowths to develop where clay coatings are present, incipient overgrowths must project through the coatings. Where this condition exists, the terminated overgrowths simply incorporate the clay to form a "dust ring" as observed by Heald (1956) and Pittman (1972). As an overgrowth enlarges, it first attaches to the points of incipient overgrowths. There is often unfilled space between the advancing overgrowth and the quartz grain (Fig. 11C) as previously described by Pittman (1972). The faces of terminated overgrowths are usually free of clay minerals. There is no obvious relation between the apparent degree of pressure solution and the volume of terminated overgrowths.

Pressure solution.—The significance of pressure solution in the cementation of some sandstones has been described by Heald (1950), Siever (1959), and others. In the St. Peter sections studied, the total amount of pressure solution is actually small. The amount of pressure solution is evaluated from the depth of solution pits (Pittman, 1972) and the degree of penetration of quartz grains (Heald, 1956). Both the apparent depth of solution pits and the interpenetration of grains in the St. Peter is increased by encrusting and incipient overgrowth development. The thickness of encrusting overgrowths is approximately the same as the depth of apparent pressure solution pits. Pressure solution pits also show greater relief where illite has developed around the margins of the pits (Fig. 3C). Pressure solution is not necessarily greater where clay minerals are abundant.

Paragenetic sequence.—The results previously discussed show that the paragenesis of authigenic minerals in the St. Peter is complex. The observed mineral suite and its sequence of development are, however, in general agreement with the stability relations in the K_2O-Na_2O-Al_2O_3-SiO_2-H_2O system described by Garrels and Christ (1965) and Hess (1966), and the following generalized interpretations of the pore fluid geochemistry are based largely on the work of these authors. A more comprehensive regional study of the authigenic minerals in the St. Peter is now in progress, which, it is hoped, will provide greater insight into the total geochemistry involved.

Although there is considerable regional and stratigraphic variation in the abundance and type of authigenic minerals in the St. Peter, the sequential order of mineral formation is reasonably clear. In general, the paragenesis can be divided into the following stages: (1) K-feldspar-encrust-

Fig. 13.—SEM photomicrographs of authigenic and detrital minerals in St. Peter Sandstone, Douglas County, Illinois. *A,* Detrital illite and "clean" quartz overgrowth; *B,* terminated quartz overgrowth and authigenic feldspar crystal whose shape is modified by detrital illite; *C,* impression of quartz grain in K-feldspar crystal; *D,* feldspar containing detrital(?) illite; *E,* terminated overgrowth developed over clay coating; *F,* K-feldspar associated with detrital and neoformed illite.

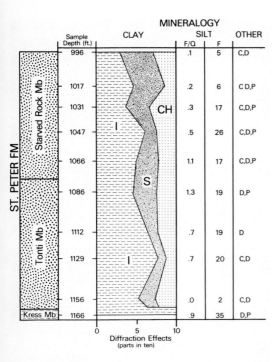

MINERALOGY

FIG. 14.—Mineralogy of the silt- and clay-size fraction from the St. Peter Sandstone, Warren County, Illinois. I = illite; S = smectite; CH = chlorite; D = dolomite; P = pyrite, C = calcite.

ing quartz overgrowths; (2) illite-smectite-chlorite-carbonate; (3) terminated quartz overgrowths; (4) pyrite; (5) kaolinite. Some of these stages, as should be expected, are transitional. As previously indicated, the precipitation of authigenic feldspar, whether as neoformed crystals or as overgrowths on detrital feldspar grains, occurred first and is a clear indication that in early diagenesis of the St. Peter the pore fluids contained at least a moderate amount of K and Al and a large amount of Si. It is believed that silica precipitated with and immediately after K-feldspar, and that both precipitated very rapidly. The early precipitation of silica suggests that the pore fluids were saturated initially with respect to amorphous silica. Although K-feldspar development was localized, silica precipitated as a thin coating on the surfaces of quartz grains not in contact with other grains to form the botryoidal-like encrusting overgrowths. It is certain that encrusting and perhaps some incipient overgrowths formed on quartz grains prior to the main stage of illite formation because illite commonly is attached to these overgrowths.

The illite stage began when the K/H ratio in

the fluids moving through the St. Peter was sufficiently low to bring the pore fluid geochemistry into the illite stability field. Undoubtedly, some illite initially began to form with K-feldspar, but the main stage of illite formation occurred later because neoformed illite often occurs around K-feldspar. Local chemical conditions may have permitted smectite and chlorite to form with or following illite, although some of the smectite in the St. Peter (Fig. 6) may be an alteration product of illite. Dolomite, when present, appears to have precipitated essentially at the same time as illite-smectite-chlorite. If Hess's interpretations of phase equilibria in the $K_2O-Na_2O-Al_2O_3-SiO_2H_2O$ system at 25° C and 1 atmosphere are applicable, the K/H and Na/H ratios ranged from slightly above to approximately the same as that of sea water during the illite phase. Although it cannot be positively demonstrated at this time, we believe the mixed-layer material is formed through the alteration of illite as the chemistry of the pore fluids changed from saline to fresh water.

The stage of terminated quartz overgrowth development occurred primarily after the illite-smectite-chlorite phase and indicates that the pore fluids contained considerable silicate but little potassium. Although some of the silica may have been derived from K-feldspar alteration and pressure solution, these sources do not seem to provide a satisfactory explanation for the large amount of terminated overgrowth development present in some sections. For example, the cementation of the St. Peter by interlocking terminated overgrowths in the Warren County core (Fig. 15E) required the movement of very silica-rich pore fluids through the St. Peter after the main illite-smectite-chlorite stage. The amount of silica precipitated during the terminated overgrowth stage varies greatly from section to section and within different strata at a single section, a feature undoubtedly related to permeability.

The formation of euhedral kaolinite crystals occurred after the development of terminated quartz overgrowths (Fig. 4B). The alumina necessary for kaolinite could have been supplied internally from alteration of feldspar and clay minerals. Where kaolinite is present, feldspar shows considerable dissolution, and there is sometimes mixed-layer material present, which supports our belief that mixed-layer material is an alteration product of illite. Kaolinite has been found only where the St. Peter contains fresh water. Thus, kaolinite is a "late" diagenetic mineral and records a low K/H ratio.

We have not established entirely to our satisfaction the chemical factors leading to the development of pyrite, especially the origin of sulfur. In the subsurface sections where the St. Peter

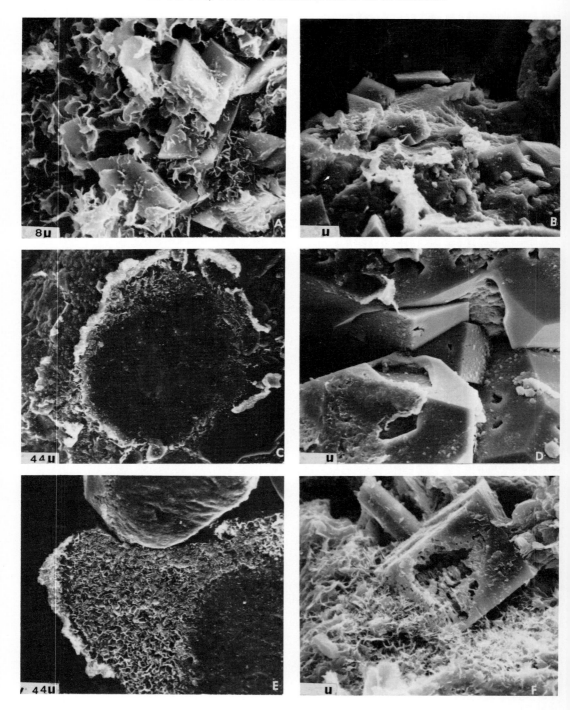

Fig. 15.—SEM photomicrographs of authigenic minerals in St. Peter Sandstone, Warren County, Illinois, *A*, K-feldspar and illite in siltstone lenses of the Kress Member; *B*, dolomite and illite on incipient quartz overgrowths; *C*, illite around pressure solution pit; *D*, terminated quartz overgrowths engulfing K-feldspar; *E*, illite-smectite-chlorite on quartz grain surface between pressure-solution pit (right) and terminated quartz overgrowth (black area on left); *F*, partially dissolved and illitized K-feldspar with illite-smectite-chlorite.

contains fresh water, it is certain that pyrite formed before kaolinite and after the major phase of terminated-overgrowth development. Pyrite is the last authigenic mineral in the St. Peter where pore fluids presently are saline. In the sections studied, there is no evidence that sulfuric acid, formed from the oxidation of pyrite, reacted with illite to form K-feldspar as proposed by Amaral (1974). Evidence from outcrop sections shows that pyrite oxidation often leads to the formation of jarosite, alunite and gypsum.

Source of cations.—It is apparent from the abundance of authigenic feldspar and quartz in some sections of the St. Peter that connate pore fluids, even if hypersaline, could not have contained the total amount of potassium, alumina, and silica required to form these minerals. A significant volume of these cations, especially silica, must have been supplied from an external source. An external source of cations is also needed to explain the immense amount of authigenic feldspar which has precipitated as overgrowths on detrital grains in the Cambrian strata of the upper Mississippi Valley. Some possible sources of cations are: hypersaline environments, which may have existed during the deposition of Cambrian and Lower and Middle Ordovician carbonates; alteration of felsic volcanics; alteration of illite during dolomitization of carbonates; and hydrothermal activity.

Authigenic K-feldspar is so abundant in Cambro-Ordovician sediments throughout the U.S. and in other areas (Swett, 1968) that it is difficult to imagine a hydrothermal source that would be so extensive. Although the alteration of volcanics is strongly favored by Buyce and Friedman (1975) for the small amounts of authigenic K-feldspar present as overgrowths in Cambrian and Lower Ordovician carbonates of New York, the known volume of volcanics in the mid-continent area is very small. In addition, there is abundant authigenic K-feldspar in Cambrian rocks throughout the western U.S. where volcanics are even less abundant. In some instances the volcanics are themselves replaced in part or wholly by K-feldspar. For example, Weiss (1954) described feldspathized shales in Middle Ordovician rocks of Minnesota, which he concluded were initially volcanic ash. Although we lack conclusive proof, we believe that the highly feldspathic siltstones occurring at Hanover (Fig. 2) and at several other locations in the Readstown directly below the Tonti Sandstone Member are replaced volcanics, although Woodward (1972) proposed that the feldspar in these beds was formed syngenetically, precipitated directly from sea water. It is noteworthy that every known occurrence of highly feldspathic siltstones in the Readstown Member is associated with a channel at the base of the Tonti Member, exactly where volcanics would most likely be preserved.

Swett (1968) proposed that K-feldspar and chert emplacements in some Cambrian and Ordovician dolomite siltstones and dolomites in Scotland are related to the alteration of detrital illite during dolomitization. We cannot fully judge the validity of this theory, but it does not seem compatible from a geochemical standpoint with the fact that illite is the primary clay mineral in the carbonates (limestones and dolomites) underlying and overlying the St. Peter. Within the St. Peter, there is no evidence that the presence of dolomite has any noticeable influence on the stability of authigenic or detrital illite. Also, most of the silty carbonates in Illinois and Wisconsin also contain authigenic K-feldspar.

It is possible that K, Al and Si required to form K-feldspar, encrusting overgrowths, illite, etc. were not supplied by exactly the same mechanism that provided the large amount of silica which formed the terminated overgrowths at a later time. The early authigenic minerals may have formed during burial diagenesis from saline pore fluids released during the compaction of associated carbonates. There is evidence of high salinity during the deposition of some of the underlying carbonates. For example, in White County, Illinois, there is massive anhydrite at the base of the St. Peter, and the Lower Ordovician carbonates contain disseminated anhydrite as well as authigenic K-feldspar (Stevenson, Chamberlain and Buschbach, 1975). With the depletion of K and Al through time, potassium silicates would cease to form, but with increasing temperature associated with burial and diagenesis of carbonates the concentration of dissolved silica might increase much above the point of amorphous silica saturation. This silica might then be precipitated as temperature decreased and fluids migrated during and following uplifts. The Al required for the kaolinite, which developed after terminated quartz overgrowths, could easily be supplied by reaction of K-feldspar and illite with fresh water. The above explanation is appealing because it would allow for the obvious time lapse which occurred between the illite-smectite-chlorite clay-mineral phase and the main phase of terminated overgrowth development. In summary, we believe that the authigenic minerals, except kaolinite, formed from saline pore fluids. Kaolinite was precipitated from fresh water. The formation of these minerals, whether from saline or fresh water, records the migration of huge volumes of pore fluids through the St. Peter.

CONCLUSIONS

Diagenetic minerals in the St. Peter Sandstone formed from pore fluids include K-feldspar, illite, smectite, chlorite, dolomite, calcite, quartz, pyrite, and kaolinite. Other diagenetic minerals such as jarosite, alunite, gypsum and lepidocrosite are sometimes present in outcrop sections as a result of "modern" weathering. The paragenetic sequence determined from SEM studies is (1) K-feldspar-encrusting quartz overgrowths, (2) illite-smectite-chlorite-carbonates, (3) terminated quartz overgrowths, (4) pyrite and (5) kaolinite. The presence of a regular mixed-layer clay mineral in many samples in which kaolinite is often abundant suggests that it formed through the transformation of illite. Some illite has also formed from the alteration of K-feldspar. There is no evidence that kaolinite forms from an alumina-silica residue remaining after feldspar alteration, as has been observed in surface weathering sequences.

Quartz grains contain three types of overgrowths: encrusting, incipient and terminated (euhedral to subhedral). The initial phase of quartz overgrowth development occurred early in the diagenetic history of the St. Peter and consisted of the precipitation of a conformable silica envelope on the surfaces of quartz grains not in contact with other grains. Additional silica precipitation in selected areas formed irregular projections called incipient overgrowths by Waugh (1970) and Pittman (1972). Some incipient overgrowths developed and coalesced to form terminated overgrowths in optical continuity with the detrital grains. The presence of clay coatings, either detrital or authigenic, inhibited the development of terminated overgrowths, but the absence of terminated overgrowths is not necessarily related to clay coatings.

The K-feldspar in the St. Peter is very K-rich, approximately 16% K_2O. Dissolution of the feldspar is most rapid along the a–b plane, probably because potassium ions are more concentrated in this plane.

Although some silica was derived from pressure solution, the volume of K-feldspar and terminated quartz overgrowths requires an external cation source. Saline pore fluids expelled during compaction of overlying and underlying carbonates and the release of silica during burial and carbonate diagenesis are believed to be the most likely sources, although the dissolution of volcanic material may have contributed some of the cations.

The pore fluid geochemistry has changed through time. The initial K/H ratio was quite high as is evident from the early precipitation of K-feldspar. Lowering of K/H ratio brought the pore fluids in equilibrium with illite, smectite and chlorite. Kaolinite is present in the St. Peter only where the pore fluids are fresh. Where fresh water is present K-feldspar shows considerable illitization and dissolution, whereas where the pore fluids are saline there is comparatively little feldspar alteration. The sequence of authigenic mineral formation and stability relations appears to agree with previously described low-temperature stability relations in the system $K_2O-Al_2O_3$-SiO_2-H_2O, except that much silica was precipitated after the K/H ratio was apparently quite low. This late silica was apparently not precipitated from fresh water because terminated overgrowths occur where the St. Peter presently contains brines.

ACKNOWLEDGEMENT

This investigation was supported by a grant from the Earth Sciences Section, National Science Foundation (EAR75-1748) to I. E. Odom.

REFERENCES

AMARAL, E. J., 1974, Oxidation of pyrite: A key factor in the formation of authigenic feldspar and chart cement in the St. Peter Sandstone [abs.]: Geol. Soc. America Abs. with Programs, v. 6, p. 1018–1019.

BUYCE, R. M., AND FRIEDMAN, G. M., 1975, Significance of authigenic K-feldspar in Cambrian-Ordovician carbonate rocks of the Proto-Atlantic shelf in North America: Journ. Sed. Petrology, v. 45, p. 808–821.

DAPPLES, E. C., 1955, General lithofacies relationship of St. Peter Sandstone and Simpson Group: Am. Assoc. Petroleum Geologists Bull., v. 39, p. 444–467.

FRASER, G. S., 1976, Sedimentology of a Middle Ordovician quartz arenite-carbonate transition in the Upper Mississippi Valley: Geol. Soc. America Bull., v. 86, p. 833–845.

GARRELS, R. M., AND CHRIST, C. L., 1965, Solutions, minerals and equilibra: New York, Harper and Row, 450 p.

GRIM, R. E., BRAY, R. H., AND BRADLEY, W. F., 1937, The mica in argillaceous sediments: Am. Mineralogist, v. 22, p. 813–829.

HEALD, M. T., 1950, Authigenesis in West Virginia sandstones: Jour. Geology, v. 58, p. 624–633.

——, 1956, Cementation of Simpson and St. Peter Sandstones in parts of Oklahoma, Arkansas, and Missouri: Jour. Geology, v. 64, p. 16–30.

HESS, P. C., 1966, Phase equilibria of some minerals in the $K_2O-Na_2O-Al_2O_3$-SiO_2-H_2O system at 25° C and 1 atmosphere: Am. Jour. Sci., v. 264, p. 289–309.

LAMAR, J. E., 1928, Geology and economic resources of the St. Peter Sandstone of Illinois: Illinois State Geol. Surv. Bull. 53, 175 p.

ODOM, I. E., 1975, Feldspar-grain size relations in Cambrian arenites, upper Mississippi Valley: Jour. Sed. Petrology, v. 45, p. 636–650.

——, Doe, T. W., and Dott, R. H., Jr., 1976, Nature of feldspar-grain size relations in some quartz-rich sandstones: Jour. Sed. Petrology, v. 46 p. 862–870.

Pittman, E. D., 1972, Diagenesis of quartz in sandstones as revealed by scanning electron microscopy: Jour. Sed. Petrology, v. 42, p. 507–519.

Siever, Raymond, 1959, Petrology and geochemistry of silica cementation in some Pennsylvanian sandstones, *in* H. A. Ireland (ed.), Silica in sediments: Soc. Econ. Paleontologists and Mineralogists Spec. Pub. 7, p. 55–79.

Stevenson, D. L., Chamberlin, T. L., and Bushbach, T. C., 1975, Insoluble residues of the Sauk Sequence (Cambrian and Lower Ordovician) rocks of the Fairfield Basin, Illinois: An aid in correlation and in petroleum exploration: Illinois State Geol. Survey, Illinois Petroleum 106, 12 p.

Swett, K., 1968, Authigenic feldspars and cherts resulting from dolomitization of illitic limestones: A hypothesis: Jour. Sed. Petrology, v. 38, p. 128–135.

Templeton, J. S., and Willman, H. B., 1963, Champlainian Series (Middle Ordovician) in Illinois: Illinois State Geol. Survey Bull. 89, 260 p.

Waugh, B., 1970, Formation of quartz overgrowths in the Penrith Sandstone (Lower Permian) of northwest England as revealed by scanning electron microscopy: Sedimentology, v. 14, p. 309–320.

Weiss, M. P., 1954, Feldspathized shales from Minnesota: Jour. Sed. Petrology, v. 24, p. 270–274.

Woodard, H. H., 1972, Syngenetic sanidine beds from Middle Ordovician Saint Peter Sandstone, Wisconsin: Jour. Geology, v. 80, p. 323–332.